BASIC ORGANIC CHEMISTRY

FRANK L. WISEMAN
Georgetown College

BASIC ORGANIC CHEMISTRY
A SHORT COURSE WITH APPLICATIONS

McGRAW-HILL BOOK COMPANY

New York   St. Louis   San Francisco   Auckland   Bogotá   Caracas   Colorado Springs
Hamburg   Lisbon   London   Madrid   Mexico   Milan   Montreal   New Delhi   Oklahoma City
Panama   Paris   San Juan   São Paulo   Singapore   Sydney   Tokyo   Toronto

BASIC ORGANIC CHEMISTRY

A SHORT COURSE WITH APPLICATIONS

2 3 4 5 6 7 8 9 0   HALHAL   8 9 3 2 1 0 9 8

ISBN   0-07-071155-0

This book was set in Times Roman by Syntax International.
The editors were Karen S. Misler and Jack Maisel;
the designer was Nicholas Krenitsky;
the production supervisor was Salvador Gonzales.
Drawings were done by Fine Line Illustrations, Inc.
Cover photograph by Phototake—N.Y.C.
Arcata Graphics/Halliday was printer and binder.

Library of Congress Cataloging-in-Publication Data

Wiseman, Frank L.
    Basic organic chemistry.

    Includes index.
    1. Chemistry, Organic.   I. Title.
QD253.W74   1988   547   87-21442
ISBN 0-07-071155-0

DEDICATION

This book is dedicated to my sons

JONATHAN

EDWARD

JOEL

who are an inspiration and joy to me

CONTENTS

PREFACE

WELCOME TO ORGANIC CHEMISTRY

You are about to begin your study of organic chemistry. Like many students who take this course, you may not be majoring in one of the fields of science. Yet you want this course to provide a sound background in science as a means of becoming more effective in your chosen profession. This book was written to help you learn organic chemistry in as efficient and enjoyable a way as possible. It was compiled with you, the student, in mind. We are aware of the special learning needs you may have as you begin this new area of study, and the following special features have been designed to aid you in mastering organic chemistry skills.

SPECIAL FEATURES

1 **Hints for studying organic chemistry** are given early in this book.

2 Short **Programmed Learning Units** aid in skill development.

3 **Applications** of organic chemistry to commerce and personal life are outlined. In addition to those applications in the main text, there are separate interchapter Applied Organic Chemistry sections throughout the book on special topics.

4 **Reaction summary flow diagrams** give an overview of the reactions in certain chapters.

5 Each chapter begins with a statement of the learning goals and ends with a **summary** of the main ideas.

6 A list of **key terms** is given at the end of each chapter to remind you of the new words and concepts just encountered.

GOALS

The main goals of this text are to teach the basic concepts of organic chemistry and to show how this very diverse field of study touches our lives in many ways.

TEACHING APPROACH

After covering bonding concepts in Chapter 1, we will spend some time in Chapter 2 presenting a broad overview of organic chemistry. This overview will help you to place each topic covered in subsequent chapters in the proper perspective.

The book includes the **synthesis of organic materials**, especially the simpler and more commercially useful ones, using reactions as you learn them. Most of you will not be synthetic organic chemists, but this approach is used as a teaching tool. It serves as a focus or theme and gives you a purpose for learning the reactions. The author's experience has shown this to be one of the most effective means by which students can learn organic chemistry. The synthesis problems given throughout the text are of the simpler type, however (one to four steps), and are used only to the extent needed to encourage learning the chemical reactions and reagents covered in the text material.

Actually, no single subject or skill in this book, taken alone, is likely to be of great importance to you unless you are planning to be a professional chemist. But there is value for you in the collective insight that can be gained by brief study and minimal skill development in the several areas covered in this course.

Because of the central importance of both synthesis and **molecular spectroscopy** to organic chemistry, these areas have been covered in separate chapters in the main body of the text. The skill required in both of these chapters is minimal, in keeping with the nature of the course. Both of these chapters may be omitted without loss of continuity to the remainder of the text if time constraints and the instructor's preference so indicate.

The presentation of detailed reaction mechanisms is limited in the body of the text to those which are needed to explain or amplify a key concept. A number of other mechanisms are given in the appendix for student interest or for required learning if the instructor so directs.

ACKNOWLEDGMENTS

I would like to express my thanks for the many useful comments and suggestions provided by colleagues who review this text during the course of its development, especially to W. M. Baldwin, Jr., University of Georgia; Neal Busch, South Dakota University; Jerry R. Dias, University of Missouri; John Eichar, Miami University; Frank Guziec, New Mexico State University; Tom R. Hays, Texas A & I University; John F. Helling, University of Florida; Elmer Jones, North eastern University; Kenneth L. Marsi, California State University; George Odell, Oklahoma State University; K. Barbara Schowen, University of Kansas; Ernest Simpson, California State Polytechnic—pomona; Gordon Wilson, Jr., Western Kentucky University; James K. Wood, University of Nebraska.

BEST WISHES

May the work and study you invest in this subject prove enjoyable and profitable, and may it aid you in your profession and help you progress toward your personal goals.

Frank Wiseman

CHAPTER 1

KEY CHEMICAL CONCEPTS

LEARNING GOALS

1 To review atomic structure and periodic chart organization

2 To understand bonding and ways of representing molecular structure

3 To develop skill in writing Lewis dot diagrams

4 To understand molecular geometry and the concept of hybridization

5 To become familiar with the textbook features and personal activities that will aid in the study of organic chemistry

We begin our study of organic chemistry by considering two examples of the many accomplishments in this field. In 1928, when World War II was not even on the horizon, a British scientist named Alexander Fleming isolated a substance called **penicillin** from mold growing in a culture medium. His discovery was to have worldwide impact—it has touched the lives and well-being of millions of people, including almost everyone reading this book. Prior to this time even simple cuts or superficial wounds could easily result in infections which could lead, in turn, to serious illness or even death. During wartime, especially, many soldiers—even more than died directly from fatal wounds—died from infections related to wounds. But this situation was about to change. In 1939, Flory and Chain recognized the value of penicillin in stopping the growth of certain kinds of bacteria in human beings. The first clinical use of this material was in 1941; in 1942 the same scientists treated bacterially caused meningitis with penicillin and demonstrated the first cure of this often fatal disease. The large scale isolation of this drug from mold cultures was then begun and penicillin was used during World War II to stop wound-related infections and many illnesses caused by bacteria. This saved lives that in previous wars would have been lost.

Penicillin had been isolated as a natural product (a substance formed in nature—not man-made), and its molecular structure was totally unknown. A large cooperative effort by British and American chemists was begun for the purpose of determining the chemical nature of this material. It involved about 300 organic chemists from both countries and was certainly one of the largest and most intensive chemical endeavors ever attempted. As a result of this effort, the structure of the penicillin molecule was discovered in the early 1950s by Kenneth Henry-Logan. This discovery led to the large scale production of partially synthetic penicillin and greatly reduced the cost and increased the availability of this drug. Knowledge of the structure of penicillin allowed investigation of the mechanism by which it stopped bacterial growth, which in turn helped in the development of other useful antibiotics.

In 1935, an organic chemist working for the Du Pont company, Wallace Carothers, was doing research aimed at producing synthetic materials that could be used to manufacture fibers for cloth. Until this time, only natural fibers such as cotton, wool, flax, and silk were known. After many trials with a number of substances, he succeeded in producing a material similar to silk. The material was strong and melted at a high enough temperature that the cloth could be washed in hot water and ironed. It was called **nylon**, and since that time it has been produced in huge quantities for fabric manufacture and for fabrication of many other items. These include gears in small appliances, fishing line, and tough protective tips for the bottoms of chair legs, to name a few. By understanding the principles of organic chemical synthesis and the relationship between molecular structure and the properties of a material, Carothers produced a totally synthetic material used by all of us and opened up the whole field of polymer chemistry. This field later produced other fibers, plastics, and coatings including polyesters (Dacron), acrylics (Orlon), butyl rubber, polyethylene, and acrylic paints. The structures of these materials and methods of producing them will be covered later in the text.

In the case of penicillin, a natural mold produced a substance, one person found it, others recognized its potential usefulness, and still others (chemists) worked to understand its chemical nature and why it acted as it did. In the case of nylon, Carothers, even with his understanding of chemical principles and his genius, had to work for years to finally make his breakthrough discovery. But without that fundamental chemical knowledge, it would have been nearly impossible for him to have succeeded.

Throughout this textbook, we will present the fundamental ideas of organic chemistry. We will also show how the knowledge of molecular structure and chemical reactions has been and will continue to be used to benefit human beings.

The study of **organic chemistry** is the study of the **compounds of carbon**, especially those in which carbon is covalently bonded to other nonmetals such as hydrogen, oxygen, nitrogen, and the halogens. Many, if not most, of the commercial products we use daily are organic in nature—medicines, plastics, synthetic fibers, and weed control agents are only a few such materials. In this book we will examine the molecular structures and uses of many organic compounds and the systems of naming them. We will also study the methods by which they are prepared and the reactions they undergo.

But before we examine the chemistry of organic compounds, we will review some general chemical ideas, especially those involving atomic structure and bonding.

ATOMIC THEORY

All matter is composed of **atoms** which, in turn, are composed of smaller particles called **neutrons**, **protons**, and **electrons**. Table 1-1 gives properties of these particles and describes their discovery.

The evidence collected by a number of scientists, chief among them Rutherford, led to the view that atoms are composed of a small dense

TABLE 1-1

PARTICLE	SYMBOL	CHARGE	MASS	DISCOVERY	SUBATOMIC PARTICLES
Electron	e^-	-1	1/1840 amu*	1890 by Thomson	
Proton	p^+	$+1$	1 amu	1898 by Wien and Thomson	
Neutron	n	0	1 amu	1932 by Chadwick	

* amu = atomic mass unit

nucleus which contains the protons and neutrons and thus most of the mass of the atom. The remainder of the atom, in which the electrons are found, is mostly empty space.

Subsequent work by chemists, physicists, and mathematicians has led to a better understanding of the distribution of electrons within atoms. Here we shall present only the basic ideas and the electron arrangements of several atoms, along with principles we will use later in the chapter.

Electrons occupy three-dimensional regions around the nucleus. We can simply think of the space around the nucleus of an atom as having within it regions which can be occupied by electrons. These regions are called **orbitals**. Each orbital has a different combination of size, shape, and orientation within the atom, and each is given a number-letter designation.

While there is a large number of such orbitals within an atom, under ordinary conditions only a relatively small number of these are occupied by electrons. Below is a list of the standard designations of the first 18 orbitals (i.e., the 18 closest to the nucleus). The number indicates the size (i.e., the average diameter) of the orbital; the letter indicates the shape. The s orbitals are spherically symmetrical about the nucleus, and the three p orbitals are dumbbell-shaped, with their axes perpendicular to each other as shown in Figure 1-1. Thus, the $1s$ orbital is the smallest and is spherical; the $2s$ orbital is larger and also spherical; the $2p$ orbitals are dumbbell-shaped with a size similar to that of the $2s$ orbital. The d orbitals are more complex. There also exist f orbitals, but we will not treat them in this textbook, since most atoms in organic compounds do not have occupied f orbitals.

A list of the first 18 atomic orbitals is as follows;

FIGURE 1-1

Orientation of atomic orbitals. The dot (·) shows the location of the nucleus of an atom.

Letter designation	Number of orientations	Drawing
s	one	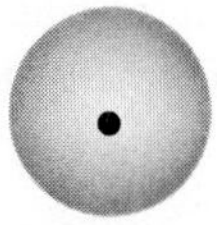
p	three	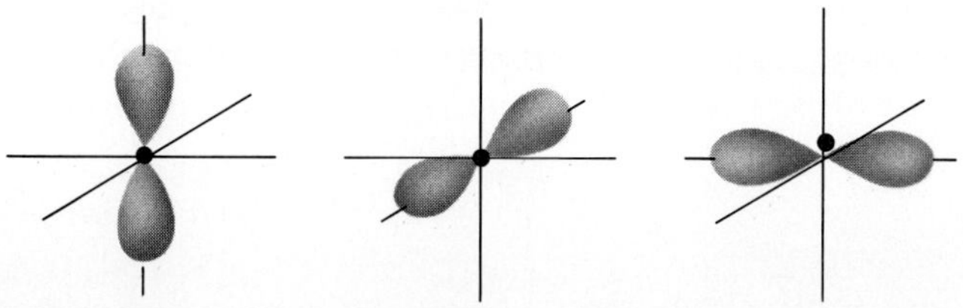

First size $1s$

Second size $2s$
$2p\ 2p\ 2p$

Third size $3s$
$3p\ 3p\ 3p$
$3d\ 3d\ 3d\ 3d\ 3d$

Fourth size $4s$
$4p\ 4p\ 4p$
plus d and f orbitals

The orbitals are grouped according to their approximate sizes, and these groups are called major **levels** or **shells**. There is only one orbital of the first size or level (the $1s$ orbital). There are four orbitals of the second size and nine orbitals of the third size. Each orbital can be empty or can hold 1 or 2 electrons. Notice that there are three p orbitals of a given size and five d orbitals of a given size. Since each orbital can hold 2 electrons, a group of p orbitals can hold 6 electrons and a group of d orbitals can hold 10 electrons. Electrons occupy orbitals of smaller size and simpler shape first (those at the top of the list); they occupy the larger ones only after the others are filled. The ease with which an orbital is filled decreases as we go down the list. In other words, electrons need higher energy to be in the orbitals at the bottom of the list above. Below, the electron configuration is shown for beryllium (Be), carbon (C), and iron (Fe). In each case the electron structures (or arrangements) are indicated by using superscripts to show the number of electrons in each orbital.

Be $1s^2\ 2s^2$

C $1s^2\ 2s^2\ 2p^1\ 2p^1$

Fe $1s^2\ 2s^2\ 2p^2\ 2p^2\ 2p^2\ 3s^2\ 3p^2\ 3p^2\ 3p^2\ 3d^2\ 3d^1\ 3d^1\ 3d^1\ 3d^1\ 4s^2$
   or $1s^2\ 2s^2\ 2p^6\ 3s^2\ 3p^6\ 3d^6\ 4s^2$

Beryllium atoms (Be) have two electrons in the $1s$ and two in the $2s$. Carbon atoms (C) have two electrons in the $1s$, two in the $2s$, and one in each of two $2p$ orbitals. The larger atoms, such as iron (Fe), have more electrons and a more complex electron structure. To simplify the writing of the electron structure of such atoms, the p and d orbitals can be designated collectively as p^6 or d^6, respectively. The electron structure of three members of each of periodic chart groups IA, VIIA, and IVA are shown below.

Group IA   Li $1s^2\ 2s^1$ ←
   Na $1s^2\ 2s^2\ 2p^6\ 3s^1$ ←
   K $1s^2\ 2s^2\ 2p^6\ 3s^2\ 3p^6\ 4s^1$ ←

One
electron in
outer shells

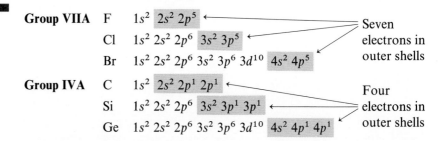

THE PERIODIC CHART

Electronic structure

From the structures given in the previous section, we can see that the electron configuration of the **outermost** levels of atoms of carbon (C), silicon (Si), and germanium (Ge) are the same—each has two electrons in an s orbital and one in each of two p orbitals. Notice that these three elements are all in the same family (IVA) of the periodic chart. **Families or groups of elements are indicated by vertical groupings on the periodic chart.** (See Figure 1-2 or the inside back cover of this book.) The outer shell configurations of fluorine (F), chlorine (Cl), and bromine (Br) are also the same, i.e., they have two electrons in an s orbital and five in p orbitals. These are also in the same family (VIIA). **All members of each family have identical outer shell configurations.** It is for this reason that they have similar chemical properties. **The chemical properties of all elements are a direct result of the electron structures of atoms of that element.** This is the most fundamental principle of modern chemistry, and explains the organization of the periodic chart. Lithium (Li), sodium (Na), and potassium (K) are all soft, silvery metals that react violently with water. They combine with chlorine to form compounds that taste salty. Fluorine (F), chlorine (Cl), and bromine (Br) are all nonmetals that react with hydrogen to form compounds that taste sour (these are acids).

The periodic chart **group numbers** indicate the **number of electrons in the outer shell** of atoms of the elements in that family, and the **period numbers** tell the **number of the highest occupied shell**. A period is indicated by the horizontal rows on the periodic chart. For example, Na and Cl are both in period 3, and each has the third shell as the largest one occupied with electrons. Strictly speaking, the outer shell electrons are indicated by the group number only for the groups designated with the letter A, such as IIA and VIIA. These are the only groups we will consider in this course.

> The electron structure of atoms determines the chemical behavior and physical properties of elements.

Atomic size

Two other kinds of information that can be obtained from the organization of the periodic chart should be discussed at this point. The first of these

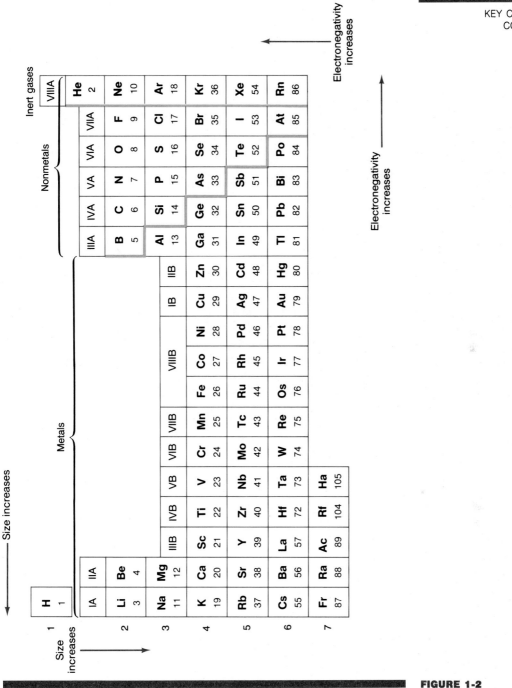

FIGURE 1-2

Summary of trends on the
periodic chart.

is the **size** (diameter) of atoms. As we move **down** a given family, with each step a whole new shell is occupied by electrons. In group IA, the last (outermost) electron of sodium (Na) is in the 3s orbital, of potassium (K) is in the 4s, of rubidium (Rb) is in the 5s, and so forth. Since the 4s orbital is larger than the 3s, K atoms are larger than Na atoms. For this reason, as we move **down** a family, the atomic diameter always **increases**. (See arrow in Figure 1-2.)

As we go from **left to right** in a given period, the atomic weight increases but atomic size **decreases** in most cases. In period 2, for example, neon (Ne) atoms are smaller than those of fluorine (F), which in turn are smaller than oxygen (O) atoms. There are a number of exceptions to this trend, but it generally holds except in the central portion of the chart.

Electronegativity

The other trend shown by the periodic chart is that of electronegativity. This is the relative attraction of atoms for electrons in a bond between different atoms. The atoms of inert gases tend not to gain or lose electrons, while metal atoms lose electrons and nonmetal atoms gain electrons. As one goes **up and to the right** in the periodic chart, electronegativity **increases**. The last group (noble gases) is not included in this trend. Fluorine (F) is thus the **most electronegative** element and francium (Fr) is the **least electronegative**. This trend is also shown by the arrows in Figure 1-2.

Using these trends we can determine, for example, that oxygen (O) is more electronegative than is sulfur (S), and sodium (Na) is less so than magnesium (Mg). This means that oxygen will have more attraction for electrons than will carbon, and that sodium will have less attraction for electrons than will magnesium (magnesium will hold onto its electrons more tightly).

Noble gas electron configuration

The elements in the last group to the right in the periodic chart are called **noble gases**; all of them except helium (He) have eight electrons in the outer shell. They are generally unreactive (there are a few exceptions); thus it is concluded that eight electrons in the outer shell is an especially stable arrangement. Other elements generally behave in such a way as to get eight electrons in their outer shells. This tendency is called the **octet rule**.

BONDING

The octet rule: Why bonding occurs

The driving force behind atoms combining with each other is the tendency for atoms to **gain**, **lose**, or **share** electrons so as to fill their outermost electronic energy levels. For the elements hydrogen (H) and helium (He), the outermost shell is the 1s shell, which requires two electrons to be full. Remember that the first shell has no p orbital. For atoms in period 2, the outside shell has one s orbital and three p orbitals, which means that eight electrons are needed to fill it because it has a total of four orbitals, each with a capacity of two electrons. Atoms tend to be especially stable (i.e., in a low energy state, which is always preferred) when the outer shell is full. Thus atoms tend to do whatever is necessary to get the "magic" eight electrons in their outer levels—except for the smaller atoms (atomic number less than 5), which tend to get two electrons in the outer shell.

The octet rule explains why the inert gases (group VIIIA) such as helium (He), neon (Ne), and argon (Ar) do not undergo chemical changes under most circumstances. **The outer shells are already full**; hence there is no need to interact with other elements to gain, lose, or share electrons. Elements in periods 3 through 7 also usually obey the octet rule (i.e., they tend to fill the outer shell s and p orbitals even though d or f orbitals may be present):

He $1s^2$ ←———— Two electrons

Ne $1s^2\ 2s^2\ 2p^6$ ←———— Eight electrons

Ar $1s^2\ 2s^2\ 2p^6\ 3s^2\ 3p^6$

Most atoms tend to gain, lose or share electrons in order to obtain eight electrons in their outer electronic level. This is called the octet rule.

Ionic bonding

There are two basic ways in which atoms fulfill the octet rule. The first of these is called **ionic bonding**. (The second is **covalent bonding**; it is discussed in the next section.) In ionic bonding, atoms of metallic elements **lose** electrons when combining, and atoms of nonmetals **gain** electrons. For instance, consider the electronic configurations of atoms of sodium (Na) and fluorine (F).

Na $1s^2\ 2s^2\ 2p^6\ 3s^1$ ←—— One electron in outer shell

F $1s^2\ 2s^2\ 2p^5$ ←—— Seven electrons in outer shell

Na has one electron in its outer shell and F has seven. If Na gives its one $3s$ electron to F, as follows,

Na $1s^2\ 2s^2\ 2p^6\ 3s^{①}$

F $1s^2\ 2s^2\ 2p^5$ ←

then the octet conditions of **both** will be satisfied. F will have eight electrons in its second shell (which is the outermost), and Na will have eight in what is now its outer shell—the second shell.

Na $1s^2\ 2s^2\ 2p^6$ ←———— Eight electrons

F $1s^2\ 2s^2\ 2p^6$ ←

Na still has 11 protons in the nucleus, but it now has a total of only 10 electrons. This means that it has one more positively charged particle than it has negatively charged particles, which gives the whole "atom" a net charge of +1. The F still has 9 protons, but it now has 10 electrons, which gives it a net charge of −1.

These charged atoms, which have gained or lost one or more electrons, are called **ions**. **Positively** charged ions are called **cations**. (This term is easily remembered because the letter *t* in it is similar to the plus sign.) **Negatively** charged ions are called **anions**.

The negatively and positively charged ions which result from a transfer of electrons from one atom to another are held together by electrostatic attraction; that is, entities of opposite charge attract each other. This attraction of ions of different charge for each other is called **ionic bonding**. It occurs when the compound contains a metal and one or more nonmetals. The following compounds fulfill this criterion and are thus ionic in nature:

$$MgCl_2 \qquad FeI_2 \qquad CuF$$

$$Na_2O \qquad Na_2SO_4 \qquad Zn(C_2H_3O_2)_2$$

Another way of showing this same transfer process is as follows:

$$\dot{Na} \quad + \quad \overset{\times\times}{\underset{\times}{\times}}\overset{}{F}\overset{\times}{} \quad \longrightarrow \quad Na^{1+} \quad + \quad \left[\overset{\times\times}{\underset{\bullet\times}{\times}}\overset{}{F}\overset{\times}{} \right]^{1-}$$

Sodium atom   Fluorine atom   Sodium ion   Fluoride ion

In this diagram, the **outer electrons only** (called **valence electrons**) are represented by symbols such as dots, circle, or ×'s. The electrons are then moved so that the octet rules of all atoms are satisfied, and the ions are formed. These representations are called **Lewis dot diagrams** after G. N. Lewis, one of the pioneers, along with Linus Pauling, in the study of chemical bonding (see Figure 1-3).

The transfer of electrons from atoms of metals to atoms of nonmetals to form ions is possible because metals have a low ability to attract electrons while nonmetals have a high attraction for electrons. Because of the strong attraction of ions for each other, ionic materials have high melting points and are solids at room temperature (see Table 1-3).

Ionic bonding occurs when electrons transfer from atoms of a metal to atoms of a nonmetal. The resulting ions are held together by electrostatic attraction.

Covalent bonding

When two nonmetals react chemically, both atoms involved have high electronegativity and a transfer of electrons is not possible. Neither atom will easily give up electrons. In this case, a **sharing** of the electrons is necessary in order to fulfill the octet rule.

For example, consider the interaction of atoms of hydrogen and chlorine:

H $\quad 1s^1$ ⟵——————— One electron in outer shell

Cl $\quad 1s^2\,2s^2\,2p^6\;\boxed{3s^2\,3p^5}$ ⟵—— Seven electrons in outer shell

The H and Cl atoms both need one more electron to fill the outer shells. If the two atoms come into physical proximity and each shares one electron, then the octet conditions of both will be met. This situation is shown below using the Lewis dot method.

$$\dot{\text{H}} + {}^{\times}_{\times}\ddot{\text{Cl}}{}^{\times}_{\times} \longrightarrow \left(\text{H}\overset{\times\times}{\underset{\times\times}{\vdots}}\text{Cl}\,{}^{\times}_{\times}\right)$$

Two electrons available $\qquad$ Eight electrons available

The orbital "picture" for this process is illustrated in Figure 1-4.

The shared electrons now belong to **both** atoms (a situation similar to a joint bank account). Hydrogen now has two electrons available to it (its original electron plus the one shared with chlorine), and chlorine has eight (its original seven plus the one shared with hydrogen). These two shared electrons cause the H and Cl atoms to be physically linked to each other (bonded); this link is called a **covalent bond**. The resulting unit is called a **molecule**. The region occupied by the shared electrons is called a **molecular orbital**.

Covalent bonding, as has been noted, occurs between **two nonmetals**. It is usually represented by a straight line (or dash). That is

$$\text{H}\overset{\times}{\text{Cl}}: \quad \text{equals} \quad \text{H}—\ddot{\text{Cl}}:$$

Covalent bonding can occur between two identical nonmetal atoms. For example

FIGURE 1-4

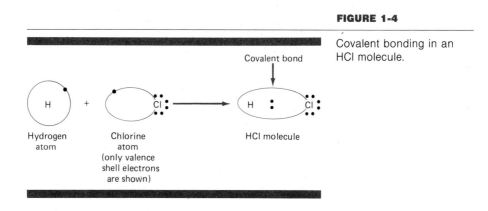

Covalent bonding in an HCl molecule.

Hydrogen atom $\qquad$ Chlorine atom (only valence shell electrons are shown) $\qquad$ HCl molecule

Covalent bond

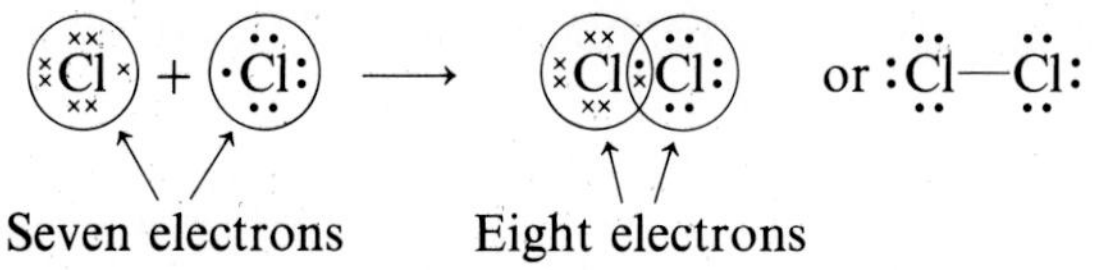

$$\overset{\times\times}{\underset{\times\times}{\times}}\text{Cl}\overset{\times}{}\; + \;\cdot\overset{\cdot\cdot}{\underset{\cdot\cdot}{\text{Cl}}}: \quad\longrightarrow\quad \overset{\times\times}{\underset{\times\times}{\times}}\text{Cl}\overset{\times}{}\text{Cl}: \quad \text{or} \quad :\overset{\cdot\cdot}{\underset{\cdot\cdot}{\text{Cl}}}-\overset{\cdot\cdot}{\underset{\cdot\cdot}{\text{Cl}}}:$$

Seven electrons   Eight electrons

This explains the diatomic nature of chlorine (Cl_2). The individual atoms, by pairing up and sharing two electrons, can fulfill the octet rule of both atoms of chlorine.

A second aspect of covalent bonding is illustrated by molecules of formaldehyde (CH_2O).

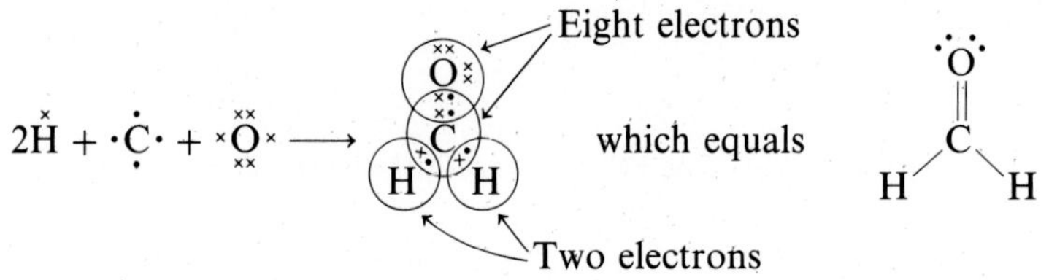

Eight electrons

$$2\overset{\times}{\text{H}} + \cdot\overset{\cdot}{\underset{\cdot}{\text{C}}}\cdot + {}^{\times}\overset{\times\times}{\underset{\times\times}{\text{O}}}{}^{\times} \longrightarrow$$

which equals

Two electrons

In this situation, the carbon atom must share two pairs of electrons with the oxygen atom in order to help gain the four additional electrons it needs to complete its octet. This is called **double covalent bond** and is represented by two straight lines between the atoms involved.

A third way atoms can bond covalently is by a **triple bond**. Such a bond is found, for instance, in molecules of nitrogen (N_2). Atoms of nitrogen have five electrons in the valence shell, and so three more are needed to fulfill the octet rule. These can be obtained by two nitrogen atoms sharing **three** pairs of electrons as shown below:

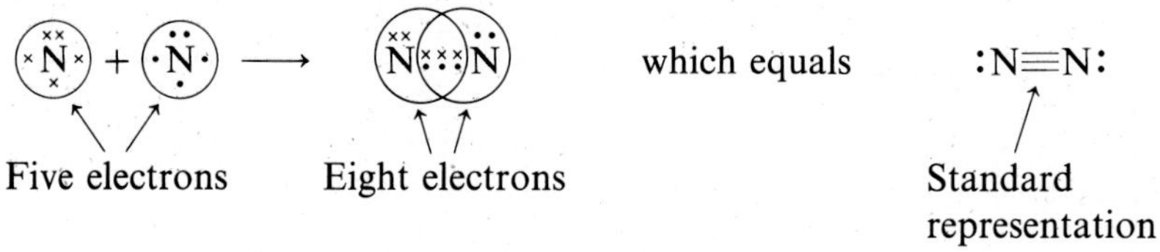

$$\overset{\times\times}{\underset{\times}{\times}}\text{N}\overset{\times}{}\; + \;\cdot\overset{\cdot\cdot}{\underset{\cdot}{\text{N}}}\cdot \quad\longrightarrow\quad \overset{\times\times}{}\text{N}{}^{\times\times\times}_{\cdot\cdot\cdot}\text{N}\overset{\cdot\cdot}{} \quad \text{which equals} \quad :\text{N}\equiv\text{N}:$$

Five electrons   Eight electrons   Standard representation

Covalent materials are usually gases, liquids, or relatively low melting solids. (An exception, among others, is diamond, which melts above 3500°C. This very high melting point occurs because diamond consists of a network of carbon atoms covalently bonded together rather than independent molecules. Essentially, a diamond, whatever its size, is thus one enormous molecule.)

Covalent bonding occurs when two nonmetallic atoms share electrons. The resulting structure is called a molecule.

Polar covalent bonding

In most covalent bonds, the two atoms sharing the electrons have somewhat different electronegativities, and the electrons in the bond are **not**

being shared equally. They spend more of their time closer to one of the atoms than to the other. In HCl, for example, the two electrons in the bond spend more time near the Cl atom because it is more electronegative than the H atom. The difference in electron-attracting abilities is not great enough to allow a complete transfer of electrons and can be thought of as intermediate between an ionic bond (complete transfer) and a pure covalent bond (equal sharing):

$$\delta + \quad \boxed{\text{H} \quad \text{:Cl:}} \quad \delta -$$

The Greek letter delta (δ) is used as a symbol for partial.

The Cl end of the molecule has a partial negative charge, and the H end has a partial positive charge. This is called a **polar covalent bond**, and the molecule is said to be **polar**—that is, it has a negative end and a positive end.

As a general rule, only identical atoms bonded to each other exhibit pure covalent bonding (that is, equally shared nonpolar bonding). In most other cases there is a small difference in electronegativities, and a slightly polar bond results. Therefore, the H—H and C—C bonds are pure covalent bonds and bonds such as C=O, C—Cl, and O—H are polar. When a molecule has nonpolar bonds, the molecule is nonpolar also. If the bonds are polar, the shape of the molecule determines whether the molecule is polar or not. Carbon dioxide (CO_2) is a linear (straight) molecule (its bond angles are 180°). The oxygen atoms must get as far away from each other as possible because their valence electrons repel each other, and a linear arrangement allows for a maximum distance. While each double bond is polar, the molecule as a whole is not polar.

$$\begin{array}{cccc} \delta - & \delta + & \delta + & \delta - \\ \text{O} & = & \text{C} & = \text{O} \end{array}$$

Both ends of the molecule are negative, and the center is positive, because of the relative electronegativities of carbon and oxygen; but since the two **ends** do not have opposite charges, it is **not a polar molecule**. The polarities of the two bonds cancel each other.

Water molecules, on the other hand, are bent, or angular, so that the bond polarities do not cancel. The angle formed by the two H—O bonds is 105°. The oxygen end is negative and the hydrogen end is positive, resulting in a polar molecule:

This geometry is assumed by the water molecule because the electrons in the O—H bonds are repelling each other and also are simultaneously being repelled by the nonbonding electrons on the oxygen atom.

Table 1-2 summarizes bonding types, and Table 1-3 gives the kinds of bonding in some common materials.

LEWIS DOT DIAGRAMS

n the preceding section, we used Lewis dot diagrams to indicate covalent bonding within small molecules such as H_2, CH_2O, and N_2. For molecules that are more complex than these, the Lewis dot diagrams are more difficult to draw. The table on page 15 gives such diagrams for several organic compounds. In each case, the unbonded atoms along with valence electrons are shown, followed by the molecule in which all atoms have a complete octet. In addition, a line diagram called the **Kekulé formula** is given.

TABLE 1-2

SUMMARY OF BONDING	TYPE OF BOND	TYPES OF ATOMS	EXAMPLES
	Ionic	Metal and nonmetal	ZnF_2
			CsCl
	Covalent	Two nonmetals	
	Pure covalent	Identical nonmetal atoms	Cl_2
			N_2
	Polar covalent	Two nonmetals with different electronegativities	HI
			CO

TABLE 1-3

BONDING IN COMMON SUBSTANCES	MATERIAL	FORMULA	TYPE OF BONDING	STATE (AT ROOM TEMPERATURE)	MELTING POINT (°C)
	Calcium chloride	$CaCl_2$	Ionic	Solid	772
	Salt	NaCl	Ionic	Solid	801
	Sodium fluoride	NaF	Ionic	Solid	990
	Boric acid	H_3BO_3	Covalent	Solid	185
	Octane	C_8H_{18}	Covalent	Liquid	−56
	Ethyl alcohol	C_2H_6O	Covalent	Liquid	−117
	Aspirin	$C_9H_8O_4$	Covalent	Solid	143
	Oxygen	O_2	Covalent	Gas	−218
	Ammonia	NH_3	Covalent	Gas	−78

Name	FORMULA	UNBONDED ATOMS	LEWIS DOT DIAGRAM	KEKULÉ FORMULA
Ethane	C_2H_6			
Methanol	CH_4O			
Acetylene	C_2H_2			

In the Lewis dot diagrams each circle contains either eight or two electrons, showing that the circled atom has either eight or two electrons available to it.

Writing these Lewis diagrams requires a little practice and is partly a creative process in which trial and error is a legitimate approach. However, there are certain steps that make the process easier; these are given in the following Programmed Learning unit. You should learn the six steps outlined and follow them through the worked examples. Then try to do the student problems **without looking at the answers**. You should then be able to write Lewis diagrams for the smaller organic molecules and polyatomic anions.

WRITING LEWIS DOT DIAGRAMS

The following steps, used in the order indicated, will allow you to write Lewis dot diagrams with reasonable facility. There is always some creativity involved, and this can be developed by much practice. The first steps are essentially mechanical, while the last ones may require some thought or trial and error.

1 **Write** the **symbols** of the elements in a **symmetrical** fashion. That is, place a single atom in the center of the array with the remaining atoms around it. Carbon, most especially, should be placed at or near the center, and those atoms which can form only one bond (such as hydrogen and the halogens) should be placed at the outer extremities. For example, using SO_2, you would write the following:

$$O \quad S \quad O$$

2 Place the correct number of **valence electrons** around each symbol. The number of valence electrons is equal to the group number (in the periodic chart) in which the element is found. Use ×'s for electrons on some atoms and o's or dots for electrons on others. All electrons are alike—using different symbols simply allows for easier "mental bookkeeping." Place the electrons at four positions (top, bottom, and two sides) on each symbol, placing one in each position before doubling them up. If pairing is required (when there are more than four electrons) place the pairs away from the symbols for the other elements. For example, sulfur has six electrons and the two pairs are placed above and below the symbol and away from the oxygens rather than on either side near the oxygens.

$$\overset{\times\times}{\underset{\times}{\times\ddot{O}\times}} \quad \cdot\ddot{S}\cdot \quad \overset{\times\times}{\times\ddot{O}\overset{}{\times}}$$

3 **Share one electron from each atom** so as to form a single covalent bond between atoms.

$$\overset{\times\times}{\underset{\times}{\times}}O\!\cdot\!\!\cdot\!\!\cdot\!S\!\cdot\!\!\cdot\!\!\cdot\!\overset{\times\times}{O}\overset{\times}{\times} \longrightarrow \overset{..}{\underset{..}{\times O}}\overset{..}{\times}S\overset{..}{\underset{..}{O\times}}$$

4 **Check** the structure to see that each atom (except hydrogen) has **eight electrons** available to it. (Hydrogen should have only two electrons.) If so, then the structure is complete. If not all atoms have complete octets, then follow steps 5 and/or 6.

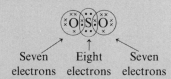

Seven   Eight   Seven
electrons   electrons   electrons

5 **Share one or two more pairs** between adjacent atoms, and/or **move** one or more **electrons anywhere** in the molecule so as to fulfill the octet rule of all atoms.

$$\overset{\times\times}{\underset{\times}{\times}}\underline{O}\overset{..}{\underset{..}{S}}\underline{O}\overset{\times\times}{\underset{\times}{\times}} \longrightarrow \times O\overset{..}{\underset{..}{S}}O\times$$

Share Move   Eight electrons each

Molecular SO_2 can be represented in Kekulé form as follows:

$$:\ddot{O}\!=\!\overset{+}{\ddot{S}}\!-\!\ddot{\underset{..}{O}}\!:^{-}$$

Note that charges on certain atoms result from moving (rather than sharing) electrons. This is called formal charge (see page 19).

6 If the species has a charge, **add one electron** to any position for each negative charge. **Remove one electron** for each positive charge (not applicable to our molecular SO_2 example).

Worked example

Write the Lewis dot diagram for CO_2

1   O   C   O

2   :Ö·   ×C×   ·Ö:
                        ×

3   :Ö:×C:×Ö:
                       ×

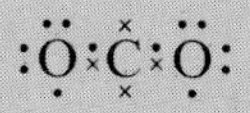

4 Structure is not complete.

5 Share one more pair of electrons between each C—O pair.

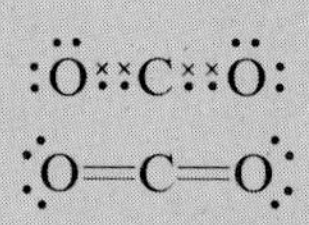

:Ö××C××Ö:

:O̤=C=O̤:

Worked example

Write the Lewis dot diagram for $CHO_2{}^-$

1   O   C   O

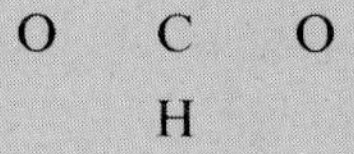

                          H

2   :Ö·   ×C×   ·Ö:
                        ×
                          H

3   :Ö:×C:Ö:
                     ××
                      Ḧ

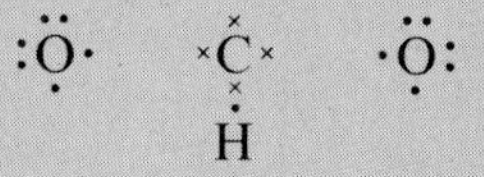

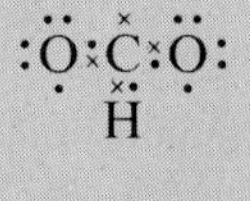

4 Structure is not complete.

5 Share one more pair of electrons between the carbon and one oxygen.

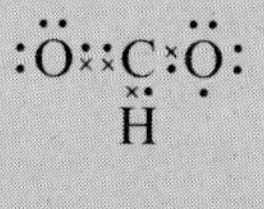

:Ö××C:Ö:
     ××
      Ḧ

6 Add one electron (because of the negative charge).

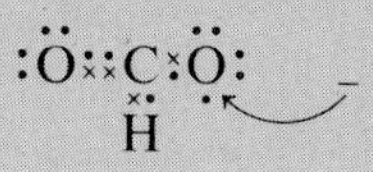

:Ö××C:Ö: ⁻
     ×× ·
      Ḧ

Rewrite:

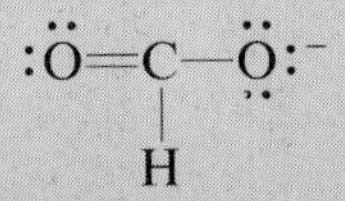

$$:\ddot{O}{=}C{-}\ddot{O}:^{-}$$

$$|$$

$$H$$

Problems

Try each of these, then look below to see if you arrived at the correct answer. Sometimes there is more than one correct way to write a formula—see the section "*Resonance*" which follows later in this chapter.

1 CH_4

2 C_2H_6

3 $CO_3{}^{2-}$

4 $NO_2{}^{-}$

5 C_3H_6

Solutions

1

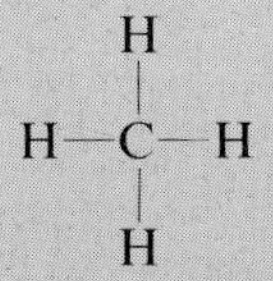

$$H{-}\underset{\underset{\displaystyle H}{|}}{\overset{\overset{\displaystyle H}{|}}{C}}{-}H$$

2

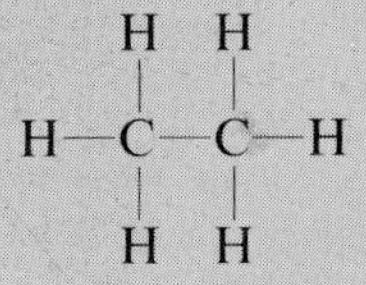

$$H{-}\underset{\underset{\displaystyle H}{|}\,\,\underset{\displaystyle H}{|}}{\overset{\overset{\displaystyle H}{|}\,\,\overset{\displaystyle H}{|}}{C{-}C}}{-}H$$

3

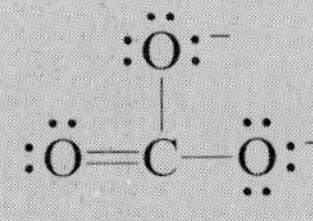

$$:\ddot{O}:^{-}$$

$$|$$

$$:\ddot{O}{=}C{-}\ddot{O}:^{-}$$

4

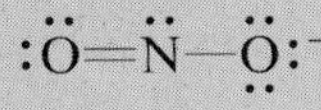

$$:\ddot{O}{=}\ddot{N}{-}\ddot{O}:^{-}$$

5

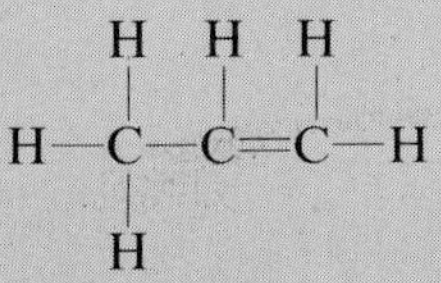

$$H{-}\underset{\underset{\displaystyle H}{|}}{\overset{\overset{\displaystyle H}{|}}{C}}{-}\overset{\overset{\displaystyle H}{|}}{C}{=}C{-}H \quad \text{or} \quad H{-}\underset{\underset{\displaystyle H}{|}}{C}\overset{\overset{\displaystyle H}{\diagdown}\,\,\overset{\displaystyle H}{\diagup}}{\underset{\displaystyle}{C}}\underset{\underset{\displaystyle H}{|}}{C}{-}H$$

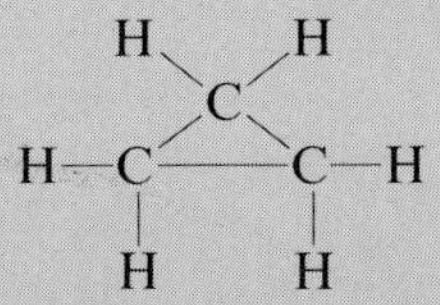

FORMAL CHARGE

Sometimes covalently bonded atoms have a charge. When we wrote the Lewis dot structure of SO_2 in the preceding section, we saw that the sulfur atom and one of the oxygen atoms have charges. The charge on an atom, which depends on the electrons available to it and the number of protons in its nucleus, is usually called the **formal charge**. The number of electrons in the valence (outer) shell of a neutral (uncharged) atom is given by its group number on the periodic chart. In a covalent bonding situation, bonding electrons (those involved in forming bonds) are "half owned" by each atom involved in bonding, and nonbonding electrons (those not involved in forming bonds) are "fully owned" by the atom on which they are found. Each atom, therefore, has all of its nonbonding electrons and as many bonding electrons as it has bonds. If the number of electrons available to a given atom is the same as the number of valence electrons in the neutral atom, then that atom will be neutral—it has no net charge. If there are more electrons than there are in the neutral atom, then that atom will bear a negative charge; if it has fewer electrons than the neutral atom, then it will be positively charged. The following relationship allows one to calculate the formal charge on any atom within a structure. The examples which follow illustrate the use of this relationship.

Formal charge = valence electrons − [nonbonding electrons
+ number of bonds]

Formal charge is the charge on a covalently bonded atom resulting from an effective transfer of electrons which occurs in addition to the sharing of electrons.

RESONANCE

Sometimes it is possible to write more than one correct Lewis dot formula or to write the same formula with different individual atoms bonded in alternative ways. For example:

ONE

1

$$H_3C-C(=\ddot{O})-\ddot{N}-H \longleftrightarrow H_3C-C(-\ddot{\ddot{O}}:^-)=\overset{+}{N}-H$$
(with H below each nitrogen)

2

$$H-C(=\dot{\ddot{O}})-\ddot{\ddot{O}}:^- \longleftrightarrow H-C(-\ddot{\ddot{O}}:^-)=\ddot{O}:$$

3

$$:\ddot{O}=\overset{+}{\ddot{S}}-\ddot{O}:^- \longleftrightarrow :\ddot{O}^--\overset{+}{\ddot{S}}=\ddot{O}:$$

In each case, two ways can be found to complete the octets of each atom. When we can write two or more such structures with the atoms in the same sequence, they are called **resonance forms** or **classical resonance structures**. They are written as shown above, connected with a double-headed arrow. In such cases, the actual structure of the species is not exactly like either classical form, nor is it changing back and forth between the two. It exists constantly in a form somewhere between the two extremes and is called the **resonance hybrid**. In the first example above, the resonance hybrid is most like the structure on the left but has some of the characteristics of the charged structure written on the right. For the other two examples above, the actual form is half way between the two classical forms, with each bond to oxygen existing as $1\frac{1}{2}$ bonds all the time. The resonance hybrids for these three examples are shown below; the dotted lines stand for partial bonds.

1

$$H_3C-C\cdots\overset{\delta+}{N}-H$$
(with $\delta-O$ above C by partial bond, H below N)

2

$$H-C\big(\cdots O^{\frac{1}{2}-}\big)\big(\cdots O^{\frac{1}{2}}\big)$$

3

$$^{\frac{1}{2}-}O\cdots\overset{+}{S}\cdots O^{\frac{1}{2}-}$$

Resonance is important because compounds that exhibit resonance tend to be more stable than those that do not. For example, in the second example above, the negative charge is equally distributed over **two** oxygen atoms rather than being concentrated on just one. This lowering of the intensity of charge is a stabilizing factor.

In the first example, the C—N bond does not behave as though it is an ordinary single bond, and the electron pair on the nitrogen is not readily available for sharing with other molecules. The fact that we can write its second (right) resonance form helps to explain these unusual facts.

Remember that the usefulness of most theories is their power to explain known facts and predict others.

> **Resonance is the delocalization of electrons over a covalently bonded structure. It adds stability to the species involved and is indicated by drawing several resonance structures connected by double-headed arrows or by drawing a resonance hybrid.**

MOLECULAR GEOMETRY

Primarily through the techniques of x-ray crystallography and electron diffraction, the shapes of molecules can be determined experimentally. By "shapes" we mean the spatial arrangement or geometry of the atoms composing molecules. This includes bond angles, bond distances, and the manner in which bonds radiate out from a central atom.

The following terms are important to an understanding of molecular geometry:

Bond angle   The average angle formed by two covalent bonds. The size of the angle fluctuates with the natural vibration of the atoms involved, but the average value is used.

Molecule   An electrically neutral structural unit composed of two or more covalently bonded atoms.

Bond length   The average distance between the nuclei of two atoms in a covalent bond. Actually bonded atoms oscillate, thus lengthening and shortening the bonds, but the average value is used.

Carbocation of carbonium ion   A group of covalently bonded atoms containing a carbon atom with a positive charge, such as H_3C^+.

Carbanion   A group of covalently bonded atoms containing a carbon atom with a negative charge, such as $H_3C\colon^-$.

Free radical   An atom or group of atoms containing an unpaired (or lone) electron, such as $H_3C\cdot$ or $Cl\cdot$.

For organic molecules there are only three basic geometries. These arrangements are illustrated by the following three simple molecules.

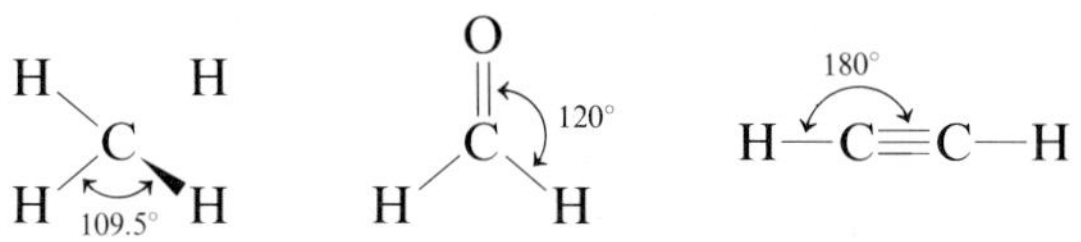

Methane,
tetrahedral

Formaldehyde,
trigonal planar

Acetylene,
linear

Figure 1-5 shows molecular models of three materials. All bond angles of methane (CH_4) are 109.5°; it is called **tetrahedral** (see Fig. 1-5). All carbon

Ball-and-stick molecular models of (from left to right) methane (CH_4), formaldehyde (H_2CO), and ethylene (C_2H_4).

FIGURE 1-5

atoms with four separate single bonds and no unshared electrons exhibit this approximate shape, even when they are in larger molecules.

Formaldehyde (CH_2O) is a flat (**planar**) molecule with the three atoms pointing in such a way as to form a triangular (**trigonal**) arrangement (see Fig. 1-5). The bond angles are all approximately 120°. All carbon atoms with one double bond, two single bonds, and no unshared electrons show this geometry, as does ethylene, as shown in Fig. 1-5. It should be noted that the bond angles in tetrahedral or trigonal planar shapes can vary by a few degrees from one molecule to another. This variation depends on the sizes of the atoms to which the central atom is bonded. For example, in CH_2Cl_2 the two chlorine atoms are farther apart than the two hydrogen

FIGURE 1-6

Ball-and-stick molecular model of dichloromethane (CH_2Cl_2).

atoms (owing to the smaller size of the hydrogen atoms). Figure 1-6 is a photograph of a model of this molecule showing the relative sizes of the various atoms. The angles are close to the standard value of 109.5°, and the basic tetrahedral geometry is the same, however.

The third shape encountered is illustrated by acetylene (C_2H_4) (see p. 21) in which all four atoms lie in a straight line. This shape is called (not surprisingly) **linear** and the bond angle is 180°. All carbon atoms with one triple and one single bond show this geometry.

Oxygen and nitrogen atoms are also found in organic molecules and usually show modifications of the tetrahedral bond angles, since there are four pairs of electrons around each atom. Inorganic molecules containing these atoms are shown below.

Water, angular   Ammonia, trigonal pyramid

The geometries are approximately the same when oxygen and nitrogen atoms are found in larger molecules, as shown by the complex molecular structure below. While it is not possible to give one name for the shape of the whole molecule, the arrangement of each part can be described by the labels shown.

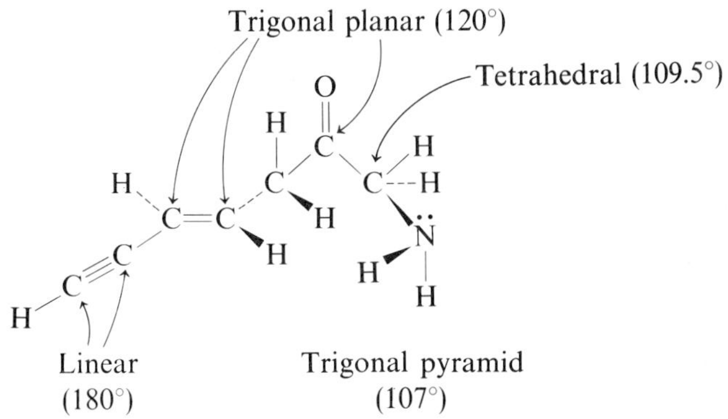

Trigonal planar (120°)
Tetrahedral (109.5°)
Linear (180°)
Trigonal pyramid (107°)

In drawings such as the one above, the regular solid lines (——) mean that the bond is in the plane of the paper, the dashed lines (–––) represent bonds that are going away from the reader, and the foreshortened bonds (——) are coming out toward the reader. Drawings which show bonds in this way are referred to as **stereo drawings**.

HYBRIDIZATION

As we discussed in the preceding section, three types of geometry are shown by carbon atoms. The carbon atom has outer shell electrons in one $2s$ and two $2p$ orbitals. The two $2p$ orbitals are at 90° to each other, and the 2s orbital is nondirectional (see the drawing below). These atomic orbitals, therefore, do not form angles which could explain the 109.5°, 120°, or 180° shapes found in organic molecules.

The concept of **hybridization** has been postulated to explain (or rationalize) how carbon atoms with certain orbital angles can form molecules with different geometries. Since there are only three basic types of geometry in organic molecules, only three types of hybridization are needed.

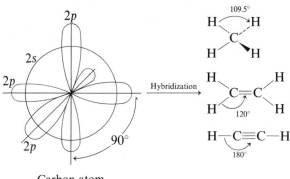

Carbon atom

The idea of hybridization comes from the genius of Linus Pauling, who is largely responsible for many of our ideas in the areas of bonding and electronegativity (see Figure 1-7). The following description of hybridization in carbon explains how carbon atoms modify their orbitals as compounds are formed. The steps in the process used to describe hybridization are imaginary to a certain extent, but the postulated steps allow us to do our mental bookkeeping. At any rate, the resulting geometries are real. We will consider only outer shell (valence) electrons.

Consider Figure 1-8. We start with carbon in the usual electron configuration. We then promote one of the 2s electrons to the empty 2p orbital (step 1). Next, and this is the abstract concept, the one 2s and three 2p orbitals mix in such a way as to change themselves into four new orbitals. Each of the newly formed orbitals is one-quarter like an s and three-quarters like a p orbital. They are called sp^3 **hybrid orbitals**. Here the superscript 3 does not stand for the number of electrons in the orbital; instead, it stands for the number of p orbitals used in the hybridization. Each hybrid orbital has one electron, and since there are four identically shaped unidirectional orbitals, they form a tetrahedron. In step 3, these 4 orbitals now form four single bonds with four other atoms such as hydrogen to produce 109.5° bond angles. Orbital pictures are drawn beside the standard notation to facilitate the development of a useful mental image.

To arrive at 120° planar molecules, we follow the process shown in Figure 1-9. First, in step 1, promotion occurs, just as in the sp^3 case. In step 2, the hybridization involves the 2s and only two of the 2p orbitals, which form three sp^2 orbitals. This leaves an unhybridized 2p orbital that will be available later (step 4) to form the side-to-side overlap needed for

FIGURE 1-7

Linus Pauling, a pioneer in developing current ideas about chemical bonding. (*Smithsonian Institution.*)

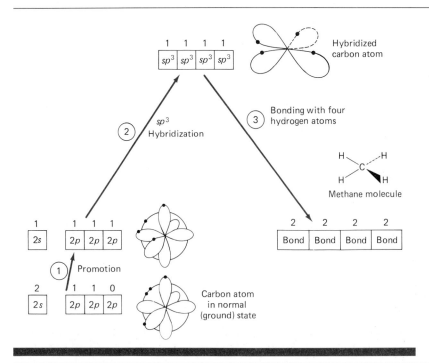

Sp^3 hybridization in methane.

FIGURE 1-8

the second bond. In step 3, two of the **sp^2 hybrid orbitals** from two such carbon atoms share their electrons to form a covalent bond between carbon atoms. This is called a **sigma bond** (σ bond) (end-to-end overlap of atomic orbitals). Step 4 shows the two unhybridized $2p$ orbitals from the two carbon atoms sharing their electrons in a side-to-side fashion to form a **pi bond** (π bond). The new molecular orbital has two areas above and below the σ bond. The σ and π bonds between the two carbon atoms constitute a **double bond**. Finally, in step 5, four hydrogen atoms bond to the remaining sp^2 orbitals to form four σ bonds. Since there are three atoms around each carbon atom and there are no nonbonding electrons, a trigonal planar arrangement is assumed by the bonds.

The third, and last, type of hybridization is illustrated by the simplest molecule containing the carbon-carbon triple bond (acetylene). It is shown in Figure 1-10. Step 1 is the same as before. In the second step, two of the $2p$ orbitals are left unchanged because later we will need to make two π bonds. The $2s$ orbital and one of the $2p$ orbitals mix to form two **sp hybrid orbitals**. After this is done for two carbon atoms, bonding occurs. Step 3 shows the σ bond forming from two sp orbitals of two carbon atoms and steps 4 and 5 show the two π bonds forming by side-to-side overlap of the unhybridized $2p$ orbitals. The one σ and two π bonds constitute a **triple bond**. Finally, in step 6, two hydrogen atoms bond to the remaining sp orbitals to form sigma bonds. Since there are only two atoms around each carbon atom and no nonbonding electrons, a linear geometry results.

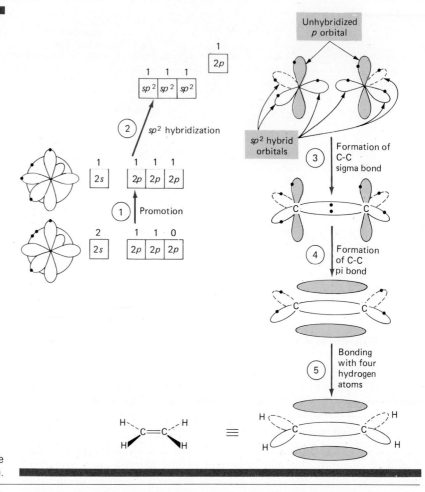

Sp² hybridization in ethene
(ethylene).

FIGURE 1-9

We have shown how the three basic geometries of organic compounds can be formed by combining the atomic orbitals of carbon atoms in three different ways. In order to identify the hybridization type in various atoms in a structure the following two methods can be used:

1   For all molecules the most general method uses bond angles:
    (*a*)   Bond angles 109.5°, 107°, and 105°—*sp³*
    (*b*)   Bond angles about 120°—*sp²*
    (*c*)   Bond angles 180°—*sp*

2   For ordinary whole organic molecules, since the types of bonds (i.e., single, double, or triple) are related to geometries, we can simply examine the bonds about the atom to determine the type of hybridization:
    (*a*)   All single bonds—*sp³*
    (*b*)   One double bond—*sp²*
    (*c*)   One triple bond—*sp*

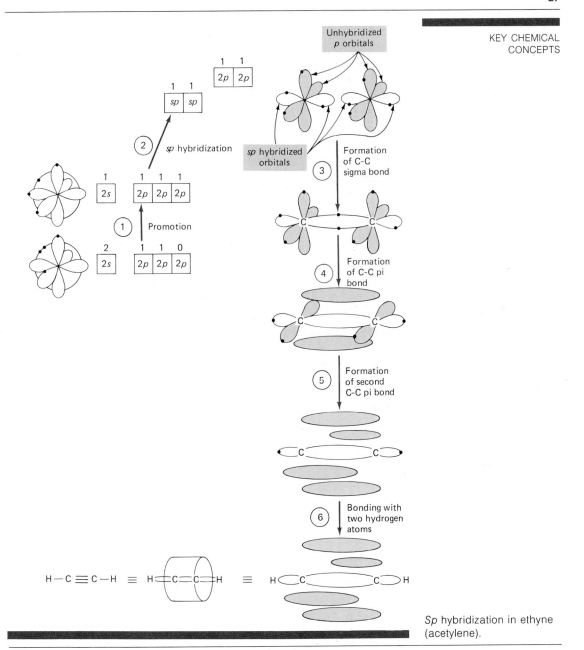

Sp hybridization in ethyne (acetylene).

FIGURE 1-10

For charged species, and for compounds containing unusual atoms such as boron (B) or beryllium (Be), we must consider the bond angles from the Lewis dot diagrams (refer to your general chemistry text, if necessary, for a review of this procedure) and use method 1 above.

For ordinary whole organic molecules, method 2 above, which is much easier and faster), is the recommended method for this course.

Hybridization is a mental construct in which we say that atoms re-organize their normal (ground state) atomic orbitals into new orbitals; this can explain observed molecular geometries.

CHEMICAL FORMULAS

Let's look at chemical formulas, especially the type used in organic chemistry, in more detail. The formula of a compound expresses the type and number of atoms in a compound. The **empirical formula** is the simplest ratio of atoms of the elements in a compound. The **molecular formula** is the actual number of each type of atom in a single molecule of the substance. For example, the molecular formula of benzene is C_6H_6, which means that there are six atoms of carbon and six atoms of hydrogen in a molecule of benzene. The ratio of carbon atoms to hydrogen atoms is 1:1; therefore, the empirical formula of benzene is simply CH. Other examples are shown in Table 1-4.

Since organic chemistry deals almost exclusively with covalent compounds, we will consider the various ways of indicating molecular structures. These are properly called **molecular diagrams** since they indicate what atoms are bonded to each other and the shapes involved. If we could see molecules they would not look exactly like their diagrams. Figure 1-11 gives a better indication of how chemists believe molecules actually appear. Four kinds of molecular diagrams are shown on the next page.

TABLE 1-4

Examples of molecular and empirical formulas	NAME	MOLECULAR FORMULA	DIAGRAM OF MOLECULE	EMPIRICAL FORMULA
	Water	H_2O	O—H / H	H_2O*
	Ethane	C_2H_6	H H | | H—C—C—H | | H H	CH_3
	Methanol	CH_4O	H | H—C—O—H | H	CH_4O
	Ethylene glycol	$C_2H_6O_2$	H H | | H—C———C—H | | O—H O—H	CH_3O

* Two hydrogen atoms to one oxygen atom is the simplest ratio possible for this molecule; therefore, the empirical and molecular formulas are the same.

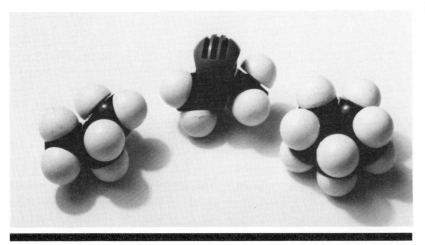

Space-filled (scale model) molecular models of (from left to right) propane (C_3H_8), acetone, (C_3H_6O), and cyclopentane (C_5H_{10}).

FIGURE 1-11

1 Complete structure:

propane   acetone   cyclopentane

2 Condensed formula:

$CH_3-CH_2-CH_3$ $CH_3-\overset{\overset{O}{\|}}{C}-CH_3$

$$\begin{array}{c} CH_2 \\ CH_2 \quad CH_2 \\ CH_2-CH_2 \end{array}$$

3 Abbreviated formula (hydrogens are omitted):

$C-C-C$ $C-\overset{\overset{O}{\|}}{C}-C$

4 Line diagram (there are carbon atoms at the end of each straight line and hydrogens are omitted. Oxygens, nitrogens and halogens are indicated):

HINTS FOR THE STUDY
OF ORGANIC CHEMISTRY

You have begun the study of organic chemistry. For many of you this is an entirely new field; whatever your reason for becoming involved in this study, you may be somewhat apprehensive about this subject and your chance of success. What follow are some practical suggestions about how these fears can be overcome, along with some study hints that will aid in bringing about your success.

Programmed learning units

In this textbook, every attempt will be made to give a careful, stepwise development of each reasoning procedure or skill. In many chapters, programmed learning units will help you to develop the skills necessary for your success in learning organic chemistry. In these programmed units, you will find examples of each type of skill worked out, with each step explained. You should follow these steps carefully in your own mind. After several worked examples are presented, a problem will be presented for you to work. You should attempt to solve the problem using the procedure shown in the worked examples. Only after you have tried to solve the problem should you turn to the solution. After repeating this procedure several times you will be asked to work problems for which only the answers are given. Don't be discouraged by any errors you make; sometimes a fuller understanding can result from a corrected mistake than from getting the correct answer the first time. Any skill needs practice; therefore, you should work all the examples given.

FIGURE 1-12

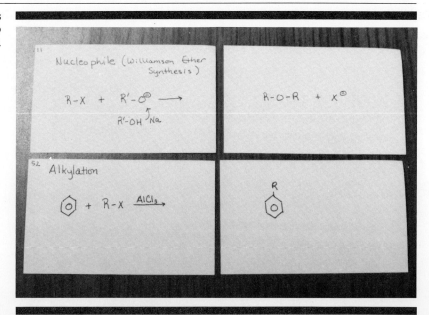

Photograph of flash cards prepared by a student to aid in learning reactions.

Flow diagrams

In chapters where chemical reactions are emphasized, flow diagrams outlining the reactions are included. These serve as "road maps," showing how to get from one chemical substance to another. You should study and essentially memorize these diagrams, or better still, draw similar diagrams of your own design. (See page 107 for such a flow diagram.)

Flash cards

A large number of reactions must be learned in organic chemistry, and before the flow diagrams mentioned above can be used, the individual reactions must be mastered. Flash cards are helpful to many students. You can obtain a package of 3×5 cards. Write the reactants on one side of the card and products on the other. For example, for the reaction shown below the cards would appear as shown. Figure 1-12 shows student-made cards. The study guide for this text contains a set of flash cards.

$$\overset{\overset{\displaystyle O}{\displaystyle \|}}{R—C—H} + LiAlH_4 \longrightarrow R—CH_2OH$$

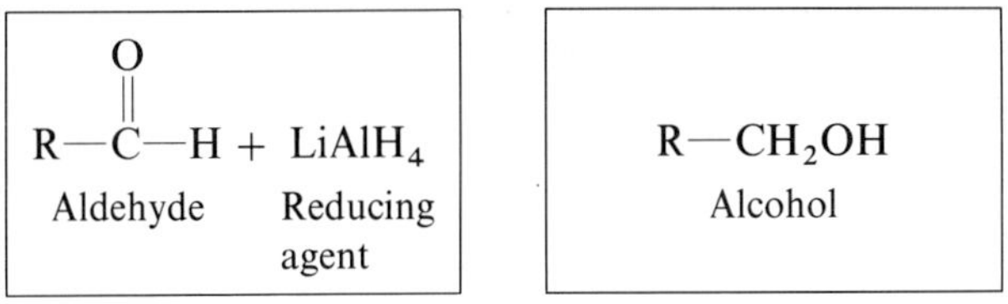

$\overset{\overset{\displaystyle O}{\displaystyle \|}}{R—C—H} + LiAlH_4$	$R—CH_2OH$
Aldehyde Reducing agent	Alcohol
Front	Back

These cards can be carried and reviewed during short blocks of time during the day. Several short periods of study (5 to 10 minutes) are better than one longer period.

Constant review

Organic chemistry, like a foreign language, is a discipline that is cumulative—later parts are based on knowledge acquired earlier. Therefore, at the end of each chapter of this book there are questions that refer back to previous chapters for review.

Molecular model sets

Since the study of molecular shapes is important to the study of organic chemistry, it is a good idea to purchase an inexpensive molecular model set. These are available at most college and university bookstores and will allow you to construct actual models which can be manipulated, examined, measured, and so forth to aid in understanding certain aspects of molecular structure.

Peer study

This textbook has been organized to facilitate learning, but it is also necessary for you to apply yourself diligently. For most chemistry courses, you should study 2 to 3 hours outside of class for every hour in class. Study could include reading the text, reading lecture notes, working problems, and memorizing facts. No teachers, text, or method will work without this most important of all factors. It is also assumed that you will attend class and do all assigned work.

At times, even a student who is spending enough time and applying enough effort will encounter difficulties, or a student may find that the hours spent studying do not seem to be productive. In this situation, students should feel free to approach the instructor for help, either as individuals or as small groups, or to seek assistance from the resources within the school. **Peer teaching**, which takes place in study groups of three to five students from the same course meeting on a regular basis, can be of great help. Study groups are not intimidating, and one member of the group may understand a given concept and be able to explain it to the others. Each member can prepare practice test questions for the others; preparing your own questions and answering those of the other students can be of value in mastering the material.

FIGURE 1-13

Processes involved in learning new subject matter.

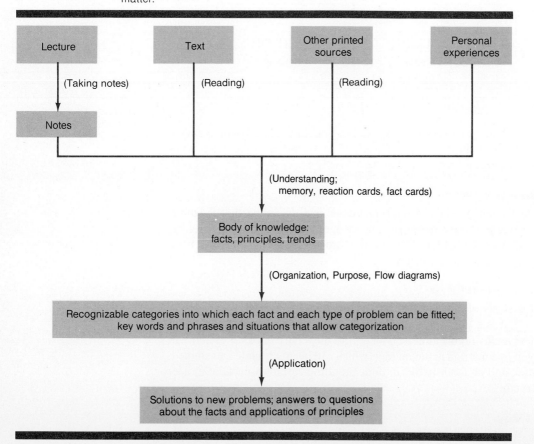

General study skills

Keep in mind that careful attention to new vocabulary is important in organic chemistry, as in any discipline. It is also true that reading in science usually takes longer than reading in other areas. You cannot expect to "speedread" most of this text. To understand it well, you should read it slowly and carefully. Some people prefer two readings—one for a rapid overview and a second for more attention to detail.

Figure 1-13 shows the organization of the processes involved in mastering a new subject; Table 1-5 lists problems commonly encountered in a chemistry course and some suggested remedies. The words in Figure 1-14 should be the motto of all beginning chemistry students.

KEY CHEMICAL CONCEPTS

Go ahead— ask dumb questions. They're easier to cope with than stupid mistakes.

The chemistry student's motto.

FIGURE 1-14

TABLE 1-5

COMMONLY ENCOUNTERED DIFFICULTIES AND SUGGESTED REMEDIES

PROBLEM	AID
Many new facts to learn	Study 2 to 3 h outside of class for each 1 h in class Prepare lists of facts or flash cards, or both, for short, frequent drills
Concepts abstract	Pay close attention to diagrams, models, and analogies **Consciously** try to develop a mental picture of each abstraction
Lethargy	Exercise regularly and follow a nutritious diet
Attitude	Develop confidence in your own ability. Try simple tasks, and the success gained will help in the more complex ones
Lack of understanding	Reread the text, and when necessary get your instructor to reexplain the concept in question
Lack of skills such as reading comprehension, note taking, effective studying, test taking	Seek advice from your instructor, a fellow student who has been successful, or the study skills office if your college or university has one. Outline the material. Prepare practice exams and take them
Lack of precision in learning	Arrange peer study groups to answer questions, explain concepts, and prepare practice tests

SUMMARY

1 The outer shell electron configuration of atoms determines the chemical behavior of elements.

2 Chemical bonding occurs by a transfer of electrons to produce ions (**ionic bonding**) or by a mutual sharing of electrons to produce molecules (**covalent bonding**).

3 **Lewis dot diagrams** are representations of molecules which indicate the position of the atoms and the location of all valence (outer shell) electrons.

4 **Molecular geometry** involves a description of the general shapes of molecules as well as the average bond angles and bond lengths.

5 **Hybridization** is a concept in which atomic orbitals are thought to re-form into new orbitals prior to covalent bonding. These new orbitals explain the experimentally observed shapes of molecules.

6 **Resonance** is a phenomenon in which electrons are distributed in molecules in a nonclassical way. There is delocalization of electrons, which causes an increased stability in a molecule or charged species.

7 Through the use of programmed learning units, chapter summaries, flow diagrams, flash cards, molecular model sets, and peer study groups the study of organic chemistry can be facilitated. Personal health care is another important factor in success.

KEY TERMS

Bond angle	Formal charge	Molecular shape
Bond length	Free radical	Molecule
Bonding	Hybridization	Octet rule
Carbanion	Ionic bonding	Orbital
Carbocation	Kekulé structure	Polar bond
Covalent bond	Lewis diagram	Resonance
Electronegativity	Molecular orbital	

SKILL PRACTICE PROBLEMS

1 Write the Lewis diagrams of
   (*a*) C_3H_8

(b) $NO_3{}^{2-}$
(c) C_5H_{10}

2 Write the Lewis diagrams of
(a) C_4H_{10}
(b) CH_4O
(c) $CHO_2{}^-$

3 Indicate the bond angles and hybridization for each atom in the following structure.

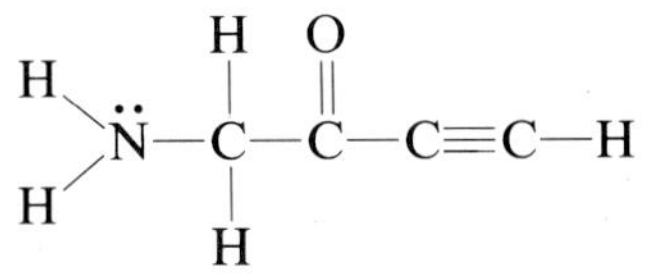

4 Indicate the bond angles and hybridization for each atom in the following structure.

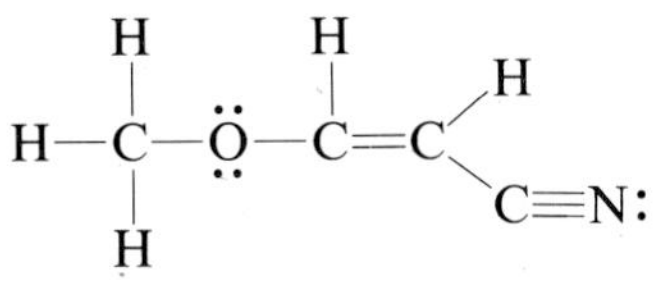

5 Define
(a) Polar covalent bond
(b) Carbanion

6 Define
(a) Carbocation
(b) Trigonal planar arrangement

7 Draw condensed, abbreviated, and line formulas for the following substance.

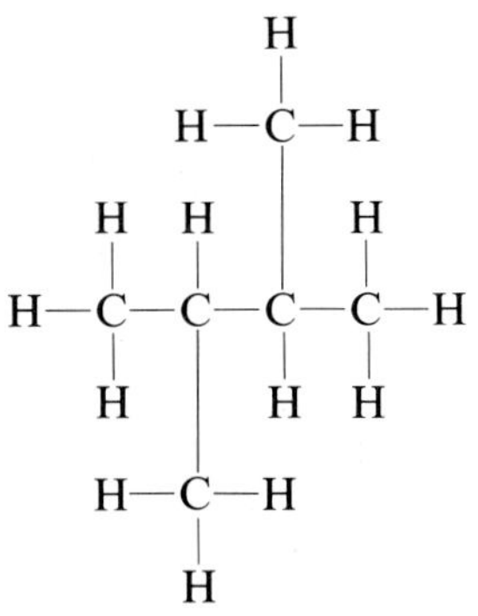

8 Draw condensed, abbreviated and line formulas for the following substance.

9 Write the **complete** structural formula for the compound whose line formula is given below.

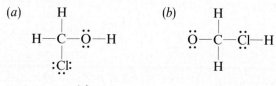

10 Which of the following molecular structures is *not* written correctly? What is wrong with it?

(*a*)

$$H—C—\ddot{O}—H$$

with H above C and :$\ddot{C}$l: below C

(*b*)

$$\ddot{O}—C—\ddot{C}l—H$$

with H above C and H below C

(*c*)

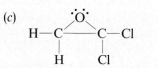

11 How many electrons are in the outer shell of each of the following atoms? (Refer to a periodic chart.)
(*a*) C   (*b*) P   (*c*) Xe   (*d*) Al

12 For each of the bonds below, indicate whether it is polar, and if so, which end is negative and which positive.
(*a*) C—O   (*b*) C—C   (*c*) N—H   (*d*) C—Cl

13 Why is the concept of hybridization useful?

14 Give the formal charge on each atom in each structure shown below.

(*a*) $H—C—\ddot{O}:$ with $\underset{\parallel}{O}$ below C

(*b*) $:\ddot{O}=C=\ddot{O}:$

(*c*) $H—C=N—H$ with H above N and $:\ddot{O}:$ below C

CHAPTER 2

OVERVIEW OF ORGANIC CHEMISTRY

LEARNING GOALS

1 To gain a perspective on the nature and scope of organic chemistry

2 To develop skill in classifying compounds according to functional group categories

3 To develop skill in recognizing and writing structures of isomers

This chapter is an overview of organic chemistry and its relation to other natural sciences. See Figure 2-1. First, let us look at a formal definition of chemistry and then briefly describe each area of chemistry.

Chemistry is a natural science which involves the study of the matter of the universe. Chemistry has three aspects:

1 Understanding all individual pure **substances** and mixtures

2 Understanding the **changes** those substances can undergo and how they interact with each other

3 Studying the **energy** changes associated with the changes in matter

Matter, in turn, can be formally defined as **that which has mass and occupies space**. However, we intuitively know what matter is: it is material, or substance, or "stuff."

AREAS OF CHEMISTRY

The field of chemistry has traditionally been divided into several subdisciplines (see Figure 2-1). Most chemistry departments at colleges and universities are thus divided into organic, inorganic, physical, and analytical chemistry and biochemistry on the basis of the exact nature of the chemistry being studied and the kinds of skills being developed in the students.

Organic chemistry   Organic chemistry is the study of carbon-containing substances and the synthesis of such materials. Since so many consumer

FIGURE 2-1

Relationship of organic chemistry to other academic disciplines.

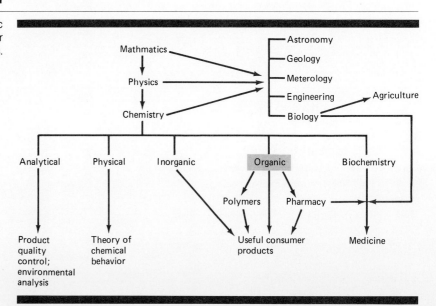

products are organic compounds, there is a large demand for organic chemists and organic chemistry is one of the larger areas in terms of number of chemists.

Inorganic chemistry   Inorganic chemistry is the study of the properties and synthesis of materials containing all elements other than carbon. This is an area that is growing rapidly now, and many exciting discoveries will likely be made in it in the near future.

Physical chemistry   Physical chemistry is the measurement of various quantitative physical properties of matter, along with an effort to correlate large amounts of data. These activities are aimed at understanding the underlying principles of chemistry rather than developing methods of synthesis. Physical chemistry is especially concerned with understanding energy changes in chemical process.

Analytical chemistry   Analytical chemistry is the study of methods used to determine the presence of materials and to establish how much of a material is present. Although this is a well established discipline, methods for analyzing new materials must be found, as well as easier ways of doing previously known analyses. With increasing concern over the environment, we also must find ways of detecting smaller and smaller amounts of harmful materials.

Biochemistry   Biochemistry is the study of all substances and processes in living systems. Many of the skills used in the other areas of chemistry are used here in specialized ways. It is generally thought that many serious medical problems can be solved only by a more complete understanding of the chemical processes in the normal organism and by an understanding of the chemical basis for malfunctions. This is an area in which present knowledge is slight compared with the vast areas that still remain unknown.

This textbook concentrates on organic chemistry and deals more briefly with biochemistry.

SYNTHETIC ORGANIC CHEMISTRY

Chemists are involved in the synthesis of materials. Research chemists in college and university laboratories as well as in industrial laboratories are constantly attempting to prepare new materials (ones that have not been made before) from materials that are already available. They are also attempting to prepare **synthetically** materials which are found in nature (Figure 2-2) but which for some reason cannot be isolated in large enough quantities or are too expensive. Such materials include, for example, aspirin, sodium benzoate, and poly(ethylene terephthalate). (Do not be concerned with learning these names now; just remember that they are pure substances which are synthesized in a laboratory by chemists. The task of the synthetic organic chemist is to produce new organic materials of

A chemist at work in a laboratory producing a new synthetic material to solve human problems or meet human needs.

FIGURE 2-2

theoretical interest (that is, for testing a hypothesis) or practical value (for solving a problem or making life more convenient).

In carrying out this task, the chemist has available many different methods of **building carbon chains** and **changing functional groups**. (See page 45 for a definition of a functional group.) By using a variety of different methods and reaction sequences, chemists can change available materials into new, heretofore unknown materials. Before beginning the actual synthesis, researchers must first familiarize themselves with the different methods available. This information is acquired from chemistry courses, from personal experience, and from a search of the chemical literature to find how another chemist effected a particular kind of change in the structure of a molecule. The researcher then has to decide if any of these methods can be applied to the problem at hand.

Envisioning a compound for a special purpose

The first step in any problem in synthetic organic chemistry is working out the general approach to the problem. This step can be illustrated by looking at a typical research project. Let us consider a search for new drugs to control seizures in people with epilepsy. The National Institutes of Health announced such a search because the approximately 15 drugs currently used either have adverse side effects or do not adequately control seizures in some patients.

A chemist working on such a problem would first examine the molecular structure of known anticonvulsants (compounds that stop seizures).

Two of the most widely used are shown below.

Phenobarbital

Diphenylhydantoin
(Dilantin)

Notice that both these compounds have portions with six-membered carbon rings, and each has a ring of atoms containing nitrogens and carbons doubly bonded to oxygen.

A chemist seeking to synthesize previously unknown compounds that could reasonably be expected to have anticonvulsant properties would first envision molecular structures that had these same features and would search for methods of preparing these compounds. This attempt at synthesis may or may not be successful; even if it is successful, the new compound may not prove to be an anticonvulsant.

Preparing the envisioned compound

The second aspect of a synthesis problem is the technique used in the laboratory to actually prepare the envisioned compound.

Chemistry—indeed, all science—is a creative endeavor involving technical skill and creativity. Both art (creativity) and science (technical skills) are required of a good research chemist. For this reason, some synthetic organic chemists are better than others—they have an inborn or developed ability that their colleagues do not have (this is true in most areas of life). This ability to bring together bits of knowledge from various places and to think about new ways of effecting chemical changes, which no one else has conceived of before, is what makes great chemists. Such a chemist was the late R. B. Woodward of Harvard University (Figure 2-4), who, along with Albert Eschenmoser of the Swiss Federal Institute of Technology, over a period of 7 years developed a 90-step synthetic procedure for vitamin B_{12} and was able to prepare in the laboratory a vitamin B_{12} that was identical to the natural material. As you can see from Figure 2-5, this is an extremely complex molecule; a lesser chemist would not have even attempted to synthesize it.

Biosynthesis   A relatively new area of study, and one that holds a great deal of promise for the future, is biosynthesis. This area involves a co-operation between biology and chemistry, and is the production of useful materials by a microorganism. First, **genetic engineering** is performed on the microorganism—its genetic material is changed so that it produces a

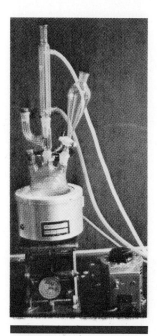

FIGURE 2-3

A typical apparatus used to synthesize organic compounds in a laboratory.

FIGURE 2-4

R. B. Woodward. (*From a drawing by the author.*)

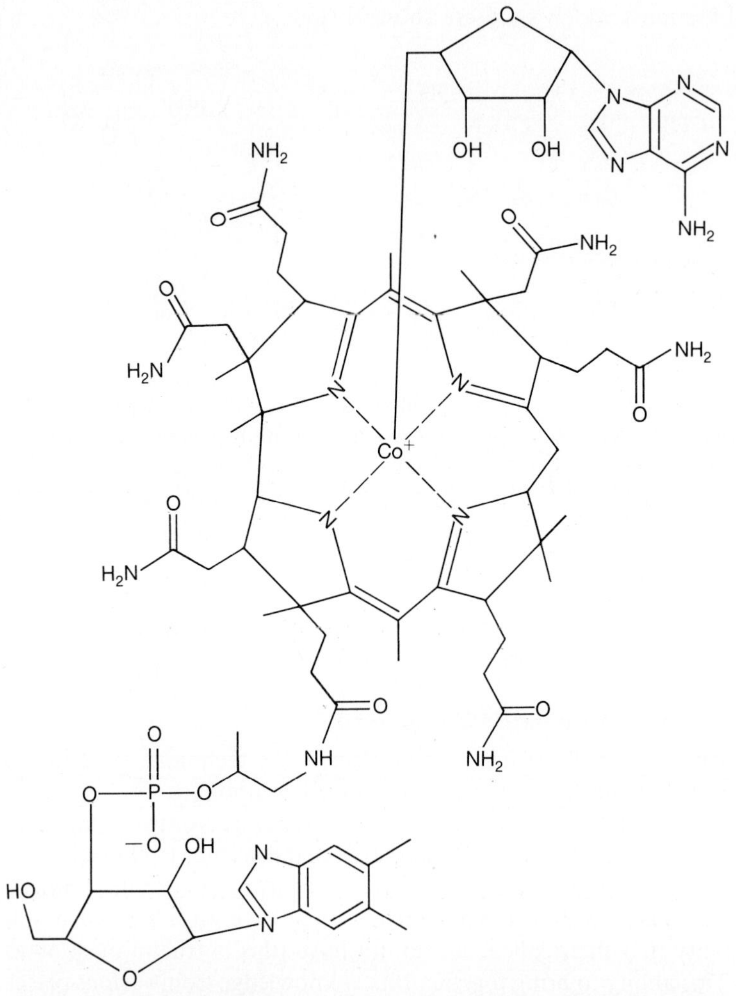

Molecular structure of
vitamin B_{12} (cobalamin).

FIGURE 2-5

material useful to human beings in addition to its normal biochemical substances. This new compound could be almost anything, theoretically, but biosynthesis is of special value when the desired material has a complex molecular structure and when its ordinary chemical synthesis is long and expensive. The most notable example of biosynthesis is the success of the Eli Lilly pharmaceutical company in preparing microbes that produce human insulin. The trade name for this microbe-produced insulin is Humulin, and it is molecularly identical to human insulin. It can be given to diabetics without the allergy problems sometimes associated with hog or cow insulin, which was previously isolated and used to treat people with diabetes.

Natural organism $\xrightarrow[\text{engineering}]{\text{genetic}}$ new organism

Biochemicals
associated with
its own life
processes

Chemical substance
needed by
humans

Determination of properties

Testing for (or discovering) the **properties** of these new materials is done either to find a new product for a specific purpose (as in Figure 2-6) or as a matter of academic interest (curiosity). Properties may also be discovered by accident as a chemist is working with the material. Examples of properties are the ability of aspirin to stop or reduce pain in the human body, of aluminum chlorhydrate to stop perspiration, and of sodium benzoate to prevent growth of microorganisms such as bacteria and mold; another example is the nature of poly(ethylene terephthalate) as a flexible solid with a high melting point. We can think of **physical properties** (how substances look, smell, and taste), **chemical properties** (how they interact with other substances), and **physiological properties** (how they affect living systems).

Theory

Last, but by no means least, many chemists are concerned with gaining a better **understanding** of chemical substances. Only out of theories about matter—only out of our understanding of how chemistry works—can we develop synthetic procedures, methods of analysis, and manufacturing

FIGURE 2-6

Animals are used to test drugs that are potentially useful for improving human health.

procedures. This fundamental knowledge is gained primarily in university laboratories by instructors and graduate students in the basic sciences.

ORGANIC CONSUMER PRODUCTS

Table 2-1 lists some products produced by organic chemists. We will look at some of these later in this book in relation to specific areas of interest to consumers.

TABLE 2-1

CONSUMER PRODUCTS PRODUCED BY ORGANIC CHEMISTS

MATERIAL	USE
Sodium lauryl sulfate	Laundry detergent
Maleic hydrazide	Growth inhibitor for preventing tobacco suckers and for preventing sprouting of vegetables during storage
2,4-Dichlorophenoxyacetic acid (2,4-D)	Herbicide for control of broad-leafed weeds
Acetylsalicylic acid (aspirin)	Analgesic—control of pain, fever, and inflammation
Sodium benzoate	Preservative for foods and beverages
Polyethylene	Plastic food containers
Poly(ethylene terephthalate) (polyester)	Strong flexible material for fibers and recording tapes
Carbaryl (Sevin)	Insecticide
Acetone	Solvent for glues and fingernail polish
Ethyl alcohol	Beverage and solvent for medications
Gasoline (heptane, octane, nonane)	Automobile fuel
Insulin	Isolated from living systems or produced by cultured bacteria to provide treatment for diabetics
n-Pentyl acetate	Used to give artificial banana flavor to candy
Cyclopropane	General anesthetic
para-Aminobenzoic acid (PABA)	Sunscreen used to prevent sunburn
Propylene glycol	Moisturizer for pastries and other foods

CLASSIFICATION OF ORGANIC COMPOUNDS: FUNCTIONAL GROUPS

As part of our overview, we will take a brief look at the various types of organic compounds to be studied. A familiarity with the full range of compounds should make the study of each type in subsequent chapters more understandable. Organic compounds are covalent in nature and as such are composed of molecules with definite arrangements of atoms. For purposes of organization and naming, all organic compounds have been divided into classes according to the characteristic groups of atoms they contain. These unique groupings of atoms are called **functional groups**. It is these groups within molecules that determine the chemical and physical behavior of organic compounds. The functional group idea is, therefore, central to the study of organic chemistry. The following pages briefly describe the more commonly encountered classes of functional groups and give examples of each. The common functional groups are summarized in Table 2-2 and on the inside front cover of this textbook.

In the description that follows, the functional groups that characterize each class are shown in color.

Alkanes   Alkanes are compounds containing **only carbon and hydrogen** and having only **single bonds**. Examples follow.

NAME	STRUCTURAL FORMULA	USE
Methane		Natural gas
Butane		Fuel for portable stoves
Pentane (see Figure 2-7)		Cigaratte lighter fluid
Octane		Component of gasoline

TABLE 2-2

NAME OF CLASS	CHARACTERISTICS FUNCTIONAL GROUP
Alkanes	$-\overset{\mid}{\underset{\mid}{C}}-\overset{\mid}{\underset{\mid}{C}}-H$
Cycloalkanes	$(CH_2)_n$
Alkenes	$>C=C<$
Alkynes	$-C\equiv C-$
Aromatics	⬡
Substituted alkanes (alkyl halides)	$-C-X$ where X is F, Cl, Br, or I
Alcohols	$-OH$
Carboxylic acids	$-\overset{O}{\overset{\|}{C}}-OH$
Esters	$-\overset{O}{\overset{\|}{C}}-O-C$
Ketones	$C-\overset{O}{\overset{\|}{C}}-C$
Aldehydes	$-\overset{O}{\overset{\|}{C}}-H$
Ethers	$C-O-C$
Amines	$\overset{\diagdown}{\underset{\mid}{N}}$
Amides	$-\overset{O}{\overset{\|}{C}}-\overset{\mid}{N}-$
Heterocyclics	$(CH_2)_nZ$ where Z is O, N or S,
Phenols	⬡$-OH$

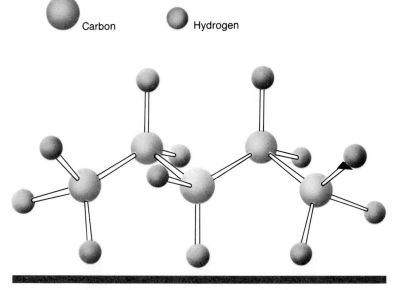

Carbon Hydrogen

Molecular model of
pentane.

FIGURE 2-7

Substituted alkanes (alkyl halides) In substituted alkanes, one or more of the hydrogen atoms have been replaced by a **halogen atom** (F, Cl, Br, I). Examples follow.

NAME	STRUCTURAL FORMULA	USE
Chloroform	$$Cl-\overset{\overset{\displaystyle H}{\vert}}{\underset{\underset{\displaystyle Cl}{\vert}}{C}}-Cl$$	Solvent
Carbon tetrachloride	$$Cl-\overset{\overset{\displaystyle Cl}{\vert}}{\underset{\underset{\displaystyle Cl}{\vert}}{C}}-Cl$$	Used in some types of fire extinguishers
1,2-Dichloroethane (ethylene chloride)	$$H-\overset{\overset{\displaystyle H}{\vert}}{\underset{\underset{\displaystyle Cl}{\vert}}{C}}-\overset{\overset{\displaystyle H}{\vert}}{\underset{\underset{\displaystyle Cl}{\vert}}{C}}-H$$	Solvent

Cycloalkanes Cycloalkanes are compounds containing only carbon and hydrogen (all single bonds) and also containing a **ring** of carbon atoms. Examples follow.

NAME	STRUCTURAL FORMULA*	USE
Cyclopropane		General anesthesia
Cyclopentane		Solvent

* These are often abbreviated by simply drawing a geometric figure with the same number of points as the carbon atoms in the ring, as shown.

Alkenes Alkenes are compounds that contain only carbon and hydrogen atoms and have at least one carbon-carbon **double bond**. Examples follow.

NAME	STRUCTURAL FORMULA	USE
Ethene (ethylene)		Production of polyethylene
1,3-Butadiene		Production of butyl rubber

Alkynes Alkynes contain only carbon and hydrogen and have one carbon-carbon **triple bond**. Acetylene, also called ethyne, is the only alkyne used widely in industry. It is used as a fuel for welding torches (see Figure 2-8) and in the synthesis of other industrial chemicals. Its formula is

$$\text{H}-\text{C}\equiv\text{C}-\text{H}$$

Aromatic hydrocarbons Aromatics are compounds containing one or more **rings** of carbon atoms, with **alternating double and single bonds** in the rings. The rings are usually six-membered. These double bonds are not localized, however. The six electrons in the three bonds are spread

Welding operation using
acetylene fuel (in tank).

FIGURE 2-8

equally around the ring. This is an example of the concept of resonance,
discussed in Chapter 1. This delocalization of the electrons around the
ring accounts for the unusual stability of aromatic compounds and, in
effect, produces a $1\frac{1}{2}$ bond between each two carbon atoms. This is shown
in Figure 2-9 as rings of electron density above and below the carbon
atoms. Examples of aromatics follow.

FIGURE 2-9

Molecular model of
benzene.

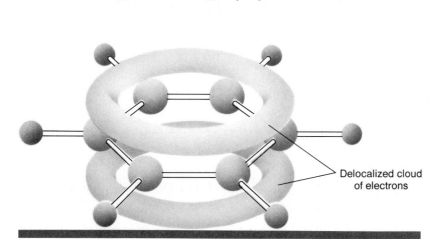

Carbon   Hydrogen

Delocalized cloud
of electrons

NAME	STRUCTURE		USE
Benzene			Solvent
Toluene		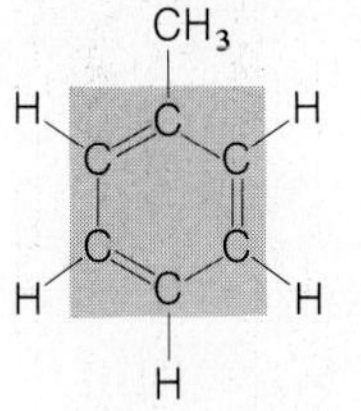 or 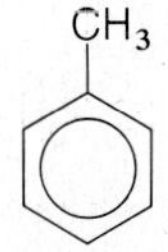	Solvent in glues, gasoline component
Naphthalene		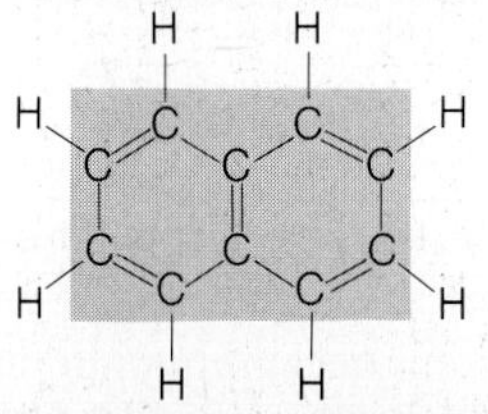 or 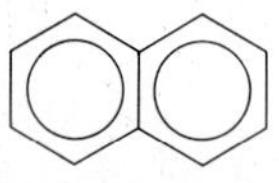	Mothballs, chemical synthesis

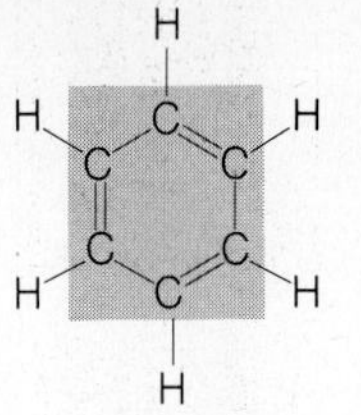

Because the benzene ring occurs so often in compounds, it is abbreviated thus:

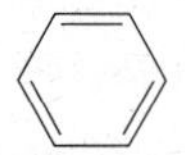

where each point on the hexagon symbolizes a carbon atom and the hydrogens are understood to be present. Alternatively, the double bonds are designated by drawing a circle to indicate the delocalization of electrons. Thus:

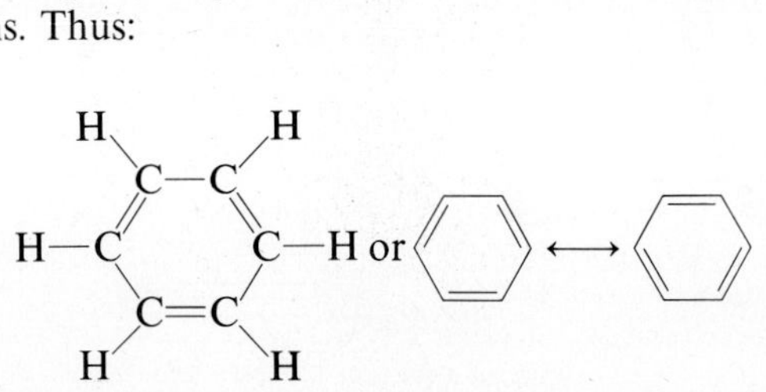

Best representation

Benzene's use is now more controlled than it was in the past because of its very weak carcinogenicity.

Alcohols Alcohols are compounds containing a **hydroxyl** (—OH) group attached to a carbon atom that is not aromatic. The remainder of the molecule has the structure of an alkane (it contains only carbon and hydrogen with single bonds). Examples follow.

NAME	STRUCTURAL FORMULA	USE
Methyl alcohol (wood alcohol, methanol)	CH_3—OH	Solvent, disinfectant
Ethyl alcohol (see Figure 2-10) (grain alcohol, ethanol; major component in denatured alcohol, proprietary solvents)	CH_3—CH_2—OH	Chemical solvent, alcoholic beverages, some rubbing alcohol formulations, solvent for medication, disinfectant
Isopropyl alcohol (2-propanol) (see Figure 2-10)	CH_3 CH—OH CH_3	Disinfectant, most rubbing alcohols (most are 70% isopropyl alcohol and 30% water)

FIGURE 2-10

Commonly encountered products containing alcohols.

Carboxylic acids Carboxylic acids are compounds with the following group of atoms, where the unattached line may be attached to either a carbon atom or a hydrogen atom:

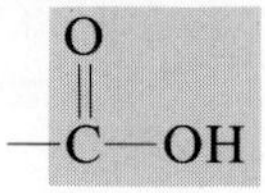

$$\begin{matrix} & O \\ & \parallel \\ -&C-OH \end{matrix}$$

Examples are

NAME	STRUCTURAL FORMULA	USE
Acetic acid (ethanoic acid)	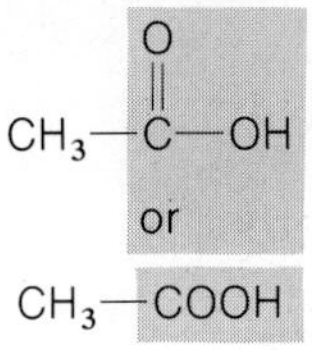 $CH_3-\overset{\overset{\textstyle O}{\parallel}}{C}-OH$ or CH_3-COOH	Vinegar is 5% acetic acid
Butyric acid (butanoic acid)	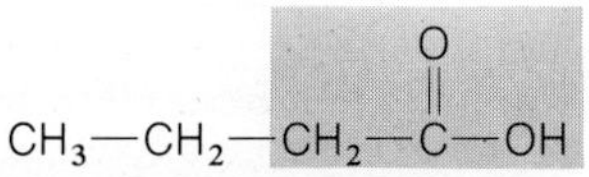 $CH_3-CH_2-CH_2-\overset{\overset{\textstyle O}{\parallel}}{C}-OH$	Responsible for the foul odor in perspiration and rancid butter

Esters Esters are compounds containing the group shown below. Again, either a hydrogen atom or a carbon atom may be located at an unattached line. Most fruit flavors, both natural and artificial, are esters. In other words, "tasting" a banana is really "experiencing" the stimulation of the olfactory organs by the ester *n*-pentyl acetate. Most fats and oils are triesters (three ester groups in the same molecule).

Names of esters are derived from the names of the acid and the alcohol from which they are prepared. Thus, the ester prepared from ethyl alcohol and acetic acid is called ethyl acetate. Note also that it does not matter if the ester group is drawn "backward" instead of the more common way. The ester group is

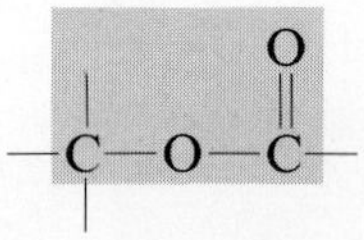

$$\begin{matrix} & & O & \\ & \mid & \parallel & \\ -&C-O-C&- \\ & \mid & & \end{matrix} \qquad \text{or} \qquad \begin{matrix} & O & & \\ & \parallel & & \mid \\ -&C-O-C&- \\ & & & \mid \end{matrix}$$

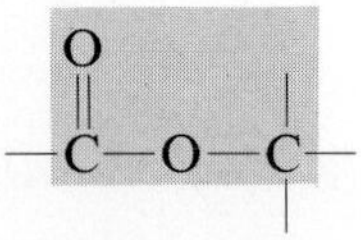

The bonding relationships are the same, and that is all that matters. This same idea holds for any functional group. Examples of esters follow.

NAME	STRUCTURAL FORMULA	USE
Ethyl acetate	$CH_3-\overset{\displaystyle O}{\overset{\|}{C}}-O-CH_2-CH_3$	Solvent, fingernail polish remover
n-Pentyl acetate	$CH_3-\overset{\displaystyle O}{\overset{\|}{C}}-O-(CH_2)_4-CH_3$	Banana flavor
Tristereoyl glycerol	$H_2C-O-\overset{\displaystyle O}{\overset{\|}{C}}-(CH_2)_{16}-CH_3$ $\ \ \ \ HC-O-\overset{\displaystyle O}{\overset{\|}{C}}-(CH_2)_{16}-CH_3$ $H_2C-O-\overset{\displaystyle O}{\overset{\|}{C}}-(CH_2)_{16}-CH_3$	Major component of lard, solid vegetable shortening

Ketones Ketones are compounds containing the $-\overset{\displaystyle}{\underset{\displaystyle \|}{C}}-\overset{\displaystyle O}{\overset{\|}{C}}-\overset{\displaystyle}{\underset{\displaystyle \|}{C}}-$ group. Examples follow.

NAME	STRUCTURAL FORMULA	USE
Acetone (propanone, dimethyl ketone)	$H_3C-\overset{\displaystyle O}{\overset{\|}{C}}-CH_3$	Solvent, fingernail polish remover, found in some glues
Methyl ethyl ketone (2-butanone)	$H_3C-\overset{\displaystyle O}{\overset{\|}{C}}-CH_2-CH_3$	Solvent, used in glues

Aldehydes   Aldehydes are compounds containing the $-\overset{\overset{\displaystyle O}{\|}}{C}-H$ group. Examples follow.

NAME	STRUCTURAL FORMULA	USE
Formaldehyde (methanal)	$H-\overset{\overset{\displaystyle O}{\|}}{C}-H$	Preserving biological specimens, embalming fluid
Acetaldehyde (ethanal)	$CH_3-\overset{\overset{\displaystyle O}{\|}}{C}-H$	Chemical reagent

Ethers   Ethers are compounds containing the $-\overset{\displaystyle |}{C}-O-\overset{\displaystyle |}{C}-$ group. Two alkyl (alkane-like) groups are connected by an oxygen atom. Examples follow.

NAME	STRUCTURAL FORMULA	USE
Diethyl ether	$CH_3-H_2C-O-CH_2-CH_3$	Chemical solvent
Diisopropyl ether	$\begin{matrix} CH_3 \\ \\ CH_3 \end{matrix}\!\!\!\diagdown_{\diagup} HC-O-CH \diagdown_{\diagup}\!\!\!\begin{matrix} CH_3 \\ \\ CH_3 \end{matrix}$	General anesthesia during surgery

Amines   Amines are compounds containing the $-\overset{\displaystyle |}{N}-$ group. Examples follow.

NAME	STRUCTURAL FORMULA	USE
Methylamine	CH_3-NH_2	Flavor and odor of fish
Propylamine	$CH_3-CH_2-CH_2-NH_2$	Chemical reagent
Trimethylamine	$CH_3-\overset{\overset{\displaystyle }{\|}}{\underset{\underset{\displaystyle CH_3}{\|}}{N}}-CH_3$	Chemical reagent

Amides   Amides are compounds containing the $-\overset{\overset{\displaystyle O}{\|}}{C}-\overset{|}{N}-$ group. An example follows.

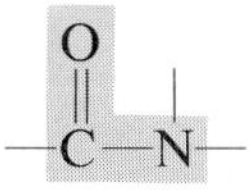

NAME	STRUCTURAL FORMULA	USE
Acetanilide	$CH_3-\overset{\overset{\displaystyle O}{\|}}{C}-\overset{\overset{\displaystyle H}{\ }}{N}-\bigcirc$	Analgesic (general painkiller)

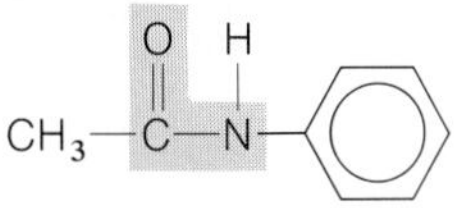

Heterocyclics   Heterocyclics are compounds containing a ring of atoms, **one of which is not a carbon**. When the structures are written as shown below, the points on the cyclic structures each indicate a carbon atom and accompanying hydrogens. Examples follow.

NAME	STRUCTURAL FORMULA	USE
Pyrrolidine	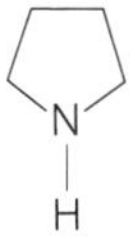	Chemical reagent used in synthesis of other compounds
Tetrahydrofuran		Solvent

Phenols   Phenols are compounds with an —OH group attached to one carbon atom of an aromatic ring. Examples follow.

NAME	STRUCTURAL FORMULA	USE
Phenol	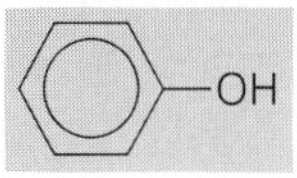 $\bigcirc-OH$	Antiseptic, disinfectant, mouthwash ingredient
Acetaminophen	$CH_3-\overset{\overset{\displaystyle O}{\|}}{C}-NH-\bigcirc-OH$	Pain killer and fever-lowering agent (active ingredient in Tylenol)

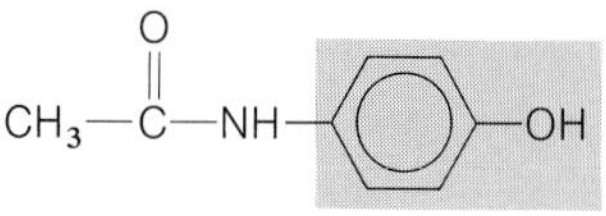

Learning the functional groups

You should learn to recognize the class to which a compound belongs by looking at its structural formula and identifying the functional group or groups present. It is suggested that you prepare a set of flash cards with the name of the class of functional group on one side and the characteristic structural features on the other. Later in the course, after you are more familiar with the various functional groups, they will be easily recognized, but for now, since some of the groups have similar bonding arrangements, carefully memorizing each one will be of value to you.

> **Functional groups are groups of atoms within molecules that impart characteristic chemical and physical behavior to various classes of organic compounds.**

ISOMERS

A carbon atom has four electrons in its outer shell. When carbon combines with other nonmetals such as hydrogen, oxygen, nitrogen, and the halogens, it forms four bonds to complete its octet (see Chapter 1). Because carbon atoms can readily form covalent bonds with other carbon atoms as well as with other nonmetals, chains of carbon atoms can be formed. Since the number of carbon atoms in a molecule can vary, and because these atoms can be arranged in a number of ways, there are a very large number of organic compounds possible. Several million organic compounds have actually been isolated and their structures determined. By comparison, for example, sodium and bromine form only one compound, NaBr.

Let's consider the number of different compounds, all containing four carbon atoms, one oxygen atom, and ten hydrogen atoms, that are possible. All possible ways of arranging these atoms in a molecule are shown in Figure 2-11. Each of these compounds has the formula $C_4H_{10}O$, but each one has different physical, chemical, and physiological (medically related) properties.

Such compounds—compounds that have the same molecular formula, but whose atoms are bonded differently—are called **isomers**. The structures shown in Figure 2-11 illustrate the concept of isomerism and suggest why so many organic compounds are possible. This is further illustrated by the fact that for the formula C_6H_{14} there are 5 isomers, for $C_{10}H_{22}$ there are 75, and for $C_{20}H_{42}$ there is an almost unbelievable number of isomers—366,319.

Let's take a closer look at isomers. Methyl ether and ethyl alcohol have the same molecular formula, but they are quite different compounds. Table 2-3 indicates the different properties possessed by these two materials, and Figure 2-12 shows their different molecular structures. The differences in properties and structure between these two isomers are an excellent illustration of the **structure-function principle**. This principle states that all properties of a compound (its function) are a consequence of the

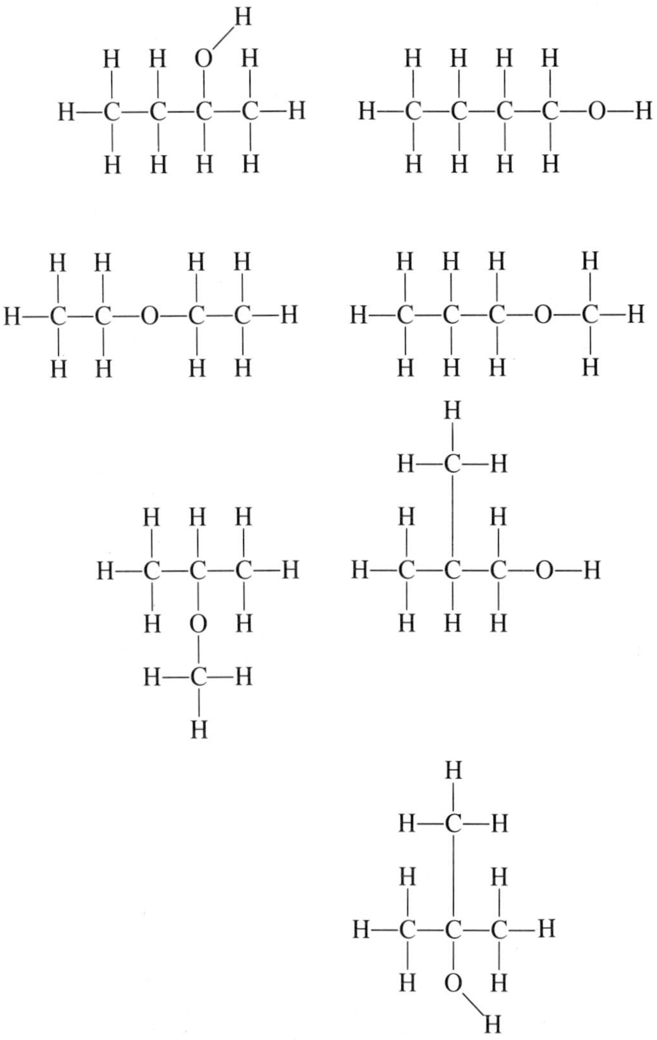

Isomers of $C_4H_{10}O$.

FIGURE 2-11

atoms in molecules of that substance and the arrangement of those atoms (its structure). While methyl ether and ethyl alcohol have different types of bonds (different functional groups) some isomers, like some of those shown in Figure 2-11, have even more subtle differences. They have the same functional groups, but the carbon atoms are arranged differently. The following Programmed Learning Unit will help you to develop skill in writing isomers of the smaller alkanes and alkyl halides.

Isomers are different compounds with the same molecular formula, but which have different arrangements of atoms within their molecules.

TABLE 2-3

SUMMARY OF VARIOUS
DIFFERENCES BETWEEN
ETHYL ALCOHOL AND
METHYL ETHER

NAME	ARRANGEMENTS	KINDS OF BONDS	MOLECULAR FORMULA	PROPERTIES
Methyl ether	CH_3—O—CH_3	O—C C—H	C_2H_6O	Gas at room temperature, chemically inert
Ethyl alcohol	CH_3—CH_2—OH	C—C C—H O—C O—H	C_2H_6O	Liquid at room temperature, chemically reactive, an intoxicating beverage

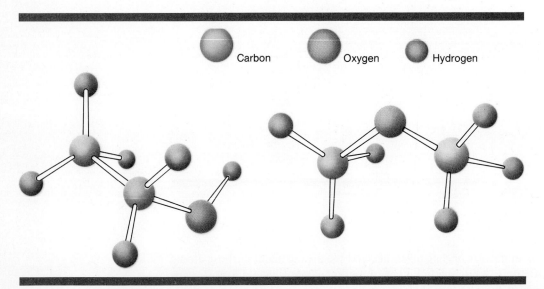

Carbon   Oxygen   Hydrogen

FIGURE 2-12

Molecular models of, left,
ethyl alcohol and, right,
dimethyl ether.

DRAWING ISOMERS

When drawing all isomers of a given molecular formula, the following steps should be followed.

1 Draw all possible arrangements for the carbon atoms. These include one continuous sequence and all possible branched arrangements. Remember that a carbon atom can have a maximum of four other carbon atoms attached.

2 Place functional groups such as halogen atoms on all locations in the structures drawn in step 1. Include all that are different, and be careful not to duplicate any of them.

3 Add enough hydrogen atoms to each carbon atom to give four bonds (a complete octet) to each carbon atom. Check to make sure you have used as many hydrogen atoms as are indicated by the molecular formula.

Worked example

Draw all isomers of C_4H_{10}.

1 Carbon arrangements:

$$C-C-C-C \quad \text{and} \quad \underset{\underset{C}{|}}{C-C-C}$$

2 Functional groups—not applicable here.

3 Put enough hydrogens in place to give the two isomers of C_4H_{10}.

Worked example

Write the structural formulas for all isomers of C_4H_9Cl.

1 Carbon atom arrangements:

$$C-C-C-C \quad \text{and} \quad \underset{\displaystyle C}{C-C-C}$$

2 Place Cl atoms on all different locations of both structures drawn in step 1.

(*a*) C—C—C—C—Cl or Cl—C—C—C—C or $\underset{\displaystyle \underset{\displaystyle C}{\overset{\displaystyle C}{\underset{\displaystyle C}{|}}}}{C-Cl}$

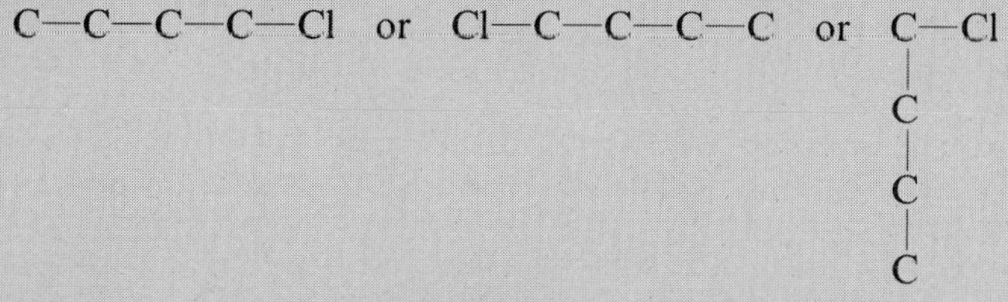

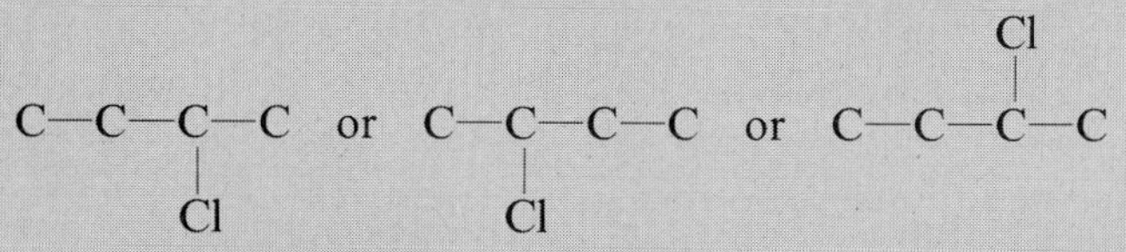

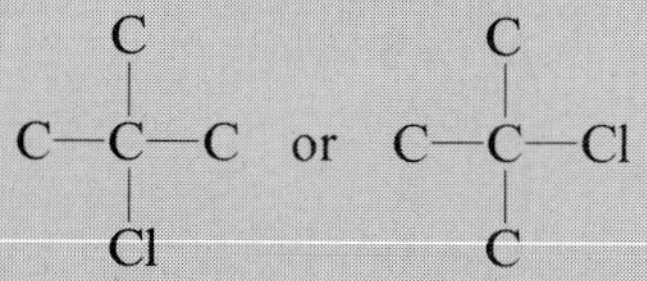

(*b*)

C—C—C—C or C—C—C—C or C—C—C—C
  | | |
  Cl   Cl   Cl

(*c*)   C   C
        | |
C—C—C or C—C—Cl
        | |
        Cl   C

(*d*)   Cl
                                               |
        C   C—Cl   C
        | | |
C—C—C—Cl or C—C—C or C—C—C

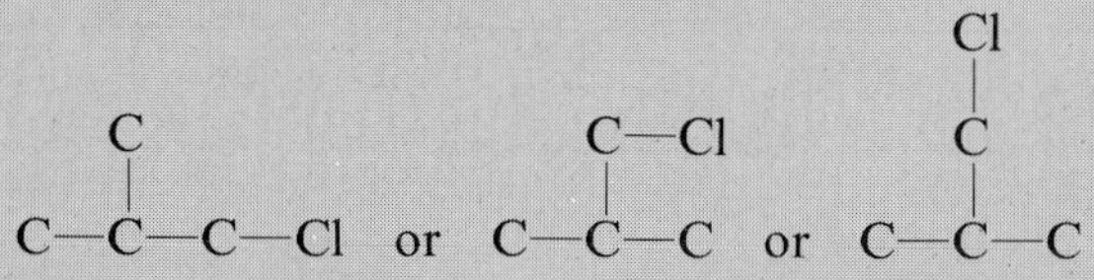

Note You must recognize duplicate structures as being equivalent. Duplicate structures are drawn above to emphasize the point that the same structure can be oriented on the paper in different ways. Since single bonds can rotate freely, bonding relationships can be indicated on paper in any direction. For example, in the first structure above (*a*), the Cl atom is on the first carbon atom (the end) in the sequence in all cases. In the second example shown above (*b*), the Cl atom is on the second carbon atom from the end in each case.

3 Adding the nine hydrogen atoms to give each carbon atom four bonds gives these four isomers with the formula C_4H_9Cl.

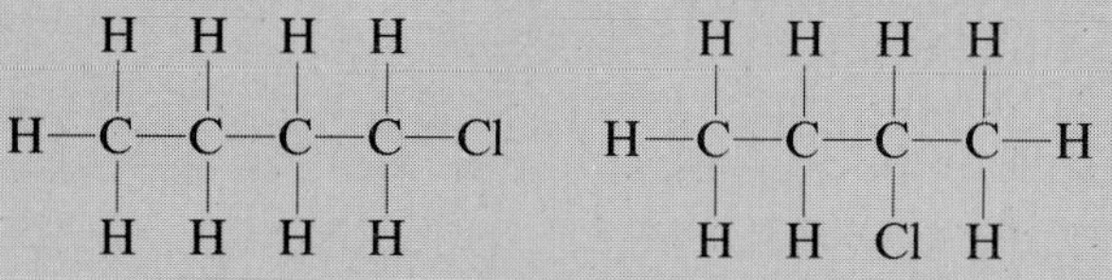

        H   H   H   H   H   H   H   H
        | | | | | | | |
    H—C—C—C—C—Cl   H—C—C—C—C—H
        | | | | | | | |
        H   H   H   H   H   H   Cl H

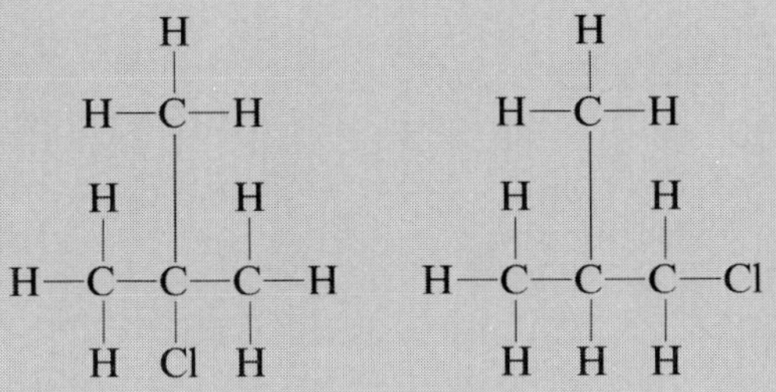

```
         H                      H
         |                      |
     H—C—H                  H—C—H
         |                      |
     H   H                  H   H
     |   |                  |   |
 H—C—C—C—H              H—C—C—C—Cl
     |   |   |              |   |   |
     H   Cl  H              H   H   H
```

Problem

Draw all isomers of $C_3H_6Br_2$. Work this problem before you look at the solution shown below.

Solution

1 There is only one arrangement for three carbons that will leave enough places for six hydrogen and two bromine atoms.

$$C—C—C$$

2 Place two Br atoms in all possible locations.

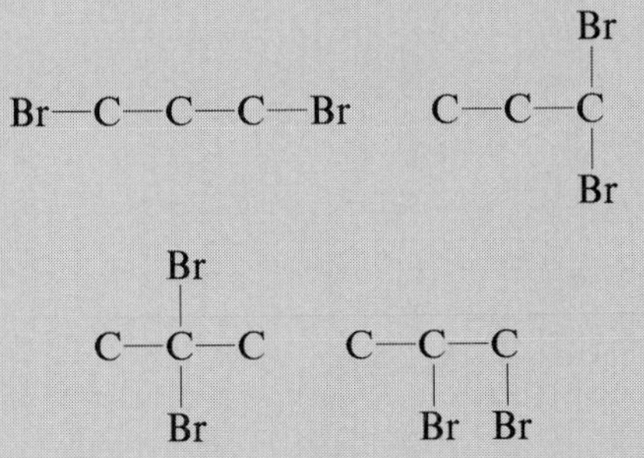

```
                                       Br
                                       |
   Br—C—C—C—Br          C—C—C
                                       |
                                       Br
```

```
        Br
        |
    C—C—C              C—C—C
        |                  |  |
        Br                Br Br
```

Note It does not matter if the Br atoms are drawn up, down, or sideways on a carbon atom.

3 Complete each structure with the appropriate number of hydrogen atoms.

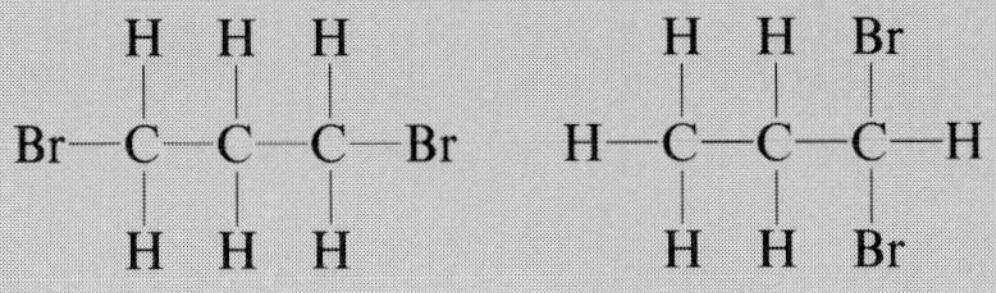

```
      H  H  H                H  H  Br
      |  |  |                |  |  |
 Br—C—C—C—Br            H—C—C—C—H
      |  |  |                |  |  |
      H  H  H                H  H  Br
```

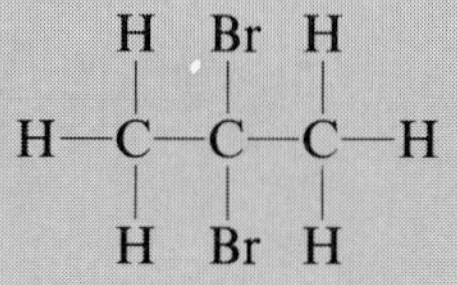

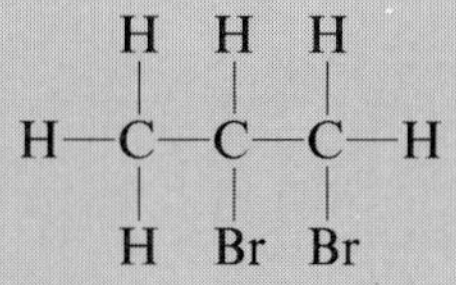

H Br H   H H H
| | | | | |
H—C—C—C—H   H—C—C—C—H
| | | | | |
H Br H   H Br Br

Problem

Write all isomers of C_5H_{12}.

Solution

1

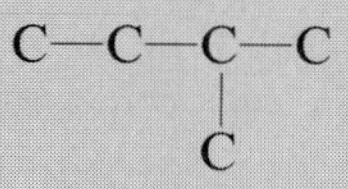

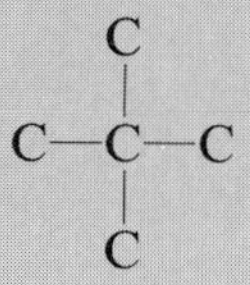

C—C—C—C—C   C—C—C—C   C
                   | |
                   C   C—C—C
                             |
                             C

2 Not applicable here.

3

H H H H H
| | | | |
H—C—C—C—C—C—H
| | | | |
H H H H H

H H H H
| | | |
H—C—C—C—C—H
| | | |
H H | H
      |
   H—C—H
      |
      H

      H
      |
   H—C—H
      |
   H | H
   | | |
H—C—C—C—H
   | | |
   H | H
      |
   H—C—H
      |
      H

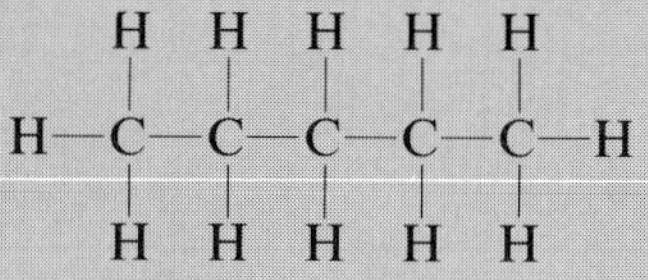

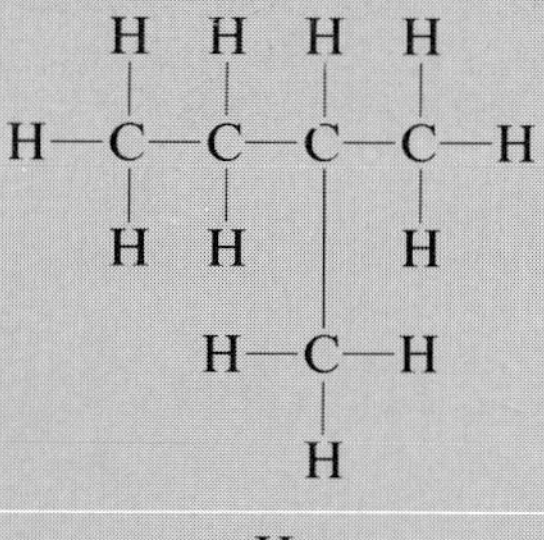

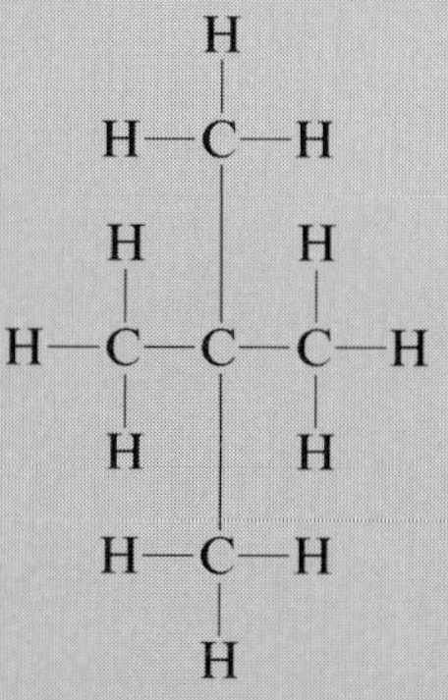

Problems

Draw all isomers with the following formulas:

(a) CH_2Cl_2
(b) $C_2H_4Cl_2$
(c) C_3H_7F

Solutions

(a)
```
        H
        |
    H—C—Cl      (Only one structure is possible)
        |
        Cl
```

(b)
```
    H   Cl              Cl  Cl
    |   |               |   |
H—C—C—H          H—C—C—H
    |   |               |   |
    H   Cl              H   H
```

(c)
```
    H   H   H           H   H   H
    |   |   |           |   |   |
H—C—C—C—F      H—C—C—C—H
    |   |   |           |   |   |
    H   H   H           H   F   H
```

SUMMARY

1 **Organic chemistry** is the study of the structure, preparation, and re-activity, as well as the physical properties, of covalently bonded **carbon-containing compounds**.

2 Organic compounds are classified according to the **functional groups** which are part of their molecular structures. These functional group categories, such as alcohols and amines, have unique physical and chemical characteristics.

3 Two or more covalent compounds with the same molecular formula but different arrangements of the atoms within the molecule are called **isomers**. All isomers of a given molecular formula can be written by considering all possible arrangements which fulfill the octet conditions of all atoms. Each compound drawn will have different chemical and physical properties.

KEY TERMS

Acid	Amine	Isomer
Alcohol	Aromatic	Isomerization
Aldehyde	Carboxylic acid	Ketone
Alkane	Cycloalkane	Phenol
Alkene	Ester	Properties
Alkyl halide	Ether	Structure-function
Alkyne	Functional groups	principle
Amide	Heterocyclic	Synthesis

SKILL PRACTICE PROBLEMS

1 Draw all the isomers of C_6H_{14}. Arrange the carbon atoms in all possible ways, then add enough hydrogen atoms to each carbon atom to give it four bonds.

2 Draw all isomers of C_3H_8O.

3 Give uses for each of the following:
   (a) Acetone
   (b) Acetylene
   (c) Butane
   (d) Acetaminophen
   (e) Naphthalene

4 Give uses for each of the following:
   (a) 2,4-D
   (b) Cyclopropane
   (c) PABA
   (d) Ethyl alcohol
   (e) Carbaryl (Sevin)

5 Identify the functional groups and name the class to which each of the following compounds belongs.

(a) ⬠—O—CH_3

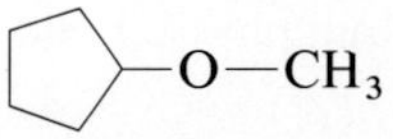

(b) CH_3—$C{\equiv}C$—H

(c)
$$HO-\overset{\displaystyle O}{\overset{\|}{C}}-(CH_2)_{16}-CH_3$$

(d)
$$CH_3-CH_2-CH_2-\overset{\displaystyle O}{\overset{\|}{C}}-H$$

(e) ⬡—OH

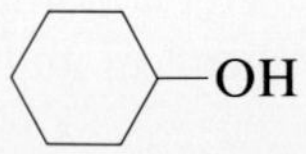

(f)
$$CH_3-\overset{\displaystyle O}{\overset{\|}{C}}-O-CH_3$$

6 Identify the functional groups in these compounds. (There may be several in each compound.)

(a)

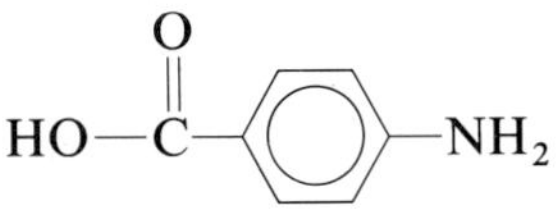

$$HO-\overset{\overset{\displaystyle O}{\|}}{C}-\bigcirc\!\!\!\!\bigcirc-NH_2$$

(b)

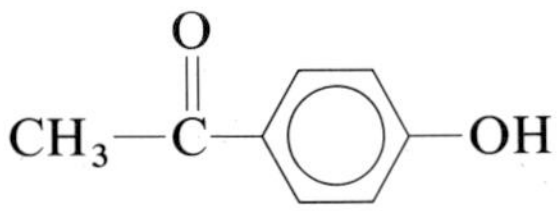

$$CH_3-\overset{\overset{\displaystyle O}{\|}}{C}-\bigcirc\!\!\!\!\bigcirc-OH$$

(c)

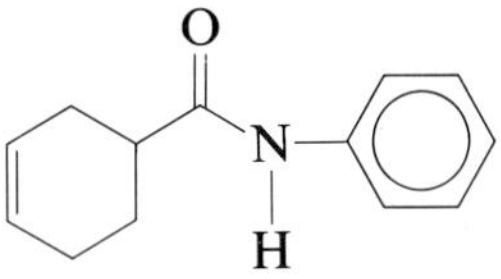

(d)

$$\underset{\begin{matrix}\ |\ \\ Cl\end{matrix}}{CH_3-}\underset{\begin{matrix}\ |\ \\ OH\end{matrix}}{CH-}CH-CH_3$$

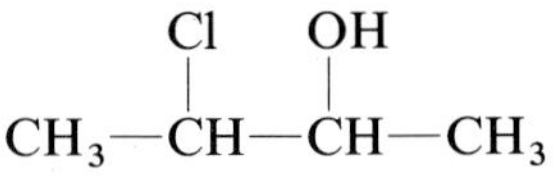

(e)

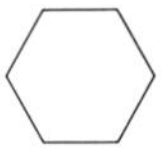

7 Define these terms
(a) Isomer
(b) Functional group
(c) Heterocyclic compound
(d) Organic synthesis

8 Write the molecular formulas for each of the compounds in question 5.

9 Match the compound whose structure is given with the functional group class to which it belongs.

(a) $CH_3-CH_2-\underset{\begin{matrix}\ |\ \\ OH\end{matrix}}{CH}-CH_3$ 1 Ketone

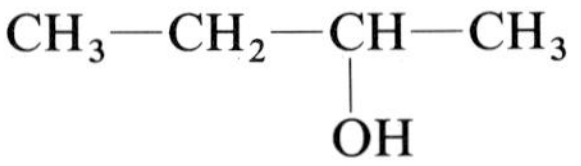

(b) $H_2N-CH_2-CH_2-CH_3$ 2 Aldehyde

(c) $CH_3-CH_2-O-\overset{\overset{\displaystyle O}{\|}}{C}-CH_3$ 3 Alkyl halide

(d) $H-\underset{\begin{matrix}\ |\ \\ H\end{matrix}}{\overset{\begin{matrix}\ H\ \\ |\ \end{matrix}}{C}}-Br$ 4 Alcohol

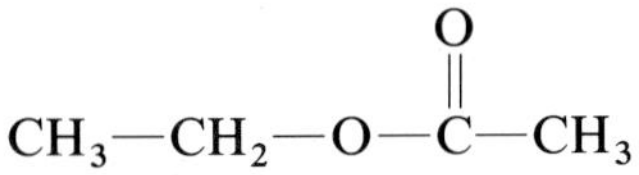

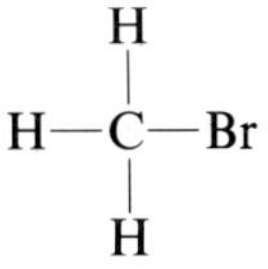

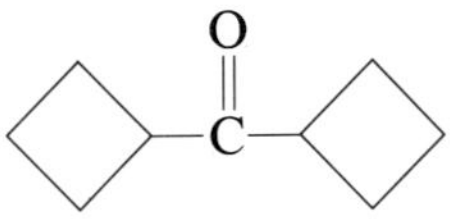

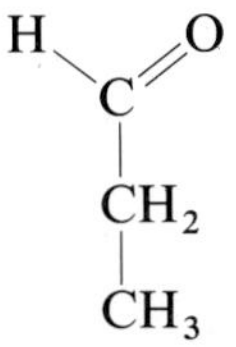

(e)

5 Ester

(f) $\underset{\begin{matrix}|\\ CH_2\\ |\\ CH_3\end{matrix}}{\overset{H}{\underset{}{}}C}\overset{O}{\diagup}$ 6 Amine

10 Give a complete definition of organic chemistry in your own words.

11 List 10 materials you have used or have been in contact with in the past week that were synthesized by organic chemists.

12 List those classes of organic compounds which contain nitrogen. Repeat for oxygen.

13 For the two isomers shown below, which of the following properties or data would you expect to be identical? Base your decision on what you know about the properties of isomers in general.

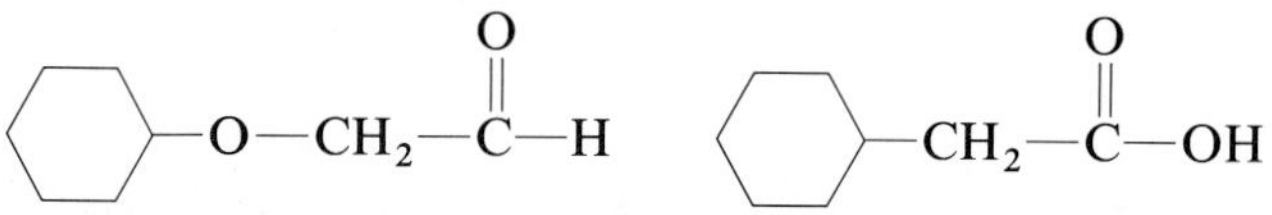

(a) Molecular formula   (b) Solubility in water
(c) Reaction with NaOH   (d) Human toxicity
(e) Molecular weight   (f) Melting point

14 Write the structural formula of acetanilide (found on page 55) in at least four different orientations. What does this indicate about the importance of drawing structures in one particular direction?

15 Draw structures of the following compounds. There are several correct answers in some cases.
(a) An alkane with the formula C_4H_{10}
(b) An alkyne with the formula C_4H_6
(c) An aldehyde with the formula C_4H_8O
(d) An ether with the formula $C_4H_{10}O$
(e) An amide with the formula C_3H_7NO
(f) An ester with the formula $C_3H_6O_2$

16 Which of the following pairs of compounds are isomers?

(a) $CH_3CH_2CH_2CH_3$ and $CH_3CH_2CH{=}CH_2$

(b) $CH_3CH_2CH_2CH_3$ and $CH_3{-}CH{-}CH_3$
                                                CH_3

(c) $CH_3{-}NH_2$ and $CH_3{-}C{-}NH_2$
                                                     O

(d) CH_3CH_2OH and

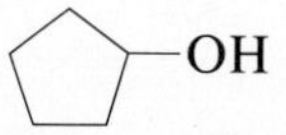

(e)
$$CH_3{-}\underset{\underset{OH}{|}}{\overset{\overset{CH_3}{|}}{C}}{-}CH_3 \quad \text{and} \quad CH_3{-}O{-}\underset{\underset{CH_3}{|}}{\overset{\overset{CH_3}{|}}{CH}}$$

(*f*)

$$CH_3-\overset{\displaystyle O}{\overset{\|}{C}}-CH_2CH_3 \quad \text{and} \quad CH_3CH_2CH_2-\overset{\displaystyle O}{\overset{\|}{C}}-H$$

17 In which of the pairs in question 16 do both members belong to the same functional group class?

REVIEW QUESTIONS

18 When we write structural formulas for molecules, how many bonds must each carbon atom have? How many bonds should each oxygen atom have?

19 Draw the Lewis dot formula for $C_2H_4O_2$. To which functional group class does this compound belong? There is more than one possible answer.

20 Which functional groups have highly polar bonds? Which do not?

SYNTHETIC CHEMISTRY—MEDICINAL RESEARCH

All medicinal drugs were first synthesized, and their medicinal properties discovered, as a result of research by professional scientists (chemists, biologists, and physicians). While most research is tedious and expensive, and sometimes it is discouraging for the experimenter, it is the only way progress can be made in lowering the suffering due to sickness. Though there are a number of diseases such as AIDS and the common cold where research is still needed, much progress has been made in bringing infectious diseases under control. In other areas there has been less success. These include treatment of cancer, cardiovascular diseases such as high blood pressure and heart attacks, central nervous system disorders such as epilepsy and mental illness, and degenerative disorders such as muscular dystrophy and Alzheimer's disease.

There are two approaches one can take to such problems.

The first and most fundamental, but also the most difficult, is to try to **understand the cause** of the malfunction. Once it was realized that diabetes is caused by a deficiency of insulin, animal insulin was used to treat it. However, although it became possible to treat diabetes, no one understood the biochemical error in the body that prevents insulin from being produced and no cure has been discovered. Since our knowledge of the normal human biosystem is limited and techniques for studying it are still being developed, there have been no major successes using this approach to date. It must be continued, however, because some problems will, no doubt, be solved eventually only by this method. This does not mean that we have had no success with the rational approach.

The second approach to treating medical problems involves the **synthesis of drugs which are similar in molecular structure** to those already known to be useful in treating a particular disease. For example, once the structure of natural penicillin was determined (see page 1), parts of its structure could be changed by chemical reactions in an attempt to produce even more useful types of penicillin. Once the medicinal chemists had prepared each new material, biologists and laboratory technicians could test it to see if it inhibited the growth of bacteria in a culture medium. This approach was used to prepare many different members of the penicillin, sulfa drug, and barbiturate families. Those that proved effective— a small number compared to the number originally synthesized—are the ones in use today. This is a somewhat random approach, but it has proved to be a practical method of discovering new medications.

Let's consider a currently active area of medicinal chemical research as an example of molecular structure modification to find better drugs. An approach similar to that described above is being sponsored by the National Institutes of Health (NIH) in an effort to develop better drugs for the treatment of epilepsy. This disease, which affects about 2 percent of the population, is sometimes called seizure disorder, and the drugs used to treat it are called anticonvulsants. There are about 15 currently used drugs, but many patients are not completely controlled (prevented from having seizures), and some have debilitating side effects from the medications they are now taking.

It is known that phenobarbital (shown below) is a good anticonvulsant, and it has been used for many years as a medication for the treatment of epilepsy. It has also been shown recently that the structure labeled A below (called *N*-phenyl-*cis*-4-cyclohexene-1,2-dicarboximide) stops seizures in test animals but is effective only at too high a concentration to be useful as a potential drug. It also shows toxicity in test animals. Notice that compound A has many of the same structural features as phenobarbital, which is the reason why it was chosen for testing. Common structural features include a nitrogen heterocyclic ring with $C=O$ groups and an aromatic ring attached.

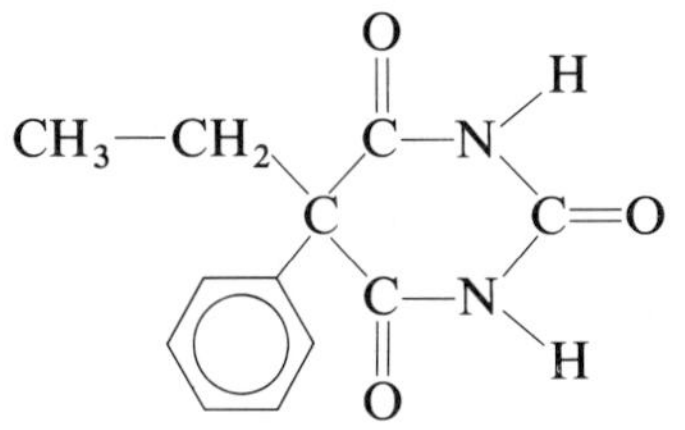

Phenobarbital 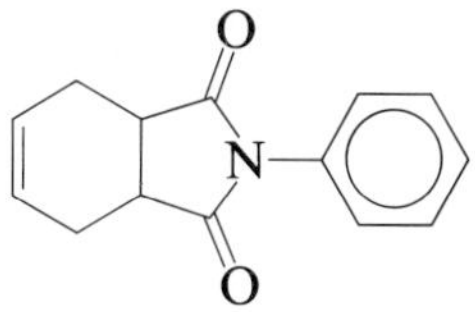   Compound A

Anticonvulsant data are determined as follows. Several compounds are known to cause seizures in animals. If a known anticonvulsant such as phenobarbital is given to the animal before the seizure-producing stimulus is administered, no convulsions occur. In the screening method, the suspected anticonvulsant drug is given to several rats, and a little while later they are given one of the seizure-producing drugs. If no convulsions are observed, then the compound is considered to have anticonvulsant properties.

With the above structural information and the above mentioned animal test data about compound A in hand, a medicinal chemist proceeded as follows. Since a small change in molecular structure frequently has a profound effect on medical properties, more compounds were synthesized with other groups attached to the aromatic portion of the molecule. The molecular structures of three of the resulting compounds are shown below, along with notes indicating the animal test results.

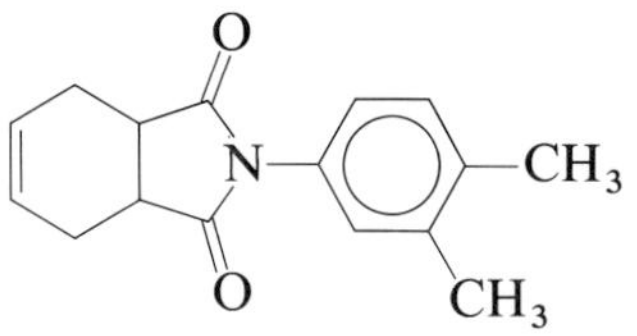

Not active; no anticonvulsant or toxic properties.

Compound B

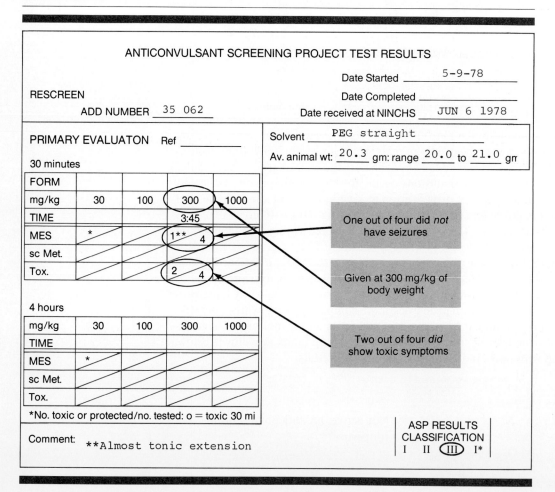

Compound C

Active in stopping seizures, but less active than compound A; showed toxicity.

Compound D

More active in controlling seizures than compound A; stopped them in four out of five test animals and showed no immediate toxicity.

FIGURE A-1 A typical drug screening report. This one is for dimethyl maleic hydrazide tested as an anticovalent

---

ANTICONVULSANT SCREENING PROJECT TEST RESULTS

Date Started _____ 5-9-78 _____

RESCREEN

Date Completed _____

ADD NUMBER _____ 35 062 _____

Date received at NINCHS _____ JUN 6 1978 _____

PRIMARY EVALUATON   Ref _____

Solvent _____ PEG straight _____

Av. animal wt: _____ 20.3 _____ gm: range _____ 20.0 _____ to _____ 21.0 _____ gm

30 minutes

FORM				
mg/kg	30	100	300	1000
TIME			3:45	
MES	*		1**	4
sc Met.				
Tox.			2	4

One out of four did *not* have seizures

Given at 300 mg/kg of body weight

4 hours

mg/kg	30	100	300	1000
TIME				
MES	*			
sc Met.				
Tox.				

Two out of four *did* show toxic symptoms

*No. toxic or protected/no. tested: o = toxic 30 mi

Comment: **Almost tonic extension

ASP RESULTS
CLASSIFICATION
I   II   III   I*

Notice the great difference in medicinal properties caused by moving the CH_3 groups to the various positions shown (a small change in such a large molecule). With this information, the chemist may now proceed to synthesize other compounds with similar (or quite different) groups in various positions in an attempt to modify structure in order to maximize anticonvulsancy and minimize toxicity. Perhaps one of the compounds will be sufficiently active to be tested on human beings and developed into a commercially useful drug. Figure A-1 shows a typical drug screening report.

Another way to find new materials for particular uses is to routinely screen all materials produced in a laboratory for a number of useful purposes, regardless of the purpose for which they were originally synthesized. For example, when a chemist working for a pharmaceutical company

FIGURE A-2

Overall scheme for development of a drug along with the approximate cost.

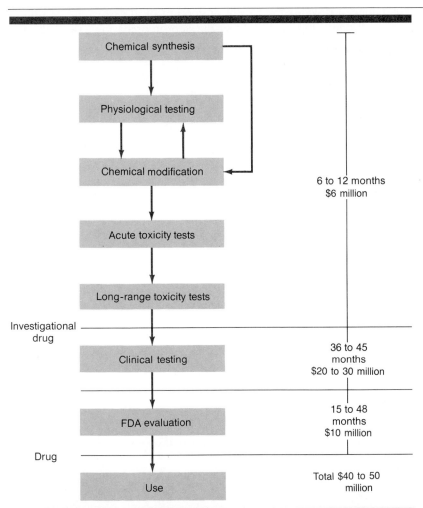

prepares a compound for testing as an anticancer drug, the company will also test it for antibacterial, antiviral, and antifungicidal properties as well as for as many as 30 or 40 other possible properties. This is to help ensure that the company will not miss a marketable material which could help solve a medical problem. Academic chemists can also submit newly prepared compounds to these screening programs.

Only 1 compound out of about 8000 tested is finally marketed. Not only must a chemical be effective in solving a problem but it must also have a low toxicity for both long term and short term use. Toxicity is tested first in test animals and finally, if the drug is considered safe on the basis of these animal tests, in human beings. Determining the effectiveness and safety of a drug is expensive and time-consuming. In order to recover the costs of development and testing, a drug company, therefore, has to have a high profit margin on the drugs eventually sold. It takes either company profits or tax money to pay for the discovery and marketing of drugs. The public, if it wants the benefit of good medical care, must be willing to bear this cost. Figure A-2 shows the steps in preparing a drug and the approximate times and amounts of money required.

CHAPTER 3

ALKANES

LEARNING GOALS

1 To develop skill in naming alkanes and substituted alkanes

2 To understand the structural features of alkane molecules and how structures are related to physical properties

3 To learn ways of preparing alkanes from compounds with other functional groups

4 To learn the reactions of alkanes

5 To understand the role of alkanes in commerce and understand the technology of petroleum refining

6 To develop personal study skills for effectively learning chemical reactions

As we have seen, alkanes are composed of carbon and hydrogen only and have only single bonds. All compounds containing only carbon and hydrogen are called **hydrocarbons**; alkanes are one type of hydrocarbon.

NOMENCLATURE OF ALKANES AND SUBSTITUTED ALKANES

Compounds are designated by names as well as by formulas, and the relationship between the two is called a **system of nomenclature**. Because there are so many compounds which carbon can form with other elements, carbon-containing compounds (organic compounds) are named using a self-contained system of organic nomenclature (all compounds of all other elements are named using a system of inorganic nomenclature).

The International Union of Pure and Applied Chemistry (IUPAC) is the international organization that has determined the official system of naming to be used in professional journals and other chemical literature. Before the development of the **IUPAC system** compounds were named using a variety of methods. Some compounds had what are now called common names. Whole systems (now called **classical systems**) for naming different kinds of compounds were in use prior to the development of the IUPAC system and were widely used by chemists. These non-IUPAC names are still used by many chemists and are still found on labels and in older books; they will therefore be presented in this chapter along with the IUPAC names.

Names in the IUPAC system

Ideally, the name of a compound should be unique to that compound. The IUPAC system reaches that goal by having the name describe the structure of the molecule. The name reveals which atoms are present, how they are arranged in the molecule, and what types of bonds hold them together. The names are systematic—that is, they are formed by following a system of rules. Given the name of a compound, the structure can be deduced. And if the structure is known, the name can be written.

In forming a name, the IUPAC system first assigns a molecule to a certain **class of compounds**. The name of the molecule reflects the class that it belongs to. One such class is the **alkanes**. All hydrocarbons that have only single bonds are classified as alkanes, and they are all given names that end in "-ane."

The base name of an alkane reveals the longest sequence of carbons in its molecules. Butane has four carbons, pentane five, for example. Naming is more complicated when a chain is branched or when a halogen atom has been substituted for a hydrogen atom. To uniquely describe the molecule, the name must tell what atom or group has been substituted. It must also tell where the branch occurs or where the halogen atom is attached.

The rules for formulating names in the IUPAC system provide for branched chain molecules and substitution. This is done by attaching a name for the branch and/or for the halogen atom to the base name of the molecule. Then a number is used to indicate the point at which the groups are attached.

The Programmed Learning Unit that follows gives the rules for forming IUPAC names and shows how to use them in naming molecules.

NAMING ALKANES AND SUBSTITUTED ALKANES

The purpose of this programmed learning unit is to teach the IUPAC naming (nomenclature) system for alkanes and substituted alkanes. After finishing this unit, you should be able to write the name for any alkane or substituted alkane (alkyl halide) whose structure is given and to draw the structure for any whose name is given (the latter is the easier for most students).

Prefixes are used to indicate the number of carbon atoms in a given molecule or part of the molecule. These prefixes are listed in Table 3-1 for one to ten carbon atoms.

From structure to name

Rules for constructing IUPAC names follow.

1 For straight-chain alkanes (no branching) the name is constructed as follows:

> (Prefix for number of carbon atoms) + *ane*

Note All alkane names end in -ane.

2 For branched alkanes
(*a*) Find the longest continuous chain or sequence of carbon atoms.
(*b*) Decide what groups are attached to this longest chain and name each group as follows:

> (Prefix for number of carbons) + *yl*

(*c*) Assign numbers to the carbons in the longest chain so that the branches are at the lowest numbers.
(*d*) Construct the IUPAC name by following this formula:

TABLE 3-1

PREFIXES DENOTING
NUMBER OF CARBON
ATOMS

NUMBER OF CARBON ATOMS	PREFIX
1	meth-
2	eth-
3	prop-
4	but-
5	pent-
6	hex-
7	hept-
8	oct-
9	non-
10	dec-

> (Position where group is attached to longest chain)
>   + (prefix for number of carbons in group + *yl*)
>   + (prefix for number of carbons in longest chain + ane).

3 When more than one group is attached to the longest chain, list the groups **alphabetically**.

Worked example

Name the compound whose structure is shown below.

$$CH_3—CH_2—CH_2—CH_2—CH_2—CH_3$$

1 Since there are no branches, rule 1 above applies. Simply count the number of carbons in the molecule.

There are six carbon atoms.

2 Find the prefix that designates six.

Hex-

3 Combine hex- and -ane into one word.

Hexane

Worked example

Name the compound whose structure is written below.

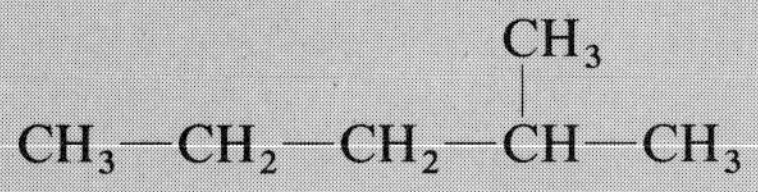

$$
\begin{array}{c}
CH_3 \\
| \\
CH_3—CH_2—CH_2—CH—CH_3
\end{array}
$$

1 Find the longest carbon sequence and draw a box around it:

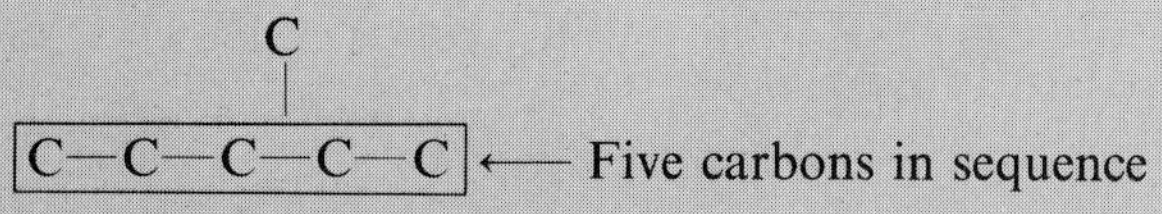

$$
\begin{array}{c}
C \\
| \\
\boxed{C—C—C—C—C} \longleftarrow \text{Five carbons in sequence}
\end{array}
$$

Note Since this alkane is branched, we use rule 2 above.

2 Write the base name by using the prefix for five carbons:

Pent-

3 Add an ending to indicate that only single bonds are present. This is the name of the longest chain.

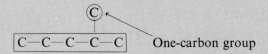

Pentane

4 Draw a circle or circles around any group or groups **attached** to this longest sequence of carbons.

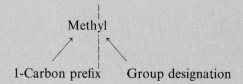

One-carbon group

5 To name this group, first write the prefix for the number of carbons in this group. Next add the ending -yl (to designate that it is a group attached to the longest chain):

Methyl

1-Carbon prefix   Group designation

6 Place numbers next to each carbon in the longest carbon chain chosen in step 1. Start at one end and continue sequentially to the other end. Start at the end **closest** to the attached group. If there is more than one group present, start at the end with a group closest to it. (This gives the position of the first attached group the lowest number possible.)

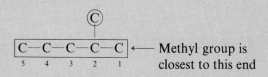

Methyl group is closest to this end

7 Construct the name of this compound as follows using rule 2 above:

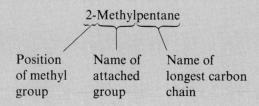

2-Methylpentane

Position of methyl group   Name of attached group   Name of longest carbon chain

Ball-and-stick (left) and
space-filled (scale model)
molecular models of
2-methylpentane.

FIGURE 3-1

Worked example

Name the compound whose structure is written below.

$$
\begin{array}{c}
\qquad\qquad\qquad\qquad\quad CH_3 \\
\qquad\qquad\qquad\qquad\quad | \\
\qquad\qquad\qquad\qquad\quad CH_2 \\
\qquad\qquad\qquad\qquad\quad | \\
CH_3{-}CH_2{-}CH{-}CH{-}CH{-}CH_3 \\
\qquad\qquad\quad | \qquad\qquad | \\
\qquad\qquad\quad Cl \qquad\quad CH_2 \\
\qquad\qquad\qquad\qquad\quad | \\
\qquad\qquad\qquad\qquad\quad CH_2 \\
\qquad\qquad\qquad\qquad\quad | \\
\qquad\qquad\qquad\qquad\quad CH_3
\end{array}
$$

1   Find the longest carbon chain and name it.

$$
\begin{array}{c}
\qquad\qquad\qquad C \\
\qquad\qquad\qquad | \\
\qquad\qquad\qquad C \\
\qquad\qquad\qquad | \\
C{-}C{-}C{-}C{-}C{-}C \\
\qquad\quad | \qquad\quad | \\
\qquad\quad Cl \qquad\quad C \\
\qquad\qquad\qquad\; | \\
\qquad\qquad\qquad\; C \\
\qquad\qquad\qquad\; | \\
\qquad\qquad\qquad\; C \;\;\longleftarrow\; \text{Octane}
\end{array}
$$

Caution The longest chain (or sequence) is not always written in a straight line.

2 Circle the groups attached to the longest chain and name them.

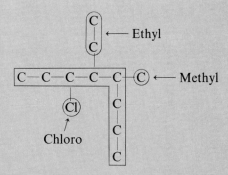

Note The names for halogen groups all end in -*o*; thus: fluoro-, chloro-, bromo-, iodo-.

3 Assign numbers to the longest chain (in this case there is a group closer to the left end, so we start numbering from the left end).

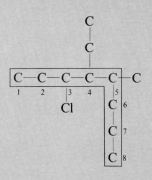

4 Write the name of the longest chain.

Octane

5 List the attached groups before the word *octane* alphabetically.

Chloro   *ethyl*   *methyl*octane

6 Place numbers before each group name to show at which carbon atom on the longest chain the group is attached.

The chloro group is attached at carbon 3.

The ethyl group is attached at carbon 4.

The methyl group is attached at carbon 5.

7 Write the name of the structure. This is the complete name:

3-Chloro-4-ethyl-5-methyloctane

Note Always place hyphens between numbers and letters in chemical names.

Worked example

Name the compound whose structure is written below.

$$
\begin{array}{c}
\qquad\qquad\;\; CH_3 \\
\qquad\qquad\;\; | \\
CH_3 \;\; CH_2 \qquad\quad CH_3 \\
\;\;| \qquad | \qquad\qquad | \\
CH_3\!-\!CH\!-\!CH\!-\!CH_2\!-\!CH\!-\!CH_3
\end{array}
$$

1 Find the longest carbon chain and name it. When there is more than one chain of the same length, choose the one that leaves the groups with the simplest structures attached to it.

$$
\begin{array}{c}
\qquad\quad C \\
\qquad\quad | \\
\;\; C \;\; C \qquad\; C \\
\;\;| \quad | \qquad\quad | \\
\boxed{C\!-\!C\!-\!C\!-\!C\!-\!C\!-\!C} \longleftarrow \text{Hexane}
\end{array}
$$

2 Circle the groups and name them.

Ethyl $\longrightarrow$

Methyl $\longrightarrow$ Methyl

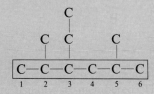

3 Number the longest chain.

$$
\begin{array}{c}
\qquad\quad C \\
\qquad\quad | \\
\;\; C \;\; C \qquad\; C \\
\;\;| \quad | \qquad\quad | \\
\boxed{C\!-\!C\!-\!C\!-\!C\!-\!C\!-\!C} \\
\;\;1 \quad\; 2 \quad\; 3 \quad\; 4 \quad\; 5 \quad\; 6
\end{array}
$$

Note This numbering system places the groups on carbons 2, 3, and 5. Starting at the other end would place the groups on carbons 2, 4, and 5, which gives a larger number at the first point of difference.

4 Write the name of the longest chain:

Hexane

5 List the attached groups alphabetically before the word *hexane*. Since there are two methyl groups, rather than listing them twice use a prefix to indicate how many are present (*di*methyl). Prefixes are shown in Table 3-2.

Ethyl-   dimethyl-

Note In alphabetizing, the prefixes designating the number of groups are not considered. For instance, in di*methyl* the *m* is used for alphabetizing, not the *d*.

6 Place numbers before the group names to show where they are attached to the longest chain. When there are two or more of the same group, there should be a number designation for each one. Then combine these parts to form the complete name.

3-Ethyl-2,5-dimethylhexane

Shows where
both methyl groups
are attached

Note A comma is placed between two adjacent numbers in a chemical name.

Problem

Name the following compound. **After** you have tried, examine the solution to see if you reasoned correctly.

$$CH_3-\underset{\underset{Cl}{|}}{\overset{\overset{CH_3}{|}}{CH}}-CH-CH_2-CH_3$$

TABLE 3-2

PREFIXES DENOTING
NUMBER OF GROUPS

NUMBER OF GROUPS OF A GIVEN TYPE	PREFIX
2	di-
3	tri-
4	tetra-
5	penta-
6	hexa-

Solution

1 Find the longest chain and name it.

$$
\begin{array}{c}
\text{C} \\
|
\end{array}
$$

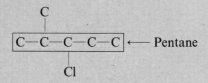

C—C—C—C—C ◄—— Pentane
|
Cl

2 Circle and name each group.

Ⓒ ◄—— Methyl

C—C—C—C—C

Ⓒⓛ ◄—— Chloro

3 Number the longest chain from the left end.

C
|
C—C—C—C—C
1   2   3   4   5
|
Cl

4 Write out the name of the compound.

3-Chloro-2-methylpentane

Problem

Name the following compound.

$$
\begin{array}{ccccccc}
& & & \text{Cl} & & \text{CH}_3 & \\
& & & | & & | & \\
\text{CH}_3\!-\!\text{CH}_2\!-\!\text{CH}_2\!-\!\text{C}\!-\!\text{CH}_2\!-\!\text{C}\!-\!\text{CH}_3 \\
& & & | & & | & \\
& & & \text{CH}_2 & & \text{CH}_3 & \\
& & & | & & & \\
& & & \text{CH}_2 & & & \\
& & & | & & & \\
& & & \text{CH}_3 & & & \\
\end{array}
$$

Solution

1 Find the longest chain and name it.

3 Number the longest chain from the right end.

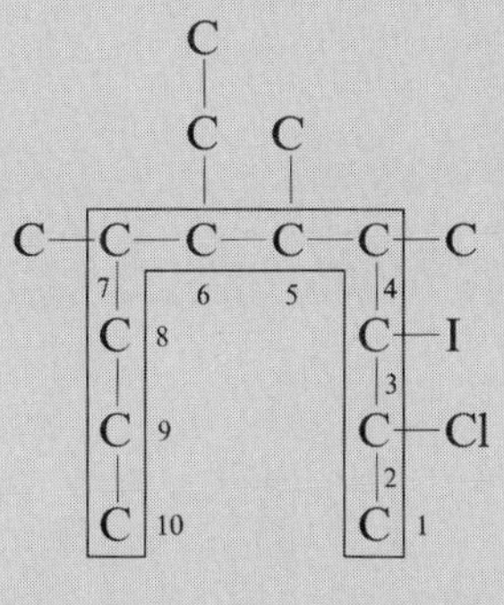

$$
\begin{array}{c}
\text{C} \\
| \\
\text{C}\quad\text{C} \\
| \quad\quad | \\
\text{C}-\text{C}-\text{C}-\text{C}-\text{C}-\text{C} \\
\end{array}
$$

4 Write out the complete name.

2-Chloro-6-*ethyl*-3-*iodo*-4,5,7-trimethyldecane

That is a complicated name. But because a systematic approach is used, it is really not difficult to decipher.

Problems

Try to name each of the following (names only are given as answers).

(*a*)

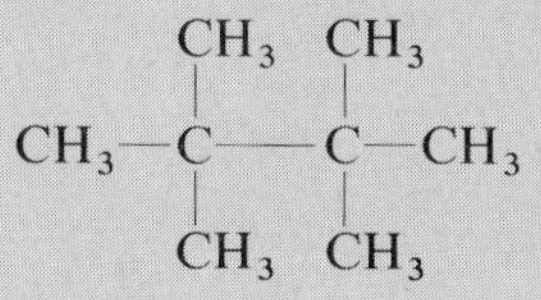

$$
\begin{array}{cc}
\text{CH}_3 & \text{CH}_3 \\
| & | \\
\text{CH}_3-\text{C}-\!\!-\!\!-\text{C}-\text{CH}_3 \\
| & | \\
\text{CH}_3 & \text{CH}_3
\end{array}
$$

(*b*)

$$
\begin{array}{c}
\text{Br} \\
| \\
\text{CH}_3-\text{CH}_2-\text{CH}-\text{CH}-\text{CH}_3 \\
| \\
\text{CH}_2 \\
| \\
\text{CH}_2 \\
| \\
\text{CH}_3
\end{array}
$$

(*c*)

$$
\begin{array}{c}
\text{CH}_3-\text{CH}_2-\text{CH}_2-\text{CH}_2-\text{CH}_2-\text{CH}-\text{CH}_2-\text{CH}_2-\text{CH}_2-\text{CH}_3 \\
| \\
\text{CH}_2 \\
| \\
\text{CH}_2 \\
| \\
\text{CH}_2 \\
| \\
\text{CH}_3
\end{array}
$$

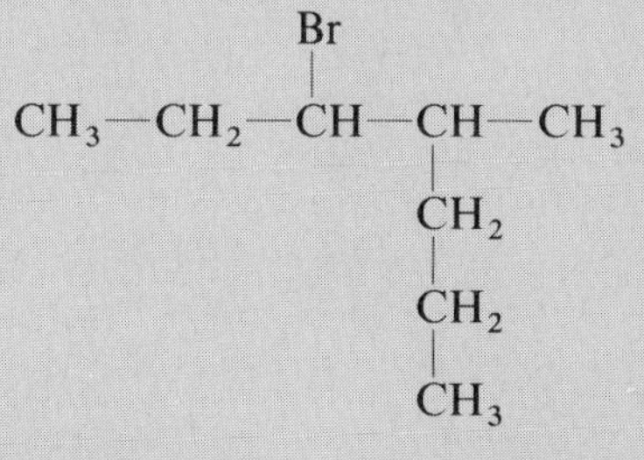

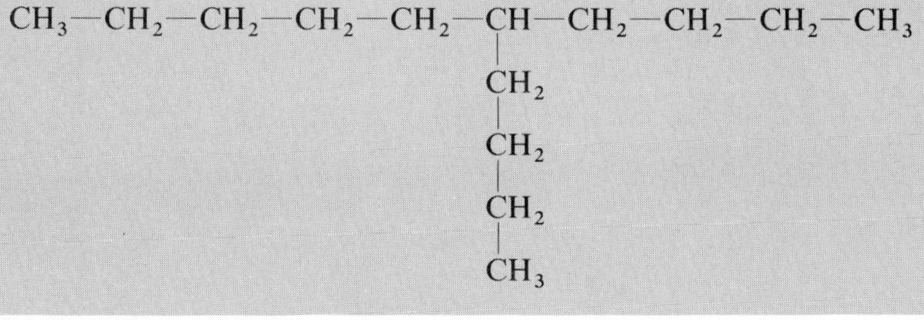

Answers

   (a) 2,2,3,3-Tetramethylbutane
   (b) 3-Bromo-4-methylheptane
   (c) 5-Butyldecane

From name to structure

Worked example

Draw the structure of 2,2-dimethylpropane.

1 Link carbons together to make a chain of the length indicated by the last part of the name (*propane*, in this case). The prefix prop- indicates three carbons.

$$C—C—C$$

2 Number this chain from either end.

$$\underset{1}{C}—\underset{2}{C}—\underset{3}{C}$$

3 Attach the indicated groups at the designated carbons. In this case, attach two methyl groups to carbon 2.

$$\begin{array}{c} CH_3 \\ | \\ \underset{1}{C}—\underset{2}{C}—\underset{3}{C} \\ | \\ CH_3 \end{array}$$

4 Attach hydrogen atoms to any carbons that do not have four bonds, so that each carbon now has four bonds.

$$\begin{array}{c} H \quad CH_3 \ H \\ | \quad\ | \quad\ | \\ H—C—C—C—H \\ | \quad\ | \quad\ | \\ H \quad CH_3 \ H \end{array}$$

5 Write out the formula in standard (condensed) form:

$$\begin{array}{c} CH_3 \\ | \\ CH_3—C—CH_3 \\ | \\ CH_3 \end{array}$$

Problem

Now, you try one. Draw the structure of 3,3-dibromo-1-chloro-5-ethylheptane.

Solution

1 Link seven carbons in a row.

$$C—C—C—C—C—C—C$$

2 Number them.

$$\underset{1\quad2\quad3\quad4\quad5\quad6\quad7}{C—C—C—C—C—C—C}$$

3 Attach the indicated groups.

4 Attach hydrogen atoms to any carbon atoms that do not have four bonds.

5 Write the structure in condensed form.

Names in the classical system

In addition to the IUPAC system, there are a number of names of structures in wide use which are part of what is known as the **classical system**. The following table gives some of the most frequently encountered names.

STRUCTURE	CLASSICAL NAME	EXAMPLE
CH_3—CH_2—CH_2—	*n*-Propyl *n* means that the carbons are not branched and the group is attached at its end	$CH_3CH_2CH_2$—Br *n*-Propyl bromide
CH_3 $\quad$CH— CH_3	Isopropyl a 3-carbon group attached at its center carbon	CH_3 $\quad$CH—OH CH_3 Isopropyl alcohol
CH_3—CH_2—CH_2—CH_2—	*n*-Butyl	Cl—CH_2—CH_2—CH_2—CH_3 *n*-Butyl chloride
CH_3—CH_2—CH—CH_3	*sec*-Butyl a consecutive 4-carbon chain attached at one of the center atoms	CH_3—CH—CH_2—CH_3 *sec*-Butyl iodide
CH_3—CH—CH_2— $\quad\quad$$CH_3$	Isobutyl a branched 4-carbon group attached at the end of one of the branches	CH_3 —CH_2—CH—CH_3 Isobutyl benzene
CH_3 CH_3—C—CH_3	*tert*-Butyl a branched 4-carbon group attached at the center atom	CH_3 CH_3—C—CH_3 OH *tert*-Butyl alcohol
CH_3 CH_3—C—CH_2— CH_3	Neopentyl a 3-carbon chain with two methyl groups attached to the center carbon	CH_3 Cl—CH_2—C—CH_3 CH_3 Neopentyl chloride

Note The prefixes "*n*-," "*sec*-," and "*tert*-" are separated from the main name by a hyphen, and they are italicized. They are not used in alphabetizing groups within a compound name. The prefixes "iso" and "neo" (which are not italicized) are part of the actual name and are used in alphabetizing.

Classification of atoms in alkanes

Both carbon atoms and the hydrogen or halogen atoms attached to them are, for purposes of easy reference, classified as primary (1°), secondary (2°), or tertiary (3°). Primary carbon atoms are those at the end of a chain or those attached to only one other carbon atom; secondary carbon atoms are those attached to two other carbon atoms; tertiary carbon atoms are those attached to three other carbon atoms (those at a branch in a carbon chain). Hydrogen atoms (as well as halogen atoms and certain other functional groups) are classified as primary, secondary, or tertiary according to **the nature of the carbon atom to which they are attached**. These assignments are illustrated in the structure shown below.

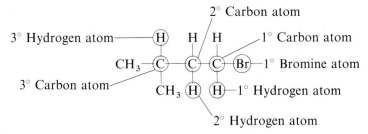

Cyclic alkanes

An alkane of this type has the same molecular structure features as other alkanes—it contains carbon and hydrogen and has only single bonds—but here the carbon atoms form a ring or cycle. Nomenclature of those compounds containing a ring of carbon atoms follows basically the rules already discussed. The cycle is named with the prefix "cyclo-" followed by a syllable for the number of carbons in the cycle and then by the ending "-ane." Any substituents (halogens or alkyl groups) are numbered and named as in open chain (acyclic) alkanes. The numbering system in the cycle places number 1 at one of the substituents and continues around the ring in the direction that assigns the smallest numbers to all the substituents. In numbering, a carbon substituent is given a lower number than is a halogen. The following examples will illustrate these points:

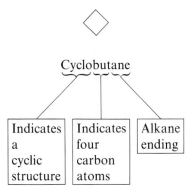

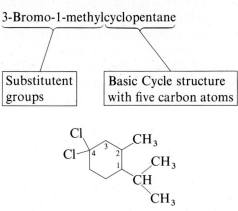

3-Bromo-1-methylcyclopentane

| Substitutent groups | Basic Cycle structure with five carbon atoms |

4,4-Dichloro-1-isopropyl-2-methylcyclohexane

Alkanes are hydrocarbons (compounds composed of only carbon and hydrogen) with sp^3 hybridized carbon atoms and thus only single bonds. They are named by considering the longest sequence or ring of carbon atoms and any groups attached, using either the IUPAC or the classical system.

PHYSICAL PROPERTIES

Most commonly encountered alkanes are liquids at room temperature and are of a nonpolar nature. They are, therefore, insoluble in water and other polar solvents. Table 3-3 shows the melting and boiling points and the physical state at room temperature of several alkanes.

The following trends usually hold for boiling points:

1 The higher the molecular weight, the higher the boiling point. Compare butane ($-1°$), pentane ($36°$) and hexane ($69°$). All temperatures are in degrees Celsius (°C).

2 Branching usually lowers boiling points if compounds have the same molecular weight. Compare the boiling points of hexane (69°), 2-methylpentane, with one branch (60°), and 2,2-dimethylbutane, with two branches (50°).

3 Cyclic compounds have higher boiling points than do their open chain equivalents. Compare hexane (69°) with cyclohexane (81°) and pentane (36°) with cyclopentane (49°).

Alkanes are low density compounds. Most open chain compounds in this class have densities of 0.6 to 0.7 g/mL, and cyclic ones have densities between 0.7 and 0.8 g/mL. Since water has a density of 1.0 g/mL, alkanes float on top of aqueous solutions or pure water.

Alkanes are low density, nonpolar materials. Boiling points are lower for compounds with lower molecular weight and are lower for branched isomers than they are for unbranched ones with the same number of carbons. Boiling points are higher for cyclic compounds than for acyclic ones with the same number of carbon atoms.

STRUCTURE

The carbon atoms in alkanes are sp^3 hybridized, with bond angles of about 109.5° and a basically tetrahedral geometry. There is free rotation around the carbon-carbon bonds; this allows the parts of the molecule to be constantly moving. The noncyclic alkanes have the general formula C_xH_{2x+2}. This means that if a molecule has a given number of carbon atoms, it will have two more than twice that number of hydrogen atoms.

Methane (CH₄)   Propane (C₃H₈)

TABLE 3-3

COMPOUND	MELTING POINT, °C	BOILING POINT, °C	STATE AT ROOM TEMPERATURE	PHYSICAL DATA OF SELECTED ALKANES
Methane	−184	−161	Gas	
Ethane	−172	−88	Gas	
Propane	−190	−42	Gas	
Cyclopropane	−127	−34	Gas	
Butane	−134	−1	Gas	
Pentane	−131	36	Liquid	
Cyclopentane	−93	49	Liquid	
Hexane	−94	69	Liquid	
Cyclohexane	6	81	Liquid	
2-Methylpentane	——	60	Liquid	
2,2-Dimethylbutane	−98	50	Liquid	
C₁₆H₃₄ (many isomers)	——	——	Oil	
C₂₀H₄₂ (many isomers)	——	——	Semi-solid	
C₂₄H₅₀ (many isomers)	——	——	Soft solid	

For propane the C—C—C bond angle is a little greater than 109.5° (about 112°) because the two methyl groups on the central carbon atom are larger than the two hydrogen atoms and tend to spread out more. Notice also that propane has 3 carbon atoms and $(3 \times 2 + 2) = 8$ hydrogen atoms, which follows the general formula for alkanes given above. Figure 3-2 shows molecular models of methane and propane.

To further consider the structure of alkane molecules, we will use a type of representation called a **Newman projection**. This is a drawing of approximately what we would see by sighting along one of the carbon-carbon bonds.

"Perspective" drawing

Butane

For butane, if we looked approximately in the direction indicated by the arrow we would see the view shown below.

"Sawhorse" drawing

FIGURE 3-2

Ball-and-stick models of methane (left) and propane molecules.

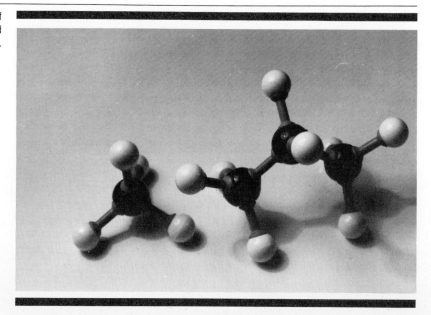

If we looked straight down the C-2 to C-3 bond, we would see the Newman projection shown below.

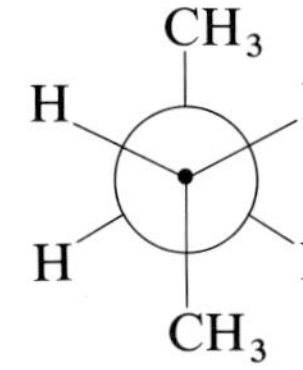

The dot in the center of the circle represents the carbon atom closest to the eye. The circle represents the carbon atom behind the first one.

We can rotate the rear part of the molecule about the C-2 to C-3 bond and progress in six steps of 60° each as shown below.

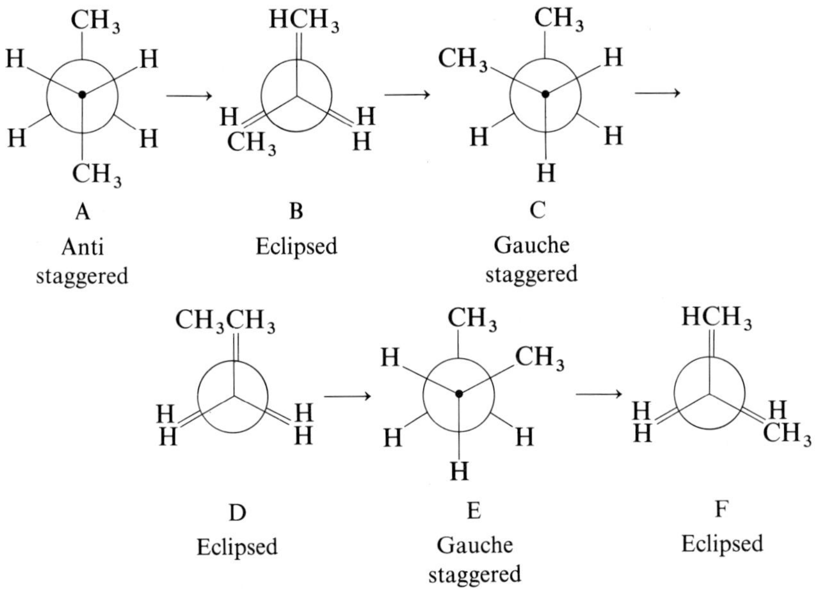

	A		B		C
	Anti staggered		Eclipsed		Gauche staggered

	D		E		F
	Eclipsed		Gauche staggered		Eclipsed

These different forms are called **conformations**. This term refers to the different forms a compound can assume by rotating around single bonds. Forms A, C, and E are called **staggered** because the attached atoms or groups alternate in space. Forms B, D, and F are called **eclipsed** because the groups appear to overlap from our perspective.

At room temperature, the molecules of butane are rotating and passing through all possible conformations. The anti staggered conformation A is the preferred state, however, since the CH_3 groups are as far apart as possible. This conformation is called **anti** because the largest groups (methyl in this case) are **opposite** each other. Generally, a molecule will assume the state in which least crowding occurs—i.e, where the largest groups are farthest apart. This means that all staggered conformations are preferred (they have lower energy and are more stable) over the eclipsed ones. It also means that the anti conformation A is preferred over the **gauche** forms C or E because there is less crowding of the methyl groups in A. While alkane molecules are constantly rotating and "flopping around," the average molecule at a given time is most likely to be in a sort of zig-zag conformation, such as that shown below for pentane, CH_3—CH_2—CH_2—CH_2—CH_3.

$$CH_3 \diagup ^{CH_2} \diagdown _{CH_2} \diagup ^{CH_2} \diagdown _{CH_3}$$

Figure 3-3 shows a molecular model of butane in the anti conformation (form A).

Figure 3-4 shows the conformations or shapes of several cyclic alkanes. The general formula for cyclic alkanes is C_xH_{2x}, which indicates that they have two fewer hydrogen atoms per molecule than the open chain alkanes have. This is the case because two hydrogen atoms must be removed from an open structure in order to form a cyclic structure.

Cyclopropane and cyclobutane are both rather high energy substances because the molecules are forced to be in eclipsed forms. This destabilizing force is called **torsional strain** and the bond angles must deviate a great deal from the preferred 112° (see page 92). Cyclopropane has C—C—C bond angles of 60°, those of cyclobutane are about 90°. This produces

FIGURE 3-3

Stick molecular model of the Newman perspective of butane in the anti staggered conformation.

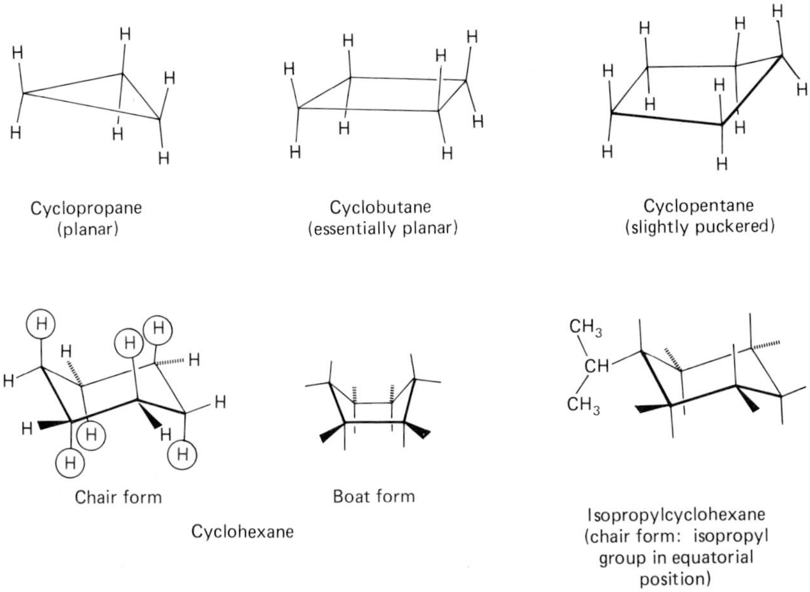

Cyclopropane
(planar)

Cyclobutane
(essentially planar)

Cyclopentane
(slightly puckered)

Chair form

Boat form

Cyclohexane

Isopropylcyclohexane
(chair form: isopropyl
group in equatorial
position)

Conformations of small
cyclic alkanes.

FIGURE 3-4

what is called **angle strain**. These factors cause cyclopropane and cyclo-butane molecules to be less stable than their open chain counterparts are. Cyclopentane has no angle strain. It would be helpful for you to build models of these molecules using a molecular model set. This would help you to both envision the shapes being described here and understand the idea of angle strain. It is difficult to build models of cyclopropane or cyclobutane without breaking the model parts if they are rigid plastic or metal.

Cyclohexane can change between two forms, a **chair form** and a **boat form**. The chair form is the more stable and is preferred because there is no eclipsing of bonds. Again, looking at a model will make this clearer. Figure 3-5 shows the Newman perspective for both forms, demonstrating the eclipsing in the boat forms. In the chair form, there are two types of positions on each carbon atom. Those hydrogen atoms shown in color in Figure 3-4 are called **axial** and those in black are called **equatorial**. The equatorial positions are less crowded; when a substituent group such as the isopropyl group is present, the molecule will take a conformation that will place this group in an equatorial position (Figure 3-4).

Acyclic (open chain) alkanes exist as dynamic molecular structures with rotation about the single carbon-carbon bonds. The more stable rotational states (conformations) are those in which less crowding occurs. Cyclic alkanes assume the conformation with the least torsional strain (eclipsing) and least angle strain.

(a)

(b)

Newman perspective of molecular models of cyclohexane in the (a) chair and (b) boat conformations. Note the destabilizing eclipsing interactions in the boat form.

FIGURE 3-5

PREPARATION OF ALKANES

We now introduce a new type of study—one that will become quite familiar to you as the course progresses. It is the learning of chemical reactions. Here you will learn what materials must be reacted and what conditions must be used to bring about a desired change in molecular structure. This new structure or functional group will cause new physical, chemical, and physiological properties. At the end of the chapter (page 107) there is a flow diagram summarizing the reactions contained in this and the following section. Now we will discuss each process and give some examples of each.

Preparation of methane

The simplest of alkanes can be prepared in the laboratory by mixing sodium acetate with sodium hydroxide and heating.

$$CH_3-\overset{\overset{\displaystyle O}{\|}}{C}-O^- + Na^+ + NaOH \xrightarrow{\Delta} CH_4 + Na_2CO_3$$

The CH_4 is a gas and evolves from the mixture; it must be collected by means of stoppers and tubes if it is to be used for further experiments. Figure 3-6 shows the apparatus for generating methane in the laboratory.

Alkanes from alkenes

Hydrogen gas can react with the double bond of alkenes to produce alkanes. This must be done in the presence of a small amount of finely

FIGURE 3-6

The apparatus used to generate methane in the laboratory.

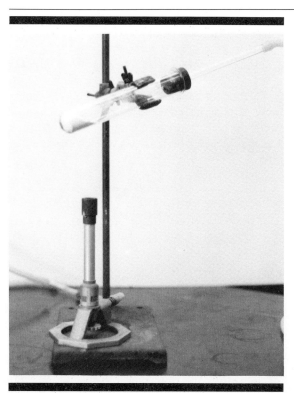

A Parr hydrogenation apparatus. This is used to hydrogenate under mild conditions—low pressures and room temperature.

FIGURE 3-7

powdered metal such as Ni, Pt or Pd. The metal is a **catalyst**—its presence is required but it is not consumed, and it may be reused a number of times. This reaction is called **catalytic hydrogenation**. The apparatus used for hydrogenation is shown in Figure 3-7.

$$\text{>C=C<} \xrightarrow{\text{catalyst}} \underset{\underset{H}{|}}{-}C\underset{\underset{H}{|}}{-}C-$$

This way of showing a reaction is called a **general equation**; it shows only those parts of the molecule which undergo change. The lines indicate other entities, usually hydrogen atoms or alkyl groups, which do not change. Specific examples of reactions which produce alkanes from alkenes are as follows:

$$CH_3-CH=CH_2 \xrightarrow{H_2}{Pt} CH_3CH_2CH_3$$
Alkene   Alkane (propane)

In the reaction, the two hydrogen atoms are held on the surface of the metal catalyst and both go on the double bond from the same side. This is called a **syn reaction** (from the same side). Sometimes, as in the last example above, this has stereochemical implications. Since the new hydrogen atoms are added onto the same side of the molecule, the CH_3 groups bend away and also end up on the same side of the ring. The product is said to have **cis geometry**—i.e., both groups are on the same side of the ring.

Another reaction that will produce alkanes is that of an alkene with lithium (Li) in liquefied ammonia (NH_3).

$$\text{C}=\text{C} \xrightarrow[\text{NH}_3]{\text{Li}} \overset{\text{H}}{\underset{\text{H}}{-\text{C}-\text{C}-}} + \text{LiNH}_2$$

This reaction is carried out at $-33°C$ (the boiling point of ammonia) and proceeds in two steps. The two new hydrogen atoms add on from opposite sides, which in certain cases makes a difference in the molecular stereochemistry of the product. This is an **anti** (opposite) addition.

Examples:

$$CH_3-CH=CH-CH_3 \xrightarrow[\text{NH}_3]{\text{Li}} CH_3-CH_2-CH_2-CH_3 + LiNH_2$$

In the first two examples, the products are the same as if we used hydrogen and a catalyst. In the last one, the two methyl groups end up on opposite sides of the ring or in a **trans** relationship to each other. The geometric considerations are summarized below for another cyclic alkene.

Syn addition to produce *cis*-1,2-dimethyl cyclobutane

Anti addition to produce *trans*-1,2-dimethyl cyclobutane

Both of these reactions are used to change alkenes to alkanes with the same carbon skeleton.

Alkanes from alkynes

In a manner similar to that for changing alkenes into alkanes, two moles of hydrogen (H_2) can be added to an alkyne.

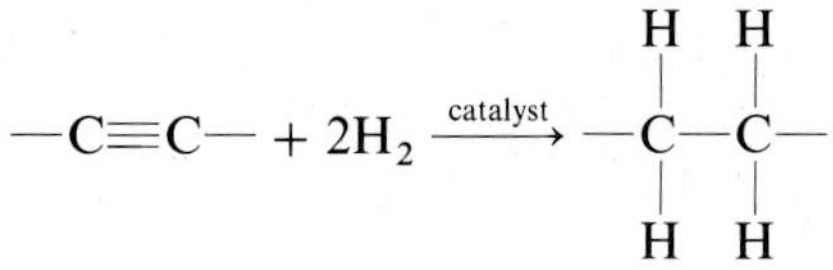

$$-C \equiv C- + 2H_2 \xrightarrow{\text{catalyst}} \begin{matrix} H & H \\ | & | \\ -C-C- \\ | & | \\ H & H \end{matrix}$$

Examples:

$$H-C \equiv C-H + 2H_2 \xrightarrow{Pt} \begin{matrix} H & H \\ | & | \\ H-C-C-H \\ | & | \\ H & H \end{matrix}$$

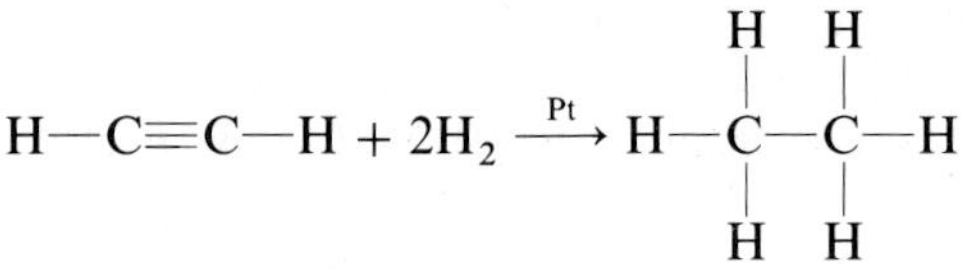

$$CH_3-CH_2-C \equiv C-CH_3 + 2H_2 \xrightarrow{Ni}$$
$$CH_3-CH_2-CH_2-CH_2-CH_3$$

There are few cyclic alkynes, so the geometric considerations discussed for hydrogenation of alkenes are not relevant here.

Alkanes from alkyl halides

The next reaction allows us to remove a halogen atom from an alkyl halide and replace it with a hydrogen atom, to produce an alkane.

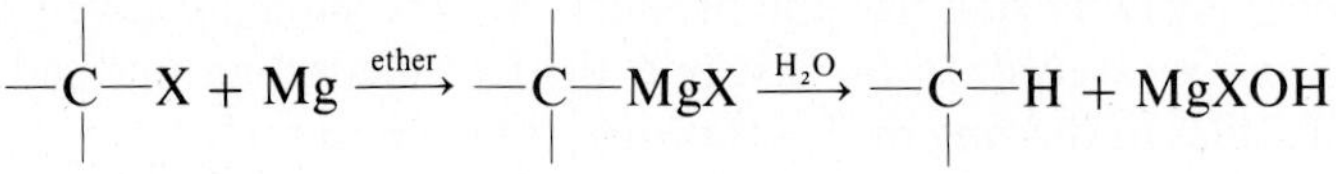

$$\begin{matrix} | \\ -C-X \\ | \end{matrix} + Mg \xrightarrow{\text{ether}} \begin{matrix} | \\ -C-MgX \\ | \end{matrix} \xrightarrow{H_2O} \begin{matrix} | \\ -C-H \\ | \end{matrix} + MgXOH$$

Grignard reagent

Here, X represents any halogen atom. The first step is called the **Grignard reaction**, and the resulting Grignard reagent is useful for many purposes. We will encounter the Grignard reagent several more times, but for now, the reaction of it with water to give an alkane is our focus.
Examples:

$$CH_3-CH_2-Cl + Mg \xrightarrow{\text{ether}} CH_3-CH_2-MgCl \xrightarrow{H_2O} CH_3-CH_3$$

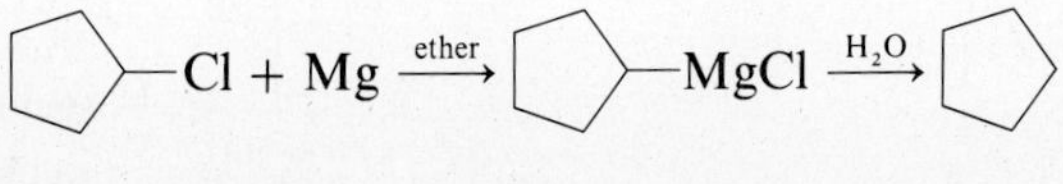

$$\text{⬠}-Cl + Mg \xrightarrow{\text{ether}} \text{⬠}-MgCl \xrightarrow{H_2O} \text{⬠}$$

Coupling reactions

It is possible to directly produce alkanes from smaller alkyl halide molecules. This reaction is versatile because it can link together two different alkyl groups to make alkane molecules having either an odd or an even number of carbon atoms, with or without symmetry. The general reaction is shown below and is called the **Cory-House reaction**. (Here, R and R′ stand for any alkyl groups; X stands for a halogen atom.)

$$2R\!-\!X \xrightarrow{\text{Li}} 2R\!-\!Li \xrightarrow{\text{CuX}} R_2CuLi \xrightarrow{R'-X} R\!-\!R' + RCu + LiX$$

One alkyl halide is reacted with lithium and the resulting compound is added to CuBr, CuCl, or CuI. The R_2CuLi salt is called a **lithium dialkylcuprate**—the material for which this procedure is sometimes named. The lithium dialkylcuprate is then reacted with a mole of another alkyl halide to produce the desired alkane.

The first alkyl halide (RX) can have any structure, but the second one (R′X) must have the halogen atom on a carbon atom at the end of a carbon chain. This is called the **primary position**; it was discussed in more detail on page 89. The overall effect of this reaction sequence is that the alkyl groups from the two alkyl halides bond together where each was formerly bonded to a halogen atom. Various inorganic materials are produced also, and while they are shown in the general equations, we will not discuss them, nor necessarily include them in the specific examples. Here, and elsewhere, we will focus on the changes in organic molecules.

Examples:

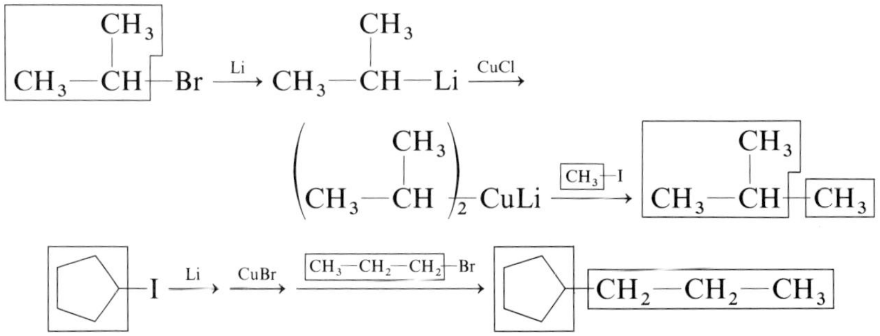

REACTIONS OF ALKANES

Alkanes are notably unreactive and undergo only three common types of reactions. Only one of these can be used to produce other organic materials in the laboratory.

Combustion

Combustion is defined as reaction with oxygen at high temperature to produce CO_2 and H_2O. This destroys the organic molecules, but since heat is given off it is a useful reaction for producing energy.

$$CH_4 + 2O_2 \longrightarrow CO_2 + 2H_2O + \text{heat}$$

When 16 g of methane (CH_4) is burned (as in Figure 3-8) 211,000 cal of heat (211 kcal) is given off. This is enough heat to change the temperature of 211,000 g (211 kg) of water by 1°C or 3 kg (about 1 gal) of soup from room temperature to boiling. Where does the heat come from? The law of conservation of energy says that energy cannot be created or destroyed—the total energy of the reactants before a chemical change must be equal to the total energy of the products after the reaction. Therefore the energy that is given off as heat must have been within the CH_4 and O_2 before the chemical change. It also means that the rearranged forms of these same atoms (CO_2 and H_2O) must have less energy within themselves than they had when they were CH_4 and O_2. The energy given off as heat (**kinetic energy**) was formerly stored as **potential energy** in the chemical bonds of the CH_4 and O_2 molecules. The potential energy contained in the bonds of molecules is called **chemical energy**. This is diagrammed in Figure 3-9.

In the burning of methane

$$CH_4 + 2O_2 \longrightarrow CO_2 + 2H_2O + 211 \text{ kcal}$$
$$\quad 16 \text{ g} \quad\; 64 \text{ g} \qquad\;\; 44 \text{ g} \quad 36 \text{ g}$$

Total energy before reaction = total energy after the reaction

211 kcal of potential energy $\longrightarrow$ 211 kcal of kinetic energy

FIGURE 3-8

Gas flames serve as an important source of energy

$$\begin{array}{c} H \\ | \\ H-C-H \\ | \\ H \end{array} + O-O + O-O \longrightarrow$$

Four C—H bonds and two O—O bonds have a certain amount of internal energy.

$$O{=}C{=}O + H-O-H + H-O-H$$

Two C=O bonds and four O—H bonds have 211 kcal less energy. They are more stable than the former arrangement.

Chemical reactions in which energy is given off in large amounts can provide energy for various human needs. When fuel oil is burned, for example, it gives off 10.5 kcal/g according to the following reaction:

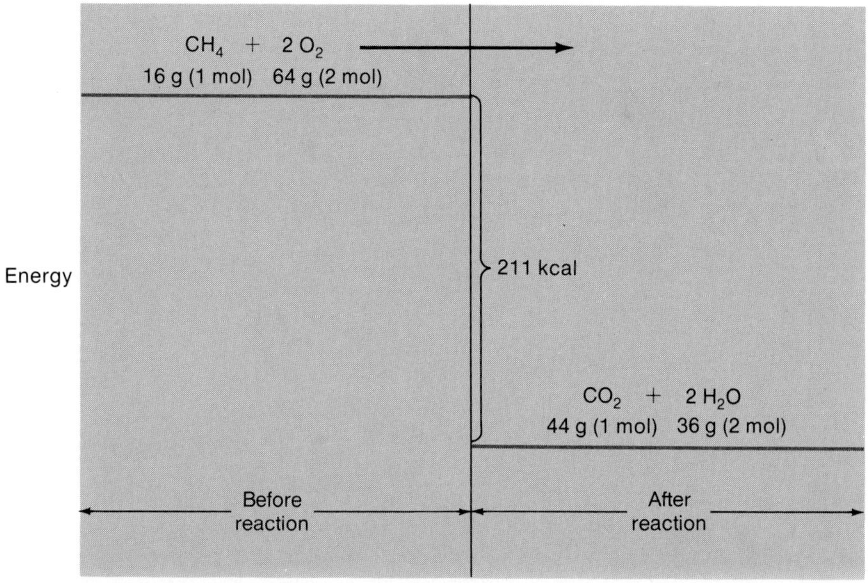

FIGURE 3-9

Energy diagram for the combustion of methane.

$$2C_{16}H_{34} + 49O_2 \longrightarrow 32CO_2 + 34H_2O + 10.5 \text{ kcal/g}$$
Fuel oil

Pyrolysis or cracking

In the absence of oxygen (to prevent combustion) at high temperature and in the presence of a catalyst, large alkanes split into smaller hydrocarbon molecules. The symbol Δ means heat.

$$C_{20}H_{42} \xrightarrow[\text{catalyst}]{\Delta} \text{smaller alkanes} + \text{alkenes}$$

The commercial reasons for doing this and more details about the process are given on page 110 in the section on petroleum refining. Pyrolysis of alkanes is carried out in industrial facilities and is rarely used in the laboratory for synthetic purposes.

Halogenation

This reaction is useful to produce alkyl halides for their own sake or for use as intermediates to produce compounds containing other functional groups. The general reaction is:

$$R—H + X_2 \xrightarrow{hv} R—X + HX$$

This works for Cl_2 and Br_2 but not for I_2. The "catalyst" needed here is light, which is symbolized by hv; it is needed to provide energy for the first step in the reaction, as shown below. If the reagents are kept in a dark place, no reaction occurs. Let's look at the mechanism for halogenation. A **mechanism** is a series of steps by which a molecular change is thought to occur. For halogenation the general mechanism is thought to be as follows:

Initiation step

(a) $X_2 \xrightarrow{h\nu} 2X\cdot$

Propagation steps

(b) $X\cdot + R{-}H \longrightarrow R\cdot + HX$

(c) $R\cdot + X_2 \longrightarrow RX + X\cdot$

Termination steps

(d) $2Cl\cdot \longrightarrow Cl_2$

(e) $R\cdot + Cl\cdot \longrightarrow R{-}Cl$

(f) $2R\cdot \longrightarrow R{-}R$

The reaction begins when light causes a few of the halogen molecules to break into two free radicals, step (a). (See Chapter 1 for a review of free radicals.) These free radicals are very reactive and pull a hydrogen atom from the alkane (R—H), leaving an alkyl free radical, step (b). This new free radical is also reactive and bonds with one of the halogen atoms from a new halogen molecule with which it happens to collide, step (c). This leaves another halogen free radical, which **starts the chain of events over again**. This process continues until all the alkane molecules have been halogenated or until one of the reagents is used up. Termination steps, in which no free radical is produced, also sometimes occur. The possible termination reactions are shown as steps (d) to (f) above, but we will not consider them in the mechanisms given in the remainder of the chapter, since a negligibly small portion of the molecules undergoes these processes. For bromination (halogenation with bromine) of ethane the specific mechanism is

$$Br_2 \xrightarrow{h\nu} 2Br\cdot$$

$$Br\cdot + CH_3{-}CH_3 \longrightarrow CH_3{-}CH_2\cdot + HBr$$

$$CH_3{-}CH_2\cdot + Br_2 \longrightarrow CH_3{-}CH_2{-}Br + Br\cdot$$

In ethane, all the hydrogen atoms are equal—they are all primary. That is, they are all attached to carbon atoms at the end of a chain. In a molecule like 2-methylbutane (shown below) there are several types of hydrogen atoms.

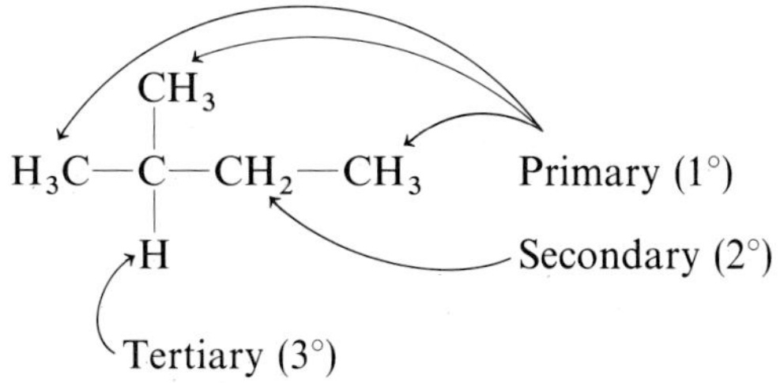

$$H_3C - \overset{\overset{\displaystyle CH_3}{|}}{\underset{\underset{\displaystyle H}{|}}{C}} - CH_2 - CH_3$$

Primary (1°)

Secondary (2°)

Tertiary (3°)

In addition to the primary ones (at the ends) there are secondary hydrogen atoms (those bonded to a carbon atom within a chain, or to a carbon atom which is bonded to two other carbon atoms), and one tertiary hydrogen atom (one bonded to a carbon atom at a point of branching, or to a carbon atom which is bonded to three other carbon atoms). In alkanes, the tertiary hydrogen atoms are replaced most easily by a halogen atom, the secondary hydrogen atoms are replaced less easily, and primary hydrogen atoms are the least easily replaced. This is especially true for bromination. For example, in the following reaction the tertiary hydrogen

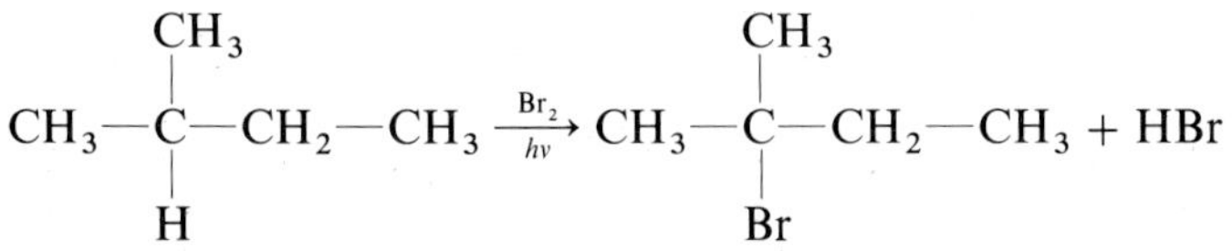

$$CH_3 - \overset{\overset{\displaystyle CH_3}{|}}{\underset{\underset{\displaystyle H}{|}}{C}} - CH_2 - CH_3 \xrightarrow[hv]{Br_2} CH_3 - \overset{\overset{\displaystyle CH_3}{|}}{\underset{\underset{\displaystyle Br}{|}}{C}} - CH_2 - CH_3 + HBr$$

atom is replaced almost exclusively. It is possible to calculate the exact amounts of other products produced by bromination or chlorination, but that is beyond the scope of this textbook. Just remember that for bromination especially, if a tertiary hydrogen atom is present, it will be replaced; if secondary and primary hydrogen atoms are the only types present, the secondary ones will be replaced.

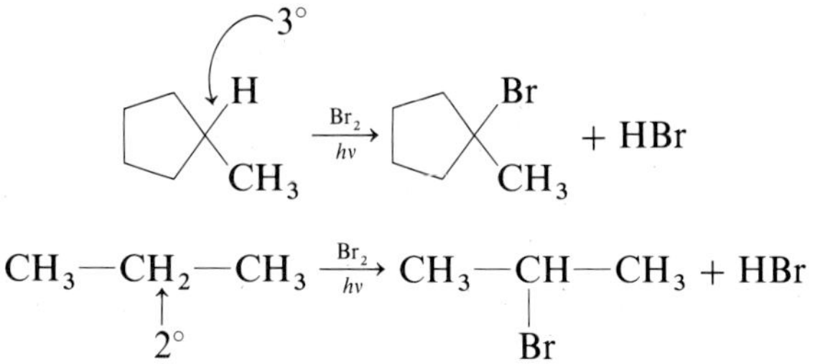

$$CH_3 - CH_2 - CH_3 \xrightarrow[hv]{Br_2} CH_3 - \overset{}{\underset{\underset{\displaystyle Br}{|}}{CH}} - CH_3 + HBr$$

The reason that halogenation is selective involves the relative stability of the several possible free radicals. For alkyl free radical $(R \cdot)$ intermediates, the order of stability is 3° > 2° > 1°. This means that 3° free radicals are more stable than are 2° free radicals and are therefore formed more easily. If a free radical is formed more easily, then halogenation at that position occurs more readily. The four possibilities for free radical formation are shown below for 2-methylbutane.

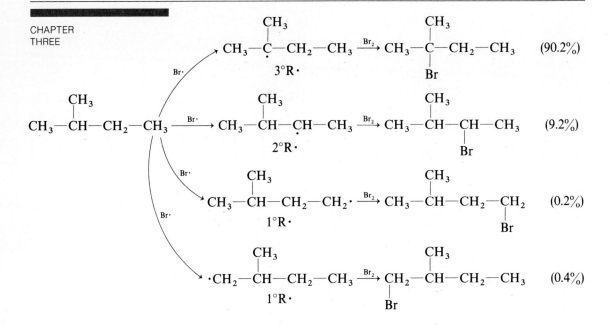

Energy profiles

The energy profile of a halogenation reaction can be drawn as shown in Figure 3-10 for the bromination of methane. While you will not be asked to construct such profiles, you should be able to read and understand them. Similar diagrams will be used at several points later in this textbook to explain certain facts.

In an energy profile, the vertical axis is a plot of the potential energy of the various species in a mechanism. Each step in this mechanism involves one bond breaking and one bond forming. Each step involves a **transition state** (TS)—a high energy state where the bonds are partially broken and/or partially formed. To reach this high energy state, the molecules need to obtain an infusion of energy called the **activation energy** (E_a). Once the activation energy has been obtained (usually from the collision of the two molecules) and the transition state is reached, the bonds proceed to go to the arrangement in the next "valley" spontaneously. The higher the TS energy, the fewer molecules have enough energy at a given temperature to surmount this barrier, and the slower the reaction proceeds.

In Figure 3-10 the first step, which involves E_{a1}, is the slowest because E_{a1} is the greatest. The second step is rapid, because E_{a2} is smaller.

The products of an isolated reaction are always lower in energy than the reactants under the reaction conditions. This energy difference is called **Gibbs free energy** (ΔG) and must be negative if the reaction is to proceed spontaneously. Nature always goes to a lower energy state—rocks roll downhill but never uphill. Similarly, molecules do not go spontaneously to higher energy states but always to lower states. Sometimes, especially in biosystems, energy lost by one reaction can be used to cause another otherwise nonspontaneous reaction to proceed. This is called **coupling of**

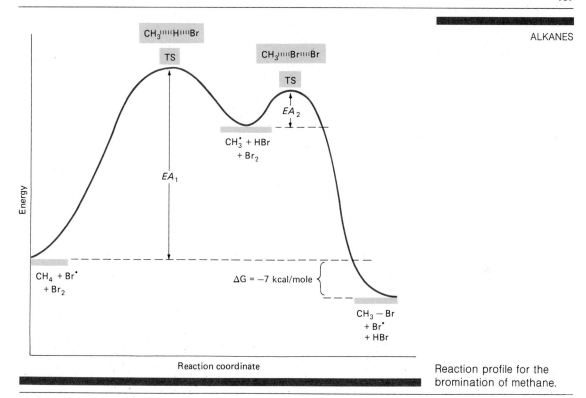

Reaction profile for the
bromination of methane.

reactions, but it is not something we need concern ourselves with for organic reactions in the laboratory.

FIGURE 3-10

REACTION SUMMARY FLOW DIAGRAM FOR ALKANES

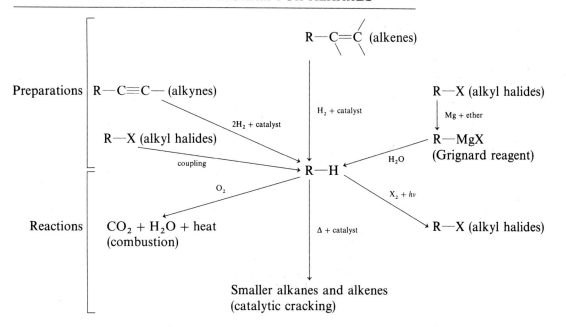

Note R stands for any alkyl (alkane-like) group. In these diagrams, R does not represent the same alkyl group in each general formula; it simply indicates that an alkyl group is present in each formula where R appears.

PETROLEUM CHEMISTRY

Since most organic chemicals are prepared from petroleum products, the petroleum industry is one of the largest in industrial societies. Let us take a look at petroleum refining processes.

Crude oil is found in pockets in sedimentary rock (rock laid down in

FIGURE 3-11

Fractional distillation apparatus used in a laboratory.

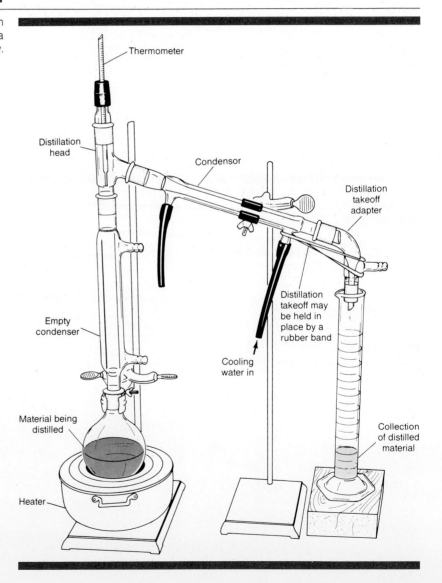

layers, generally by the action of water). It was formed, as far as we can tell, from large quantities of decaying plants. It is a mixture of alkanes and aromatic hydrocarbons. Crude oils from the eastern United States and Texas-Oklahoma region are mostly alkanes; California oils contain a large amount of aromatics as well.

The process of refining crude oil begins with a separation into various components. Actually, each compound is not purified; rather, groups of compounds with similar physical and chemical properties are isolated as a mixture for particular commercial uses. The method used in the separation is called **fractional distillation** (see Figure 3-11). This involves heating the crude mixture to successively higher temperatures and collecting the components that boil out of the mixture (i.e., change to the gaseous state) over certain temperature ranges. This vapor is cooled, and the cooling causes it to change back to the liquid state again (condensation). Table 3-4 shows the various boiling temperature ranges used, the name of the material collected at each temperature range (fraction), and the commercial use of that material.

Figure 3-12 shows an oil refinery. Once the various fractions have been collected by the refinery, they are sent by pipeline, truck, or railroad tank car to distribution points.

Crude oil contains more of the heavy compounds in the motor oil range than are needed and much less gasoline than is required; therefore a process has been developed to convert heavy oils, composed mostly of molecules characterized by high molecular weight and long carbon chains, into

FIGURE 3-12

Petroleum refinery.
(*Ashland Oil Company.*)

gasoline composed of relatively short chain-compounds (5- to 10-carbon atom chains). The oils are heated in the absence of oxygen (to prevent them from burning) in the presence of a **catalyst**. When the oil is heated with a catalyst, the long oil molecules break down into shorter molecules of the gasoline type. This is called **catalytic cracking.**

For example:

$$C_{18}H_{38} \xrightarrow[\Delta]{\text{catalyst}} C_9H_{18} + C_9H_{20}$$
$$\text{Alkene} \quad \text{Alkane}$$

A mixture of low molecular weight alkanes and alkenes is produced. Figure 3-13 shows a catalytic cracker, and Figure 3-14 shows the catalyst used to bring about this change. (See also page 103.)

HINTS FOR STUDYING ORGANIC CHEMISTRY: STUDYING REACTIONS

When you study a reaction, be aware of its purposes. Learn it not for its own sake, but rather as a means of accomplishing something. Some examples of the purposes of organic reactions are as follows:

1 To change a functional group

2 To produce a particular type of compound

3 To identify a compound

TABLE 3-4

VARIOUS FRACTIONS ISOLATED IN THE REFINING OF CRUDE OIL	TEMPERATURE, °C	COMPOSITION	USE
	Below 20	Methane, ethane, propane, butane	Natural gas for fuel
	30–200	Alkanes containing from 5 to 10 carbons per molecule	Gasoline
	200–325	Alkanes containing from 10 to 15 carbons per molecule	Kerosene (coal oil)
	325–400	Alkanes containing from 15 to 18 carbons per molecule	Diesel fuel and fuel oil for fuel and heating
	Above 400	Alkanes with greater than 18 carbons	Paraffin, lubricating oils
	Solids left after distillation	Complex mixture	Asphalt

Catalytic cracking unit. (*Ashland Oil Company.*)

FIGURE 3-13

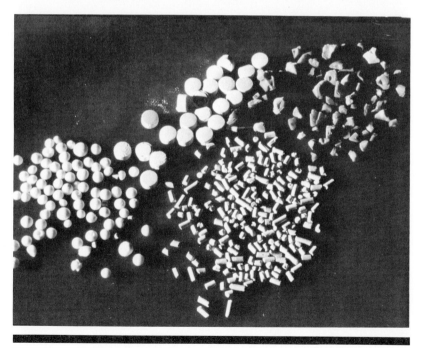

Solid catalyst used in cracking petroleum products. (*Ashland Oil Company.*)

FIGURE 3-14

4 To block a group so that the group will not be changed later

5 To be part of a standard multistep sequence used to produce a drug, polymer, or other useful product

As mentioned in Chapter 1, you will likely want to place each reaction on a review card and arrange these in a logical array such as that shown on page 107. Even after this is done, or rather as a part of it, keep a purpose in mind and note this on your cards and flow diagrams. As an example, for the Cory-House reaction you should not be concerned about the isolated fact that lithium will react with an alkyl halide. Better to see the reaction as a **tool** to link carbon chains together in order to build larger molecules. We will be studying synthesis in this text, not only because synthesis is one of the main purposes of organic reactions but also because these processes show how individual reactions are used. The study of synthesis will make the reactions easier to learn.

Flash cards should be reviewed once each day, and the flow diagrams should be learned like a map of a state or a diagram for an upcoming football play. The purpose of the diagrams is to give a visual perspective or overview that will aid in organizing the various reactions that are related. Of course, each reaction must be understood and learned before the overview has much meaning, but the facts themselves are difficult to use unless they are seen as part of a larger scheme. Below is a list of the steps one may want to use in studying reactions.

ACTIVITY	EXAMPLE
1 Learn from class notes and text	
(a) Specific equations	$CH_4 + Cl_2 \longrightarrow CH_3Cl + HCl$
(b) The mechanism	$Cl_2 \xrightarrow{hv} 2Cl\cdot$
	$CH_4 + Cl\cdot \longrightarrow CH_3\cdot + HCl$
	$CH_3\cdot + Cl_2 \longrightarrow CH_3Cl + Cl\cdot$
(c) The energetics	2 steps
	First step has higher activation energy
2 Generalize	
(a) What other compounds enter into this or a similar reaction?	All alkanes will react with Cl_2, and Br_2 but not with I_2
(b) What is the purpose of doing this reaction?	Producing alkyl halides for commercial use or as intermediates in chemical syntheses

SUMMARY

1   Alkanes, cycloalkanes, and halogen substituted alkanes are named by both the **IUPAC** and **classical systems**.

2   **Physical properties** of alkanes, including solubilities and boiling points, are the result of **molecular structures**.

3 Molecules of alkanes contain tetrahedral carbon atoms and exhibit free rotation around single bonds. The various rotational states are called **conformations** and are represented by Newman projections or sawhorse drawings.

4 The smaller cyclic alkanes (C_3 to C_5) are higher in energy than their open chain counterparts because of **angle strain** and/or **torsional strain.** They exist as essentially planar molecules.

5 Cyclohexane exists in two puckered conformations (**chair** and **boat**). The chair form is the more stable. Substituents on the chair form of cyclohexane rings tend to assume an equatorial position as opposed to the more crowded axial position.

6 Alkanes can be prepared by a number of reactions, including **hydrogenation** of alkenes and alkynes and **reduction** of alkyl halides. **Larger carbon skeletons** can be prepared by the lithium dialkylcuprate (Corey-House) method.

7 Alkanes undergo only three common types of reactions: **combustion, pyrolysis**, and **halogenation**. Only the last of these is useful for laboratory synthesis of alkyl halides and hence other classes of organic compounds.

8 A **mechanism** is a series of steps by which a reaction is thought to proceed. An **energy profile** is a graphic representation of the energy associated with each step in the mechanism.

9 **Petroleum** is a mixture of alkanes and is processed into commercially useful materials by catalytic cracking and fractional distillation.

10 By focusing on the **purpose of a reaction** and regularly reviewing reaction flash cards or lists you can more efficiently learn organic reactions.

KEY TERMS

Activation energy	Classical nomenclature	Grignard reagent
Alkane	Combustion	Halogenation
Angle strain	Concerted reaction	Hydrogenation
Anti addition	Conformation	IUPAC naming system
Anti conformation	Corey-House reaction	Lithium dialkylcuprate reaction
Axial position in cyclohexane	Coupling reaction	
Boat conformation of cyclohexane	Eclipsed conformation	Mechanism
Catalyst	Energy profile	Newman projection
Catalytic cracking	Equatorial position in cyclohexane	Primary hydrogen atoms
Chair conformation of cyclohexane	Fractional distillation	Pyrolysis
	Gauche conformation	"Sawhorse" drawings

Secondary hydrogen
  atoms
Staggered
  conformation

Syn addition
Tertiary hydrogen
  atoms

Torsional strain
Transition state

SKILL PRACTICE PROBLEMS

1 Using the general formula for acyclic alkanes, write the molecular formula for alkanes with 15 and 91 carbons, respectively.

2 Draw structures for all isomers of C_7H_{16}. Name each one.

3 Draw structures for the following:
(a) a *sec*-butyl group
(b) 2,3,3-trimethylpentane
(c) 2-chloro-1-isobutylcyclohexane
(d) 1-bromo-4-ethyl-2,3-dimethyloctane
(e) 2,2,3,3-tetramethylhexane
(f) 1,1-dicyclobutylcyclopentane

4 What is wrong with the names shown below? Give correct names for the structure indicated by each one.
(a) 2-dimethylnonane
(b) 1-ethylheptane
(c) 2-propylbutane
(d) 3,3-chloro-1-methylcyclohexane

5 Name each compound shown below.

(a)

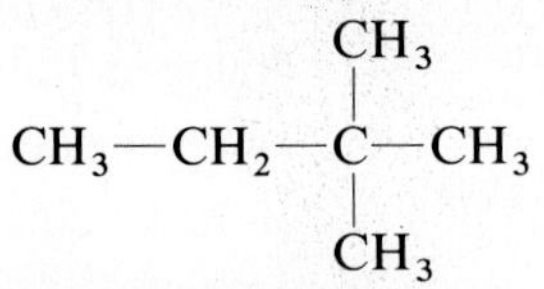

$$CH_3-CH_2-\underset{\underset{CH_3}{|}}{\overset{\overset{CH_3}{|}}{C}}-CH_3$$

(b) CH₃—⬡—Cl, Br

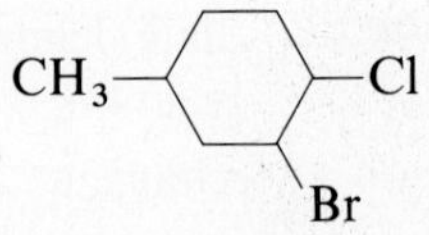

(c)

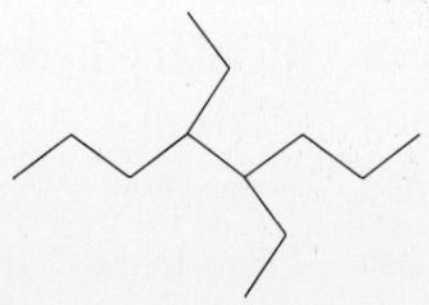

(*d*)

$$CH_3-\overset{\overset{\displaystyle Br}{|}}{\underset{\underset{\displaystyle CH_2-CH_2-CH_2-CH_2-\overset{\overset{\displaystyle}{}}{\underset{\underset{\displaystyle CH_3-CH-CH_3}{|}}{CH}}-I}{|}}{C}}-CH_2-CH_3$$

(*e*) $CH_3-CH_2-CH-CH_2-CH_2-CH_3$

with cyclopropyl group

6 Name these alkanes and substituted alkanes.

(*a*) $CH_3-CH_2-CH_2-\overset{\overset{\displaystyle}{}}{\underset{\underset{\displaystyle Br}{|}}{CH}}-\overset{\overset{\displaystyle}{}}{\underset{\underset{\displaystyle CH_3}{|}}{CH}}-CH_3$

(*b*) $CH_3-CH_2-CH-CH_3$

with cyclobutyl group

(*c*)

(*d*) cyclopentyl $\overset{CH_2-CH_2-CH_3}{\underset{CH_2-CH_2-CH_3}{}}$

(*e*)

$$\underset{\underset{\displaystyle CH_3}{\overset{\displaystyle |}{\underset{\displaystyle CH_2}{\overset{\displaystyle |}{CH_2}}}}}{CH_2}-CH_2-\overset{\overset{\displaystyle CH_3}{|}}{CH}-\overset{\overset{\displaystyle CH_3}{|}}{CH} \qquad Cl-\overset{\overset{\displaystyle}{}}{\underset{\underset{\displaystyle Cl}{|}}{C}}-CH_2-CH_3$$

7 Write the product(s) you would expect for each of these reactions.

(*a*)

$$CH_3-CH_2-\overset{\overset{\displaystyle CH_3}{|}}{CH}-CH_2-CH_3 + Br_2 \overset{h\nu}{\longrightarrow}$$

(*b*) $CH_3Br + Mg/ether \longrightarrow \overset{H_2O}{\longrightarrow}$

(*c*) cyclopentene $+ H_2 \overset{Pt}{\longrightarrow}$

(*d*) $C_6H_{14} + O_2 \longrightarrow$

(*e*) $CH_3-CH_3 + H_2O \longrightarrow$

(*f*) cyclohexyl$-Cl \overset{Li}{\longrightarrow} \overset{CuI}{\longrightarrow} \overset{CH_3CH_2CH_2CH_2-I}{\longrightarrow}$

8 Complete these reactions.

(a) $CH_3-CH_2-CH=CH-CH_3 + H_2 \xrightarrow{Ni}$

(b) $CH_3-C\equiv CH + 2H_2 \xrightarrow{catalyst}$

(c) $+ Cl_2 \xrightarrow{hv}$

(d)

$$CH_3-CH_2-\overset{\overset{\displaystyle CH_3}{|}}{C}H-Br \xrightarrow{Li} \xrightarrow{CuBr} \xrightarrow{CH_3-Cl}$$

(e)

$$CH_3-\overset{\overset{\displaystyle CH_3}{|}}{\underset{\underset{\displaystyle CH_3}{|}}{C}}-MgBr + H_2O \longrightarrow$$

(f) $\xrightarrow[Pt]{H_2}$

(g) $\xrightarrow[NH_3]{Li}$

9 Write the mechanism for the reaction of bromine with cyclohexane.

10 Draw the most stable conformation of ethylcyclohexane.

11 Which one of the following pairs of compounds would you expect to have the highest boiling point?
(a) C_5H_{12} or C_7H_{16}
(b) Octane or cyclooctane
(c) Heptane or 3,3-dimethylpentane
(d) 3-Ethylhexane or 2,2,3,3-tetramethylbutane

12 In which fuel product would you be likely to find the following alkanes?
(a) 3-Methylhexane
(b) Ethane
(c) 5,6-Diethyldecane

13 From what you know about factors affecting the stabilities of various conformations, which would you expect to be lower in energy, the cis or trans isomer of 1,2-dimethylcyclobutane?

14 How much heat energy is produced per gallon of fuel oil? (A gallon of fuel oil weighs about 3050 g.)

15 A cubic foot of natural gas (mostly methane) contains about 0.2 moles of methane. How many calories of heat is produced from the burning of a cubic foot of natural gas?

16 Write definitions in your own words for the following terms:
   (a) Mechanism
   (b) Catalyst
   (c) Transition state
   (d) Conformation
   (e) Angle strain
   (f) Combustion

17 Classify each hydrogen atom in the following molecule as $1°$, $2°$, or $3°$.

18 Draw the Newman projection for the most stable conformation of pentane looking down the C-2 to C-3 bond (carbon atom number 2 should be closest to your eye).

19 Repeat question 18 for pentane looking down the C-1 to C-2 bond (carbon atom number 1 should be closest to your eye).

20 Name the groups attached to the cyclohexane ring below using the classical system.

21 An alkane with molecular weight of 86 forms only two monochlorination isomers. What is the structure of the alkane? Name the alkane and both products that could be formed.

22 Two alkanes, A and B, both have a molecular weight of 72. Compound A gives four possible monobromination products, while compound B gives only one monobromination product. What are the structures and names of A and B?

CHAPTER 4

STEREOCHEMISTRY AND OPTICAL ACTIVITY

LEARNING GOALS

1 To understand optical activity

2 To understand the concept of chirality and the terms associated with it

3 To develop the skill of determining the absolute configuration of chiral molecules

4 To develop the skill of translating between stereo drawings and Fischer representations of molecules

5 To understand the relevance of optical activity

We have already discussed the concept of isomers—compounds which have the same molecular formula but have the atoms arranged differently. The skeletal isomers of alkanes and the cis and trans forms of substituted cyclic alkanes are examples. In these cases, the several isomers have different physical and chemical properties. In this chapter, we will be considering a type of isomerism which involves an even more subtle difference in structure.

CONCEPT OF CHIRALITY AND OPTICAL ACTIVITY

The molecule below (1-bromo-1-iodoethane) has a tetrahedral carbon atom with four **different** atoms or groups attached. This means that there is no symmetry of any kind in the molecule—it is totally lacking in symmetry. We call such a molecule **asymmetric** or **chiral**.

H   CH₃
    C
I   Br   } Chiral molecule

Chiral carbon

At this point we need to consider the concept of polarized light, since we will be using it to describe the behavior of chiral molecules. **Polarized light** is produced by passing ordinary light through a polarizing (Polaroid) filter as shown in Figure 4-1.

When we obtain a source of polarized light and pass it through a solution containing a chiral compound, the plane of vibration of the light is rotated, and the compound is said to be **optically active**. In the laboratory, the exact amount of rotation can be measured by an instrument called a

FIGURE 4-1

Diagram of the operation of a polarizing filter.

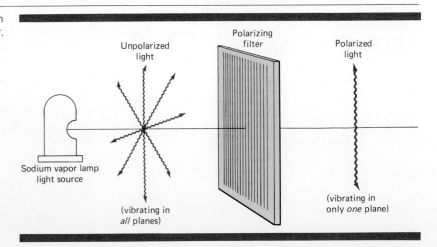

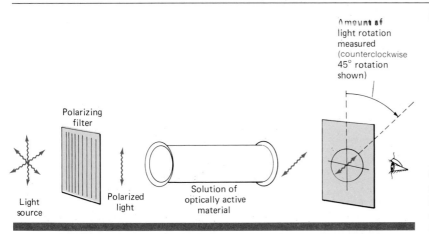

Schematic diagram of the rotation of plane polarized light by an optically active compound, in a polarimeter.

FIGURE 4-2

polarimeter. Such an instrument is diagrammed in Figure 4-2, and a photograph of one is shown in Figure 4-3.

The amount of light rotation caused by a particular chiral compound is usually expressed in terms of its **specific rotation**. The **specific rotation** of a compound is defined as the rotation produced by a solution containing 1 gram (g) of chiral material per milliliter (mL) of solution when the light is passing through a tube 0.10 meter (1.0 decimeter or dm) in length. The observed rotation of light is affected by the length of the tube (the longer the tube, the greater the rotation) and by the concentration (lower con-

FIGURE 4-3

A polarimeter used to experimentally determine the amount of rotation of plane polarized light by an optically active compound.

centrations give less rotation). The rotation is also affected by both the temperature and the wavelength of the light used, so both of these factors must be carefully controlled. The specific rotation is symbolized by $[\alpha]_D^{25}$. The 25 represents 25°C, which is standard temperature for such measurements, and the D indicates that we are using the D line, with a wavelength of 589.6 nanometers (nm), produced by a sodium vapor lamp light source.

When light is rotated to the right (clockwise, cw) from the observer's point of view (see Figure 4-2), the compound is said to be **dextrorotatory** and the specific rotation is given a plus sign (+). When light is rotated to the left (counterclockwise, ccw) the compound is said to be **levorotatory** and the specific rotation is given a minus sign (−).

For example, the compound below has the indicated specific rotation of $[\alpha]_D^{25} = +5.8°$. This means that 1 g/mL solution at 25°C in a 1.0 dm tube will rotate light 5.8° to the right from the observer's perspective.

$$CH_2CH_3 \quad CH_2OH$$
$$C$$
$$CH_3 \qquad H$$

$$[\alpha]_D^{25} = +5.8°$$

Let's examine the relationship between molecular structure and optical activity. Below you will see a stereodrawing of a chiral molecule and its mirror image.

$$Cl \quad H \qquad H \quad Cl$$
$$C \qquad C$$
$$CH_3 \quad Br \quad Br \quad CH_3$$

mirror

1-Bromo-1-chloroethane

It may seem at first glance that these mirror images are really the same molecule drawn two ways. But if we build models of both forms and then attempt to move them so that every atom matches, it soon becomes obvious that this cannot be done. That is, the mirror images are **not superimposable**. Figure 4-4 shows the mirror image molecular models, and Figure 4-5 shows an attempt to superimpose them. Note that two groups match but the other two are reversed. No matter how they are turned, two groups will match and two will not.

A molecule that is chiral is, therefore, not the same as its mirror image. The two are different compounds (isomers) and are given the name **enantiomers**. Most of the chemical and physical properties of a pair of enantiomers are identical. These identical properties include melting point, density, boiling point, surface tension, solubility, stability, bond angles, and reaction with most chemical reagents. Enantiomers do differ from each other, however, in two ways:

Models of two molecules
that are mirror images of
each other (enantiomers).

FIGURE 4-4

An attempt to superimpose
models of enantiomers.
Note that the back and left
groups match, but the
upper and right groups
are reversed.

FIGURE 4-5

1   They respond to polarized light differently. One enantiomer will rotate
polarized light in one direction by an amount determined experimentally
(it cannot be predicted). The other enantiomer (the first one's mirror image)
will rotate polarized light by the same amount but in the opposite direction. If one enantiomer has a specific rotation of $+10°$ (clockwise to the
observer), the other enantiomer will have a specific rotation of $-10°$

(counterclockwise). We cannot predict either the direction or the magnitude of the rotation of light by examining the molecular structure of the enantiomers, but if we know the value for one isomer, we know that the other isomer will have the same value but in the opposite direction.

2 In chemical reactions, enantiomers respond differently to other chiral molecules. Such chiral molecules include, among others, those found in biosystems. For example, if one enantiomer is toxic, the other one may not be. If one is a vitamin, the other may be inactive. The reason for this is that all biological processes are catalyzed by **enzymes**. Enzymes are protein molecules that have a chiral structure themselves. For a compound to be biologically active, it must match the shape of the enzyme, as shown in Figure 4-6. In the left-hand drawing, there is a match between the halogen atoms on the molecule and the site on the enzyme that corresponds to it. In the right-hand drawing, the I and Br atoms do not match their respective sites on the enzyme, and no reaction will occur. We will deal more with enzymes in Chapter 15.

> Molecules that lack symmetry are said to be chiral. Such molecules have the unusual property of rotating the plane of polarized light. The magnitude of rotation is measured by a polarimeter. Mirror image isomers of chiral molecules are called enantiomers and have identical physical and chemical properties, except that they differ in the direction of rotation of plane polarized light and in their reactions with other chiral compounds, including enzymes in biosystems.

FIGURE 4-6

Interaction of enantiomers with an enzyme.

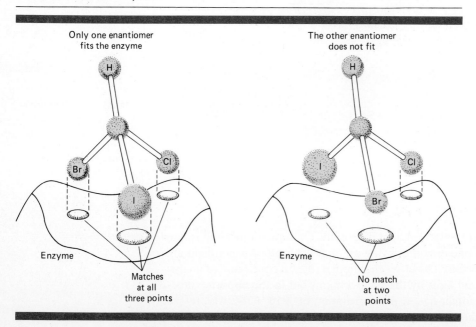

Only one enantiomer fits the enzyme

The other enantiomer does not fit

Enzyme

Matches at all three points

Enzyme

No match at two points

DESIGNATING CONFIGURATION

For purposes of communication, a concise means of differentiating between enantiomers must be developed.

Before such systems are presented, however, we must consider ways of indicating molecular structure on paper. The most obvious is the stereochemical drawing illustrated below for the two enantiomers of 2-bromo-2-iodobutane.

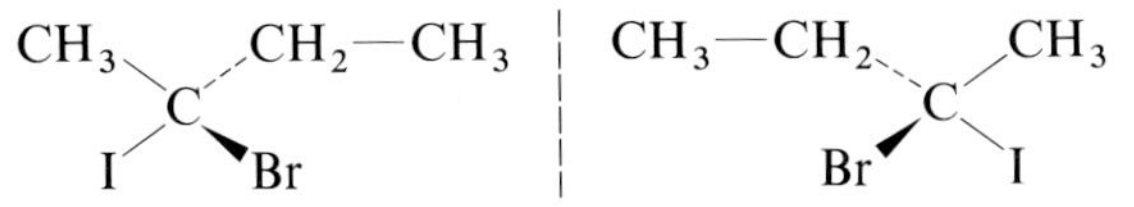

Mirror

Since these are somewhat difficult to draw, a shorthand method called a **Fischer Projection** was developed by the great sugar chemist Emil Fischer. Fischer projections are flat drawings in which the four groups are shown at the ends of four lines at 90° to each other. By convention, it is understood that **the vertical lines are going away from the reader, the horizontal ones are coming out of the paper**, and at the intersection of the lines is the chiral atom **in the plane of the paper**. Thus:

Stereodrawing   Fischer projection

1-Bromo-1-chloroethane

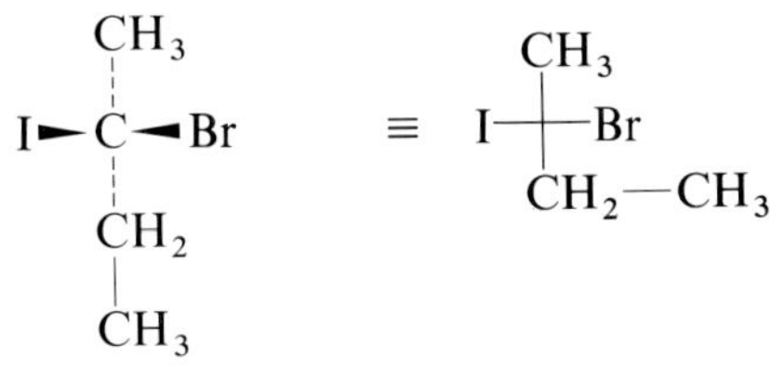

2-Bromo-2-iodobutane

ABSOLUTE CONFIGURATION

Now let's look at a system for differentiating between enantiomers. The **absolute configuration** (spatial arrangement) about a chiral center (atom) can be designated by the following steps. This system is called the **Cahn-Ingold-Prelog** system. We will illustrate this system by using 1-bromo-1-chloroethane, which was drawn above in the illustration of Fischer projections.

1 First assign a rank to the four atoms or groups attached to the chiral carbon.

(*a*) The atom with the highest atomic number has the highest rank (rank 1). Here we consider the atomic numbers of the atoms attached directly to the chiral atom. The atom with the second highest atomic number is rank 2, etc. Thus for Cl, C, H and Br, the correct ordering would be:

ATOM	ATOMIC NUMBER	RANK
Br	35	1
Cl	17	2
C	6	3
H	1	4

(*b*) If two groups have the same atom attached directly to the chiral center, we go out from the chiral center one more step to see if a differentiation in atomic number can be made. If so, the one with the highest number "wins" and has a higher priority than the other. For some groups, we must go several more steps away from the chiral center to make a distinction.

(*c*) When we encounter multiple bonding, we count it as though it were multiple atoms of the same element. For example, C=O is considered to be a carbon atom bonded to **two** oxygen atoms and an oxygen atom bonded to **two** carbon atoms.

$$\text{C=O} \quad \text{is considered to be} \quad \begin{array}{c} | \\ -\text{C}-\text{O} \\ | \quad | \\ \text{O} \quad \text{C} \end{array}$$

and

$$-\text{C}\equiv\text{C}- \quad \text{is considered to be} \quad \begin{array}{c} \text{C} \quad \text{C} \\ | \quad | \\ -\text{C}-\text{C}- \\ | \quad | \\ \text{C} \quad \text{C} \end{array}$$

2 Once the four priorities are assigned, we orient the chiral atom so that the group with the lowest priority (4) is pointing away from the viewer. This automatically establishes that groups 1, 2, and 3 point toward the viewer. We then draw a circular line beginning at 1 and going to 2 and then to 3. If this line points clockwise (cw), the enantiomer is said to be (R); if counterclockwise (ccw), it is called the (S) isomer. (R stands for *rectus* and S for *sinister*.)

The drawing above shows the (S) enantiomer of 1-bromo-1-chloro-ethane. Note that in progressing from rank 1, to 2, to 3, we move in a counterclockwise direction. The group with the fourth priority (H) is back, away from the viewer.

When using stereodrawings or actual models we manipulate (actually or mentally) the model to get the priority 4 atom or group away from the viewer so that the arrangement of the groups with priorities 1, 2, and 3 can be examined.

For Fischer projections, the process is easier for students who have difficulty visualizing in three dimensions. If the fourth priority is at the top or bottom of the Fischer projection, then it is already pointed away from the viewer (remember that in Fischer projections, the vertical groups always go back into the paper by convention). If this is the case, simply draw a circle on the paper from priority 1 to priority 2 to priority 3 and observe whether the circle is pointing in a clockwise (R) or counterclockwise (S) direction.

If, on the other hand, the fourth priority is on a side in the Fischer projection, it is coming toward you. This means that you ought to look at the molecule from the other side of the paper. Instead of trying to imagine yourself walking over to the other side (which is a perfectly valid method, but difficult for some students), reverse the way it appears on the paper. For example, if priority 4 is on a side, draw a line from priorities $1 \rightarrow 2 \rightarrow 3$. If it is counterclockwise, change it to clockwise and label it the (R) isomer. This method works because something that is moving clockwise from one perspective will always appear to be moving counterclockwise when viewed from the opposite direction. If this is not obvious to you, try observing a fan blade or other rotating object from one side and then look at it from the other side—it will appear to be going in the opposite direction.

Steps for determining absolute configuration

The steps in the Cahn-Ingold-Prelog method for designating the configuration of chiral centers are listed below for easy reference.

1   Convert to Fischer projection

2   Determine priorities of the four atoms or groups on the chiral center

3 Draw an arrow 1 → 2 → 3

4 If priority 4 is on a side, then reverse the arrow direction determined in step 3

5 If the arrow direction is clockwise, then the isomer is assigned an (R) configuration; if the arrow is counterclockwise, then (S) is assigned.

The following Programmed Learning Unit will illustrate these steps and allow you to develop skill in determining the absolute configuration of a chiral center.

DETERMINING ABSOLUTE CONFIGURATION AT CHIRAL CENTER

Worked example

Which isomer of 1-chloro-1-fluoroethane is drawn below?

$$CH_3 \overset{\displaystyle Cl}{\underset{\displaystyle H}{\rule[0.5ex]{1em}{0.4pt}\!\!\!\!\!\vert\!\!\!\!\!\rule[0.5ex]{1em}{0.4pt}}} F$$

Solution

1 The Fischer projection is already drawn.

2 The atomic number and priority assignments of the four atoms attached to the chiral atom are:

ATOM	ATOMIC NUMBER	RANK
Cl	17	1
F	9	2
C	6	3
H	1	4

3 Drawing an arrow 1 → 2 → 3 gives a cw rotation.

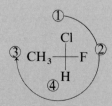

4 Priority 4 is down, so no reversal is needed.

5 This is the (R) isomer.

Worked example

Give the absolute configuration of the compound whose stereo drawing is shown below.

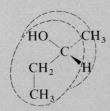

Solution

1 Change this to a Fischer Projection. There are several different ways to correctly draw this, and all of them will give the same configuration. Look at the drawing, holding your head as indicated by the outline. From this perspective, the OH and H are left and right, respectively, and coming toward you. Therefore, draw them on the sides in the Fischer projection, as follows:

$$
\begin{array}{c}
CH_3 \\
HO \!-\!\!\!-\!\!\!-\! H \\
CH_2 \\
CH_3
\end{array}
$$

Note By convention, in Fischer projections the longest carbon chain containing the chiral atom is drawn vertically.

2 Atomic numbers and priorities are as follows:

ATOM	ATOMIC NUMBER	RANK
O	8	1
C	6	2 & 3
C	6	
H	1	4

3 We have two carbon atoms. To distinguish between them, we go out one more step in all directions in these groups. Remember that we have already determined that the —OH group is priority 1 and that H is priority 4. We are now only finding which carbon group is priority 2 and which is 3.

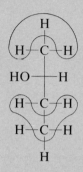

One more step in the methyl (upper) group shows three H's; going one more step in the ethyl (lower) group gives 2 H's and one C. The atomic numbers of the latter add to $1 + 1 + 6 = 8$; the atomic numbers of the former give $1 + 1 + 1 = 3$. The ethyl group's 8 gives it the higher priority; therefore it is assigned a priority of 2, leaving the methyl group to be priority 3. The priorities are shown below.

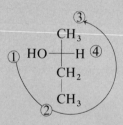

4 Drawing an arrow $1 \rightarrow 2 \rightarrow 3$ gives counterclockwise direction, as shown.

5 Since the fourth group is on a side, we reverse the arrow direction determined in step 4.

6 This is therefore an (R) compound.

Worked example

Give the configuration of the starred atom in this compound.

$$
\begin{array}{c}
\overset{\displaystyle O}{\diagdown}\overset{\displaystyle H}{\diagup} \\
C \\
HO-CH_2-\overset{\displaystyle *}{|}-H \\
CH_2 \\
CH_2 \\
CH_3
\end{array}
$$

Solution

1 The molecule is already in Fischer form.

2 The H is number 4 priority. The other three atoms attached to the chiral center are all carbons. Going one more step in the three alkyl groups gives the following:

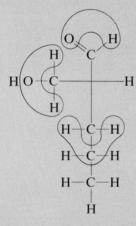

The left group has one oxygen and two hydrogens ($8 + 1 + 1 = 10$). The bottom group has one carbon and two hydrogens ($6 + 1 + 1 = 8$). The top group has one hydrogen and one **doubly bonded** oxygen, which counts as two oxygen atoms ($1 + 8 + 8 = 17$).

Note For multiple bonds, each atom is thought of as though it were bonded to another atom of the same element. Thus,

$$
\begin{array}{c}
O \\
\parallel \\
-C-H
\end{array}
\qquad \text{is considered} \qquad
\begin{array}{c}
O\diagdown \\
-C-O \\
| \\
H
\end{array}C
$$

is considered to be

ATOM OR GROUP ON CHIRAL CENTER	ATOMIC NUMBER OF ATOMS ATTACHED TO CHIRAL CENTER	SUM OF ATOMIC NUMBERS AT THE SECOND STEP OUT	RANK
$\overset{\displaystyle O}{\overset{\|}{-C}}-H$	6	17	1
$-CH_2-OH$	6	10	2
$-CH_2-CH_2-CH_3$	6	8	3
H	1	——	4

3 Drawing the arrow $1 \to 2 \to 3$ gives a counterclockwise direction.

4 Since priority 4 is on a side, change the direction to clockwise.

5 Thus the configuration is (R)

Worked example

Give the configuration of the starred atom in this compound:

Solution

1 This is already in Fischer form.

2 All the atoms attached to the chiral carbon are themselves carbons. Taking one more step in all directions from the chiral center, as indicated by the colored loops, shows the following:

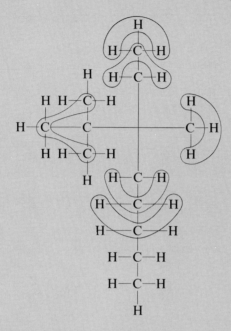

This gives priority 1 to the *tert*-butyl (left) group and priority 4 to the CH_3 (right) group. The ethyl (upper) and *n*-pentyl (lower) groups both have equal rank at this stage. Going one more step from the chiral center for these two groups only shows that the *n*-pentyl group has a higher rank than the ethyl group. The ranking for the groups is therefore as follows:

Rank 1 *tert*-butyl group

Rank 2 *n*-pentyl group

Rank 3 ethyl group

Rank 4 methyl group

Note This shows that priorities are not always in line with total group size. The *tert*-butyl group has one fewer carbon atoms than the *n*-pentyl group, but a higher rank. It is usually true in hydrocarbon groups that the group having branches closer to the chiral center will have the higher rank.

3 Drawing arrows gives a ccw direction.

4 Priority 4 is on a side, therefore, reverse direction to cw.

5 Give an (R) assignment.

Problem

Give the configuration of the following molecule:

$$H \quad CH_3$$
$$C$$
$$CH_3CH_2 \quad NH_2$$

Solution

1 Redraw as a Fischer projection.

$$CH_3$$
$$H—NH_2$$
$$CH_2$$
$$CH_3$$

2 Determine priorities.

$$③$$
$$④ \quad CH_3 \quad ①$$
$$H—NH_2$$
$$CH_2 \quad ②$$
$$CH_3$$

3 Note clockwise direction.

4 Since priority 4 is on a side, assign the isomer (S).

Problem

What is the configuration of the isomer of 1-bromo-1-cyclopentyl-propane shown below? Draw its enantiomer.

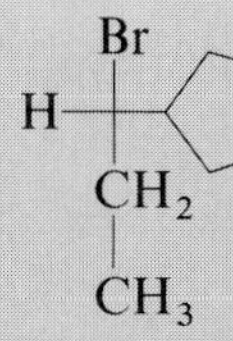

Solution

1 Assign priorities.

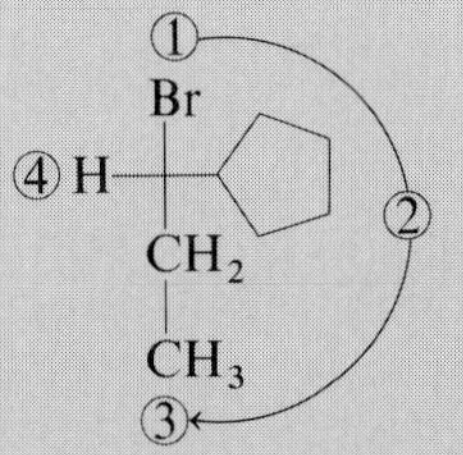

2 Note clockwise rotation.

3 Since priority 4 is on the side, reverse to counterclockwise and give a designation of (S). The (R) enantiomer is shown below, drawn two ways.

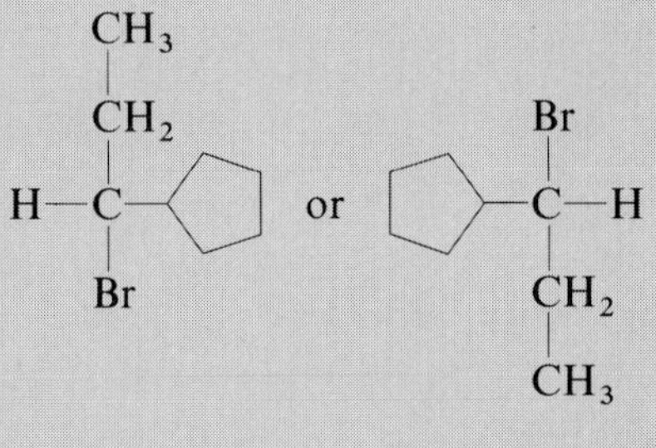

Problem

Are the two drawings below identical or are the molecules enantiomers?

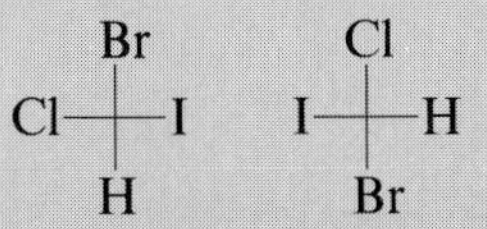

Solution

1 Determine the absolute configuration at each chiral atom.

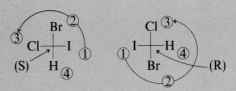

2 Since they have **opposite** configurations, they are enantiomers.

Chiral compounds are designated as (R) or (S) based on the Cahn-Ingold-Prelog system. This method uses a process of assigning priorities to the 4 atoms or groups attached to the chiral atom, followed by an observation of the direction of progress from first to second to third priority groups, while the fourth priority group is oriented away from the observer. Clockwise is assigned a designation of (R); counterclockwise is assigned (S).

NAMING CHIRAL MOLECULES

When a compound has one chiral atom, the (R) or (S) designation is placed before other parts of the name. If there are several chiral atoms, each is indicated by number. The direction of **light rotation** is sometimes also given as part of the name by including a (+) for clockwise rotation or (−) for counterclockwise rotation. Examples are as follows:

$$CH_3$$
$$H\!-\!\!\overset{|}{\underset{|}{}}\!\!-\!I \quad (S)$$
$$CH_2$$
$$CH_3$$

$$CH_3$$
$$H\!-\!\!\overset{|}{\underset{|}{}}\!\!-\!I \quad (S)$$
$$H\!-\!\!\overset{|}{\underset{|}{}}\!\!-\!CH_3$$
$$CH_2 \quad (R)$$
$$CH_3$$

(S)-(+)-2-iodobutane   (2S, 3R)-2-iodo-3-methylpentane

Note   There is **NO** correlation between the direction of light rotation and the direction of the arrows in the Cahn-Ingold-Prelog System.

CHANGING DRAWINGS TO OPPOSITE CONFIGURATION

When we have one enantiomer and want to draw the other one, we perform **any one** of the following operations:

1   Draw the mirror image of the chiral molecule

2   Rotate the chiral molecule 90°

3 Switch any **two** groups on the chiral carbon.

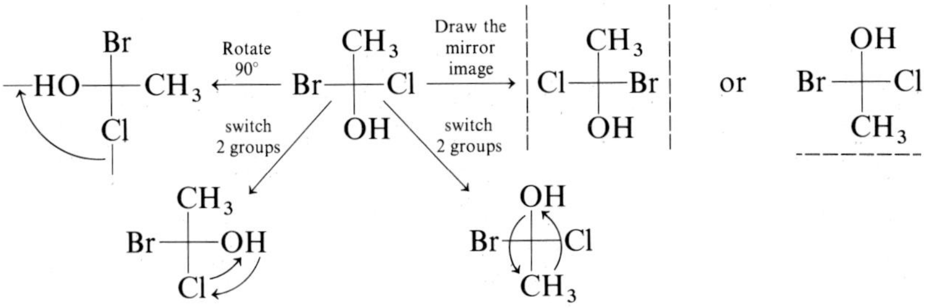

RELATIVE CONFIGURATION

An older method of designating configuration is based on an arbitrary standard compound—glyceraldehyde.

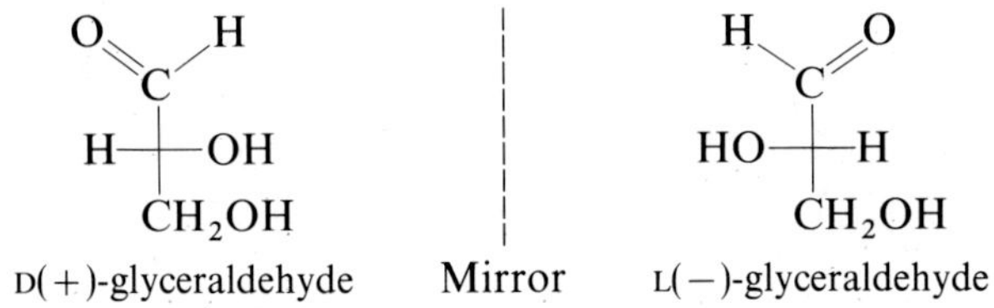

D(+)-glyceraldehyde   Mirror   L(−)-glyceraldehyde

The isomer shown at the left rotates light clockwise [it is dextrorotatory or (+)] and is called the D enantiomer. The other one rotates light to the left [it is levorotatory or (−)] and is called the L isomer. The D isomer of glyceraldehyde happens to be (R) in the absolute system while the L isomer is (S). This is not a general rule, however. Either the D or L designation for a given compound could be (R) or (S).

In this **relative** system, any chiral center which has the same configuration as the chiral center of D-glyceraldehyde is called a D isomer **regardless of its experimentally determined direction of light rotation**. This older system is still used to name some medically active materials, such as dextroamphetamine and dextromethorphan, a stimulant ("upper") and cough suppressant, respectively. Also, biochemists still use the older system to designate the configuration of sugars and amino acids (see Chapters 14 and 15). Below are shown the structures of a D-glucose (a sugar) and L-alanine (an amino acid).

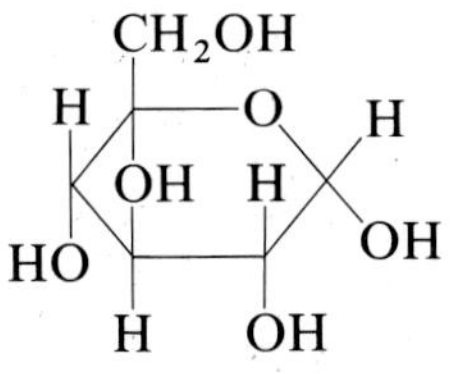

α-D-(+)-glucose 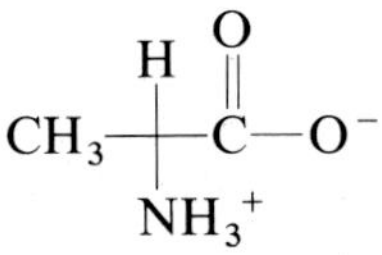   L-alanine

TERMS USED FOR CHIRAL MOLECULES

Enantiomers   This term has already been discussed. It is the special name given to chiral isomers that are nonsuperimposable mirror images of each other.

Diasteriomers   These are stereoisomers that are **not** mirror images. They have the same skeleton and the same functional groups on the same carbons, but the spatial arrangements are different. This term is applied to compounds with more than one chiral center. For example, for 2,3-dihydroxybutane we can draw 4 isomers:

$$
\begin{array}{ccc}
& \text{CH}_3 & \\
\text{H} & \!\!\!-\!\!\! & \text{OH} \\
\text{H} & \!\!\!-\!\!\! & \text{OH} \\
& \text{CH}_3 &
\end{array}
\qquad \text{Mirror} \qquad
\begin{array}{ccc}
& \text{CH}_3 & \\
\text{HO} & \!\!\!-\!\!\! & \text{H} \\
\text{HO} & \!\!\!-\!\!\! & \text{H} \\
& \text{CH}_3 &
\end{array}
$$

Compound A   Mirror   Compound B

$$
\begin{array}{ccc}
& \text{CH}_3 & \\
\text{H} & \!\!\!-\!\!\! & \text{OH} \\
\text{HO} & \!\!\!-\!\!\! & \text{H} \\
& \text{CH}_3 &
\end{array}
\qquad \text{Mirror} \qquad
\begin{array}{ccc}
& \text{CH}_3 & \\
\text{HO} & \!\!\!-\!\!\! & \text{H} \\
\text{H} & \!\!\!-\!\!\! & \text{OH} \\
& \text{CH}_3 &
\end{array}
$$

Compound C   Mirror   Compound D

Compounds C and D are enantiomers (mirror images of each other), but A and C as well as A and D are disasteriomers—they are not reflections of each other, but they are stereoisomers.

Meso   This term is used to describe a molecule which has chiral atoms, but which is not itself chiral. A meso compound's mirror image is superimposable on itself. Therefore, a meso compound and its drawn mirror image are really the same molecule—not two different ones as was the case for chiral molecules (enantiomers). Compounds A and B above are such a case. They are drawn as mirror reflections, but they are not two different compounds. If we build molecular models of A and B, we can superimpose B on A and get a perfect match.

We can recognize meso compounds on paper by observing a mirror plane within the molecule. That is, if one half of the molecule is a reflection of the other half, the molecule is meso. Of course, there must be the same groups on symmetrically oriented chiral centers before one half the molecule can be the reflection of the other half. We can also determine that a molecule is meso by observing the same functional groups on symmetrically oriented chiral atoms and noting that mirror image chiral centers have opposite (R) or (S) designations. Figure 4-7 shows a photograph of a molecular model and the mirror plane.

Molecular model of a *meso* compound. The piece of cardboard indicates the imaginary mirror plane of symmetry in the molecule.

FIGURE 4-7

meso-2,3-Dihydroxybutane

Meso compounds do not rotate polarized light. One end will be of the (R) configuration and tend to rotate light in one direction, while the other end, which is the mirror reflection, will necessarily be (S) and will tend to rotate light in the opposite direction. Thus, the rotations cancel each other and no net rotation is observed.

Not meso; not the same four atoms or groups on both chiral atoms

Not meso; no mirror plane; both chiral centers are (S)

$$\begin{array}{c}
\text{Br} \\
\text{H}\!-\!\!\!\!-\!\!\!\!\text{O}\!-\!\text{CH}_3 \quad \text{(S)}\\
\text{------------------Mirror}\\
\text{H}\!-\!\!\!\!-\!\!\!\!\text{O}\!-\!\text{CH}_3\\
\text{Br} \quad \text{(R)}
\end{array}$$

Meso; same four groups on both chiral atoms; internal mirror plane; one (R) and one (S) chiral center

Scheme I gives a flowchart with which to determine optical activity. We start at the top and answer each question. This leads us to one of the boxes containing the correct answer for the material in question. For example, consider the following compound:

$$\begin{array}{ccc}
\text{Br} & \text{Cl} & \text{Cl}\\
| & | & |\\
\text{CH}_3\!-\!\text{C}\!-\!\text{C}\!-\!\text{C}\!-\!\text{CH}_2\!-\!\text{CH}_3\\
| & | & |\\
\text{I} & \text{Br} & \text{CH}_3
\end{array}$$

Are there chiral centers? Yes there are three of them. Is there a plane of symmetry? No, therefore this material will rotate polarized light.

Racemic mixtures and optical activity   A mixture of equal amounts of two enantiomers will not rotate polarized light. This is because the isomers will rotate light in opposite directions; thus each cancels the other's effect. Such a mixture is called a **racemic mixture**, sometimes also called a **racemic modification**. When a sample contains only one enantiomer, it is said to be **optically pure**.

SCHEME 1

Determining optical activity. Follow this flowchart, asking the appropriate question which is indicated by the answer to the previous question. **Active** means that the compound will rotate polarized light.

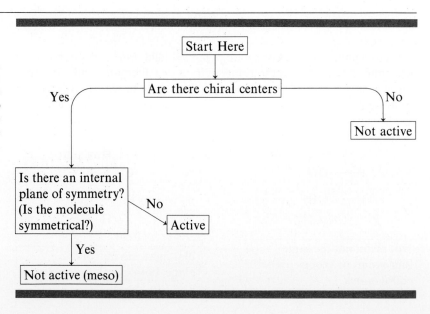

Number of isomers   We find the number of stereoisomers that can be drawn as follows: Number of isomers $= 2^n$, where n is the number of chiral centers. This number includes the mirror reflection of a meso compound, since it can be drawn. Therefore, the actual number of isomers is $(2^n -$ number of meso compounds). For the compound drawn below there are 2 chiral centers, so the number of drawings would be $2^2 = 4$. Since a mirror plane is possible, the meso compound and its mirror image are the same molecule, and there are only 3 isomers (see page 138).

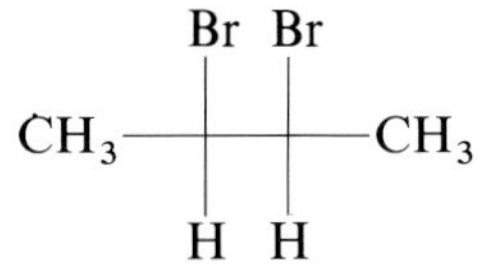

$$\text{CH}_3 \underset{\underset{\text{H}\quad\text{H}}{|\quad|}}{\overset{\overset{\text{Br}\quad\text{Br}}{|\quad|}}{\rule{2cm}{0.4pt}}} \text{CH}_3$$

For the following compound no mirror plane is possible, so for this compound with 3 chiral centers there would be $2^3 = 8$ isomers.

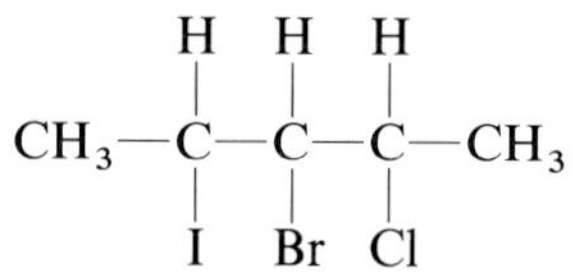

$$\text{CH}_3 - \underset{\underset{\text{I}}{|}}{\overset{\overset{\text{H}}{|}}{\text{C}}} - \underset{\underset{\text{Br}}{|}}{\overset{\overset{\text{H}}{|}}{\text{C}}} - \underset{\underset{\text{Cl}}{|}}{\overset{\overset{\text{H}}{|}}{\text{C}}} - \text{CH}_3$$

APPLICATIONS OF OPTICAL ACTIVITY

We have already mentioned that biochemical processes are catalyzed by enzymes, and that enzymes have a unique three-dimensional structure that causes them to be spatially matched to only one enantiomer. This means that of all biologically active materials, if a chiral center is present, usually only one enantiomer will exhibit biological activity. The other enantiomer will be biologically inactive or show a greatly reduced activity. Materials with chiral centers include drugs (both medicinal and non-medicinal), vitamins, and most foods.

Figure 4-8 shows the structure of lysergic acid *diethylamide* (LSD) and indicates the chiral centers (*). If one or both of them is of the opposite configuration, the material will not have its normal hallucinatory effect.

Mystery novels sometimes include the use of optical activity to prove the guilt of a murderer. **Naturally produced chiral materials are always optically pure.** This means that only one of two possible enantiomers is produced by plants and animals. The enantiomer produced naturally is the most biologically active one. Most synthetic organic procedures produce a racemic mixture of the two enantiomers. Such a mixture, you will remember, does not rotate polarized light. Thus, if someone has been poisoned by strychnine (see below), the stomach contents can be examined to determine whether the strychnine is optically active or not.

If the strychnine rotates light, it could be of natural origin and our sleuth might assume that its source was a poisonous plant (berry, root,

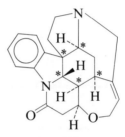

FIGURE 4-8

Structure of lysergic acid
diethylamide (LSD).

or bark) which was accidentally consumed. On the other hand, if the strychnine does not rotate light (is a racemic mixture) it is surely of synthetic origin, which suggests that the victim was murdered.

Strychnine

The optical activity of biological compounds can be used to determine the age of certain fossils. All natural amino acids are of the (S) absolute configuration (L in the relative system). Once an organism has died, the amino acids in the protein portions of the body (such as bones, dried skin, flesh, and hair) begin very slowly to racemize. That is, the amino acids change to the (R) configuration until, after a very long time, there is a racemic (50:50) mixture of the two isomers.

This fact can be used to determine the ages of proteinaceous artifacts. If we know the rate of change to the (R) isomer, an analysis of the amount of (R) present in a sample can be used to find the age of the sample. This is a significant method, since it bridges the gap between the carbon-14 method, which is of little value for samples older than about 30,000 years, and the potassium-argon or uranium-lead methods, which are useful for mineral samples which are on the order of billions of years old.

Samples which are between several hundred thousand and several million years old can be dated using the amino acid racemization method. It is during this period that human evolution may have occurred, and there is considerable interest in artifacts in this age range. An amino acid analyzer used to determine the (R/S) ratio of ancient protein samples is discussed in Chapter 15.

Plants and animals synthesize only one of the two possible enantiomers of any chiral compounds they produce. Furthermore, only one enantiomer of chiral drugs and other biologically active materials exhibits significant biological activity. The other enantiomer is either inactive or greatly reduced in activity. Racemization of optically active amino acids in proteins can be used to determine the ages of certain artifacts.

SUMMARY

1 Compounds whose molecules are **chiral** (asymmetric) rotate **polarized light**. This phenomenon is called **optical activity** and is determined experimentally by an instrument called a **polarimeter**.

2 **Enantiomers** are stereoisomers which are chiral and are mirror images of each other. The chemical and physical properties of the two enantiomers are identical except for the rotation of polarized light and the reactions with other chiral materials including enzymes in biological systems.

3 Chiral atoms within molecules are designated as (R) or (S) according to the arrangement of the four atoms or groups attached. An older system uses D and L assignments according to the relationship to arbitrarily assigned D- or L-glyceraldehyde.

4 Natural chiral materials (those produced by plants and animals) contain only one stereoisomer and are said to be optically pure. Usually, only one enantiomer of a given pair is biologically active. The optical activity of amino acids in proteins can be used to determine the age of certain artifacts.

KEY TERMS

Absolute configuration	Diasteriomers	Polarimeter
Asymmetric	Fischer projection	Polarized light
Cahn-Ingold-Prelog priority system	Levorotatory	Racemic mixture
Chiral	Meso	Relative configuration
Configuration	Mirror image	Rotation of polarized light
Enantiomers	Mirror plane	Superimposable
Enzymes	Optical activity	
Dextrorotatory	Optical purity	

SKILL PRACTICE PROBLEMS

1 Which of the following objects are chiral (totally lacking in symmetry)?
- (*a*) Electric table lamp
- (*b*) Golf ball
- (*c*) Bicycle
- (*d*) Human hand
- (*e*) Human body (external shape only)
- (*f*) Light switch cover plate

2 Draw the Fischer projection for each of the following compounds.

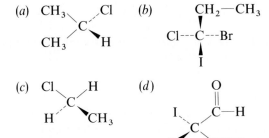

3 Which of those compounds in question 2 are chiral? Give each one its (R) or (S) designation.

4 Draw Fischer projections of both enantiomers of the following:
- (*a*) 3-Bromohexane
- (*b*) 1,2-Dichloropropane

5 Draw Fischer projections of all isomers of the following:
- (*a*) Tartaric acid: $HOOC—CH(OH)—CH(OH)—COOH$
- (*b*) 4-Iodo-3-methylhexane

6 Identify any meso structures in question 5.

7 Give the (R) and (S) designations for the chiral atoms in question 5.

8 Give the absolute configurations of all the chiral atoms in the structures below:

(*a*)
```
       CH₃
       |
  H ——+—— NO₂
       |
      CH₂
       |
      CH₃
```

(*b*)
```
      CH₃
       |
      CH₂
       |
  Br ——+—— Cl
       |
      CH₂
       |
      CH₂
       |
      CH₂
       |
      CH₃
```

(*c*)
```
          CH₃
           |
  CH₃ —— C —— Br
           
  I —— C —— H
           |
          CH₃
```

9 Which of the following compounds would be optically active? (Use scheme I, p 140.)

(a)

$$CH_3-CH_2-\underset{\underset{H}{|}}{\overset{\overset{Br}{|}}{C}}-CH_2-CH_3$$

(b)

$$CH_3-\underset{\underset{H}{|}}{\overset{\overset{OH}{|}}{C}}-CH_2-\underset{\underset{H}{|}}{\overset{\overset{OH}{|}}{C}}-CH_3$$

(c)

$$H-\underset{\underset{CH_3}{|}}{\overset{\overset{Br}{|}}{C}}-\underset{\underset{Br}{|}}{\overset{\overset{CH_3}{|}}{C}}-H$$

(d)

$$CH_3-\underset{\underset{H}{|}}{\overset{\overset{I}{|}}{C}}-\underset{\underset{H}{|}}{\overset{\overset{Cl}{|}}{C}}-\underset{\underset{H}{|}}{\overset{\overset{Br}{|}}{C}}-CH_3$$

10 Given the following properties for (R)-2-bromobutane, give the values for (S)-2-bromobutane.
  (a) Density = 1.258 g/ml
  (b) Boiling point = 91.3°C
  (c) Specific rotation = +50°
  (d) Relative configuration = D
  (e) Refractive index = 1.4344
  (f) Insoluble in H_2O

11 How many stereo isomers are there for

$$CH_3-\underset{\underset{H}{|}}{\overset{\overset{F}{|}}{C}}-\underset{\underset{Cl}{|}}{\overset{\overset{H}{|}}{C}}-\underset{\underset{I}{|}}{\overset{\overset{H}{|}}{C}}-\underset{\underset{H}{|}}{\overset{\overset{Br}{|}}{C}}-CH_3$$

12 Name the following compounds [include the (R) or (S) designation].

(a)
$$\begin{array}{c} CH_3 \\ H-\!\!\!\!-Br \\ CH_2 \\ CH_2 \\ CH_3 \end{array}$$

(b)
$$\begin{array}{c} CH_3 \\ CH_2 \\ Cl-\!\!\!\!-CH_3 \\ CH_2 \\ CH_2 \\ CH_3 \end{array}$$

(c)
$$\begin{array}{c} CH_3 \\ Cl-\!\!\!\!-Br \\ CH_2 \\ CH_2Cl \end{array}$$

13 Define the following terms:
  (a) Optical purity
  (b) Meso compound
  (c) Racemic mixture
  (d) Optical activity
  (e) Chiral

CHAPTER 5

ORGANIC HALOGEN COMPOUNDS

LEARNING GOALS

1 To review the nomenclature of halogen substituted alkanes

2 To learn the most useful laboratory methods of preparing halogen-containing compounds

3 To understand the importance of reaction mechanisms and the stabilities of the reactive intermediates in explaining why certain products are formed during a reaction

4 To learn the laboratory methods of preparing other classes of organic materials from alkyl halides

5 To examine, in detail, the mechanisms by which substitution reactions occur

6 To learn the molecular structures of some commercially useful halogen-containing compounds

The alkyl halides are useful as consumer products and as important intermediates in the synthesis of other classes of organic compounds. They are composed of molecules of the alkane type (carbon and hydrogen, and only single bonds) in which one or more of the hydrogen atoms has been replaced with a halogen atom (one of the group VIIA elements—F, Cl, Br, or I). Alkyl halides are symbolized by R—X, where R stands for the alkyl (C, H) portion and X is any halogen. Note that the terms *alkyl halide* and *halogen-substituted alkane* are synonymous. Examples of alkyl halides are

$$CH_2\text{---}CH_2 \qquad CH_3\text{---}Br \qquad \text{⬠---}I \qquad CHCl_3$$
$$\underset{Br}{|} \quad \underset{Br}{|}$$

1,2-Dibromoethane (ethylene dibromide)	Bromomethane	Iodocyclopentane	Trichloromethane (chloroform)

Figure 5-1 shows molecular models of chloromethane and iodocyclopentane. Note the difference in size between chlorine and iodine atoms. You will be asked to apply this relative size information in answering questions at the end of the chapter.

Alkyl halides are named using the same system presented for naming alkanes, with the halogen atoms being named as substituents. This system of nomenclature was covered in Chapter 3 in the Programmed Learning Unit on naming alkanes and substituted alkanes. Compounds in the alkyl halide class are relatively nonpolar compounds (usually liquids) which are insoluble in water.

FIGURE 5-1

Molecular models of chloromethane (CH_3Cl) and iodocyclopentane (C_5H_9I).

PREPARATION OF ALKYL HALIDES

Halogenation of alkanes

The most direct method of preparing alkyl halides is the reaction of Cl_2 or Br_2 with an alkane. (F_2 is too reactive to be useful in the laboratory, and I_2 will not react with alkanes.) Light (symbolized by hv) or heat is required for this reaction to begin. Examples are as follows:

$$CH_4 + Cl_2 \xrightarrow{hv} CH_3—Cl + HCl$$

$$CH_3—CH_3 + Br_2 \xrightarrow{hv} CH_3—CH_2—Br + HBr$$

These are **substitution** reactions, in which one of the hydrogens is replaced by a halogen and a molecule of HX is produced. Multiple substitution occurs if more than one mole of halogen is present per mole of alkane. (See Appendix A for an outline of the various types of organic reactions, including substitution reactions.)

$$CH_4 + 2Br_2 \xrightarrow{hv} CH_2Br_2 + 2HBr$$

$$CH_4 + 4Cl_2 \xrightarrow{hv} CCl_4 + 4HCl$$

The mechanism and other considerations of these halogen substitution reactions were covered in Chapter 3. Remember that for monosubstitution (only one halogen atom replacing one hydrogen atom), if there is more than one type of hydrogen atom present in the molecule, the higher-order position will react preferentially; i.e., tertiary hydrogen atoms are more reactive than secondary atoms and so forth. This and the other reactions in this chapter are summarized in the flow diagram on page 166.

Addition of HX to alkenes

Another convenient method of producing alkyl halides involves the addition of HX to the double bond of an alkene. This method sometimes allows the production of those alkyl halides which cannot be made by direct halogenation of alkanes.

$$CH_3—CH=CH_2 + HCl \longrightarrow CH_3—\underset{\underset{Cl}{|}}{CH}—CH_3$$

In this reaction, the **hydrogen** atom adds to the carbon atom of the double bond that already has the greatest number of **hydrogen** atoms. This is known as **Markovnikov's rule**. HBr and HI also follow this rule. However, it is possible to reverse the orientation **for HBr only** by adding a small amount of peroxide catalyst to the reaction mixture.

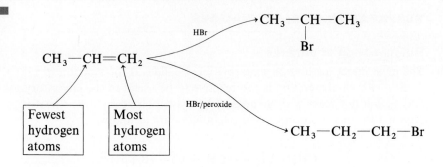

Without peroxides, the end of the double bond with the **greatest number of hydrogen atoms** gets the new **hydrogen** atom and the other end gets the bromine atom. When peroxide is present, however, the end with the **fewest hydrogen atoms** gets the **new hydrogen** atom. This is called **anti-Markovnikov addition** because the result is the reverse of the normal orientation. This only works for HBr; HCl and HI add by Markovnikov's rule with or without peroxides present. For example:

Other examples of the addition of HX to alkenes are shown below.

Stability of carbocations   The explanation for the orientation of the addition of HX to carbon-carbon double bonds, which has just been discussed, lies in the relative stabilities of the intermediates formed during the reaction. A concept that is used to explain many results in organic chemistry is the following stability series for all possible carbocations which could be formed from 2-methylbutane:

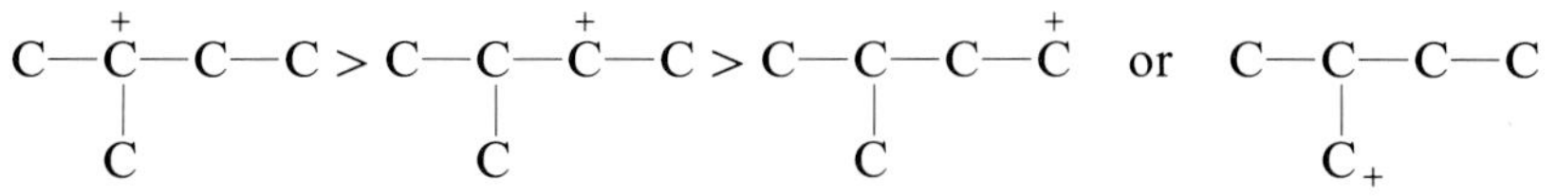

$$
\overset{\;+}{C}-\overset{|}{\underset{|}{C}}-C-C \;>\; C-\overset{|}{\underset{|}{C}}-\overset{+}{C}-C \;>\; C-C-\overset{|}{\underset{|}{C}}-\overset{+}{C} \quad \text{or} \quad C-C-\overset{|}{\underset{|}{C}}-C
$$

C	C	C	C+

Tertiary (3°)   Secondary (2°)   Primary (1°)

This order of stability is experimentally determined and is believed to be the result of the phenomenon explained in the following paragraph.

Alkyl groups tend to "feed" electrons toward a carbocation more effectively than do hydrogen atoms. These alkyl groups actually take on part of the positive charge, which tends to delocalize it. The greater the number of alkyl groups attached to a positive carbon atom of a carbocation species, the more the charge is delocalized and the more stable the carbocation will be. Delocalization of charge (positive or negative) is always a stabilizing influence. This feeding-in of electrons is called a **positive inductive effect**. Since it is the intensity of the positive charge that causes the carbocation to be unstable in the first place, the more this intensity is reduced, the more stable is the cation. The 3° cation has three alkyl groups, while the 2° and 1° cations have only two and one carbon-containing groups, respectively, that can donate electrons. The more alkyl groups present, the more stabilization occurs. The arrows in the formulas shown below indicate the positive inductive effect.

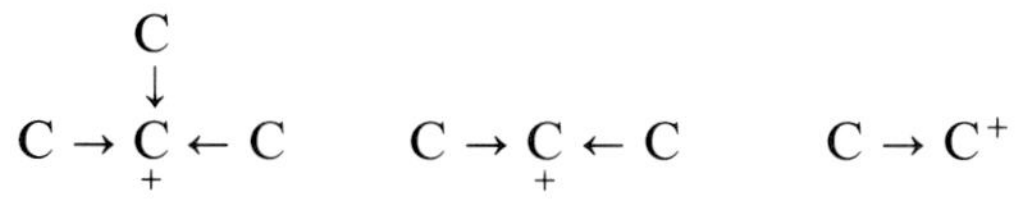

$$
\begin{array}{ccc}
C & & \\
\downarrow & & \\
C \to \underset{+}{C} \leftarrow C & \quad C \to \underset{+}{C} \leftarrow C \quad & C \to C^{+} \\
3° & 2° & 1° \\
\end{array}
$$

More stabilized   Less stabilized

If a molecule has a "choice" for forming two or more different carbocations during a reaction, it will form the one in which the C^{+} is in the most stable position.

Explanation of Markovnikov and anti-Markovnikov orientations   The Markovnikov and anti-Markovnikov additions can be explained by examining the mechanism of each type of addition and the relative stabilities of the intermediates. Without peroxides the following mechanism is operative:

$$\boxed{2°\text{---More stable}} \qquad\qquad \boxed{1°\text{---Less stable}}$$

$$CH_3-CH=CH_2 \longrightarrow CH_3-\overset{+}{C}H-CH_2 \quad \text{or} \quad CH_3-CH-\overset{+}{C}H_2$$
$$\overset{\downarrow}{H^+} \qquad\qquad\qquad\qquad \overset{|}{H} \qquad\qquad\qquad \overset{|}{H}$$

$$Br^- \searrow$$
$$CH_3-CH-CH_3$$
$$\overset{|}{Br}$$

The hydrogen ion adds to one of the carbon atoms of the double bond. This causes the carbon atom at the other end of the double bond to become positively charged. The hydrogen ion will add to the end of the double bond which will produce the more stable carbocation (2°). The Br^- ion then joins itself to the carbon atom containing the positive charge. Thus, since the higher-order carbon atom (2° in this case) will always get the positive charge, it will always get the bromine atom also. The carbon atom of the double bond which initially bonds to the hydrogen ion will always be the one with the most hydrogen atoms originally. This mechanism is referred to as an **electrophilic addition** because the H^+ ion, which initiates the process, is electron-loving—it is seeking a source of electrons because of its positive charge. Thus, it is attracted to the carbon-carbon double bond, which is electron rich.

In the presence of peroxides (R—O—O—R) the Markovnikov orientation is reversed:

$$\boxed{2°\text{---More stable}} \qquad \boxed{1°\text{---Less stable}}$$

$$R-O-O-R \xrightarrow{\Delta} 2RO\cdot$$
$$R-O\cdot + HBr \longrightarrow R-OH + Br\cdot$$
$$CH_3-CH=CH_2 \longrightarrow CH_3-\overset{\cdot}{C}H-CH_2 \quad \text{or} \quad CH_3-CH-\overset{\cdot}{C}H_2$$
$$\overset{\downarrow}{Br\cdot} \qquad\qquad\qquad\qquad \overset{|}{Br} \qquad\qquad\qquad \overset{|}{Br}$$

$$HBr \searrow$$
$$CH_3-CH-CH_2 + Br\cdot$$
$$\overset{|}{H} \quad \overset{|}{Br}$$

First, the peroxide molecule splits, and the resulting RO·reacts with HBr to produce bromine free radicals. These free radicals add to one end of the carbon-carbon double bond in such a way as to produce the more stable free radical. In this case, a 2° free radical is formed, since it is more stable than the 1° one shown in the reaction above. The stability order for free radicals is the same as that for carbocations (see page 151). This secondary free radical then pulls a hydrogen atom from another HBr molecule, leaving behind a new bromine free radical. The higher-order carbon atom will take on the free radical nature and therefore bond to the new hydrogen atom also. The peroxide, thus, changes the nature of the addition mechanism from an ionic (carbocation) mechanism to a free radical chain reaction mechanism and reverses the order of addition of the H and Br.

The addition of HCl is not reversed by peroxide because the Cl· free radical is too unstable to form under these conditions. The free radical mechanism, therefore, cannot occur. For HI, the I· free radical does form, but it is not reactive enough to add to the double bond. Here, too, the free radical mechanism does not occur. Instead, both HCl and HI must add by the carbocation mechanism; they therefore follow Markovnikov's rule under both sets of conditions.

HCl, HBr, and HI add to the double bonds of alkenes so that the carbon atom that originally has the most hydrogen atoms gets the new hydrogen atom. This is explained by considering the stability of the carbocation intermediate and is called Markovnikov addition. HBr, in the presence of peroxides, adds by the reverse orientation by a free radical mechanism. This is called anti-Markovnikov addition.

Reaction of alcohols

The following chemical equations indicate reagents used to convert alcohols to the corresponding alkyl halides.
For primary alcohols:

$$R\text{---}OH \xrightarrow[\text{or } PX_5 \text{ or } SOCl_2]{PX_3} R\text{---}X$$

For tertiary alcohols:

$$R\text{---}OH \xrightarrow[ZnCl_2]{HCl} R\text{---}X$$

Primary alcohols react best with phosphorus halides or thionyl chloride ($SOCl_2$), while tertiary alcohols react with the **Lucas reagent** (HCl/$ZnCl_2$). HBr or HI without the zinc compound will also react with tertiary alcohols. Secondary alcohols will react acceptably with any of these reagents. Examples are as follows:
Primary alcohols:

$$CH_3\text{---}CH_2\text{---}OH \xrightarrow{PCl_3} CH_3\text{---}CH_2\text{---}Cl$$

Secondary alcohols:

Tertiary alcohols:

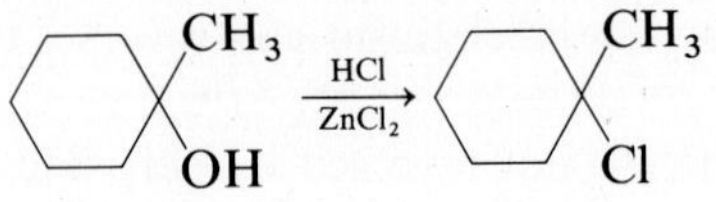

Alkyl halides can be prepared by direct halogenation of alkanes, by addition of HX to alkenes, and by replacing the —OH group of alcohols with a halogen atom. (See the flow diagram on page 166.)

REACTIONS OF ALKYL HALIDES

Nucleophilic substitution reactions

The halogen atom can be replaced rather easily by a number of other atoms or groups of atoms. The general reaction can be represented as follows:

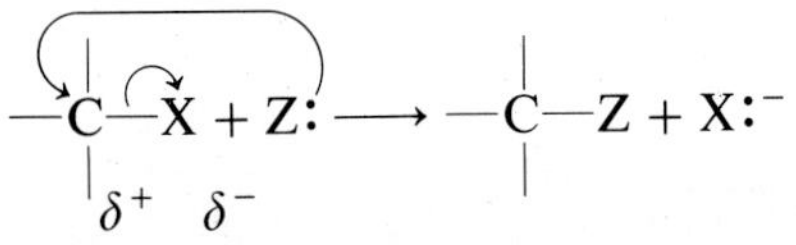

In this general reaction, Z: stands for an anion or a molecule with a pair of electrons; it is called a **nucleophile** (nucleus-loving ion). The halogen-carbon bond is polar, with the carbon atom bearing the partial positive charge. The electrons of the nucleophile attack the positive carbon atom, which causes the halogen atom to leave (it is called the **leaving group**),

TABLE 5-1

SELECTED NUCLEOPHILES			
	NUCLEOPHILE	RELATIVE DISPLACING ABILITY (NUCLEOPHILICITY)	SUBSTITUTION PRODUCT
	SH^-	500,000	R—SH (thiol)
	CN^-	5,000	R—CN (nitrile)
	I^-	4,000	R—I (alkyl iodide)
	OH^-	1,000	R—OH (alcohol)
	$R-O^-$	700	R—O—R' (ether)
	Br^-	500	R—Br (alkyl bromide)
	Cl^-	100	R—Cl (alkyl chloride)
	$H_2\ddot{O}:$	<1	R—OH (alcohol)
	$R-\ddot{O}H$	<1	R—O—R' (ether)

and the Z group becomes bonded in the place of the halogen atom. This is called a **nucleophilic substitution** reaction because the initiator of the reaction is a **nucleophile** and because the halogen atom becomes **substituted** by another group. We abbreviate these as S_N reactions (S for substitution and N for *n*ucleophilic). Table 5-1 lists several nucleophiles and the substitution products that result from their attack on an alkyl halide.

Notice that several important functional groups can be introduced into a molecule by S_N reactions, and also that one halogen atom can be replaced by another. The following examples illustrate some of the more useful S_N reactions.

1 *Preparation of alkyl iodides.* You may remember that I_2 does not react with alkanes, so that alkyl iodides cannot be prepared by directly halogenating an alkane. One way to make an alkyl iodide is to first chlorinate or brominate an alkane and then substitute, using NaI in acetone as follows:

$$CH_3-\langle\rangle-Cl + NaI \overset{acetone}{\rightleftharpoons} CH_3-\langle\rangle-I + NaCl\downarrow$$

Alkyl iodide

The acetone is present because it will dissolve the NaI but will not dissolve the resulting NaCl or NaBr. The solubility of NaI causes the I^- to be nucleophilic, but since the chloride and bromide are insoluble, they cannot act as nucleophiles to reverse the reaction. Thus, the equilibrium is shifted to the right, and the alkyl iodide can be obtained in high yield. Another way to produce alkyl iodides is to react HI with an alkene (see page 149).

2 *Williamson ether synthesis.* An alkoxide ion ($R-O^-$), which can be produced by reacting an alcohol with sodium metal, acts as a nucleophile toward certain alkyl halides. This reaction produces ethers and is called the **Williamson ether synthesis**. It works well only when the alkyl halide is primary. The alcohol which forms the alkoxide ion can be of any type, however.

(*a*) $CH_3-CH_2-Br + CH_3-O^- Na^+ \longrightarrow$

1° Alkyl halide

$CH_3OH \xrightarrow{Na}$

Alcohol

$CH_3-CH_2-O-CH_3$

Ether

(b)

$$CH_3-CH_2-CH_2 \!-\! I + CH_3-C \!-\! O^- \ Na^+ \longrightarrow$$

with CH_3, CH_3 groups on the central carbon

$$CH_3-C \!-\! OH \xrightarrow{\ \ Na\ \ }$$

$$
\begin{array}{c}
CH_3 \\
| \\
CH_2 \\
| \\
CH_2 \\
| \\
O \\
| \\
CH_3-C-CH_3 \\
| \\
CH_3
\end{array}
$$

3 *Production of amines.* Ammonia will react with alkyl halides to produce amines, and these amines will react with other alkyl halides to produce other amines. In either case, the amino $-(\ddot{N}H_2)$ group acts as a nucleophile and replaces the halogen atom. If the nitrogen atom already has an alkyl group attached, the alkyl group is simply carried along, as is the methyl group in example (b) that follows. Because the species formed at first has a nitrogen atom with four bonds (a formal charge of $+1$), a second mole of NH_3 (or other base) is needed to form the intended amine in neutral form.

(a)

$$\langle \ \rangle\!-\!I + \ddot{N}H_3 \longrightarrow \langle \ \rangle\!-\!NH_3{}^+I^- \xrightarrow{\ NH_3\ }$$

Amine salt

$$\langle \ \rangle\!-\!\ddot{N}H_2 + NH_4{}^+I^-$$

Amine

(b)

$$(CH_3-CH_2)\!-\!Cl + H_2\ddot{N}\!-\!CH_3 \longrightarrow$$

$$
\begin{array}{cc}
Cl^- & H \\
& | \\
CH_3-CH_2-N\!-\!CH_3 & \xrightarrow{\ NaOH\ } \\
& | \\
& H
\end{array}
$$

Amine salt

$$(CH_3-CH_2)\!-\!NH\!-\!CH_3 + NaCl + H_2O$$

Amine

4 *Production of alcohols.* Alcohols can be produced by reaction of any alkyl halide with dilute aqueous NaOH or by reacting tertiary alkyl halides with water. While water is a weak nucleophile, the 3° halogen atoms are easily replaced.

(a) [benzene ring]—CH_2I + NaOH $\xrightarrow{H_2O}$ [benzene ring]—CH_2—OH + NaI

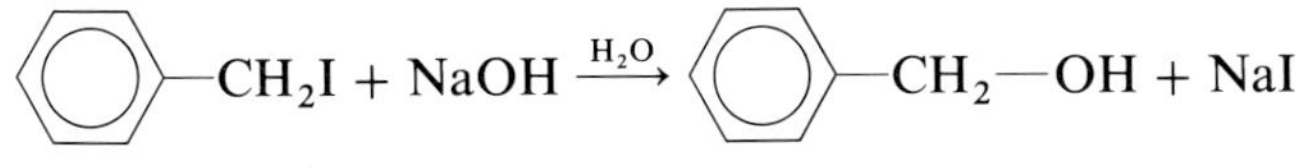

    1° Alkyl halide   Alcohol

(b)

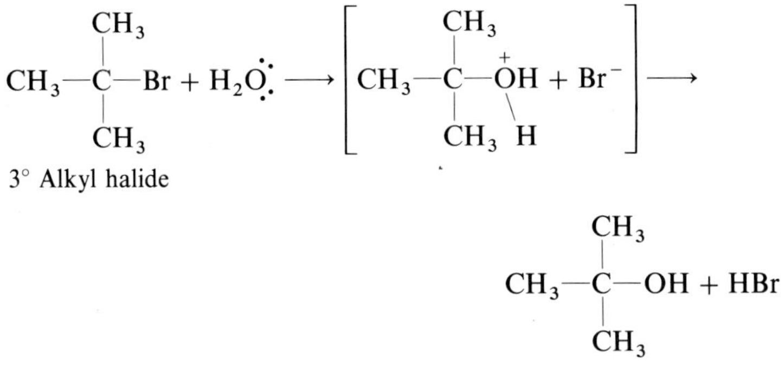

$$CH_3-\underset{\underset{CH_3}{|}}{\overset{\overset{CH_3}{|}}{C}}-Br + H_2\overset{..}{\underset{..}{O}} \longrightarrow \left[CH_3-\underset{\underset{CH_3\ H}{|}}{\overset{\overset{CH_3}{|}}{C}}-\overset{+}{O}H + Br^- \right] \longrightarrow$$

$$CH_3-\underset{\underset{CH_3}{|}}{\overset{\overset{CH_3}{|}}{C}}-OH + HBr$$

                                             Alcohol

3° Alkyl halide

5 *Production of nitriles.* The cyanide ion (CN^-) is a good nucleophile and easily reacts with alkyl halides to give organic cyanides, which are usually called **nitriles**. Nitriles are seldom useful in themselves, but they can be converted to carboxylic acids by reacting with water in the presence of either an acid or base catalyst, or to amines by reduction with hydrogen (H_2) and a catalyst.

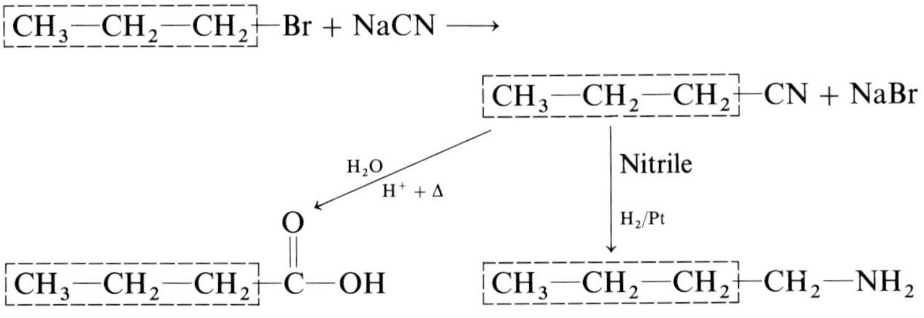

$[CH_3-CH_2-CH_2]$—Br + NaCN ⟶

                          $[CH_3-CH_2-CH_2]$—CN + NaBr

                                  Nitrile

         $\underset{H^+ + \Delta}{\overset{H_2O}{\nwarrow}}$ $\downarrow$ H_2/Pt

$[CH_3-CH_2-CH_2]-\overset{\overset{\displaystyle O}{\|}}{C}-OH$ $[CH_3-CH_2-CH_2]-CH_2-NH_2$

     Acid   Amine

Note that the nitrile, acid, and amine all have **one more carbon atom** than does the original alkyl halide. This is, therefore, a good way to add another carbon atom as well as to change the functional group.

Nucleophilic substitution reaction mechanism Nucleophilic substitution reactions occur by two different mechanisms, depending upon the nature of the alkyl halide and of the nucleophile and upon the reaction conditions. These two mechanisms are shown below for two typical cases.

    The first mechanism takes place in one step as the nucleophile attacks the carbon atom from the side opposite the halogen atom to be replaced. This mechanism is illustrated by the reaction of cyanide ion (CN^-) with bromomethane.

$$NC^- \quad \overset{H}{\underset{H}{\overset{|}{\diagdown}}} C \!-\! Br \longrightarrow \left[NC \cdots \overset{\overset{H}{|}}{\underset{\overset{|}{\underset{H}{}}}{C}} \cdots Br \right] \longrightarrow NC \!-\! \overset{H}{\underset{H}{\overset{|}{\diagdown}}} C \!-\! H + Br^-$$

Transition state

In this mechanism, all processes occur at once. That is, the C—CN bond forms at the same time that the C—Br bond breaks. When all processes occur at once, we call it a **concerted mechanism**. We refer to an S_N mechanism that is concerted as an **S_N2 mechanism**, which represents substitution *nucleophilic* with *2* reactants involved at once (bimolecular). When this mechanism is used, the rate of the reactions depends upon the concentrations of both the alkyl halide and the nucleophile.

During the S_N2 process, an **inversion** takes place. This means that as the nucleophile attacks the carbon atom from the side opposite the side where the halogen is attached, and as the halogen ion leaves, the other three atoms or groups change position to maintain a tetrahedron. Figure 5-2 illustrates this mechanism for an optically active alkyl halide. Inversion produces the opposite configuration. However, the (R) or (S) designation may or may not be different in the product compared to the reactant. This is because the relative ordering of the priorities of the four atoms or groups attached to the chiral atom may be changed by introducing a new group.

The second mechanism by which an S_N reaction can take place is called the **S_N1 mechanism** and involves two steps, as illustrated in the following example for the reaction of tert-butyl bromide with NaOH. The term S_N1 represents *substitution nucleophilic* with *1* reactant controlling the reaction rate (unimolecular).

FIGURE 5-2

The mechanism of an S_N2 reaction.

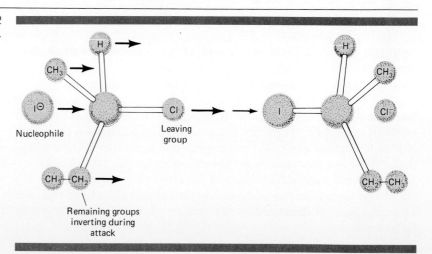

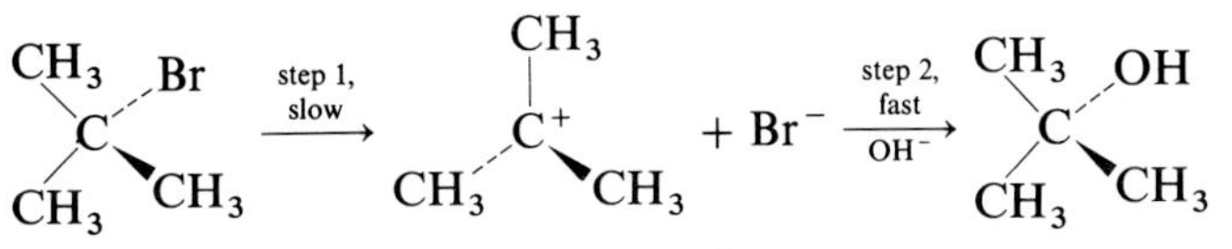

Carbocation intermediate

The first step does not involve a nucleophile—it is the spontaneous leaving of the halide ion to give a carbocation. Since 3° carbocations are more stable than 1° or 2° ones, this type of mechanism happens most readily for tertiary alkyl halides. The cation is planar, and in the second step the nucleophile can attack equally well from either side. Since the first step is the slowest (rate-controlling), the rate of the reaction is **independent of the nucleophile concentration**. Figure 5-3 illustrates this process for an optically active alkyl halide. A racemic mixture is formed when the S_N1 mechanism is operating.

One standard way to determine experimentally which mechanism is being used during a given reaction is to observe how the reaction rate is affected by the nucleophile concentration. We run the reaction with certain concentrations of both reactants and measure the rate of product formation or reactant disappearance. We then run the reaction again with a different nucleophile concentration (say, twice as much). If the reaction is following an S_N2 mechanism, the rate will double when the

FIGURE 5-3

The mechanism of an S_N1 reaction.

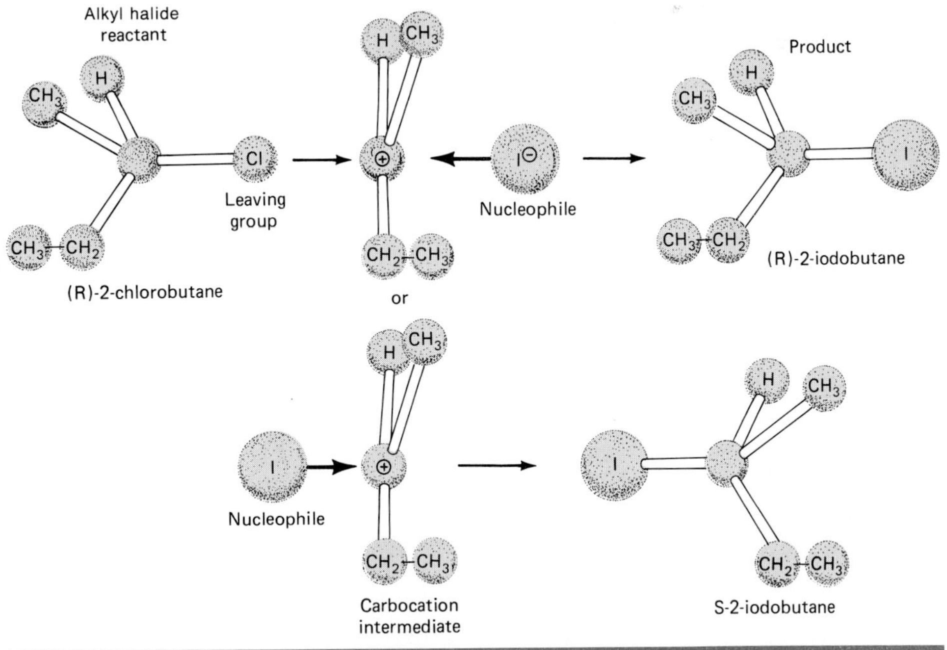

nucleophile concentration is doubled. If an S_N1 mechanism is operating, the reaction rate will be the same in the second experiment as in the first. This type of experiment is illustrated by the data in Table 5-2.

When the S_N2 mechanism is followed, we see from experiments (a) and (b) in Table 5-2 that doubling the RBr concentration, [RBr], doubles the reaction rate (while holding OH⁻ concentration, [OH⁻], constant). In experiments (a) and (c), doubling [OH⁻] also causes the rate to double (while holding [RBr] constant). Thus, the rate depends on the concentrations of **both** reactants.

When the S_N1 mechanism is followed, doubling [RBr] again doubles the reaction rate [see experiments (d) and (e), which hold [OH⁻] constant]. Note, however, in experiments (d) and (f), that doubling [OH⁻] from 0.05M to 0.10M does not cause an increase in the rate of reaction. The reaction rate, therefore, depends on the concentration of only one of the reagents, the alkyl halide.

Now we are faced with the question: "Can we tell which mechanism will be followed simply by observing the molecular structure of the alkyl halide and the nature of the nucleophile?" The answer is a qualified "yes." Table 5-3 lists those factors which tend to make a reaction follow either an S_N1 or an S_N2 mechanism.

In the extreme cases, such as the two examples which follow, the mechanism can be predicted with confidence.

For an S_N2 mechanism

Poor leaving group; the C—Cl bond is relatively strong

$$CH_3-CH_2-Cl + CN^- \longrightarrow CH_3-CH_2-CN + Cl^-$$

1° Halide   Strong nucleophile

TABLE 5-2

KINETIC DATA FOR S_N1 AND S_N2 REACTION MECHANISM FOR R—Br + OH⁻ → R—OH + Br⁻	TEST NUMBER	[R—Br]	[OH⁻]	RATE (mole/L hr)
	S_N2 reaction			
	(a)	0.1M	0.05M	10
	(b)	0.2M	0.05M	20
	(c)	0.1M	0.10M	20
	S_N1 reaction			
	(d)	0.1M	0.05M	10
	(e)	0.2M	0.05M	20
	(f)	0.1M	0.10M	10

TABLE 5-3

TYPE OF MECHANISM	FACTOR	REASON	FACTORS THAT DETERMINE THE MECHANISM OF AN S_N REACTION
S_N2	1° Alkyl halide	Little steric hindrance to prevent backside attack of the nucleophile 1° carbocation too unstable to form in an S_N1 mechanism	
	Good nucleophile (high nucleophilicity— see Table 5-1)	Ability to force the halogen atom off	
	Poor leaving group* (strong C—X bond)	Halogen will not leave on its own; it must be forced off	
	Nonpolar solvent	No stabilizing influence by solution of the intermediate carbocation is required (see "polar solvent" below)	
S_N1	3° Alkyl halide	Too much steric hindrance for nucleophile to attack on the backside; carbocation stable	
	Poor nucleophile	Not enough ability to force the halogen off, therefore it must leave of its own accord	
	Good leaving group* (weak C—X bond)	Easily leaves on its own accord	
	Polar solvent	Tends to stabilize carbocation intermediate by solvation	

* Chloride is a poor leaving group, iodide a good one; Cl < Br < I.

For an S_N1 mechanism

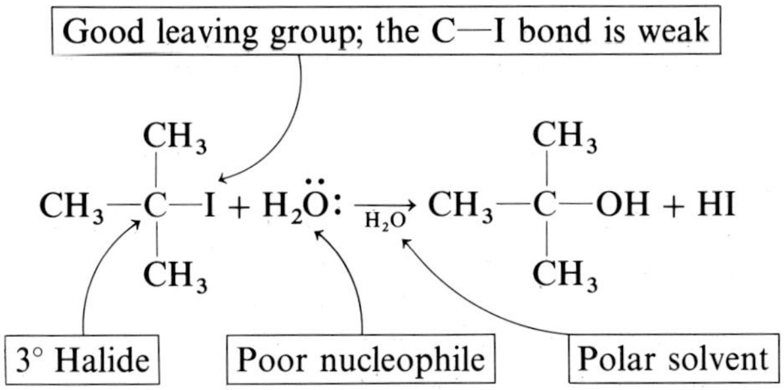

In many cases, however, there is a conflict in factors, and the mechanism is considered to be intermediate between the two mechanisms. The example shown below involves a secondary alkyl halide, a moderately good nucleophile, and a moderately good leaving group. The solvent is somewhat polar.

$$CH_3-\underset{\underset{Br}{|}}{CH}-CH_3 + CH_3-O^- \xrightarrow{CH_3OH} CH_3-\underset{\underset{O-CH_3}{|}}{CH}-CH_3$$

In a case such as this, the C—Br bond may be partly broken when the CH_3O^- attacks and pushes off the halogen atom. This reaction is said to have partial S_N1 character and partial S_N2 character. We can characterize such intermediate mechanisms as 50 percent S_N2 : 50 percent S_N1, or 30 percent S_N2 : 70 percent S_N1, and so forth, depending on the degree to which the C—X bond is broken when the nucleophile attacks.

> Nucleophilic substitution reactions are those in which an electron rich species (a nucleophile) displaces another atom or group of atoms (such as a halogen atom) from a carbon atom. This can take place in a one-step (concerted) mechanism (S_N2) or by a two-step mechanism involving a carbocation intermediate (S_N1).

Commercially useful S_N reactions. Below are shown the commercial syntheses of two consumer products using S_N reactions. First, let's look at the synthesis of the medicine **diphenhydramine hydrochloride** (Benadryl). The reaction sequence used to produce this antihistamine is as follows:

After bromination has taken place at the most reactive position, the resulting alkyl halide is treated with an alcohol, which is a weak nucleophile (see Table 5-1), to produce the final product. Because of the weakness of the alcohol as a nucleophile and the relative stability of the carbocation intermediate, the second reaction occurs via an S_N1 mechanism. The resulting amine salt may be converted to the neutral amine by a base (NaOH), but commercial Benadryl is used as the hydrochloride salt. See Chapter 13 for a description of amine salts.

The second commercial synthesis involving an S_N reaction which we will consider is the synthesis of one of the early drugs used to treat heart ailments such as angina, arrhythmia, and hypertension. It is **dichloroisoproterenol**, and it is in the class of medications called beta-blockers.

Dichloroisoproterenol

In the starting material, the primary (1°) bromine atom is replaced by the relatively strong —NH₂ nucleophile in the direct (concerted) fashion (S_N2). The resulting amine salt is then reacted with base to form the neutral amine.

Dehydrohalogenation

This term refers to the **elimination** reaction that removes a **halogen** atom and a **hydrogen** atom from adjacent carbon atoms in a molecule and forms a double bond between those carbon atoms. See Appendix A for a general description of elimination reactions. The general reaction may be represented as

While many strong bases will bring about this reaction, KOH in alcohol is particularly convenient and effective. This should be contrasted with NaOH in water, which serves as a better nucleophile and replaces the halogen with —OH (see page 156).

Note that since nucleophilicity and basicity are related, there is often competition between nucleophilic substitution and elimination. This is especially true for the stronger bases and means that both processes may occur even when one of them is dominant. In this text we will concern ourselves only with the dominant process for each set of reagents and conditions, however. The following equations give three examples of dehydrohalogenation.

1

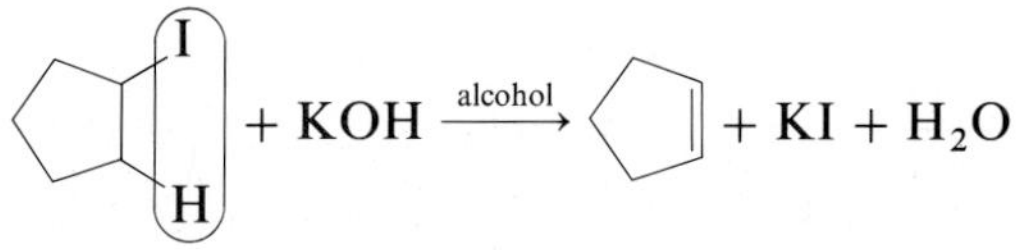

$$\text{(cyclopentane ring with I and H)} + KOH \xrightarrow{\text{alcohol}} \text{(cyclopentene ring)} + KI + H_2O$$

2

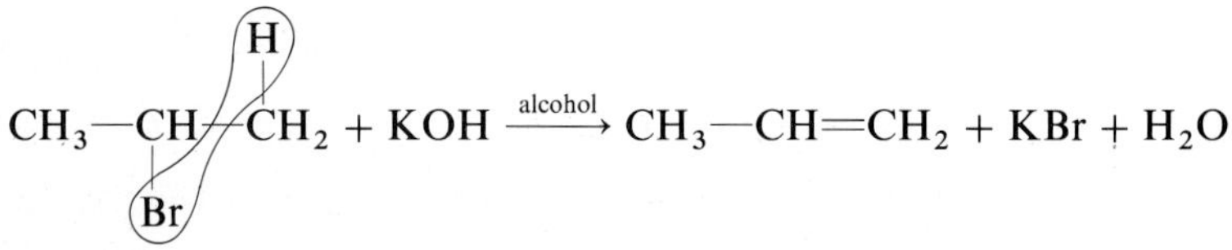

$$CH_3{-}CH{-}CH_2 (\text{with H and Br}) + KOH \xrightarrow{\text{alcohol}} CH_3{-}CH{=}CH_2 + KBr + H_2O$$

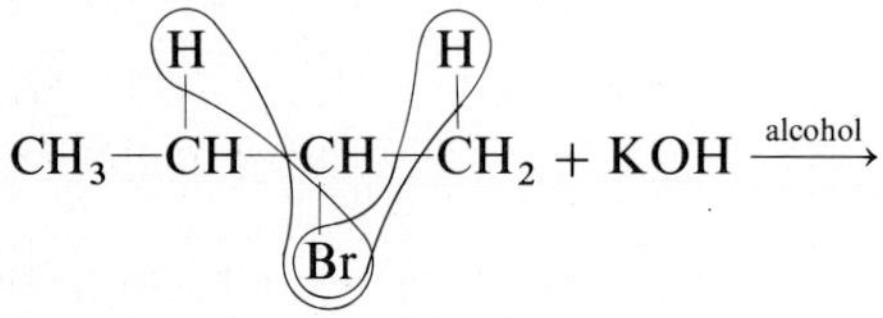

3

$$CH_3{-}CH{-}CH{-}CH_2 (\text{with H, H and Br}) + KOH \xrightarrow{\text{alcohol}}$$

$$CH_3{-}CH{=}CH{-}CH_3$$

and $\qquad + KBr + H_2O$

$$CH_3{-}CH_2{-}CH{=}CH_2$$

In example 3, there are two choices as to the position from which the H—Br pair can be eliminated. When this is the case, the alkene that forms predominantly is the **most highly substituted** one (i.e., the alkene with the most alkyl groups attached directly to the carbon atoms which are doubly bonded). Of the two products in reaction (3), one has two alkyl groups attached to the carbon atoms of the double bond. The other has only one.

$$\boxed{CH_3}{-}\boxed{CH{=}CH}{-}\boxed{CH_3} \qquad \boxed{CH_3{-}CH_2}{-}\boxed{CH{=}CH_2}$$

To choose the correct (major) product, follow these steps:

1 Draw all possibilities of forming a C=C bond between the carbon atom attached to the halogen atom and an adjacent carbon atom. In the following example there are 3 such possibilities.

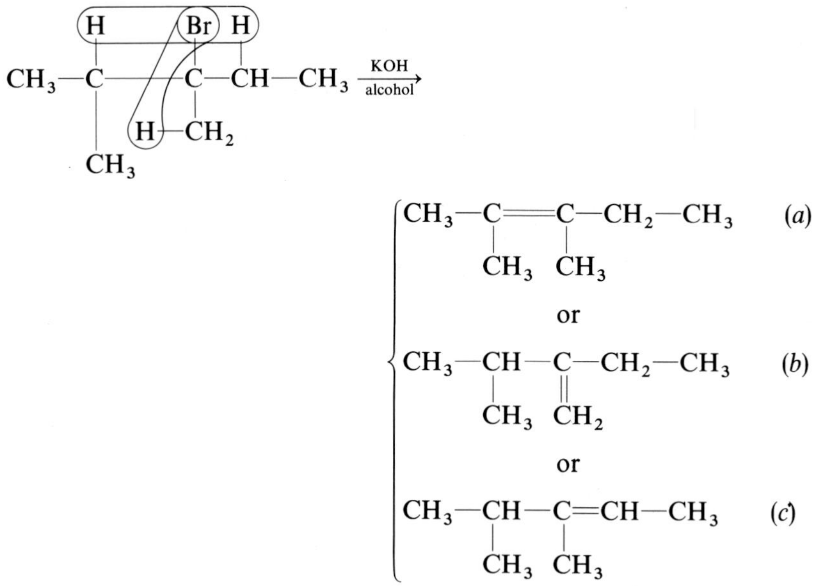

$$CH_3-\overset{H}{\underset{CH_3}{\underset{|}{C}}}-\overset{Br}{\underset{|}{\overset{|}{C}}}-CH-CH_3 \xrightarrow[\text{alcohol}]{KOH}$$

$$CH_3-\underset{CH_3}{\underset{|}{C}}=\underset{CH_3}{\underset{|}{C}}-CH_2-CH_3 \quad (a)$$

or

$$CH_3-\underset{CH_3}{\underset{|}{CH}}-\underset{CH_2}{\overset{||}{C}}-CH_2-CH_3 \quad (b)$$

or

$$CH_3-\underset{CH_3}{\underset{|}{CH}}-C=CH-CH_3 \quad (c)$$

2 Draw a box around the carbon atoms doubly bonded to each other.

(a) C—|C=C|—C—C with C C below

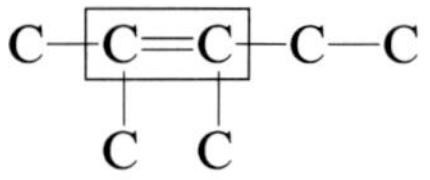

(b) C—C—|C / C|—C—C

(c) C—C—|C=C|—C

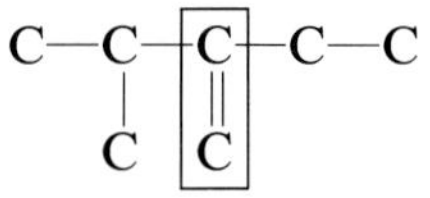

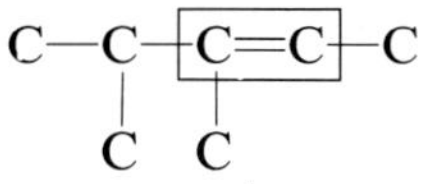

3 Draw circles around all carbon-containing groups attached to the box.

(a) (C)—|C=C|—(C—C) with (C)(C) below
Four alkyl groups

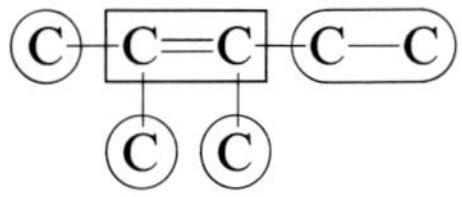

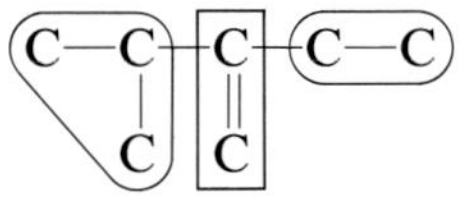

(b) (C—C)—|C / C|—(C—C)
Two alkyl groups

(c) (C—C)—|C=C|—(C)
Three alkyl groups

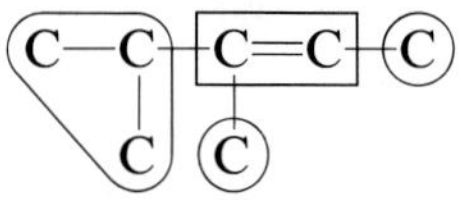

Note: The **size** of the alkyl groups does not matter. Only the **number** of them is important in this connection.

4   Choice (*a*) in the example above is the most substituted alkene of the possible products; it is therefore the one that would actually be formed in the greatest abundance.

The mechanism for dehydrohalogenation is usually a concerted one (one step) initiated by the base pulling off the hydrogen atom as the electrons move all at once as shown below. The hydrogen and the halogen atoms must be opposite each other (in the anti conformation) for this process to happen. This is called an E_2 mechanism (*E* for elimination; *2* for bimolecular—both base and alkyl halide concentrations affect the reaction rate).

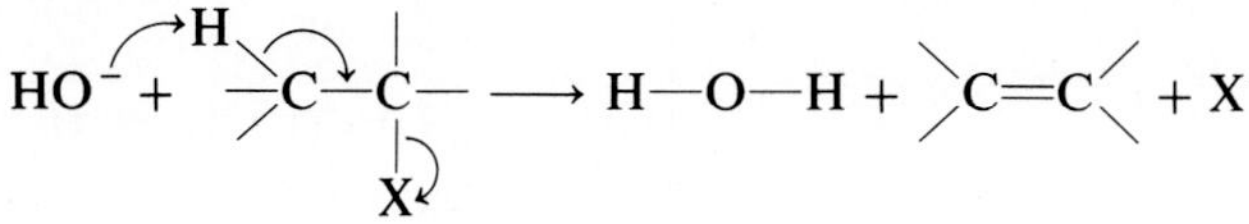

$$HO^- + \quad \overset{H}{\underset{X}{\underset{|}{C}}}\!\!-\!\!\overset{|}{\underset{|}{C}}\!\!- \quad \longrightarrow \quad H\!-\!O\!-\!H + \ \ \ \diagup{C}\!\!=\!\!C\diagdown\ + X^-$$

A base will cause an alkyl halide molecule to eliminate an HX molecule to form a carbon-carbon double bond and produce an alkene. This usually occurs by an E_2 (concerted) mechanism to produce the most highly substituted alkene as the major product.

REACTION SUMMARY FLOW DIAGRAM FOR ALKYL HALIDES

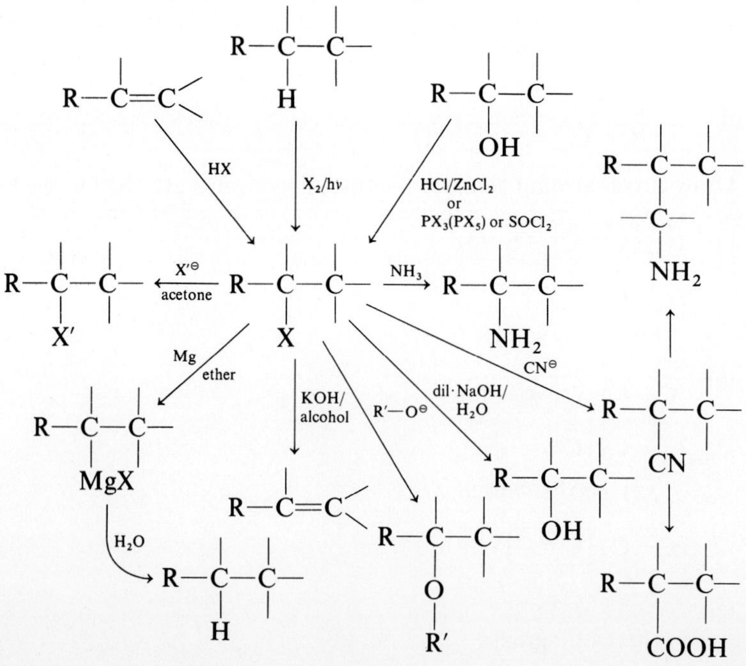

COMMERCIALLY USEFUL ALKYL HALIDES

As we have seen, alkyl halides are useful as intermediates in producing compounds with other functional groups. A number of alkyl halides are used directly as consumer products however.

Freon is a trade name for **tetrahalogenated methanes** (methanes with four halogen atoms attached) used as refrigeration fluids. There are four Freons in common use:

Freon 11 $CFCl_3$

Freon 12 CF_2Cl_2

Freon 13 CF_3Cl

Freon 14 CF_4

Both air conditioning and refrigeration are accomplished by evaporation of a liquid. In the cooling system, the refrigerant, a tetrahalogenated methane which can fairly easily be changed from a liquid to a gas and back again, is placed in a sealed tube, which passes through the space to be cooled and then through a compressor. The liquid refrigerant is allowed to evaporate (which causes cooling) and is then passed to the compressor, which forces it back into the liquid state for reevaporation later.

Tetrahalogenated methanes in the atmosphere are suspected of contributing to the depletion of the protective ozone (O_3) layer which exists high in the atmosphere. This O_3 layer prevents damaging ultraviolet rays from the sun from reaching the biosphere, and its depletion could cause harm to living organisms. In addition to being used in refrigeration units from which they can accidentally escape, tetrahalogenated methanes are used in the ubiquitous aerosol cans, although their use in the latter application is being discouraged.

Ethylene dibromide (1,2-dibromoethane)(EDB) was used as a grain fumigant until 1984, when it was found to be carcinogenic. Its use in the United States was banned at that time.

Ethylene dichloride (1,2-dichloroethane) is a solvent used for removing various stains and unwanted materials from surfaces and clothing. It is available at some drug stores and is especially useful for removing chewing gum from fabric or clothes dryers, as shown in Figure 5-4.

Carbon tetrachloride (tetrachloromethane) and **chloroform** (trichloromethane) are used as laboratory solvents under controlled conditions but are not used for public purposes because of the health hazards they pose. Carbon tetrachloride was formerly used as a dry-cleaning solvent and chloroform was used for general anesthesia. Some of the aerosol fire extinguishers contains CCl_4; they should only be used outdoors because of the toxic fumes produced when the contents come in contact with flame.

FIGURE 5-4

Using ethylene dichloride
($C_2H_4Cl_2$) to remove
chewing gum from a cloth.

$$
\begin{array}{ccc}
\underset{\underset{Cl}{|}}{CH_2}-\underset{\underset{Cl}{|}}{CH_2} & \underset{\underset{Cl}{|}}{\overset{\overset{Cl}{|}}{Cl-C-Cl}} & \underset{\underset{Cl}{|}}{\overset{\overset{Cl}{|}}{H-C-Cl}} \\
\text{Ethylene} & \text{Carbon} & \text{Chloroform} \\
\text{dichloride} & \text{tetrachloride} &
\end{array}
$$

Perchloroethylene (tetrachloroethene) is used in dry-cleaning.

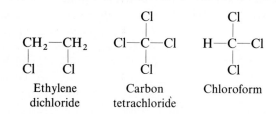

Perchloroethylene

1,1,1-Trichloroethane is used as a grease and oil remover in industrial situations. It sometimes comes in an aerosol can for spraying onto an object that needs to be degreased. After spraying, the oil and solvent (1,1,1-trichloroethane) are wiped off with a cloth.

Methylene chloride (dichloromethane) is used in paint and varnish removers and in paint brush cleaners.

SUMMARY

1   **Alkyl halides** are those compounds whose molecules contain one or more **halogen** atoms on an alkane framework.

2   Alkyl halides can be **prepared** by
(a)   Direct halogenation of alkanes

(*b*) Addition of HX to alkenes

(*c*) Replacing the OH group of alcohols with a halogen atom by using HX, PX_3, PX_5, or $SOCl_2$

(*d*) Exchanging one halogen atom for another from other alkyl halides

3 Alkyl halides can be used to prepare other classes of organic compounds such as nitriles, ethers, amines, and alcohols by substitution reactions and to prepare alkenes by elimination reactions.

4 Substitution reactions of alkyl halides take place by a **two-step (S_N1)** or **one-step (S_N2) mechanism** depending on the nature of the leaving group, the nature of the nucleophile, the nature of the carbon atom on which displacement occurs, and the nature of the solvent.

5 **Addition** of HX to the double bonds of alkenes takes place by a **Markovnikov** or an **anti-Markovnikov** orientation, depending upon the nature of the mechanism. The Markovnikov orientation occurs with ionic addition of HCl, HBr, and HI, while anti-Markovnikov orientation takes place with free radical addition of HBr only in the presence of peroxides.

6 **Elimination** of an HX molecule from an alkyl halide molecule by a base produces alkenes. The most highly substituted alkene is the most stable and is formed in the greatest abundance when several products are possible.

7 Many **industrial solvents** are alkyl halides. They are frequently toxic to human beings and should be used in a controlled environment such as a fume hood to minimize human exposure.

KEY TERMS

Alkyl halide	Halogenation	Positive inductive
Anti-Markovnikov	Leaving group	effect
addition	Markovnikov	S_N1 mechanism
Bimolecular	addition	S_N2 mechanism
Carbocation	Nucleophile	Substitution
Dehydrohalogenation	Nucleophilic	Unimolecular
E_2 mechanism	substitution	Williamson ether
Electrophilic addition	Nucleophilicity	synthesis
Free radical		

SKILL PRACTICE PROBLEMS

1 Complete the following reactions:

(*a*) $CH_3-CH(CH_3)-CH_2-CH_3 + Br_2 \longrightarrow$

(b) $CH_3—CH_2—CH_2—I + NaOH \xrightarrow{H_2O}$

(c) $CH_3—CH_2—Cl + CH_3—$⬠$—O^- \longrightarrow$

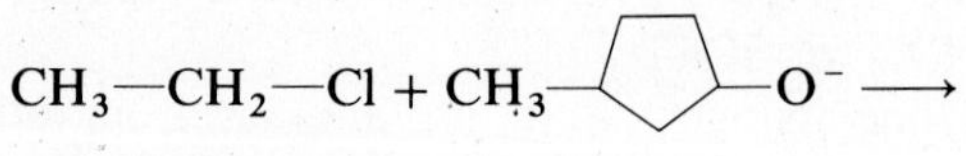

(d) $CH_3—CH=CH_2 + HI \longrightarrow$

(e) $CH_3—$⬠$\overset{Br}{} \xrightarrow[\text{alcohol}]{\text{KOH}}$

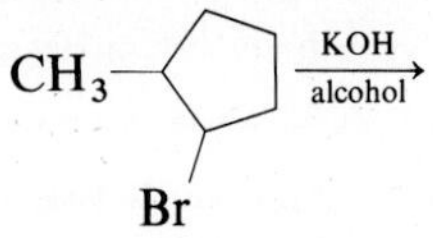

2 Give the product(s) of each of the reactions below:

(a) $CH_3—CH_2—CH_2—CH_2—Cl + NaI \xrightarrow{\text{acetone}}$

(b) ⬠$—CH_2—Cl + SH^- \longrightarrow$

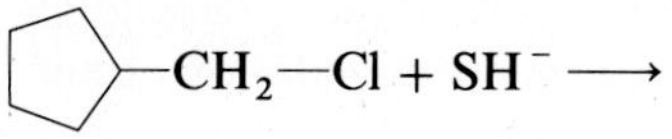

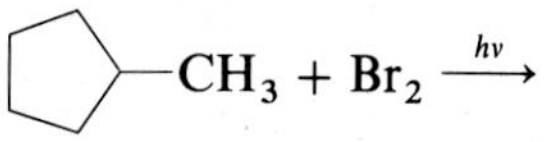

(c) ⬠$—CH_3 + Br_2 \xrightarrow{hv}$

(d) ⬡$—CH_3 + HBr \xrightarrow{\text{peroxide}}$

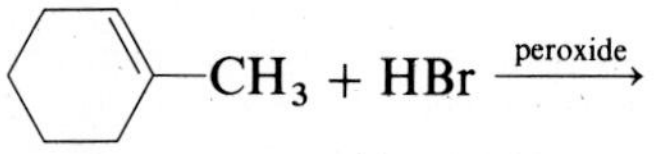

(e) $CH_3—CH_2—\underset{\underset{OH}{|}}{CH}—CH_3 + HCl \xrightarrow{ZnCl_2}$

3 Draw the molecular structure of the following:
(a) 1,3-Dibromohexane   (b) 1-Bromo-1-cyclohexylpentane
(c) tert-Butyl iodide   (d) 3-Chloro-1-ethylcyclopentane
(e) Carbon tetrachloride

4 Name the following compounds:

(a) $CH_3—\underset{\underset{Cl}{|}}{CH}—Cl$ (b)

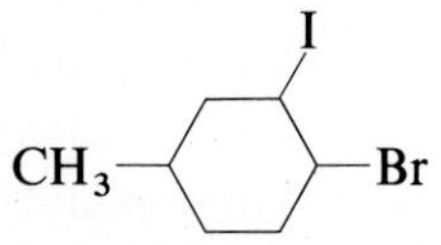

$CH_3—$⬡$\overset{I}{}—Br$

(c) $\underset{\underset{Cl}{|}}{CH_2}—\underset{\underset{Cl}{|}}{CH_2}$ (d) ◻ with Cl, Cl, Cl, F

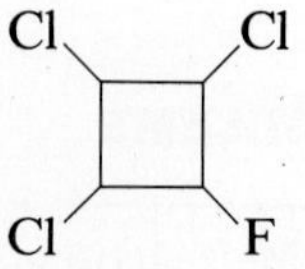

(e) $HCCl_3$

5 From the following data, decide whether the mechanism of the reaction being studied is S_N1 or S_N2.

EXPERIMENT	[RX]	[NUCLEOPHILE]	RATE (mole/L hr)
1	0.15 M	0.70 M	2.5
2	0.15 M	0.35 M	1.25
3	0.30 M	0.70 M	5.0

6 How would you synthesize 1-bromopentane from CH_3—CH_2—CH_2—CH=CH_2?

7 Show how to prepare 1-bromopropane from propane and any inorganic materials you may need.

8 On the basis of the structures and conditions given, predict the mechanisms of the reactions shown below.

(a)

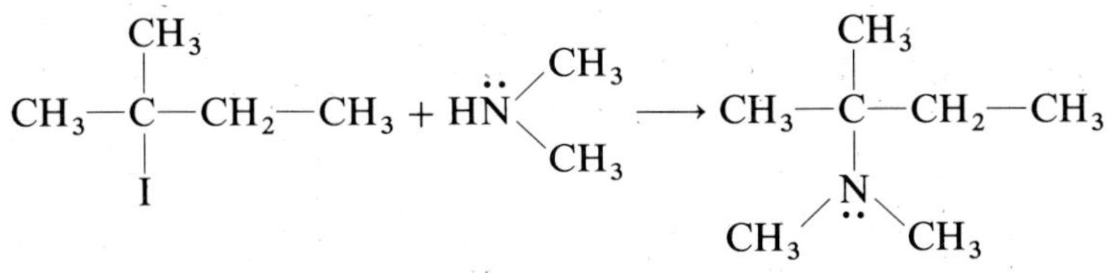

$$CH_3-\underset{\underset{I}{|}}{\overset{\overset{CH_3}{|}}{C}}-CH_2-CH_3 + HN\overset{CH_3}{\underset{CH_3}{\big<}} \longrightarrow CH_3-\underset{\underset{\underset{CH_3}{N}}{|}}{\overset{\overset{CH_3}{|}}{C}}-CH_2-CH_3$$

(b) $CH_3-CH_2-CH_2-Cl + SH^- \longrightarrow CH_3-CH_2-CH_2-SH$

(c) (cyclohexyl-Br) $+ OH^- \xrightarrow{H_2O}$ (cyclohexyl-OH)

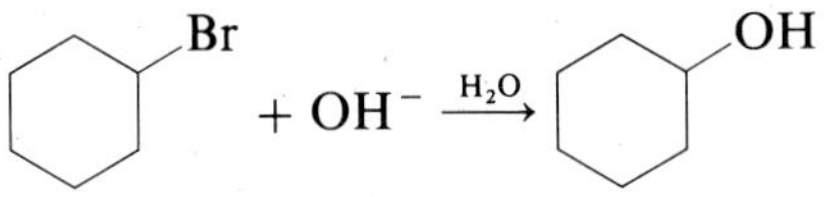

9 Draw all possible dehydrohalogenation products of 2-cyclohexyl-2-iodobutane. Which would be formed in the greatest amount?

10 Show the mechanism for the bromination of propane. (See Chapter 3 for a review, if needed.)

11 Write the steps in the mechanism of HBr reacting with the following compound:

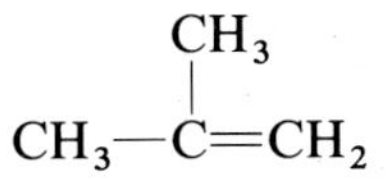

$$CH_3-\overset{\overset{CH_3}{|}}{C}=CH_2$$

12 How would you prepare 1-bromoethane from ethane?

13 Does the reaction given in question 2(d) follow Markovnikov or anti-Markovnikov addition?

14 Repeat question 13 for the reaction shown in question 1(d).

15 What kind of mechanism is operating in the reaction given in question 1(e)?

16 If (R)-2-bromopentane reacts with an SH⁻ ion as follows, what will be the absolute configuraton of the product?

$$Br \overset{\displaystyle CH_3}{\underset{\displaystyle \begin{array}{c} CH_2 \\ CH_2 \\ CH_3 \end{array}}{\overline{}}} H \xrightarrow{SH^-}$$

17 Why would the following alkyl halide undergo dehydrohalogenation very slowly, if at all?

REVIEW QUESTIONS

18 Would the following halogenated alkane be optically active? Why?

$$\begin{array}{c} CH_3 \\ H \overline{} Br \\ H \overline{} Br \\ CH_3 \end{array}$$

19 From the periodic chart trends presented in Chapter 1, can you suggest a reason why SH⁻ is a stronger nucleophile (i.e., is more willing to share its electrons) than the the OH⁻ ion is?

20 Which is more polar, CH_3F or CH_3Br?

21 In which would there be a greater difference in stability between the cis and trans isomers, 1,2-dichlorocyclobutane or 1,2-diiodocyclobutane?

22 Which would have the halogen atom in the equatorial position rather than the axial position by a greater margin, fluorocyclohexane or bromocyclohexane?

23 In the second reaction in the synthesis of diphenhydramine hydrochloride (Benadryl) (see page 162), why does the H—O— group rather than the $-\overset{+}{\underset{H}{N}}(CH_3)_2$ group act as a nucleophile and attack the C—Br bond?

ORGANIC CHEMICALS USED AS PESTICIDES

One of the reasons American farmers and gardeners produce more and more food on less and less land with less work is the availability of chemical substances to control pests. Most of these compounds are synthetic organic materials. The terms *pests* and *pesticides* should, of course, be used with care, since a given organism is not inherently bad. It is only that its presence in a particular place at a particular time is working in opposition to the goal of a particular person or group of people. For example, a rose is desirable in a rose garden but is a pest in a wheat field. Perhaps the terms *biologically active compound* or *biogenic material* would be more precise. (The term *xenobiotic* is also now being used.) At any rate, we have available many materials that will kill or repel most plants and insects without harming the plants or animals we want to grow. We will only deal with a few examples here, since a comprehensive treatise of this subject would fill an entire book.

A material used a great deal in the past as an **insecticide** was DDT (*di*chloro*di*phenyl*tri*chloroethane). The structure is given below; it kills many insects that damage plants and livestock.

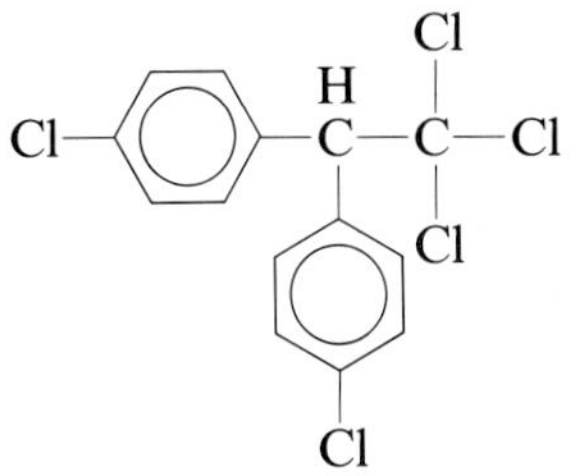

DDT is a very stable type of chlorinated hydrocarbon. These compounds do not decompose in nature but stay around and become concentrated in certain fish and birds. DDT served well for a time; but once its polluting effect was understood, its use was essentially stopped.

A currently and commonly used **herbicide** (a substance that kills selected plants) is 2,4-D (2,4-dichlorophenoxyacetic acid). It is used to spray such plants as shoestring plants and sumac plants, and kills them by stimulating their growth to the point of destruction. That is, the young plant cells divide before maturing completely; an unhealthy plant is produced, which eventually dies. The structure of 2,4-D is shown below:

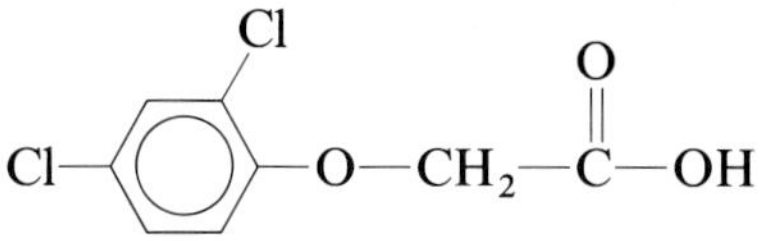

As we can see, it is a chlorinated compound, an ether, and a carboxylic acid. It is slowly degraded by nature, so that it does not pose an environmental problem as far as is presently known. It kills broad-leaved plants but does not harm grass or grain. Thus when it is sprayed on lawns or cornfields, it will kill dandelions, plantain, and many other weeds but will not harm the desired plant. This selectivity of action is what makes 2,4-D so valuable. It has been used since the 1940s and is effective at only about 1 to 2 lb/acre.

Maleic hydrazide (MH) is representative of another kind of functional group and another biochemical effect. It is a **growth inhibitor** and is used for several widely divergent applications. It is sprayed on partially grown tobacco plants to prevent new leaves from starting. The new leaves are called *suckers*; their presence reduces the growth of the tobacco leaves already growing and reduces their quality. The structure of maleic hydrazide is shown below:

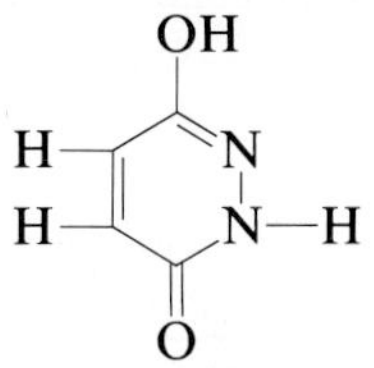

Maleic hydrazide

This material is also sprayed on potatoes to prevent sprouting and thus increases the length of time the potatoes can be stored. The result is that the potatoes arrive at the market in better condition. Shipping can therefore be more leisurely and less expensive. Maleic hydrazide is also sprayed on grass along highways to slow its growth so that mowing does not have to be done as frequently. There is no known danger to these types of exposure.

Another material, atrazine, which was introduced for agricultural use in the late 1950s, can be sprayed on the ground before corn is planted. It prevents weeds and grass from growing but does not harm the corn (or any other crop). This means that the farmer does not have to cultivate as often (or does not have to cultivate at all); this reduces costs and increases the acreage that one person can till. Atrazine is biodegradable and remains in the environment only a very short time. The structure of atrazine is shown below:

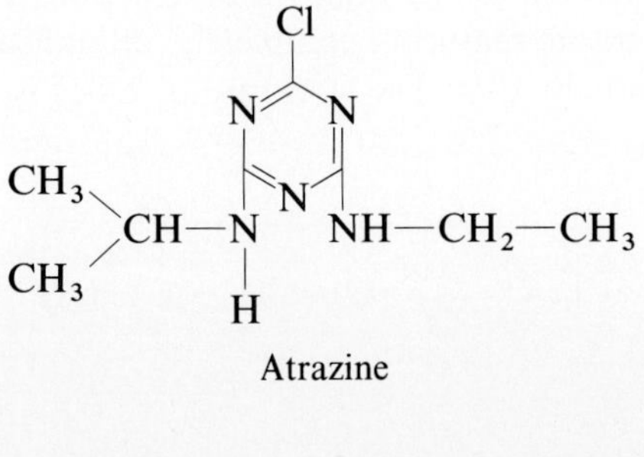

Atrazine

Another compound, commonly known as butylate and sold under the trade name Sutan, came out in 1969. It is a complex sulfur-containing material, as shown below:

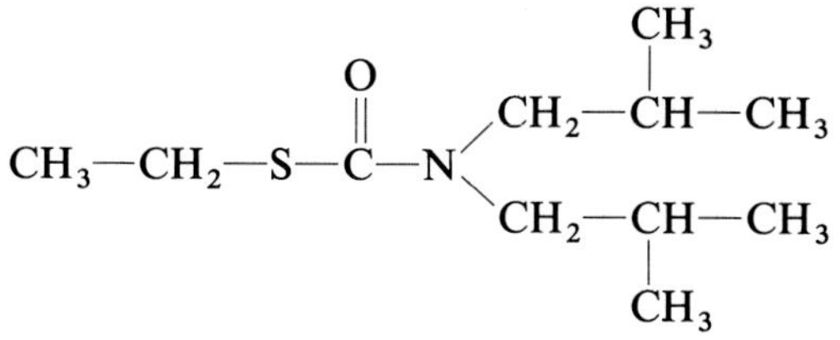

$$CH_3-CH_2-S-\overset{\overset{\displaystyle O}{\|}}{C}-N\overset{\displaystyle CH_2-\overset{\overset{\displaystyle CH_3}{|}}{CH}-CH_3}{\underset{\displaystyle CH_2-\underset{\underset{\displaystyle CH_3}{|}}{CH}-CH_3}{}}$$

Butylate

Research continues in this area, and there are now over 50 herbicides on the market.

In addition to DDT, many other materials are used to control insects. A common one is chlordane:

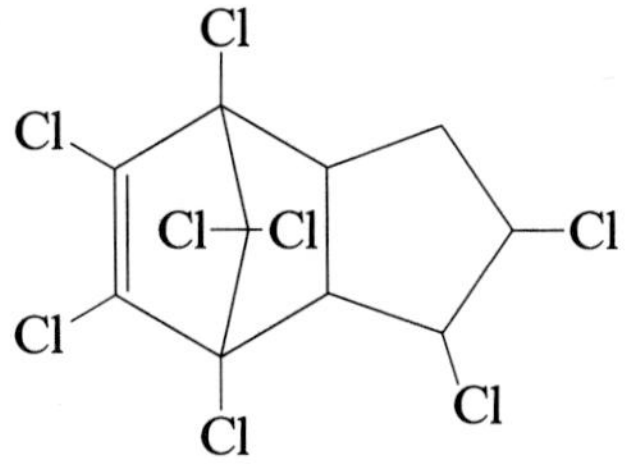

Chlordane

Chlordane controls ants, roaches, and spiders in the home and garden and kills insects on livestock.

It was noted earlier that DDT is not destroyed in the environment. Chlordane is also a chlorinated hydrocarbon, but it is degraded slowly in the environment and thus does not pose as much of a long range environment threat as does DDT. It does persist for many years, however, and should be used carefully. The response to environmental factors is a direct result of the precise molecular structure (the structure-function principle).

Two other important insecticides are carbaryl (Sevin) and malathion which also are complex organic materials:

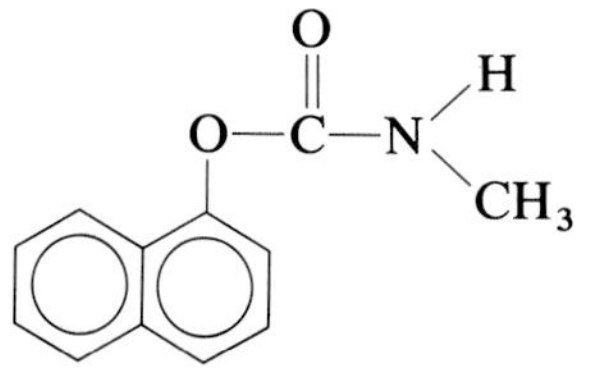

Sevin 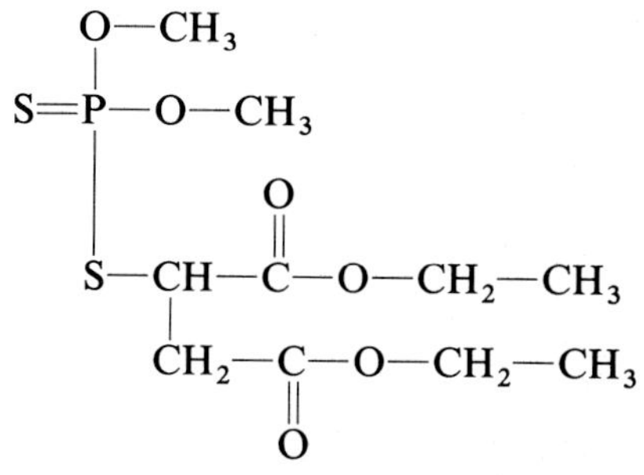   Malathion

Older, simpler organic materials, which are used to repel rather than kill moths which eat holes in valuable cloth, are naphthalene and *para*-dichlorobenzene:

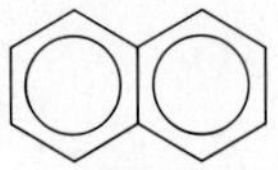

Naphthalene

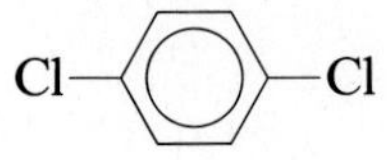

Cl —⬡— Cl

para-Dichlorobenzene

These same materials can be used to repel dogs from flower beds and rabbits and deer from gardens. This is a better approach in some respects than killing pests, because the materials are not toxic to other nearby animals, such as pets.

CHAPTER 6

UNSATURATED HYDROCARBONS

LEARNING GOALS

1 To understand the rules of nomenclature for alkenes and alkynes

2 To learn the more important methods of preparing alkenes and alkynes

3 To learn the reactions of alkenes and alkynes

4 To learn the structures of commonly encountered polymers, plastics, and coatings

5 To learn several simple laboratory procedures that allow chemists to identify the functional groups which are present in an unknown material and/or give information about molecular structure

So far, we have concentrated on the properties, preparation, and reactions of molecules having single bonds: the alkanes and alkyl halides. Now we will examine three important organic functional groups: the carbon-carbon double bond, the carbon-carbon triple bond, and the aromatic ring. These functional groups are found in **alkenes**, **alkynes**, and **aromatic** compounds respectively.

Molecules containing these groups are said to be **unsaturated**—that is, they have less than the maximum number of hydrogen atoms. Alkanes, in contrast, are **saturated** (they contain all the hydrogen atoms possible, considering the number of carbon atoms present and the four bonds each carbon atom must form). In this chapter, we will study alkenes and alkynes, and in Chapter 9 we will consider aromatic compounds.

An alkane
(ethane)
C_2H_6

An alkene
(ethene)
C_2H_4

An alkyne
(ethyne)
C_2H_2

An aromatic compound
(benzene)
C_6H_6

Saturated   Unsaturated

MULTIPLE BONDS

The general formula for noncyclic (open chain; acyclic) alkanes is C_xH_{2x+2} (see Chapter 3). Because two hydrogen atoms must be removed to form the double bond, alkenes have two fewer hydrogen atoms than do alkanes of the same carbon number. The general formula for open chain alkenes is C_xH_{2x} (assuming only one double bond per molecule). Alkynes have four fewer hydrogen atoms than do alkanes of the same carbon number, since four hydrogen atoms must be removed to form the two new carbon-carbon pi bonds in the triple bond. This gives a general formula for open chain alkynes with one triple bond of C_xH_{2x-2}. Remember from our discussion of hybridization in Chapter 1 that doubly bonded carbon atoms in alkenes are sp^2 hybridized, and that triply bonded carbon atoms in alkynes are sp hybridized. Table 6-1 summarizes unsaturation, and Figure 6-1 shows the geometry of alkenes and alkynes.

The pi bonds in double and triple bonds constitute areas of electron density. It is the electrons in these pi bonds which are the initiators of many of the electrophilic (electron-loving) reactions alkenes and alkynes undergo. The orbital pictures for multiple carbon-carbon bonds are shown in Chapter 1 (see pages 26 and 27).

NAME	EXAMPLE	FORMULA	HYBRIDIZATION	GEOMETRY
Alkane	$CH_3CH_2CH_2CH_2CH_3$ Pentane	C_5H_{12} (C_xH_{2x+2})	sp^3	Tetrahedral (109°)
Cyclic alkane	Cyclopentane	C_5H_{10} (C_xH_{2x})	sp^3	Tetrahedral (109°)
Alkene	$CH_3—CH_2—CH_2—CH=CH_2$ 1-Pentene	C_5H_{10} (C_xH_{2x})	sp^2 and sp^3	Planar at C=C (120°)
Cyclic alkene	Cyclopentene	C_5H_8 (C_xH_{2x-2})	sp^2 and sp^3	Planar
Alkyne	$CH_3CH_2CH_2—C\equiv CH$ 1-Pentyne	C_5H_8 (C_xH_{2x-2})	sp and sp^3	Linear at C≡C (180°)
Aromatic	Benzene	C_6H_6 (C_xH_x)	sp^2	Cyclic, planar

FIGURE 6-1

Models, showing the molecular geometry (shape) of alkenes (left) and alkynes.

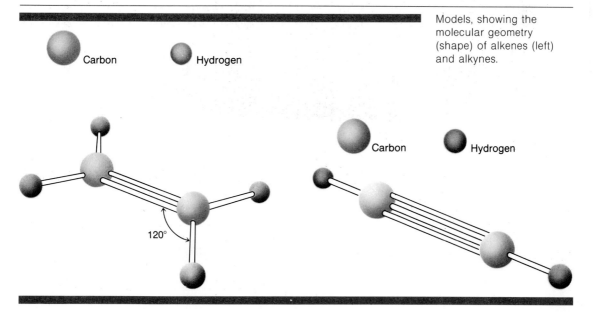

120°

ALKENES—NOMENCLATURE

Alkenes are named much like alkanes. The name reflects the **number of carbon atoms** in the longest sequence of carbon atoms **which contains the double bond**, along with any substituents. However, alkene names always end in *-ene*. The name also must indicate the **position of the double bond** and, in some cases, the stereochemistry (geometry) as well. The first two members of the alkene family are shown below. In addition to the IUPAC names, classical names are given in parentheses.

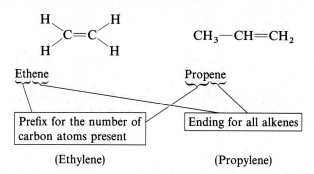

Beginning with butene, the name must indicate the placement of the double bond and, if necessary, the stereochemistry of the molecule. For butene there are two possible positions for the double bond, and one of the positional isomers exists as two possible geometric isomers.

IUPAC NAMES OF BUTENES	STRUCTURE	IUPAC NAME
	$CH_2{=}CH{-}CH_2{-}CH_3$	1-butene. The double bond **begins** at carbon atom number 1.
	CH_3 CH_3 $C{=}C$ H H	*cis*-2-Butene. The double bond begins at carbon atom number 2. Because of the rigid nature of the double bond (it cannot rotate), the methyl groups attached to it are locked into one of two basic relationships. Here they are both on the same side of the dotted line we have drawn through the double bond. Just as in cyclic alkanes, this **same side** orientation is referred to as the *cis* arrangement.
	CH_3 H $C{=}C$ H CH_3	*trans*-2-Butene. Here the two groups are on **opposite sides** of our imaginary dotted line, and this arrangement is referred to as trans.

Other examples of alkene name-structure relationships are given below:

1 The IUPAC name for the following structure can be worked out.

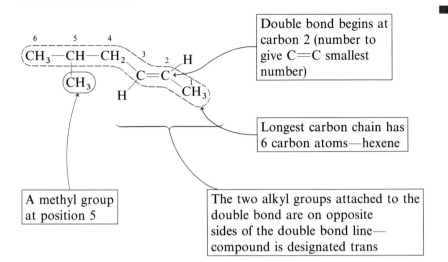

The IUPAC name is therefore as follows:

trans-5-methyl-2-hexene

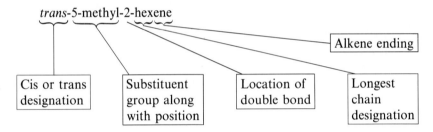

2   Let's take the following cyclic alkene:

This is 3,3-dimethylcyclohexene. In cyclic alkenes, we assign numbers so that the doubly bonded carbon atoms are 1 and 2, respectively. Since most cyclic alkenes can only exist in the cis form, it is not necessary to indicate the double bond stereochemistry.

3   Not all alkenes have two possible configurations.

$CH_3—CH_2—CH_2$

These two are identical

This is 1-pentene. Since the two groups on **one end** of the double bond are the same, there is only one configuration (arrangement) possible and no cis, trans designation is possible.

4 The following structure demonstrates the method of choosing the numbering order.

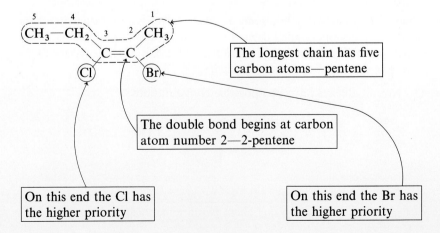

This is 3-chloro-2-methylcyclopentene. We choose the numbering order of the doubly bonded carbon atoms so as to give the substituents the lowest possible numbers. What would the name have been if we had reversed the numbering on atoms 1 and 2?

For more complex alkenes where there are more than two groups attached to the doubly bonded carbon atoms, the cis-trans system does not work since we do not have a way to indicate which groups are on the same side and which are on opposite sides. The method used in these cases is as follows:

1 Examine each end of the double bond and choose the **one** group on each end with the highest priority, based on the Cahn-Ingold-Prelog rules used for (R) and (S) determination in Chapter 4 (see page 126).

2 If the two higher priority groups (one from each end) are on the same side of the double bond line (*cis*-like) then the isomer is designated (Z) (from the German word for together—*zusammen*). If the two higher priority groups are opposite (*trans*-like), then a prefix of (E) is used for the isomer (from the German for opposite—*entgegen*).

For example

The compound is Z, since the Cl and Br (the higher priority groups) are on the **same** side of the double bond. We thus write the complete name as follows:

Z-2-bromo-3-chloro-2-pentene

Another example

$$CH_3-CH_2-CH_2 \diagdown C=C \diagup CH_2CH_2-CH_3$$
$$H \qquad\qquad H$$

cis-4-Octene

A third example

$$CH_3CH_2CH_2 \diagdown Cl$$
$$C=C$$
$$CH_3-CH_2-CH_2-CH_2 \diagup \diagdown CH_3$$

(E)-2-chloro-3-propyl-2-heptene

Note: For our base name, we choose the longest sequence of carbon atoms **containing the double bond**; this is not necessarily the longest sequence in the molecule.

Alkenes are named by indicating the number of carbon atoms in the longest sequence (chain or ring) which contains the double bond, along with an indication of any substituents and the position of the double bond. The geometry (arrangement) of the groups attached to the doubly bonded carbon atoms is also indicated, when necessary, as *cis-trans* or E-Z, and the name always ends in the syllable ene.

PREPARATION OF ALKENES

The double bond of alkenes is usually created by elimination reactions. Hydrogen halide (HX) can be removed from an alkyl halide by a strong base. Water can be removed from an alcohol by use of an elevated temperature and a substance that combines with water.

Dehydrohalogenation

This reaction involves the removal of a hydrogen atom and a halogen atom from adjacent carbon atoms using a base, such as KOH in alcohol.

$$\begin{array}{c} H \\ | | \\ -C-C- \\ | | \\ H X \end{array} + KOH \xrightarrow[\text{alcohol}]{} \diagdown C=C \diagup + KX + H_2O$$

Some specific examples follow.

Cyclopentene

$$CH_3-CH_2-CH-CH_3 \xrightarrow[\text{alcohol}]{\text{KOH}}$$

$$\underset{\text{Br}}{|}$$

$$CH_3-CH=CH-CH_3 + CH_3-CH_2-CH=CH_2$$

(Major product)	(Minor product)
2-Butene (mixture of	1-Butene
cis and *trans*)	

When more than one alkene product can be formed by removing more than one HX pair, as in the second reaction above, the product with the most R groups attached to the double bond will be the major product. This reaction and the expected orientation of the double bond were discussed more fully in Chapter 5 (see page 164).[1]

Dehydration

The term *dehydration* means loss of water. The removal of water from an alcohol molecule, using an acid catalyst such as H_2SO_4 or H_3PO_4 and heat

produces an alkene, which has a lower boiling point than the alcohol from which it was produced. The lower boiling point makes separation of the product by distillation quite easy. The reaction mixture is kept at a temperature above the boiling point of the alkene being produced, but below that of the alcohol starting material. As the alkene is formed it immediately distills out of the reaction vessel. For example, in the first reaction below, the alcohol (cyclohexanol) has a boiling point of 161°C, while the cyclohexene formed boils at 83°C. If the temperature of the reaction mixture is kept at about 100°C, the alkene will distill into another container while the alcohol will not. The examples below illustrate this reaction.

---

[1] It is frequently true that a given type of reaction can be logically discussed at more than one place. For example, dehydrohalogenation can be discussed with alkyl halides and with alkenes. When this happens, we will discuss the reaction in detail at one of the places, but mention it again and show more examples at the other place or places. Usually, the briefer discussion will refer to the detailed one.

$$\text{(cyclohexanol)}-OH \xrightarrow[100°C]{H_2SO_4} \text{(cyclohexene)} + H_2O$$

Cyclohexene

$$CH_3-CH_2-OH \xrightarrow[180°C]{H_3PO_4} CH_2{=}CH_2 + H_2O$$

Ethene

$$\begin{array}{c} CH_3 \\ | \\ CH_3-C-CH_3 \\ | \\ OH \end{array} \xrightarrow[85°C]{H_2SO_4} \begin{array}{c} CH_3 \\ | \\ CH_3-C{=}CH_2 \end{array} + H_2O$$

2-Methylpropene
(isobutylene)

Like dehydrohalogenation of alkyl halides, the dehydration of alcohols can sometimes lead to mixtures of alkenes. The mechanism and a discussion of some interesting details of dehydration reactions are given in Chapter 7 (see page 235).

Alkenes from alkynes

In addition to the elimination reactions just discussed, one mole of H_2 can be added to an alkyne, under controlled conditions, to produce an alkene. The catalyst needed to produce the cis alkene in the presence of hydrogen gas is a mixture of palladium, barium sulfate, and quinoline. The trans product can be produced by the reaction of an alkyne with lithium metal dissolved in liquefied ammonia. Quinoline has the formula

The general equations are as follows:

$$-C{\equiv}C- \xrightarrow[Pd/BaSO_4/quinoline]{H_2} \begin{array}{c} \ \ \diagdown C{=}C\diagup \\ H \diagup \ \ \ \diagdown H \end{array}$$ Syn addition to produce the cis alkene

$$-C{\equiv}C- \xrightarrow[NH_3(l)]{Li} \begin{array}{c} \diagdown \ \ \ \ H \\ C{=}C\diagup \\ H\diagup \ \ \ \diagdown \end{array}$$ Anti addition to produce the trans alkene

Some specific examples of these processes follow.

$$CH_3-C{\equiv}C-CH_3 + H_2 \xrightarrow{Pd/BaSO_4/quinoline} \begin{array}{c} CH_3 \diagdown \ \ \ \ \diagup CH_3 \\ C{=}C \\ H\diagup \ \ \ \diagdown H \end{array}$$

cis-2-Butene

$$CH_3-CH_2-CH_2-C\equiv C-CH_3 \xrightarrow[NH_3(l)]{Li}$$

$$CH_3-CH_2-CH_2 \diagdown \atop H \diagup C=C \diagup H \atop \diagdown CH_3$$

trans-2-Hexene

Remember from our discussion in Chapter 3 (see page 99) that the terms *cis* and *trans* are adjectives which describe the nature of the molecular geometry and are incorporated into the compound name. *Syn* and *anti* are terms which describe the nature of the process (mechanism) by which a reaction occurs; syn means that both groups or atoms add from the same side, while anti means the two add from opposite sides of the molecule. In Chapter 3 these terms were used in connection with alkenes being converted to alkanes; here we are using them to describe alkynes changing into alkenes, but the meanings are similar.

Alkenes can be prepared by dehydrohalogenating alkyl halides, dehydrating alcohols, or by adding hydrogen atoms to an alkyne. In the latter case, the geometry about the double bond can be controlled by using the appropriate reagent.

GENERAL REACTIONS OF ALKENES

Alkenes undergo a large number of reactions to produce other functional groups and are, therefore, quite useful intermediates in chemical synthesis. If we want to produce a compound with a particular functional group in a synthesis problem, we may want to consider first forming an alkene and then changing it into the desired product. Reactions of alkenes can be divided into two categories. Those reactions involving a stepwise electrophilic addition are summarized in the flow diagram on page 199, and all those which do not involve electrophilic addition are shown in the flow diagram on page 198 along with the preparation methods. First, we will consider the reactions that are **not** electrophilic additions.

Hydrogenation

This is the reaction with hydrogen gas and a noble metal catalyst which causes the addition of two atoms of hydrogen across the double bond of alkenes to produce alkanes. This reaction has been covered in detail in Chapter 3 (see page 98). For review, the following examples are given.

$$+ H_2 \xrightarrow{Pt}$$

1,4-Dimethylcyclohexane

$$\underset{CH_3}{\overset{CH_3}{\diagdown}}C=C\underset{CH_3}{\overset{CH_3}{\diagup}} + H_2 \xrightarrow{Ni} CH_3-\underset{\underset{H}{|}}{\overset{\overset{CH_3}{|}}{C}}-\underset{\underset{H}{|}}{\overset{\overset{CH_3}{|}}{C}}-CH_3$$

2,3-Dimethylbutane

Ozonolysis

This process is unusual in that it causes both bonds of a carbon-carbon double bond to break and the carbon skeleton to be split into two parts. It involves the reaction of the alkene with ozone (O_3) followed by treatment with zinc and water. This causes the molecule to split at the double bond and usually produces two molecules of aldehyde and/or ketone. Ozonolysis causes cyclic alkenes to form open aldehydes and/or ketones. The two carbon atoms that were doubly bonded to each other are now each doubly bonded to a separate oxygen atom.

Split   an ozonide

$$\diagup\diagdown C=O + O=C\diagdown\diagup + Zn(OH)_2$$

For example

$$\underset{CH_3}{\overset{CH_3}{\diagdown}}C\overset{\vdots}{=}C\underset{H}{\overset{CH_3}{\diagup}} \xrightarrow[H_2O]{O_3 \quad Zn} \underset{CH_3}{\overset{CH_3}{\diagdown}}C=O + O=C\underset{H}{\overset{CH_3}{\diagup}}$$

Ketone   Aldehyde

$$\underset{H}{\overset{CH_3-CH_2}{\diagdown}}C\overset{\vdots}{=}C\underset{H}{\overset{CH_2-CH_3}{\diagup}} \xrightarrow[H_2O]{O_3 \quad Zn} 2O=C\underset{H}{\overset{CH_2=CH_3}{\diagup}}$$

Two molecules of aldehyde

$$\bigcirc \cdots \xrightarrow[H_2O]{O_3 \quad Zn} H-\overset{\overset{O}{\|}}{C}-(CH_2)_4\overset{\overset{O}{\|}}{C}-H$$

A dialdehyde

$$\overset{CH_3}{\bigcirc} \cdots \xrightarrow[H_2O]{O_3 \quad Zn} CH_3-\overset{\overset{O}{\|}}{C}-CH_2-CH_2-CH_2-\overset{\overset{O}{\|}}{C}-H$$

A ketone-aldehyde

Note that in the last two examples a ring is split open to produce a single open chain molecule rather than two molecules. Ozonolysis reactions can serve two purposes. The most obvious is the production of aldehydes and ketones, but it can also be used to prove the structure of alkenes. For example, if an unknown alkene, upon ozonolysis, produced the compounds shown here

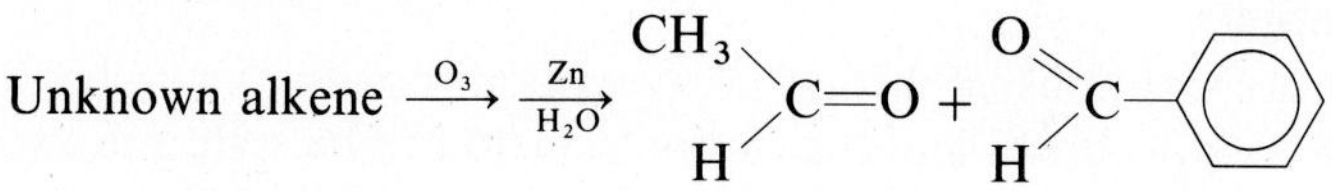

$$\text{Unknown alkene} \xrightarrow{O_3} \xrightarrow[H_2O]{Zn} \quad \begin{array}{c} CH_3 \\ \diagdown \\ H \diagup \end{array} C{=}O + \begin{array}{c} O \\ \diagdown \\ H \diagup \end{array} C{-}\bigcirc$$

its structure could be determined by the following logic. The two carbon atoms which are now doubly bonded to the two oxygen atoms must have been doubly bonded to each other in the original alkene structure. The attached groups go along with their original carbon partners.

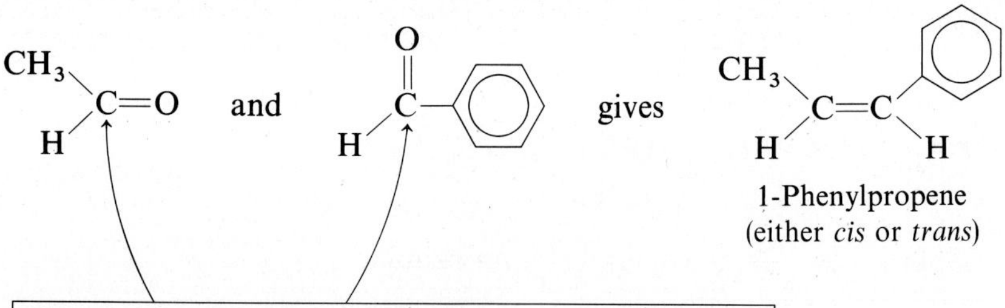

$$\begin{array}{c} CH_3 \\ \diagdown \\ H \diagup \end{array} C{=}O \quad \text{and} \quad \begin{array}{c} O \\ \parallel \\ H \diagup \end{array} C{-}\bigcirc \quad \text{gives} \quad \begin{array}{cc} CH_3 \\ \diagdown \\ H \diagup \end{array} C{=}C \begin{array}{c} \bigcirc \\ \diagup \\ \diagdown H \end{array}$$

1-Phenylpropene
(either *cis* or *trans*)

These two carbon atoms should be doubly bonded to each other to produce the structural formula of the unknown alkene

Another example is

$$\begin{array}{c} \text{Unknown alkene} \\ (C_5H_8) \end{array} \xrightarrow{O_3} \xrightarrow[H_2O]{Zn} \quad \begin{array}{ccc} O && O \\ \parallel && \parallel \\ H{-}C{-}(CH_2)_3{-}C{-}H \end{array}$$

The structure must have been cyclic, since we have to link two ends of the same compound in order to get the structure of the original alkene.

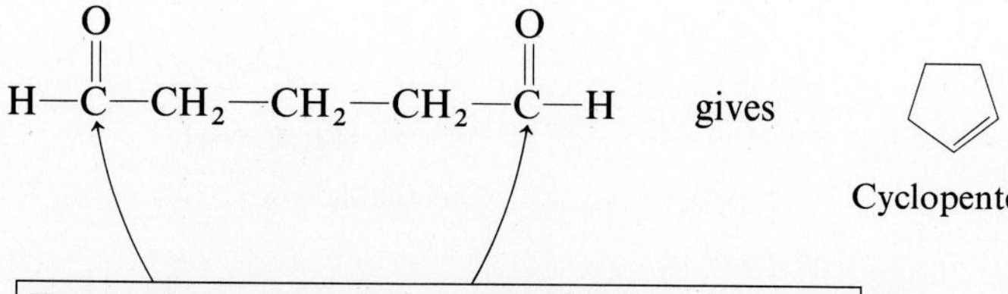

$$\begin{array}{ccccc} O &&&& O \\ \parallel &&&& \parallel \\ H{-}C{-}CH_2{-}CH_2{-}CH_2{-}C{-}H \end{array} \quad \text{gives} \quad \bigcirc$$

Cyclopentene

Two carbon atoms have to doubly bond to each other to get the unknown alkene

Oxidation

The reagent that will convert alkenes into dialcohols (**diols or glycols**) is aqueous potassium permanganate, $KMnO_4$. This reagent adds both OH groups onto the same side of the alkene (syn addition). A *cis* product results if the alkene is cyclic. The general reaction is as follows:

$$\text{>C=C<} + MnO_4^- \xrightarrow[\text{cold, dilute}]{OH^-} \underset{\underset{OH\ \ OH}{|\ \ \ |}}{-\overset{|}{C}-\overset{|}{C}-} + MnO_2$$

For example

$$CH_3-CH_2-\underset{\underset{H}{|}}{C}=C\overset{H}{\underset{H}{<}} \xrightarrow{KMnO_4} CH_3-CH_2-\underset{\underset{OH}{|}}{CH}-\underset{\underset{OH}{|}}{CH_2}$$

Diols are formed best when a base is used as a catalyst and the conditions are kept mild (i.e., low temperatures and a dilute solution of the $KMnO_4$). Under stronger conditions, such as acid catalysis and high temperatures, cleavage at the double bond occurs and carboxylic acids are produced.

The reaction with $KMnO_4$, in addition to producing glycols, gives a rapid visual test for alkenes. The $KMnO_4$ is an intense purple color, but when an alkene is present in a test tube to which a few drops of permanganate solution are added, the color immediately changes to brown. Alkynes and aldehydes also cause this color change, but most other functional groups do not under the conditions used. This procedure is called the **Baeyer test** and is shown in Figure 6-2.

FIGURE 6-2

The Baeyer test for alkenes. The test tube on the left contains a dilute aqueous $KMnO_4$ solution; the one on the right contains a $KMnO_4$ to which an alkene was added. Note the decolorization produced by the alkene.

TYPE OF COMPOUND	RESULT OF BAEYER TEST
Alkenes	Purple disappears (positive test)
Alkynes	Purple disappears (positive test)
Alkanes	Purple remains (negative test)
Alkyl halides	Purple remains (negative test)
Aromatic compounds	Purple remains (negative test)
Carboxylic acids	Purple remains (negative test)
Aldehydes	Purple disappears (positive test)
Ketones	Purple remains (negative test)

Allylic substitution

When an alkene is subjected to free radical halogenation, the carbon atoms adjacent to the double bond, which are called **allylic** carbon atoms, are the most readily halogenated.

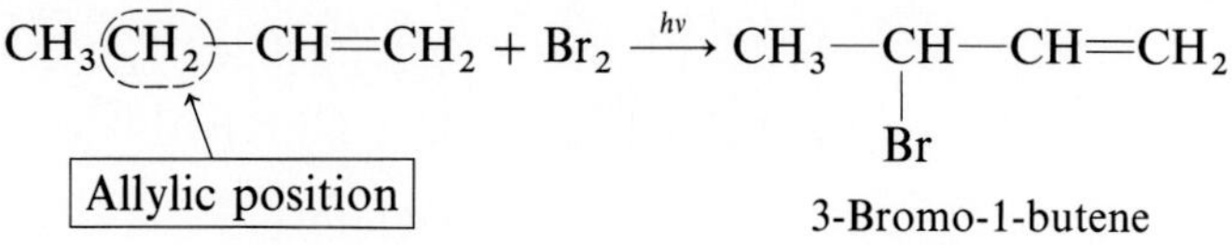

$$CH_3-(CH_2)-CH{=}CH_2 + Br_2 \xrightarrow{h\nu} CH_3-\underset{\underset{Br}{|}}{CH}-CH{=}CH_2$$

Allylic position

3-Bromo-1-butene

A reagent specific for this purpose, *N*-bromosuccinimide (NBS), can be more conveniently used in the laboratory. NBS and the peroxide catalyst (see below) are both solids and are easily handled. When they are mixed together and warmed, a source of bromine free radicals is produced. Elemental bromine, on the other hand, is toxic, volatile, and troublesome to use, as is elemental chlorine.

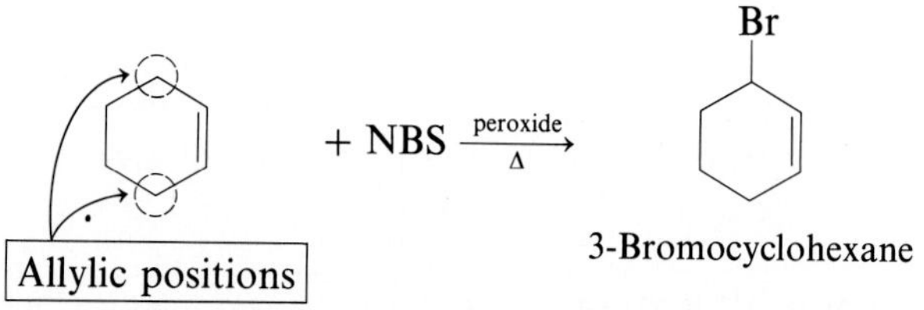

Allylic positions

$$+ NBS \xrightarrow[\Delta]{peroxide}$$

3-Bromocyclohexane

Halogenation reactions occur at the allylic position because the allylic free radical intermediate is more stable than any other that could be produced and, thus, is formed the most easily. As shown below, **resonance** stabilizes the allylic free radical—the free radical character is delocalized over two carbon atoms rather than being concentrated on only one. The mechanism for allylic bromination is shown below.

$$Br_2 \xrightarrow{h\nu} 2Br\cdot$$

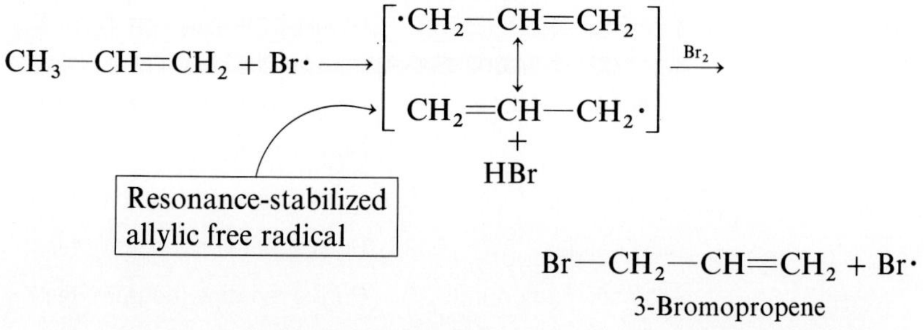

$$CH_3-CH{=}CH_2 + Br\cdot \longrightarrow \begin{bmatrix} \cdot CH_2-CH{=}CH_2 \\ \updownarrow \\ CH_2{=}CH-CH_2\cdot \end{bmatrix} \xrightarrow{Br_2}$$

+
HBr

Resonance-stabilized allylic free radical

$$Br-CH_2-CH{=}CH_2 + Br\cdot$$

3-Bromopropene

Reactions of alkenes include cleavage with ozone to produce aldehydes and ketones and to prove the structure of alkenes, hydrogenation to form alkanes, and oxidation to produce glycols. In addition to these reactions in which the double bond is changed, the position adjacent

to the double bond (allylic position) can be selectively halogenated while the double bond is left unchanged.

Electrophilic addition reactions of alkenes

Now let's consider the reactions of alkenes which are summarized in the flow diagram on page 199. These are called electrophilic addition reactions because they are initiated by the attraction of an electron deficient (electron-loving) species to the pi electron region of the double bond. These reactions differ from each other in what groups add across the double bond, but they all involve a **two-step addition** initiated by an **electrophilic reagent** such as a cation. For the general case

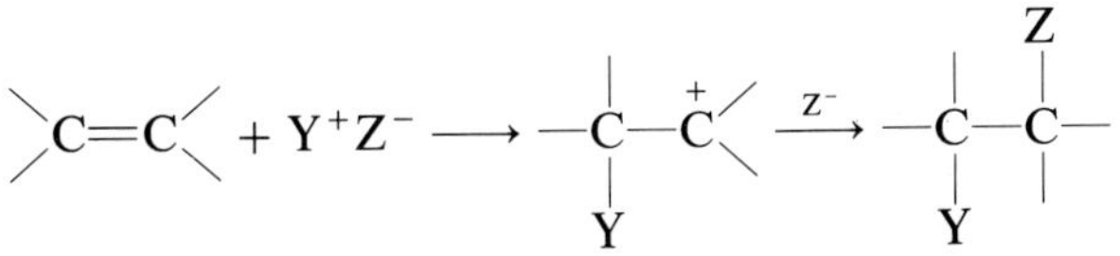

$$\diagup C=C\diagdown + Y^+Z^- \longrightarrow -\overset{|}{\underset{Y}{C}}-\overset{+}{C}\diagup \xrightarrow{Z^-} -\overset{|}{\underset{Y}{C}}-\overset{\overset{Z}{|}}{\underset{|}{C}}-$$

In most cases, these reactions follow **Markovnikov's rule**—the Y^+ goes to the end of the double bond with most hydrogens, and the Z^- goes to the other end. These electrophilic addition reactions are covered in detail in those chapters dealing with the functional groups produced. For example, the addition of HBr to produce alkyl halides is covered in Chapter 5, and reactions which add water to produce alcohols are discussed in Chapter 7. But several examples of electrophilic reactions are shown below to illustrate those shown in a general way in the flow diagram. The positive species which has **less than the desired octet of electrons** is initially attracted to the electrons in the double bond of the alkene.

$$CH_3-CH=CH_2 + \underset{\delta+\ \ -\delta}{H\dot{\div}Br} \longrightarrow CH_3-\underset{\underset{Br}{|}}{CH}-CH_3$$

$$CH_3-CH=CH_2 + \underset{\delta+\ \ -\delta}{H\dot{\div}OH} \xrightarrow{H^+} CH_3-\underset{\underset{OH}{|}}{CH}-CH_3$$

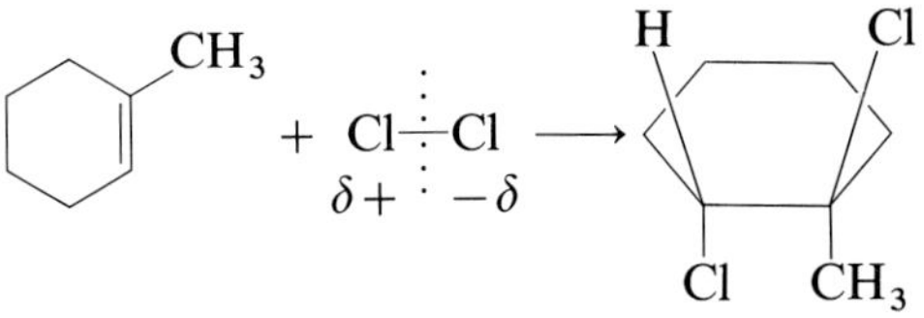

Alkenes react with those reagents that are attracted to the electrons of the double bond (electrophilic reagents). These reagents add to the doubly bonded carbon atoms in a stepwise fashion to produce a variety of important functional groups, including alkyl halides and alcohols.

POLYMERS, PLASTICS, AND COATINGS

Alkenes can be used to produce an important family of materials called **polymers**. These include such materials as plastics, rubbers, varnishes, paints, and synthetic fibers. Polymers are produced chemically by linking many individual small molecules, called **monomers**, together by covalent bonds. This produces very long, high molecular weight molecules that in many cases have unusual properties. By designing different molecular structures, chemists have been able to make many polymers with a wide range of properties and uses. These polymers are sometimes called **macromolecules** because of their very large size and high average molecular weight.

While a number of functional groups can be used in making polymers, alkenes are well suited for making several common polymers. The general reaction for a substituted alkene forming a macromolecule is

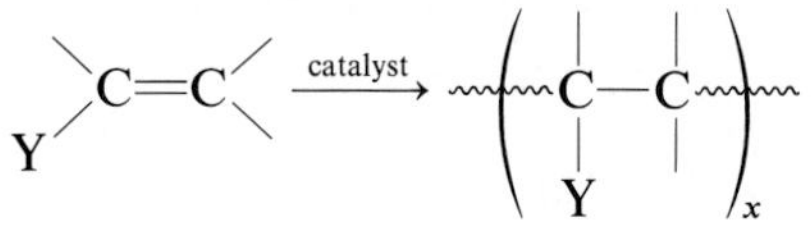

Monomer   Polymer

The pi bond in each alkene molecule is used to form a sigma bond with another molecule and produce a chain of carbons. The group or groups attached to the alkene (Y above) follow along and impart unique properties to the polymer, but they do not participate in the reaction. The x in the polymer formula, along with the wavy line ($\sim\!\!\sim\!\!\sim$) at each end, is used to indicate a large but indefinite number of repeating units (monomer units). Polymers are usually named simply by placing the prefix *poly-* before the common, classical, or IUPAC name of the monomer. Some also have trademarked commercial names. The structures of seven of the more familiar polymers derived from alkenes, along with the monomers used in their production, are shown below. Their uses are also indicated.

Commercial polymers

Polyethylene   Polyethylene (see Figure 6-3 for polyethylene products) is used to make most inexpensive household containers. The formula of all polyethylene is the same, but the manufacturing process determines the exact properties of the material.

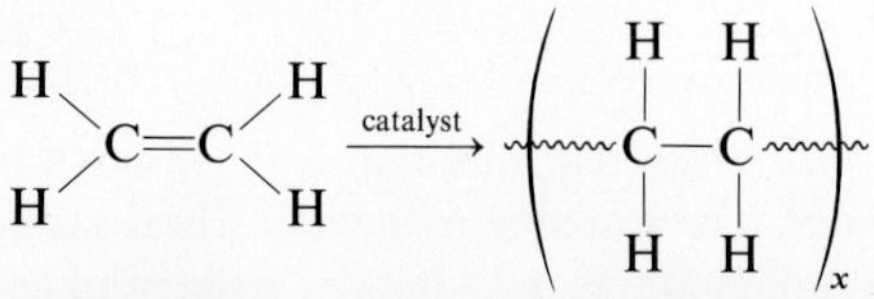

Ethylene   Polyethylene

Polyethylene products.

FIGURE 6-3

The softer translucent type is **low density polyethylene**; the colored, opaque harder type is **high density polyethylene**.

Polyvinyl chloride and polyvinylidene chloride   Vinyl floor tile and clear plastic food wrap are formed by polymerizing vinyl chloride and vinylidene chloride, respectively.

$$\underset{\text{Vinyl chloride}}{\overset{\text{H}}{\underset{\text{H}}{>}}C=C\overset{\text{H}}{\underset{\text{Cl}}{<}}} \xrightarrow{\text{catalyst}} \underset{\text{Polyvinyl chloride (PVC)}}{\left(\begin{array}{cc}\text{H} & \text{H}\\ \text{C}-\text{C}\\ \text{H} & \text{Cl}\end{array}\right)_x}$$

FIGURE 6-4

Drainpipe made from polyvinyl chloride.

$$\underset{\text{Vinylidene chloride}}{\overset{\text{H}}{\underset{\text{H}}{>}}C=C\overset{\text{Cl}}{\underset{\text{Cl}}{<}}} \longrightarrow \underset{\text{Polyvinylidene chloride (Saran)}}{\left(\begin{array}{cc}\text{H} & \text{Cl}\\ \text{C}-\text{C}\\ \text{H} & \text{Cl}\end{array}\right)_x}$$

Polyvinyl chloride can be formulated with other materials to form materials for a number of familiar products, such as water pipes (see Figure 6-4) and electrical insulation.

Poly(methyl methacrylate)   A lightweight, transparent material that is better than glass for some applications is the synthetic polymer with the trade name of Lucite or Plexiglas. It does not shatter on impact and is thus safer for functions such as windows in storm doors. A Lucite pane will bend rather than break if something or someone falls against it. It can also be cut and glued to make transparent models of buildings or machines. However, it scratches easily and will dissolve or become cloudy if it comes in contact with organic solvents such as acetone or hexane.

The chemical name and formula for this plastic, along with the corresponding monomer, are shown below:

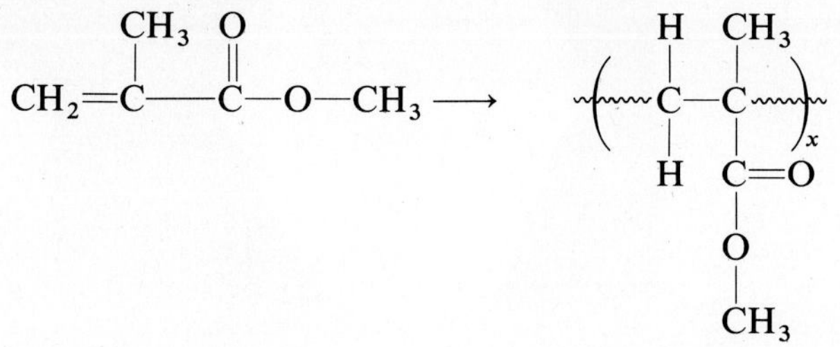

$$CH_2=\underset{\underset{CH_3}{|}}{C}-\underset{\underset{O}{||}}{C}-O-CH_3 \longrightarrow$$

Methyl methacrylate

Poly(methyl methacrylate)
(Lucite)

Polystyrene   This inexpensive material is most often found in the form of a polymerized foam (expanded polystyrene or Styrofoam) and is used for flotation devices, household thermal insulation, insulated containers for ice and cold drinks, and for decorations such as Christmas tree ornaments.

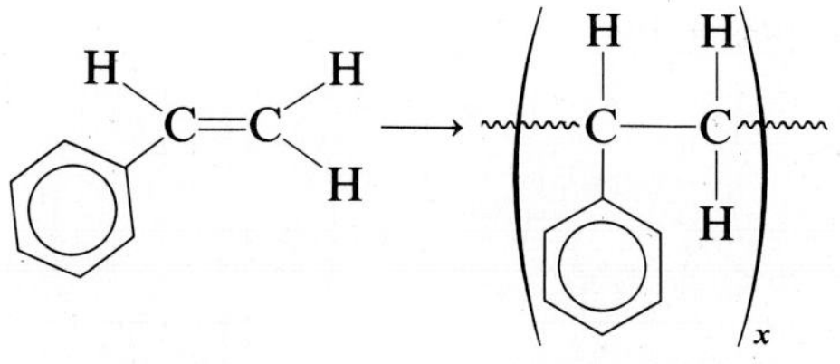

Styrene   Polystyrene

Polyacrylonitrile   This is a material usually made into fibers for use in the manufacture of socks and sweaters, since it looks and feels like wool. Its trade names include Orlon (Du Pont), Acrilan (Monsanto), and Creslan (American Cyanamid).

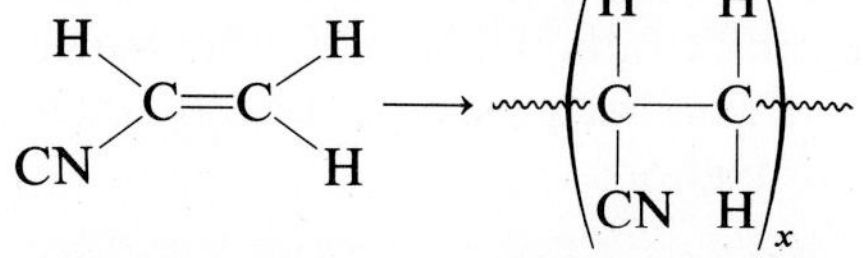

Acrylonitrile   Polyacrylonitrile

Polytetrafluoroethene   This material is marketed by Du Pont as Teflon. It is inert to most organic materials and to most acids, bases, and other materials found in the chemical laboratory and around the home. It also has a slick or "greasy" surface and a high resistance to thermal decomposition, which makes it ideal for coatings on cookware and on certain laboratory utensils.

$$\underset{\text{Tetrafluoroethene}}{\overset{F}{\underset{F}{>}}C=C\overset{F}{\underset{F}{<}}} \longrightarrow \left(\!\!\begin{array}{c} F \quad F \\ | \quad | \\ C-C \\ | \quad | \\ F \quad F \end{array}\!\!\right)_{\!x}$$

Tetrafluoroethene   Polytetrafluoroethene
(Teflon)

**Alkenes containing a variety of substituted groups can be polymerized
(allowed to react with other molecules of the same substance) to produce large molecules (macromolecules) with useful properties.**

Coatings

For purposes of protection, decoration, or both, most metals and wooden
and plastic objects and surfaces are coated. These coatings include paint,
varnish, shellac, lacquer, and fingernail polish. The last three of these can
be thought of as temporary coatings, since they are applied as a solution
of natural or synthetic polymers. They harden because the **solvent evaporates**, leaving a coating of the polymer. This polymer coating can be removed by redissolving it in the original solvent.

Fingernail polish is dissolved by rubbing with a cloth moistened in
ethyl acetate or acetone. A little oil is usually added to these solvents to
prevent excessive drying of the skin with which they come into contact.
Shellac is readily soluble in 95% denatured ethyl alcohol, which is what
shellac thinner is. We can remove shellac from furniture or other wooden
objects by rubbing with coarse steel wool which is wet with alcohol.
Lacquer is soluble in a mixture of ketones and can also be removed from
furniture.

The more permanent coatings, such as paint and varnish, involve the
application of a **partly polymerized** mixture in a solvent. During hardening,
both evaporation of the solvent and exposure to the oxygen in the air
cause **complete polymerization** to occur. Such a coating cannot simply be
redissolved in the same solvent because the new material formed (polymerization is a chemical process and a new substance is formed) is
not soluble in the solvent used for the original monomer.

Acrylic latex paints use methyl methacrylate monomers and their polymer to form the polymer that coats the wall. Latex paints contain small
particles of polymerized material. (That is why latex paints never have a
high gloss; the coarse structure is built in.) They also contain enough
monomer so that additional polymerization can occur as the paint cures.
The polymer itself is essentially colorless, and a pigment such as TiO_2 is
added to produce a white base, which is then tinted various colors. Oil-
based paints and all varnishes are prepared with either natural or
synthetic monomers dissolved in hydrocarbon solvents.

Paints often contain linseed oil, and varnishes sometimes contain tung
oil. Both these oils are in a class called **drying oils**, which react with oxy-

gen (from the air) to form a polymeric coating which holds the pigments. These oils, like others, are composed of triesters, which are molecules whose fatty acid portion contains double bonds. (See Chapter 16.) Natural (raw) oils are **not conjugated** (that is, they do not have alternating double and single bonds) and would, if untreated, produce a very slow-drying product. When these oils are boiled, their double bonds rearrange into a conjugated relationship, and these boiled oils form polymers much more rapidly than the untreated oils do.

$$H_2CO-\overset{\displaystyle O}{\overset{\|}{C}}-(CH_2)_7-\overbrace{CH=CH-CH_2-CH=CH}^{\text{Nonconjugated double bonds}}(-CH_2)_4-CH_3$$

$$HCO-\overset{\displaystyle O}{\overset{\|}{C}}-(CH_2)_7-CH=CH-CH_2-CH=CH(-CH_2)_4-CH_3 \xrightarrow[\text{(boiling)}]{\Delta}$$

$$H_2CO-\overset{\displaystyle O}{\overset{\|}{C}}-(CH_2)_7-CH=CH-CH_2-CH=CH(-CH_2)_4-CH_3$$

Linoleic ester
(65% of raw linseed oil)

$$H_2CO-\overset{\displaystyle O}{\overset{\|}{C}}-(CH_2)_8-\overbrace{CH=CH-CH=CH}^{\text{Conjugated double bonds}}-(CH_2)_4-CH_3$$

$$HCO-\overset{\displaystyle O}{\overset{\|}{C}}-(CH_2)_8-CH=CH-CH=CH-(CH_2)_4-CH_3 \xrightarrow{O_2}$$

$$H_2CO-\overset{\displaystyle O}{\overset{\|}{C}}-(CH_2)_8-CH=CH-CH=CH-(CH_2)_4-CH_3$$

Boiled linseed oil

$$H_2CO-\overset{\displaystyle O}{\overset{\|}{C}}-(CH_2)_8-\overset{|}{CH}-CH_2-CH_2-\overset{|}{CH}-(CH_2)_4-CH_3$$

$$HCO-\overset{\displaystyle O}{\overset{\|}{C}}-(CH_2)_8-\overset{|}{CH}-CH_2-CH_2-CH-(CH_2)_4-CH_3$$

$$H_2CO-\overset{\displaystyle O}{\overset{\|}{C}}-(CH_2)_8-\overset{|}{CH}-CH_2-CH_2-CH-(CH_2)_4-CH_3$$

Polymeric drying oil
(in hardened or dried paint)

Once such permanent coatings have dried, they can be removed only by destroying chemical bonds. Paint and varnish removers usually contain a strong base and organic solvents such as dichloromethane or carbon tetrachloride. Some must be scraped off; others can be washed off with water. They should always be used with plenty of ventilation, and contact with the skin should be minimized.

Medical applications of polymers

Plastics (polymeric materials) have been used for a number of medical polymeric dental filling material. The material used must be compatfillings.

Chemists develop polymers for specific medical uses by taking into account the desired properties and the exact conditions under which the material must function. For example, let's consider the development of polymeric dental filling material. The material used must be compatible with the mouth—that is, it should not irritate the mouth and must not decompose when wet. It should also be hard, look basically white, and come in various shades to match natural tooth colors. A dentist should be able to mix it easily; after mixing, it should become quite hard in a relatively short time. This hardening process is a chemical reaction in which the monomer molecules react under the influence of a catalyst to form the polymeric dental filling material.

This reaction not only must occur rapidly but must do so at body temperature (that is, no heat greater than body temperature heat should be required) and must not give off excess heat, since that would be painful to the patient and could cause burns.

The monomer found to be the best is shown below; it has ends that have the same structure as methyl methacrylate.

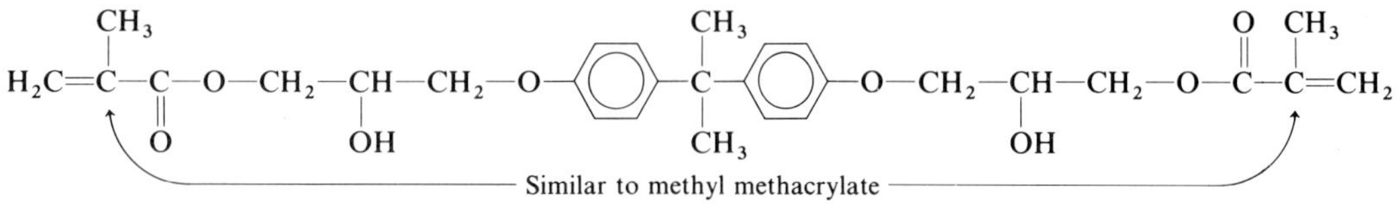

Similar to methyl methacrylate

The resulting polymer is similar to polymethyl methacrylate. The polymer is relatively soft and gives off heat when polymerization occurs. These problems are solved by adding finely powdered sand to the polymer. The sand adds hardness and greatly reduces the amount of organic material present, thus reducing the amount of heat liberated.

When the usual initiator catalyst (a peroxide) is used, some heat is required from an external source, such as a flame. A flame, of course, cannot be used in the mouth. When an amine is present along with the peroxide, the reaction goes too quickly and the material hardens in the container before it can be used. It is also true that the dentist is not usually a chemist and does not want to have bottles of the needed chemicals around. These problems are solved by dividing the monomer mixture into two parts and adding peroxide to one part and an amine to the other part. The resulting two mixtures—one containing monomer and peroxide and the other, monomer and an amine—are then stored in separate containers. The dentist has only to mix equal amounts of material from the two containers.

REACTION SUMMARY FLOW DIAGRAM— PREPARATION AND GENERAL REACTIONS OF ALKENES

REACTION SUMMARY FLOW DIAGRAM—
ELECTROPHILIC ADDITION REACTIONS
OF ALKENES

$$R—\overset{\overset{\displaystyle X}{|}}{C}—\overset{\overset{\displaystyle X}{|}}{C}—$$

Alkyl dihalides

$$R—\overset{|}{C}—\overset{\overset{\displaystyle H}{|}}{\underset{\underset{\displaystyle OH}{|}}{C}}—$$

Alcohols

$$R—C{=}C\left\langle\quad\xrightarrow[\ ]{(BH_3)_2}\quad\xrightarrow[OH^-]{H_2O_2}\quad R—\overset{|}{\underset{\underset{\displaystyle H}{|}}{C}}—\overset{|}{\underset{\underset{\displaystyle OH}{|}}{C}}—\right.$$

Alcohols
(See Chapter 7)

X₂

H₂O/H⁺

HX

HBr/peroxide

Hg(OAc)₂

NaBH₄

$$R—\overset{\overset{\displaystyle H}{|}}{\underset{\underset{\displaystyle X}{|}}{C}}—\overset{|}{C}—$$

Alkyl halides

$$R—\overset{|}{C}—\overset{\overset{\displaystyle Br}{|}}{\underset{\underset{\displaystyle H}{|}}{C}}—$$

Alkyl halides

$$R—\overset{|}{C}—\overset{\overset{\displaystyle H}{|}}{\underset{\underset{\displaystyle OH}{|}}{C}}—$$

Alcohols
(See Chapter 7)

ALKYNES

Alkynes are characterized by a triple bond between *sp* hybridized carbon atoms; they exhibit linear geometry (180° bond angles at the alkyne functional group).

$$R—C{\equiv}C—R$$
180°

Alkynes are named much as alkenes are, except that the ending *-yne* is used. The carbon chain is numbered, and the position of the triple bond and of any substituents is indicated. Because of the linear structure characteristic of the triple bond portion of the molecule, alkynes do not exhibit *cis-trans* isomerism, nor does the triple bond occur in small rings. Therefore, it is simpler to name an alkyne than an alkene. The following examples illustrate the IUPAC system of nomenclature of alkynes.

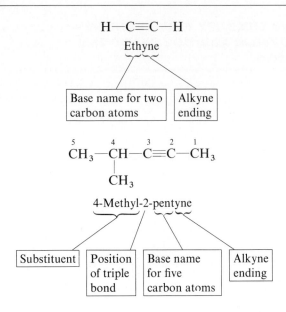

The smallest alkyne (ethyne) is commonly called **acetylene** in commercial situations and is used as a welding fuel, as shown in Figure 6-5. Other alkynes are sometimes named as substituted acetylenes, as shown below, and these names are part of the classical system of nomenclature.

$$CH_3—CH_2—C{\equiv}C—CH_3$$

IUPAC name: 2-pentyne
Classical name: methylethylacetylene

FIGURE 6-5

Acetylene is used as a welding fuel.

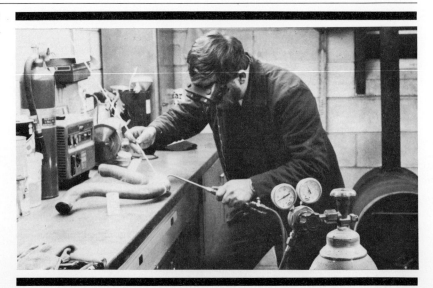

Alkynes with the triple bond at the end of the molecule are called **terminal** alkynes. Those with the triple bond in any other part of the molecule are called **nonterminal** alkynes.

Alkynes are named by indicating the longest sequence of carbon atoms containing the triple bond along with any substituents, the position of the triple bond, and the ending *yne*. Alternatively, they are named as substituted acetylenes.

PREPARATION OF ALKYNES

Production of acetylene

The smallest alkyne, acetylene (ethyne), can be prepared from inexpensive, inorganic natural materials as follows:

$$\text{Coal} \xrightarrow{\Delta} \text{coke} \xrightarrow[\Delta]{\text{CaCO}_3} \underset{\substack{\text{Calcium}\\\text{carbide}}}{\text{CaC}_2} \xrightarrow{\text{H}_2\text{O}} \underset{\text{Acetylene}}{\text{H}-\text{C}\equiv\text{C}-\text{H}} + \text{Ca(OH)}_2$$

Coal is heated in the absence of air to drive off oils and tar and leave a relatively pure carbon material called **coke**. If coke is then heated with limestone ($CaCO_3$) in an electric furnace, we obtain **calcium carbide** (CaC_2), which, when reacted with water, yields acetylene. Acetylene, a gas at ordinary temperatures, is stored under pressure in cylinders until needed for welding with an oxyacetylene torch, or for chemical synthesis. A newer and less expensive method of producing acetylene involves the pyrolysis (heating in the absence of oxygen) of methane or of low molecular weight alkanes.

Alkynes from alkyl halides

Larger alkynes can be made from smaller ones, as shown in the next section, or the triple bond can be introduced into a nonalkyne molecule, as shown below:

$$\underset{\quad}{\text{R}-\overset{\overset{\text{H}}{|}}{\text{C}}-\overset{\overset{\text{H}}{|}}{\underset{\underset{\text{X}}{|}}{\text{C}}-} + 2\text{NaNH}_2 \longrightarrow \underset{\text{An alkyne}}{\text{R}-\text{C}\equiv\text{C}-} + 2\text{NH}_3 + 2\text{NaX}$$

This process involves the double dehydrohalogenation of alkyl halides having two halogen atoms by the use of two molecules of a strong base, such as sodium amide ($NaNH_2$). The dihalide can be made from an alkene as shown in the first example below.

$$CH_3-CH=CH-CH_3 + Br_2 \longrightarrow$$

$$R-C\equiv C-H \xrightarrow{\text{NaNH}_2} R-C\equiv C^-Na^+ + NH_3$$

Alkynes are prepared from dihalides by removing two moles of HX with sodium amide ($NaNH_2$). Acetylene is produced commercially from calcium carbide and water, or by pyrolysis of methane.

REACTIONS OF ALKYNES

Hydrogenation

As we have discussed in the first part of this chapter, alkynes can be hydrogenated in two different ways to produce alkenes, and can be converted to alkanes by using two moles of hydrogen gas in the presence of a metal catalyst.

Reactions of terminal alkynes

The hydrogen atom at the end of terminal alkynes is quite acidic and can be pulled off by strong bases to produce metal salts of alkynes.

$$R-C\equiv C-H \xrightarrow{\text{NaNH}_2} R-C\equiv C^-Na^+ + NH_3$$

The resulting anion can be used as a **nucleophile** to build larger carbon chains, as shown in the following section.

Certain metal cations such as Ag^+ [in the form of $Ag(NH_3)_2{}^+OH^-$] and Cu^+ will also react with terminal alkynes to form insoluble salts. These reactions can be used in **qualitative analysis** to distinguish between terminal and nonterminal alkynes. If a terminal alkyne is present, a visible solid (a precipitate) will form when Ag^+ or Cu^+ is added; if a nonterminal alkyne is present, no visual change will occur. For example

$$CH_3CH_2-C\equiv C-H \xrightarrow{\text{Ag(NH}_3)_2{}^+\text{OH}^-}$$

$$CH_3CH_2-C\equiv C^-Ag^+ + H_2O + 2NH_3$$

Solid

$$CH_3-CH_2-C\equiv C-CH_2-CH_3 \xrightarrow{\text{Ag(NH}_3)_2{}^+\text{OH}^-}$$

no reaction   (no solid formed)

The Baeyer test for unsaturation discussed on page 189 in connection with the identification of alkenes is also positive for alkynes. Thus, the changing from purple to brown or colorless is indicative of either a double or a triple bond.

Chain lengthening

Terminal alkynes can be converted to anions, as shown in the previous section. These anions can serve as nucleophiles, which can displace halogen atoms on alkyl halides. This displacement (S_N) reaction forms **larger carbon chains** with a triple bond which can subsequently be converted to other functional groups. The concept of producing new organic molecules in this way is diagrammed for the general case by the following scheme:

$$R—C\equiv C—H \xrightarrow{\text{NaNH}_2} R—C\equiv C^- \xrightarrow{\boxed{R'}\,X}$$

$$R—C\equiv C—\boxed{R'} \longrightarrow \text{other functional groups}$$

These reactions can be used to build larger molecules and produce new functional groups, as shown by the specific examples below. In the first and second examples an alkane and an alkene, respectively, are produced, after the carbon skeleton is built.

$$\boxed{CH_3—CH_2}—Br + H—C\equiv C^- \longrightarrow$$

$$CH_3—CH_2—C\equiv C—H \xrightarrow{2H_2/\text{Pt}} CH_3—CH_2—CH_2—CH_3$$

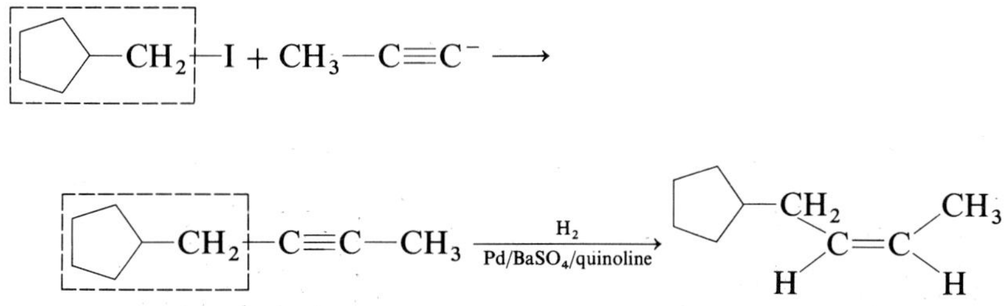

1-Butyne   Butane

$$\boxed{\langle\text{cyclopentyl}\rangle—CH_2}—I + CH_3—C\equiv C^- \longrightarrow$$

$$\boxed{\langle\text{cyclopentyl}\rangle—CH_2}—C\equiv C—CH_3 \xrightarrow[\text{Pd/BaSO}_4/\text{quinoline}]{\text{H}_2}$$

cis-1-Cyclopentyl-2-butene

1-Cyclopentyl-2-butyne

Alkynes can be partially or completely hydrogenated by one or two molecules of hydrogen to produce alkenes or alkanes, respectively. Terminal alkynes can also be reacted with strong bases to produce nucleophiles which are useful in building alkynes with larger carbon structures. Terminal alkynes (those with the triple bond at the end of the molecule) will react with Cu^+ or Ag^+ to give a precipitate. This procedure serves as a qualitative test for the terminal nature of the alkyne.

REACTION SUMMARY FLOW DIAGRAM FOR ALKYNES

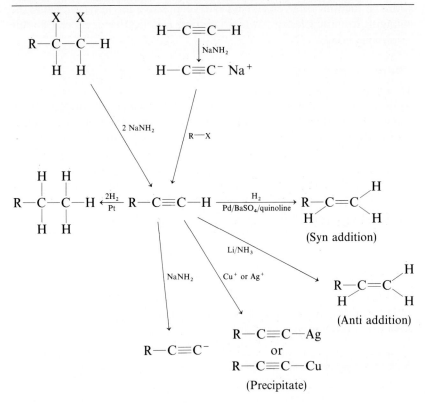

WRITING PRODUCTS OF ORGANIC REACTIONS

In this unit we will develop the skills needed to correctly write the products of organic reactions. You are sometimes asked to predict the products of the reaction of a particular reagent, or set of reagents, with an organic compound. After learning a general reaction and seeing several examples in the text, you are expected to apply this general knowledge to a specific reaction. This process involves the following steps:

1 Identifying the reaction as one of the general ones you have learned

2 Performing the expected molecular changes on the molecule at hand

In this programmed learning unit, we will show the **reasoning**

steps involved in this process by using worked examples. You will then be asked to work several problems. These examples should allow you to understand the thought process involved in correctly writing the products of organic reactions.

Worked example

Write the product or products of the following reaction:

$$CH_3CH_2-C\equiv C-CH_2CH_3 + H_2 \xrightarrow{\text{Pd/BaSO}_4\text{/quinoline}}$$

1 Identify the functional group in the starting material as an alkyne.

2 Identify the reagents and catalysts as those which add one molecule of H_2 to an alkyne molecule to produce alkenes. (This should have been previously learned.)

3 Remember that these reagents add the two hydrogen atoms in a *syn* fashion to produce the *cis* alkene.

4 Write the structure of the product.

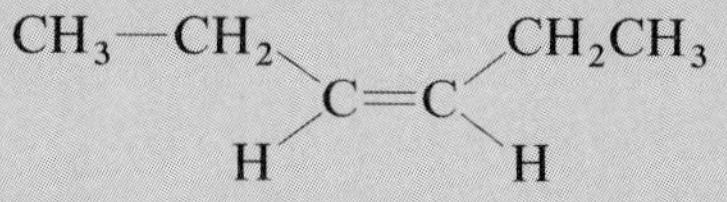

$$\underset{H}{\overset{CH_3-CH_2}{\diagdown}}C=C\underset{H}{\overset{CH_2CH_3}{\diagup}}$$

cis-3-Hexene

Worked example

Write the products of the following reaction:

$$\text{⬠} \xrightarrow[\text{alcohol}]{\text{KOH}}$$

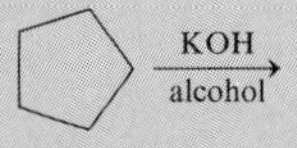

1 Identify the starting material as an alkane (cyclopentane).

2 Identify the reagents as those which cause dehydrohalogenation of alkyl halides to produce alkenes.

3 Recognize that cyclopentane is *not* an alkyl halide, and thus cannot be dehydrohalogenated (no halogen is present).

4 Also recall that alkanes are quite unreactive and only react with halogens and undergo combustion.

5 Putting these facts together, conclude that no reaction would occur between these materials.

6   Write "no reaction" as your answer.

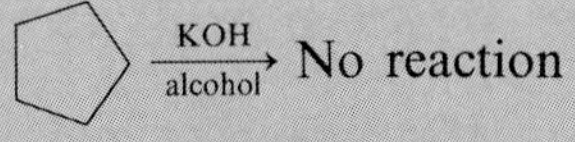

$$\bigcirc \xrightarrow[\text{alcohol}]{\text{KOH}} \text{No reaction}$$

Worked example

Write the products of the following reaction:

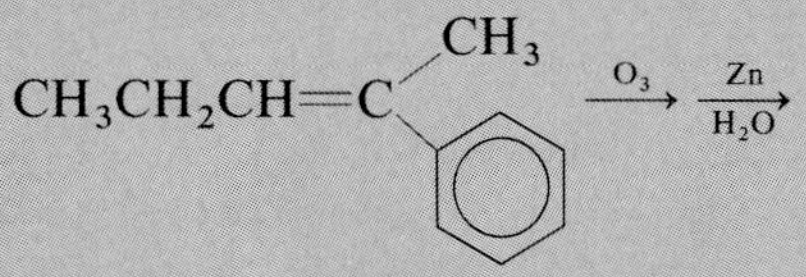

$$\text{CH}_3\text{CH}_2\text{CH}=\text{C}\underset{\bigcirc}{\overset{\text{CH}_3}{<}} \xrightarrow{\text{O}_3} \xrightarrow[\text{H}_2\text{O}]{\text{Zn}}$$

1   Identify the starting material as an alkene.

2   Recall that treatment of an alkene molecule with O_3 followed by Zn/H_2O will cleave (split) the alkene at the double bond and produce two molecules of an aldehyde or ketone type.

3   Rewrite the molecular structure in two parts by mentally splitting it at the double bond.

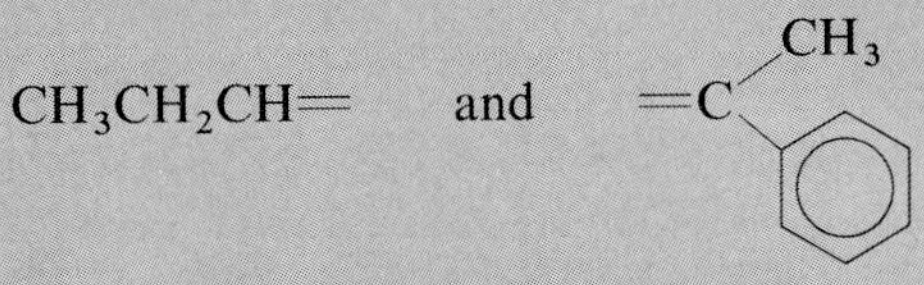

$$\text{CH}_3\text{CH}_2\text{CH}= \quad \text{and} \quad =\text{C}\underset{\bigcirc}{\overset{\text{CH}_3}{<}}$$

4   Write an oxygen atom at the points where splitting occurred in step 3.

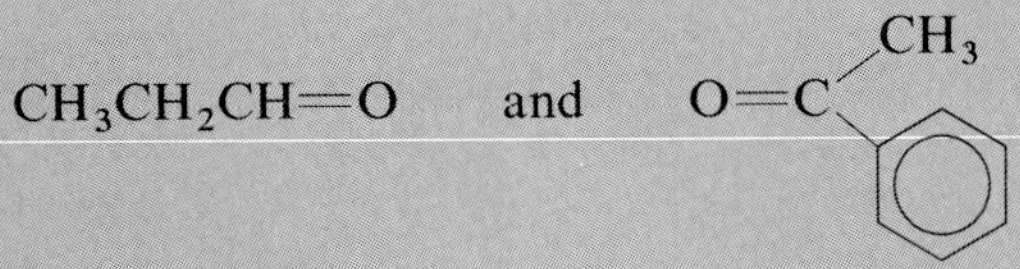

$$\text{CH}_3\text{CH}_2\text{CH}=\text{O} \quad \text{and} \quad \text{O}=\text{C}\underset{\bigcirc}{\overset{\text{CH}_3}{<}}$$

5   Write the whole equation.

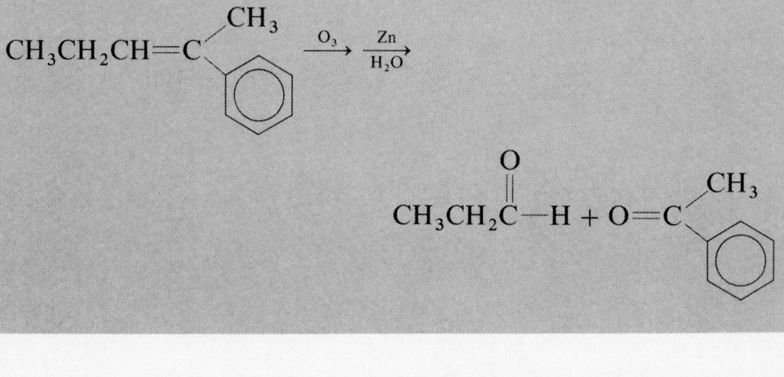

$$\text{CH}_3\text{CH}_2\text{CH}=\text{C}\underset{\bigcirc}{\overset{\text{CH}_3}{<}} \xrightarrow{\text{O}_3} \xrightarrow[\text{H}_2\text{O}]{\text{Zn}}$$

$$\text{CH}_3\text{CH}_2\overset{\overset{\text{O}}{\|}}{\text{C}}-\text{H} + \text{O}=\text{C}\underset{\bigcirc}{\overset{\text{CH}_3}{<}}$$

Problem

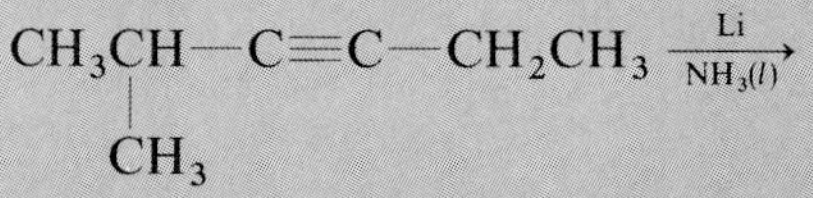

$$CH_3CH-C\equiv C-CH_2CH_3 \xrightarrow[NH_3(l)]{Li}$$

$$\quad\quad\quad | \quad\quad\quad\quad\quad\quad$$

$$\quad\quad CH_3$$

Determine the product of this reaction. **Note the steps in your reasoning** and write them down. Becoming aware of your thought processes (even simple steps in reasoning) and expressing them is a good way to develop skill in problem solving. After doing this, check your answer and compare with the method below.

Solution

1 Identify the starting material as an alkyne.

2 Remember that Li/NH$_3$ will convert alkynes into *trans* alkenes with the same carbon skeleton.

3 Write the product structure.

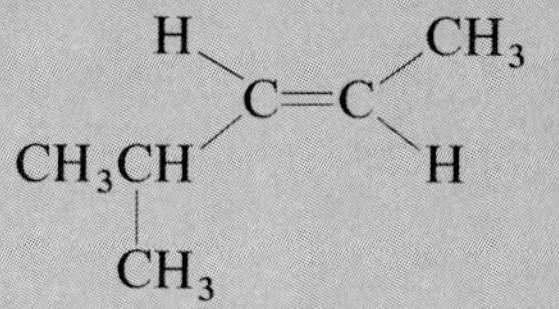

Problem

Determine the product of this reaction:

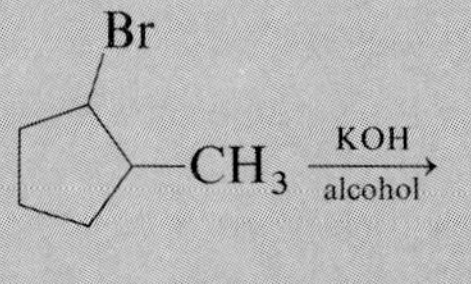

Solution

1 Identify the starting material as an alkyl halide.

2 Recall that KOH/alcohol removes a hydrogen atom and a halogen atom from adjacent carbon atoms to produce alkenes.

3 Also remember that if more than one alkene is possible, the most highly substituted one will be the major product.

4 Write all alkene products resulting from removal of all HBr pairs.

5 Choose the first one as the correct answer, since it is the more highly substituted.

Problem

Determine the products of this reaction:

$$CH_3CH_2CH=CH_2 \xrightarrow{CN^-}$$

Solution

1 Identify the starting material as an alkene.

2 Observe that nowhere have you learned that cyanide ion (CN^-) reacts with alkenes.

3 Write "no reaction."

Note You have to know your reactions well enough to be confident you have not seen this before. Of course, there are many organic reactions that do occur that are not covered in this text. You will not be asked any of those in this book, however, and the assumption that no reaction occurs is a valid one within the context of this course.

SUMMARY

1 **Alkenes** and **alkynes** are **unsaturated hydrocarbons** which contain **double** and **triple** carbon-carbon bonds, respectively. They are named by the same rules as alkanes, but in addition, the position of the double or triple bond is indicated along with the ending *ene* for alkenes or *yne* for alkynes. For alkenes, the geometry around the double bond is designated as *cis* or *trans*, or E or Z.

2 **Alkenes** are prepared from **alcohols** or **alkyl halides** by elimination of water or HX, respectively, or from **alkynes** by addition of two hydrogen atoms to the triple bond. **Alkynes** are generally prepared by removing two HX pairs from a **dihalide** by use of a strong base, or by reaction of the sodium salt of a terminal alkyne with an alkyl halide. Acetylene (ethyne) can be prepared from coal, limestone, and water; it is used for chemical synthesis and as a welding fuel.

3 Alkenes and alkynes react with various reagents which cause addition to the double or triple bonds. Thus, **alcohols**, **alkanes**, and **alkyl halides** can be produced from alkenes. Alkenes and alkanes can similarly be produced from alkynes. In addition to reactions for the preparation of other functional groups, alkenes undergo **cleavage** with ozone to produce aldehydes and/or ketones, which, when identified, allow us to deduce the structure of the alkene.

4 Many alkenes can be converted into high molecular weight **polymeric materials** with useful properties. These are formulated into structural materials, coatings, and medically useful products.

5 Certain simple **visual tests** have been developed which allow the chemist to quickly identify the functional group present in a compound. These include the **Baeyer test** for alkenes and alkynes, and the metal salt precipitate test for **terminal alkynes**.

KEY TERMS

Acetylene	Polyacrylonitrile	Polyvinylidine
Allylic position	(Orlon)	chloride
Anti addition	Polyethylene	Saturated
Baeyer test	Polymer	Syn addition
Cis alkene	Polymerization	Polytetrafluoroethene
Conjugated double	Polystyrene	(Teflon)
bonds	Polyvinyl chloride	Terminal alkyne
Dehydration	(PVC)	*Trans* alkene
E alkene	Poly(methyl	Unsaturated
Ethylene	methacrylate)	Z alkene
NBS	(Lucite)	
Ozonolysis		

SKILL PRACTICE PROBLEMS

1 Give **two** possible structures for each general formula given.
(a) C_3H_6 (b) C_6H_{10}
(c) C_4H_8 (d) C_6H_6

2 Give the hybridization of each carbon in the structures you drew for question 1.

3 Name each compound.

(a) —Br

(b) CH_3-CH_2
CH_3
$C=C$
Cl
Br

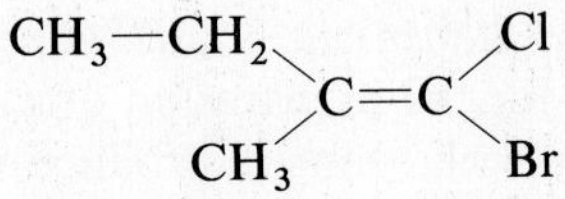

(c) CH_3-CH_2
H
$C=C$
$CH_2-CH_2-CH_3$
H

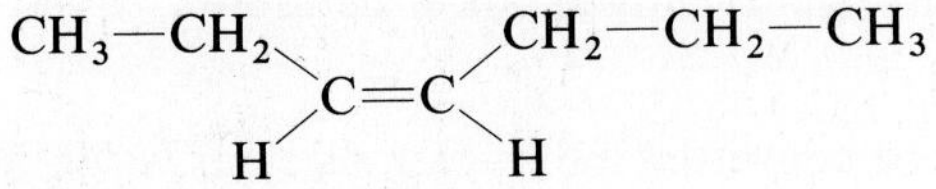

(d) $CH_3-CH_2-C{\equiv}C-H$

(e)

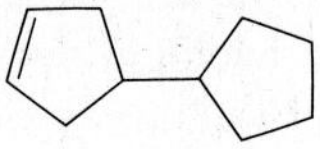

(f)
Cl
CH_3-CH
H
$C=C$
H
H

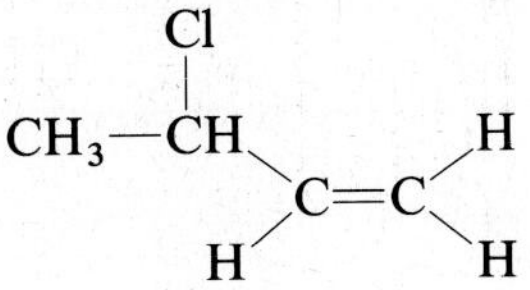

(g)
CH_3
$CH_3-C-C{\equiv}C-CH_3$
CH_3

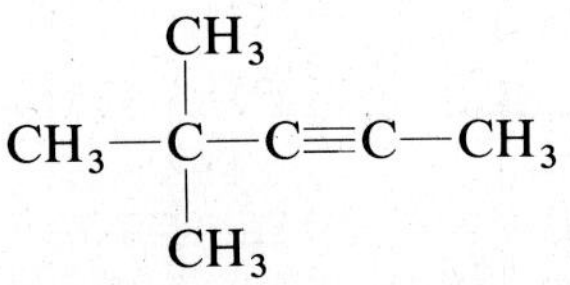

4 Draw the structures of each of the following:
   (a) *cis*-3-Hexene
   (b) 1-Hexyne
   (c) Methylisopropylacetylene
   (d) (Z)-2-chloro-3-iodo-2-pentene
   (e) *trans*-4-Decene
   (f) *trans*-3,4-Dimethylcyclohexene

5 Complete these reactions:

   (a) $+ H_2O \xrightarrow{\ H^+\ }$

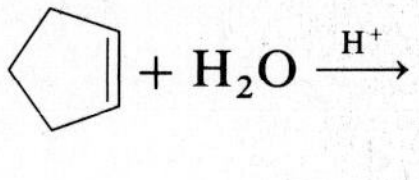

   (b)
   CH_3
   $CH_3-CH=C$
   CH_3
   $+ HI \xrightarrow{\text{peroxide}}$

   (c) $CH_3-CH_2-CH-CH_2 + 2NaNH_2 \longrightarrow$
   $\qquad\qquad\quad Br \quad\ Br$

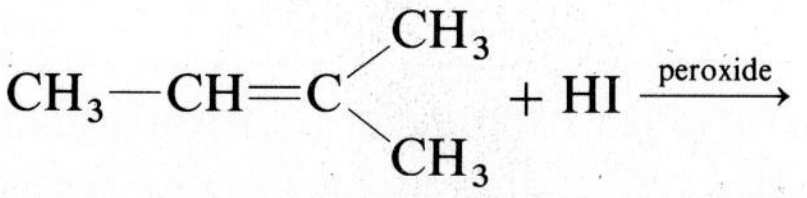

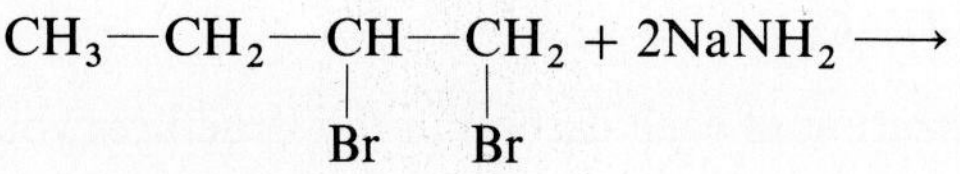

   (d)
   CH_3
   CH_3
   $\xrightarrow{O_3} \xrightarrow[H_2O]{Zn}$

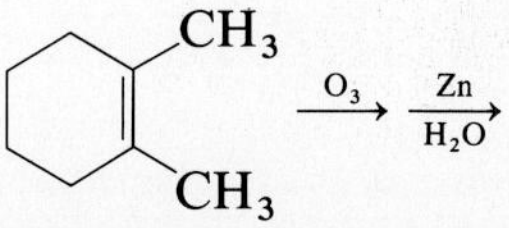

   (e) $CH_3-CH_2-CH_2-CH=CH_2 \xrightarrow[\text{peroxide}]{\text{NBS}}$

(*f*) [cyclopentyl]—C≡C—H $\xrightarrow{\text{NaNH}_2}$ $\xrightarrow{\text{CH}_3\text{I}}$

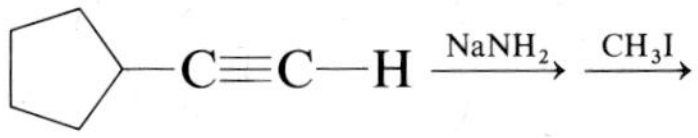

6 Give the organic products of the following reactions:

(*a*) [cyclopentenyl]—CH$_2$—CH$_3$ + HBr $\longrightarrow$

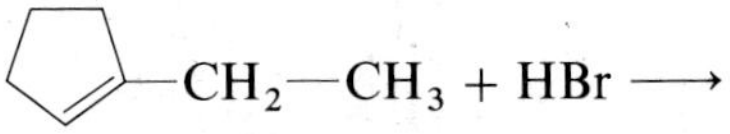

(*b*) CH$_3$—[cyclopentenyl]—CH$_2$—CH$_3$ + HBr $\xrightarrow{\text{peroxide}}$

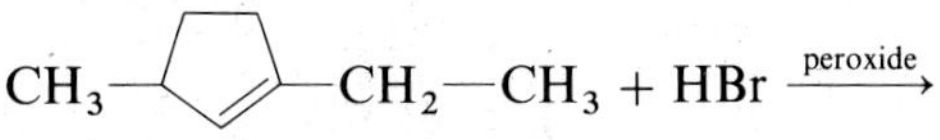

(*c*) CH$_3$—CH=CH—CH$_3$ $\xrightarrow{\text{O}_3}$ $\xrightarrow[\text{H}_2\text{O}]{\text{Zn}}$

(*d*) CH$_3$—C≡C—CH$_2$—CH$_3$ + 2H$_2$ $\xrightarrow{\text{Pt}}$

(*e*) CH$_3$—C≡C—CH$_2$—CH$_3$ + H$_2$ $\xrightarrow[\substack{\text{BaSO}_4 \\ \text{quinoline}}]{\text{Pd}}$

(*f*)

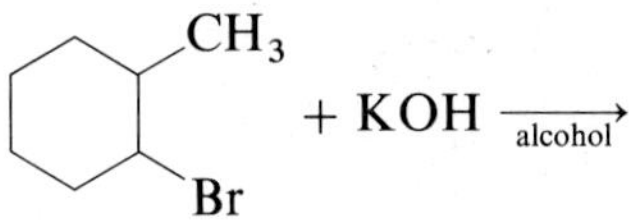

[cyclohexane with CH$_3$ and Br] + KOH $\xrightarrow{\text{alcohol}}$

(*g*) [cyclohexene] + NBS $\xrightarrow[\Delta]{\text{peroxide}}$

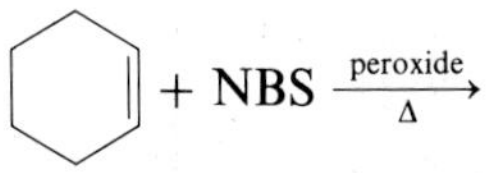

7 Suggest a series of reactions that would allow a chemist to use ace-tylene and ethane to produce butane.

8 If the following materials are obtained upon ozonolysis of unknown alkenes, what must the original alkene structure have been?

(*a*) CH$_3$—C(=O)—CH$_3$ and CH$_3$—CH$_2$—C(=O)—H

(*b*) [phenyl]—CH$_2$—C(=O)—H and CH$_3$—CH$_2$—C(=O)—CH$_2$—CH$_3$

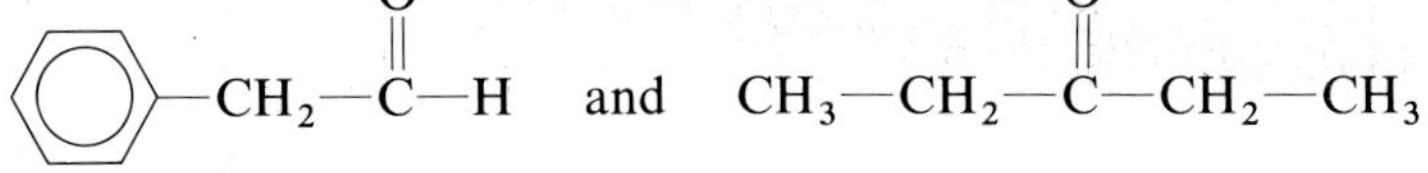

(*c*) 2 H—C(=O)—CH$_2$—C(=O)—H

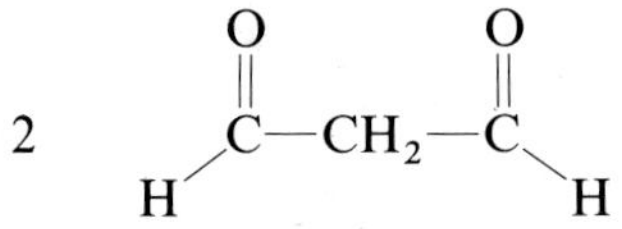

9 Give the structure of the polymer that would result from each of the following monomers. Suggest a name for each polymer.

(*a*) H$_2$C=CH—CH(Cl)—[phenyl] $\longrightarrow$

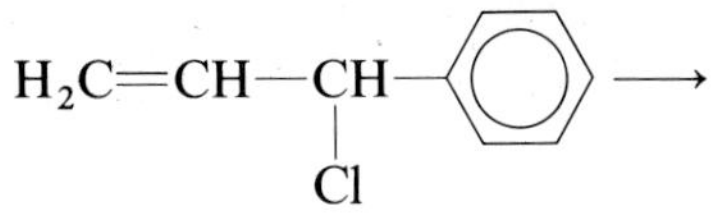

(b) $H_2C=CH-CH_3 \longrightarrow$

10 Imagine you are a chemist for a large company and must design a method of converting cyclohexane to *cis*-1,2-dihydroxycyclohexane (*cis*-1,2-cyclohexanediol). How would you propose to do it?

11 A certain compound (A) was found to react with two moles of H_2 in the presence of Pt to give compound B. When compound A was reacted with one mole of H_2/Pd $BaSO_4$, quinoline, compound C was produced. When compound C was reacted with O_3 followed by H_2O/Zn, the following two materials were produced:

$$CH_3-CH_2-\overset{\overset{\displaystyle O}{\|}}{C}-H \quad \text{and} \quad \overset{\bigcirc}{}-CH_2-\overset{\overset{\displaystyle O}{\|}}{C}-H$$

What are compounds A, B, and C? Show all the reactions.

12 Show reactions for simple tests (those involving visual changes) that would allow one to distinguish between each of the following pairs:

(a) ⬡ and ⬡

(b) $CH_3-C\equiv C-CH_3$ and $CH_3-CH_2-C\equiv C-H$
(c) $CH_3-CH_2-C\equiv C-H$ and $CH_3-CH_2-CH=CH_2$

13 Draw all isomers of C_4H_8. Include geometric as well as positional and structural isomers. Name each.

14 Repeat question 13 for C_4H_6.

15 Show the product of the following reagents reacting with 1-butene.
(a) $KMnO_4$ (b) HBr/peroxide
(c) O_3 followed by Zn/H_2O (d) H_2O/H^+
(e) H_2/Pt

16 Beginning with *cis*-2-butene, show how you would prepare each of the compounds below. (What reagents would you use to bring about the change indicated?)
(a) 2-Bromobutane   (b) *cis*-1-Bromo-2-butene
(c) 2-Butyne   (d) Butane

17 Observe the materials in the room or building you now occupy. Are any of them composed of polymers? If so, can you identify them and write their structures?

18 Draw the structures of polystyrene and polytetrafluoroethene (Teflon).

19 What reagent(s) would be used to accomplish the following changes in molecular structure?

(a) $CH_3-CH-CH_2-CH_3 \xrightarrow{?} CH_3-CH=CH-CH_3$
        |
        Br

(b)

$CH_3-CH=CH-CH_3 \xrightarrow{?} 2CH_3-\overset{\overset{O}{\|}}{C}-H$

(c) CH_3 CH_3
           | |
$CH_3-C=CH-CH_3 \xrightarrow{?} CH_3-C-CH_2-CH_3$
                                     |
                                     Br

(d) CH_3 CH_3
           | |
$CH_3-C=CH-CH_3 \xrightarrow{?} CH_3-CH-CH-CH_3$
                                     |
                                     Br

(e) $\xrightarrow{?}$

(f) $\xrightarrow{?}$ OH
                                           OH

REVIEW QUESTIONS

20 Identify the functional groups in each compound below.

(a)   (b)
$CH_3-\overset{\overset{O}{\|}}{C}-N\overset{\diagup CH_3}{\diagdown CH_3}$ $H-\overset{\overset{O}{\|}}{C}-\square$

(c) $HOOC-CH_2-COOH$ (d) $\langle\bigcirc\rangle-NH_2$

21 What is the (R)/(S) designation of the following compounds?

(a) $CH=CH_2$ (b) H
           | |
$CH_3-\overset{}{C}-Cl$ $HO-CH_2-\overset{}{C}-C\equiv C-H$
           | |
           CH_2 CH_2
           | |
           CH_3 CH_2-CH_3

22 Draw the Lewis dot representation for the following:
(a) *cis*-2-butene   (b) 2-butyne

23 Write the balanced chemical equation for the combustion of 1,3-dimethylcyclohexane (see Chapter 3).

CHAPTER 7

ALCOHOLS AND ETHERS

LEARNING GOALS

1 To understand how physical properties of compounds are related to molecular structure

2 To learn the nomenclature systems used for alcohols and ethers

3 To learn the standard methods of preparing alcohols and ethers and to learn the reactions they undergo

4 To gain a perspective on the alcoholic beverage industry

In several of the preceding chapters we encountered alcohols as starting materials for the preparation of other functional groups, such as alkyl halides and alkenes, or as the product of a change in another functional group, such as the conversion of certain alkyl halides into alcohols with OH^- ion. In this chapter we will take a detailed and systematic look at this important class of compounds. Alcohols contain the —OH (hydroxyl) group attached covalently to an sp^3 hybridized carbon atom.

PHYSICAL PROPERTIES

Most alcohols are liquids at ordinary temperatures and have unusually high boiling and melting points for their molecular weights. They are also more soluble in water than are alkanes, alkenes, alkynes, and alkyl halides. The **polar nature** of the OH functional group helps determine the interesting physical properties of alcohols.

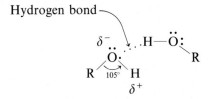

The C—O and O—H bonds are both polar, and the angular shape of the alcohol functional group causes a net dipole of considerable magnitude. **Hydrogen bonding** also occurs **between** alcohol molecules; it helps

FIGURE 7-1

Ball-and-stick molecular model of ethyl alcohol (C_2H_6O).

to explain the high boiling points and water solubility exhibited by alcohols.

As you may remember from a general chemistry course, *hydrogen bonding* is the term used for the intermolecular bonds that form between hydrogen atoms bonded to the N, O, or F atoms in one molecule and an N, O, or F atom in another molecule (or another part of the same molecule). See the diagram above. While hydrogen bonds are much weaker than covalent bonds, hydrogen bonds are stronger than the other two types of intermolecular forces—dipole-dipole attraction and London forces. Because hydrogen bonding is relatively strong, it, along with the dipole-dipole attractions, holds the alcohol molecules together rather strongly. This means that a higher temperature (more energy) is needed to vaporize an alcohol than would be required for a compound with similar molecular weight that could not participate in hydrogen bonding.

Since hydrogen bonding can also occur between an alcohol molecule and water molecules, alcohols with three or fewer carbon atoms are completely soluble in water, and those with four to six carbon atoms are somewhat soluble in water. Table 7-1 gives some comparative data for alcohols. Note that alcohols are more soluble in water and have higher boiling points than alkanes or ethers with about the same molecular weight (see Chapter 2, page 54 for a description of the ether functional group). Neither alkanes nor ethers can form hydrogen bonds; alkanes are nonpolar while ethers are only slightly polar.

For those molecules with a molecular weight of about 45, for example,

TABLE 7-1

COMPOUND	MOLECULAR WEIGHT, amu	BOILING POINT, °C	SOLUBILITY IN WATER,*g/L	SOME PHYSICAL PROPERTIES OF ALCOHOLS, ETHERS, AND ALKANES
CH_3CH_3	30	−89	0.06	
CH_3-OH	32	65	∞	
$CH_3CH_2CH_3$	44	−42	0.13	
CH_3-O-CH_3	46	−23	77	
CH_3-CH_2-OH	46	78	∞	
$CH_3CH_2CH_2CH_3$	58	−0.5	0.4	
$CH_3-O-CH_2CH_3$	60	8	——	
$CH_3CH_2CH_2-OH$	60	97	∞	
$CH_3CH_2CH_2CH_2CH_3$	72	36	0.36	
$CH_3CH_2-O-CH_2CH_3$	74	35	75	
$CH_3CH_2CH_2CH_2-OH$	74	118	79	

* Solubilities are in grams per liter, in water at about room temperature.

the alcohol boils at 78°C, the ether at −23°C, and the alkane at −42°C. This indicates that the intermolecular forces decrease in the order alcohols > ethers > alkanes. Note also that there is a relationship between the molecular weights of alcohols and their boiling points—the higher molecular weight alcohols have higher boiling points. In contrast, the water solubility decreases as a function of molecular weight. Both of these trends are commonly observed in other functional group classes as well.

The water solubility trend can be explained by the fact that as the molecular weights increase, the nonpolar alkyl portion of the molecule increases in size. This reduces the relative influence of the hydroxyl group, and the water solubility of the alcohol is reduced.

In general, as molecular weights of organic compounds increase, the boiling points increase and the water solubilities decrease. Hydrogen bonding and the polarity of the OH functional group impart unusually high boiling points and water solubilities to members of the alcohol class.

NOMENCLATURE

The IUPAC systematic name for an alcohol includes a base name indicating the longest carbon chain containing the —OH group, the ending -*ol*, names and positions of any substituents, and the position of the alcohol group. Thus the IUPAC name is made up as follows:

$$
\boxed{\begin{array}{c}\text{Position and name}\\\text{of substituent (s)}\end{array}} + \boxed{\begin{array}{c}\text{position of OH}\\\text{group}\end{array}} + \boxed{\text{base name}} + \boxed{\text{ol}}
$$

For example

$$CH_3—CH_2—OH$$

Ethanol

| Two carbon atoms | Suffix denoting an alcohol |

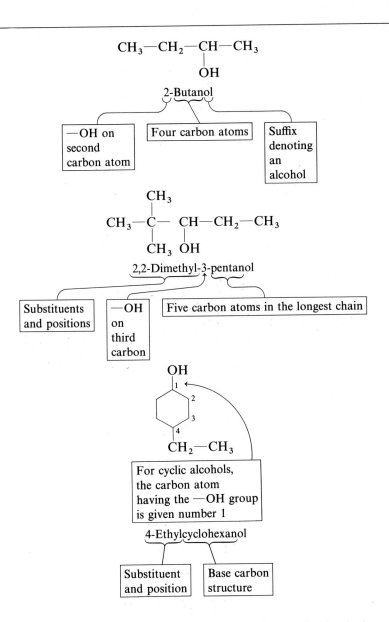

The **classical system** for naming simple alcohols uses the classical name for the alkyl group (see Chapter 3 for a list of these) followed by the term *alcohol* as a separate word.

The classical name is

$$\boxed{\text{Alkyl group name}} + \boxed{\text{alcohol}}$$

Examples of names in the classical system and the IUPAC system follow. IUPAC names are given in parentheses.

ALCOHOL	NAME
CH_3—OH	Methyl alcohol (methanol)
CH_3—CH_2—OH	Ethyl alcohol (ethanol)
CH_2—CH—CH_3 OH	Isopropyl alcohol (2-propanol)
CH_3—C—CH_3 with CH_3 above and OH below	*tert*-Butyl alcohol (2-methyl-2-propanol)
CH_3— (cyclopentane ring) —OH	3-Methylcyclopentyl alcohol (3-methylcyclopentanol)

    The first two members of the alcohol class, because of their commercial importance, are also sometimes referred to by **common names**. Names for these substances are as follows:

CH_3—CH_2—OH:
  Ethanol (IUPAC)
  Ethyl alcohol (classical)
  Grain alcohol (common)
  Proprietary solvent (common)

CH_2OH:
  Methanol (IUPAC)
  Methyl alcohol (classical)
  Wood alcohol (common)
  Carbinol (common)

    For those alcohols with several OH groups, the position of each OH, along with prefixes indicating the number of these groups, must be given. For example

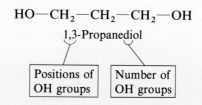

$$HO—CH_2—CH_2—CH_2—OH$$
1,3-Propanediol

| Positions of OH groups | Number of OH groups |

HO$\overset{6}{\underset{5}{\bigcirc}}$OH

$$\text{1,3,5-Cyclohexanetriol}$$

Positions of OH groups	Number of OH groups

Alcohols are named in the IUPAC system by indicating the longest carbon chain containing the OH group and the position of the OH group. Names and positions of any substituents are given and the ending *-ol* is used. The classical names of alcohols include the classical name of the alkyl portion of the molecule plus the word *alcohol*. Common names such as grain (ethyl) alcohol and wood (methyl) alcohol are used colloquially and in commerce.

FAMILIAR MATERIALS CONTAINING THE ALCOHOL GROUP

A number of useful or commonly encountered substances contain the alcohol functional group. Several of these are shown below.

$$CH_3-\underset{\underset{CH_3}{|}}{C}=CH-CH_2-CH_2-C=CH-\boxed{CH_2-OH}$$
$$\underset{CH_3}{|}$$

Geraniol
(rose oil)

Epinephrine[1]

FIGURE 7-2

Commercial product containing menthol.

---

[1] The two —OH groups attached directly to a carbon of the aromatic ring are phenol —OH groups, not alcohol —OH groups, because they are attached to an aromatic ring (sp^2 rather than sp^3 carbon atoms). This changes their behavior.

$$CH_3$$

Menthol
(gives the "cool" feeling of
lotions and cough drops)

$$CH_3-C$$

Terpin hydrate
(expectorant–anticough medication)

Cholesterol
(component of cell membranes)

$$HO-CH_2-CH_2-OH$$

1,2-Ethanediol
(ethylene glycol, antifreeze)

$$CH_2-CH-CH_2$$
$$OH \quad OH \quad OH$$

1,2,3-Propanetriol
(glycerin or glycerol, softening
agent in skin lotions)

BEVERAGE INDUSTRY—ETHYL ALCOHOL

The alcohol in alcoholic beverages is ethyl alcohol (ethanol or grain alcohol). Ethanol is the most commonly used nonmedicinal drug in our culture; it is less toxic than methanol or the propanols. Methanol can cause blindness when as little as 10 milliliters (mL) is ingested and is lethal at a dosage of 100 mL (3 ounces) or more. Isopropyl alcohol is also highly toxic.

Ethyl alcohol is produced for beverage purposes by enzymatic **fermentation** of starches or sugars from fruit or grain. The fermentation process is covered in more detail in Chapter 14.

$$(C_6H_{10}O_5)_n \xrightarrow{enzyme} C_6H_{12}O_6 \xrightarrow{enzyme} CH_3CH_2OH$$

Starch · Glucose · Ethyl alcohol

Because over 15% alcohol in the fermentation medium inactivates the enzymes which cause fermentation, once the alcohol content has reached this level, fermentation stops. In order to reach a higher concentration of ethanol, the mixture must be distilled. Ethyl alcohol boils at 78°C, while water (the other major volatile component of the fermentation mixture)

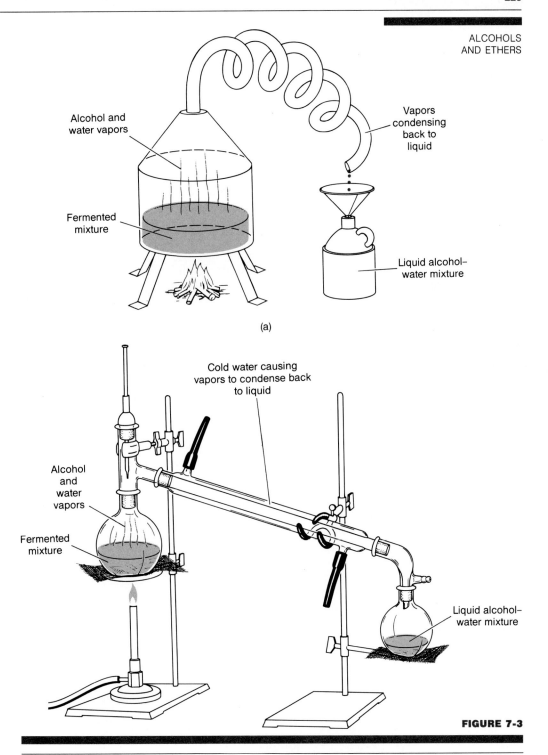

Alcohol and
water vapors

Vapors
condensing
back to
liquid

Fermented
mixture

Liquid alcohol–
water mixture

(a)

Cold water causing
vapors to condense back
to liquid

Alcohol
and
water
vapors

Fermented
mixture

Liquid alcohol–
water mixture

FIGURE 7-3

Two types of distillation apparatus used to produce
(a) crude ethyl alcohol and (b) laboratory ethyl alcohol.

boils at 100°C. When a solution containing ethanol and water is heated, however, a unique mixture consisting of 5% by volume water and 95% by volume ethanol distills. Such a constant-boiling/constant-composition mixture is called an **azeotropic mixture**. Thus, 95% ethanol is the purest ethanol mixture we can obtain from a fermentation broth by ordinary distillation.

Figure 7-3 shows the distillation of an alcoholic beverage, and Table 7-2 lists several common alcoholic beverages along with the source of starch or sugar and the percent alcohol. The term **proof** has been carried down from antiquity and is still used to designate alcohol content (see Table 7-2 for examples). In the United States, the proof value is twice the volume percent of alcohol:

$$\text{Proof} = 2 \times (\text{volume percent of ethanol})$$

The U.S. government places a heavy tax on alcoholic beverages, which greatly increases the cost of the beverage above production costs plus a reasonable profit. To render alcohol intended for industrial and laboratory use undrinkable, and thus to legally avoid paying the beverage tax, most commercial alcohol has small amounts of toxic, unpalatable materials added to it. Ethyl alcohol treated in this manner is called **denatured alcohol** or proprietary solvent. It may contain gasoline, methyl alcohol, acetone, or any one of about 100 denaturation mixtures approved for various purposes. These materials cannot be easily removed chemically or physically, and so the denatured material cannot be changed into drinkable alcohol at reasonable cost. Drinking denatured alcohol can cause blindness or death, especially if methyl alcohol is the denaturant.

Medically, ethyl alcohol is used as an antiseptic and hypnotic (soporific, sleep inducer). In general public use, it is used in beverages as a tension reliever, inhibition lowerer, and intoxicant. The dangers of drinking and

TABLE 7-2

COMMON ALCOHOLIC BEVERAGES	NAME	SOURCE OF STARCH	TREATMENT	PERCENT ALCOHOL	PROOF
	Beer	Barley	Fermented	5	10
	Wine	Grapes	Fermented	10–15	20–30
	Whiskey	Corn or other grain	Distilled	40–50	80–100
	Rum	Molasses	Distilled	40–50	80–100
	Vodka	Potatoes	Distilled	40–50	80–100
	Gin	Rye (flavored with juniper berries)	Distilled	40–50	80–100

driving and the methods used by police officers to detect this lethal practice are discussed in "Applied Organic Chemistry E" (see page 374). Figure 7-4 shows fermentation vats in a whiskey distillery.

Ethyl alcohol (ethanol) is produced for beverage purposes by fermentation. The alcohol concentration of a fermentation mixture can be increased by distilling an azeotropic mixture of alcohol and water (95:5 by volume). To render industrial ethanol undrinkable, denaturants are added.

PREPARATION OF ALCOHOLS

Commercial preparation

The preparation of the three most important commercial alcohols are shown below. The industrial preparations are frequently done in metal reaction vessels under conditions of high temperature and pressure which cannot be used in a laboratory setting. Later we will see that an acid catalyst is needed to cause water to react with an alkene in a glass laboratory vessel, but as shown by the second and third examples below, if pressure is used, the acid catalyst is not necessary.

$$CO + 2H_2 \xrightarrow[300° \text{ C, pressure}]{ZnO/Cr_2O_3} CH_3OH$$
Methanol

FIGURE 7-4

(*a*) Fermentation vats containing grain, yeast and water. (*b*) Alcohol being collected from a distillation device ("still"). (*Jim Beam Distillery*.)

$$CH_2{=}CH_2 + H_2O \xrightarrow[\text{pressure}]{\text{heat}} CH_3{-}CH_2{-}OH$$

Ethanol

$$CH_3{-}CH{=}CH_2 + H_2O \xrightarrow[\text{pressure}]{\text{heat}} CH_3{-}\underset{\underset{\displaystyle OH}{|}}{CH}{-}CH_3$$

2-Propanol
(isopropyl alcohol)

Prior to 1923, when German chemists developed the first process shown above, methyl alcohol was produced by heating wood in the absence of air—a process called **destructive distillation**. This process is the source of methyl alcohol's common name—wood alcohol.

$$\mathsf{\sim\!\!\!-(C_6H_{10}O_5)_x\!\!\sim} \xrightarrow{\Delta} CH_3OH + \text{tar} \xrightarrow[\text{distillation}]{\text{fractional}} CH_3OH$$

Hard wood   (90 percent pure)
(cellulose)

Preparation from alkyl halides

$$R{-}X + OH^- \longrightarrow R{-}OH + X^-$$

This reaction is discussed in Chapter 5 and is a way of changing alkyl halides into alcohols.

Reduction of aldehydes and ketones

$$\underset{\displaystyle C}{\overset{\displaystyle O}{\underset{\|}{}}}{-} \xrightarrow[\text{agents}]{\text{reducing}} -\underset{\underset{\displaystyle H}{|}}{\overset{\overset{\displaystyle OH}{|}}{C}}-$$

Aldehydes and ketones can be reduced to 1° and 2° alcohols, respectively, by using $NaBH_4$ (sodium borohydride), $LiAlH_4$ (lithium aluminum hydride), or catalytic hydrogenation. The finer points of the use of these reducing agents are given in Chapter 8, but the following examples illustrate their use.

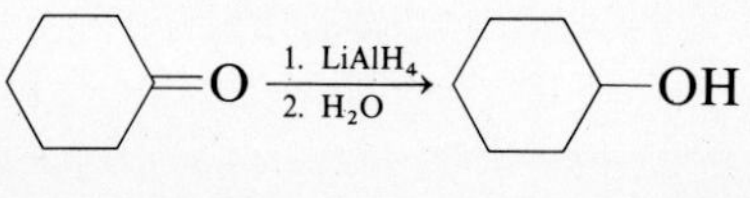

Note: The notation 1) $LiAlH_4$; 2) H_2O means that these two reagents are used **in sequence**.

$$CH_3—CH_2—\overset{\overset{\displaystyle O}{\|}}{C}—CH_3 \xrightarrow{\text{NaBH}_4} CH_3—CH_2—\overset{\overset{\displaystyle OH}{|}}{CH}—CH_3$$

$$CH_3—CH_2—\overset{\overset{\displaystyle O}{\|}}{C}—H \xrightarrow{\text{NaBH}_4} CH_3—CH_2—CH_2—OH$$

$$\bigcirc\!\!=\!\!O + H_2 \xrightarrow{\text{Pt}} \bigcirc\!\!-OH$$

Hydration of alkenes

$$R—\overset{|}{C}{=}C\diagup + H_2O \xrightarrow{\text{H}^+} R—\overset{|}{\underset{\underset{\displaystyle OH}{|}}{C}}—\overset{|}{\underset{\underset{\displaystyle H}{|}}{C}}—$$

This reaction involves the acid-catalyzed addition of water to alkenes by the following mechanism, which follows Markovnikov's rule (see page 191). The vinyl carbon atom with the greatest number of hydrogen atoms gets the new hydrogen atom; the other ends gets the —OH group.

$$CH_3—CH{=}CH_2 + H^+ \longrightarrow CH_3—\overset{+}{C}H—CH_3$$

$$H^+ + CH_3—\underset{\underset{\displaystyle H}{\diagup}}{\overset{|}{C}H}—CH_3 \longleftarrow CH_3—\underset{\underset{\displaystyle H\diagdown\overset{+}{O}\diagup H}{|}}{\overset{|}{C}H}—CH_3$$

For example

Fewest hydrogens

$$\begin{array}{c} \text{CH}_3 \\ \bigcirc \\ \text{H} \end{array} \xrightarrow[\text{H}^+]{\text{H}_2\text{O}} \begin{array}{c} \text{CH}_3 \\ \text{OH} \end{array}$$

Most hydrogens

Sometimes rearrangements will occur. The initially formed carbocation may rearrange if by doing so it becomes more stable. If the carbocation is originally 1°, it will, if possible, change to one that is 2° or 3° in nature. For this to occur, an H or R group must move.

$$CH_3-\underset{\underset{H}{|}}{\overset{\overset{CH_3}{|}}{C}}-CH=CH_2 \xrightarrow{H^+} CH_3-\underset{\underset{H}{|}}{\overset{\overset{CH_3}{|}}{C}}-\overset{+}{CH}-CH_3 \xrightarrow{\text{rearrangement}}$$

3-Methyl-1-butene

$\boxed{2° \text{ Carbocation}}$

$$CH_3-\underset{\overset{+}{}}{\overset{\overset{CH_3}{|}}{C}}-\underset{\underset{H}{|}}{CH}-CH_3$$

$\boxed{3° \text{ Carbocation} \atop \text{(more stable)}}$ $\Big\downarrow H_2O$

$$H^+ + CH_3-\underset{\underset{OH}{|}}{\overset{\overset{CH_3}{|}}{C}}-CH_2-CH_3 \longleftarrow CH_3-\underset{\underset{\overset{+}{O}}{|}}{\overset{\overset{CH_3}{|}}{C}}-CH_2-CH_3$$

2-Methyl-2-butanol $\overset{}{H} \quad \overset{}{H}$

Here the —OH appears on the 3° carbon atom and not on one of the carbon atoms originally part of the double bond.

Another set of reagents (mercuric acetate followed by sodium borohydride) can be used to add H_2O across a double bond **without rearrangements**. The overall effect is a Markovnikov orientation for the water addition. $Hg(OAc)_2$ represents mercuric acetate.

$$R-\overset{|}{C}=\overset{|}{C}\Big< \xrightarrow{Hg(OAc)_2} \xrightarrow{NaBH_4} R-\underset{\underset{OH}{|}}{\overset{|}{C}}-\underset{\underset{H}{|}}{\overset{|}{C}}-$$

Using this method on the starting material in the preceding example, the isomeric 3-methyl-2-butanol may be synthesized as shown by the following equation.

$$CH_3-\underset{\underset{H}{|}}{\overset{\overset{CH_3}{|}}{C}}-CH=CH_2 \xrightarrow{Hg(OAc)_2} \xrightarrow{NaBH_4} CH_3-\underset{\underset{H}{|}}{\overset{\overset{CH_3}{|}}{C}}-\underset{\underset{OH}{|}}{CH}-CH_3$$

In the interest of brevity, the mechanism of this reaction will not be given. Since the reaction is more difficult and the reagents are more expensive than is true for the H_2O/H^+ method, the mercuric acetate method is used only when a possible rearrangement is to be avoided.

It also is possible to accomplish the anti-Markovnikov addition of the elements of water indirectly by using a different set of reagents. Here we use diborane $(BH_3)_2$ followed by hydrogen peroxide and sodium hydroxide $(H_2O_2/NaOH)$. In this method, in the first reaction, boron and the hydrogen atoms of diborane add across the double bonds by Markovnikov's rule. The hydrogen atoms go to the carbon atom with the **least hydrogen atoms** since boron is less electronegative than is hydrogen. The replacement of the boron atom with an OH group by peroxide oxidation of the initially formed borane effectively adds H and OH across the original carbon-carbon double bond in an anti-Markovnikov fashion. No rearrangement occurs with these reagents because no carbocation intermediate is involved in the mechanism.

$$3R-\overset{|}{C}{=}C\overset{\diagup}{\diagdown} + (BH_3)_2 \longrightarrow \left(R-\overset{|}{\underset{H}{C}}-\overset{|}{C}\right)_3 B \xrightarrow{NaOH/H_2O_2}$$

Diborane   An organic borane

$$3R-\overset{|}{\underset{H}{C}}-\overset{|}{C}-OH$$

For example, it is possible to prepare 1-propanol using this method, while H_2O/H^+ would produce 2-propanol.

$$CH_3-CH=CH_2 \xrightarrow[\quad H^+ \quad]{H_2O} CH_3-\overset{|}{\underset{OH}{CH}}-CH_3$$

2-Propanol

$$CH_3-CH=CH_2 \xrightarrow{(BH_3)_2} \xrightarrow[H_2O_2]{NaOH} CH_3-CH_2-CH_2-OH$$

1-Propanol

Preparation from Grignard reagents

In the reactions we have seen so far, no change in carbon structure has been brought about. A way of producing **new carbon skeletons** and 1°, 2°, or 3° alcohols involves the reaction of a Grignard reagent (see Chapter 3; page 100) with aldehydes, ketones or esters.

The general reaction is

$$\overset{\delta^-}{O} \overset{\|}{\underset{\delta^+}{C}} + \boxed{R | MgX} \longrightarrow \left[\overset{O^- \ \overset{+}{MgX}}{\underset{R}{-\overset{|}{C}-}}\right] \xrightarrow{H^+} \overset{OH}{\underset{R}{-\overset{|}{C}-}}$$

Grignard reagent

The negative R group of the Grignard reagent adds to the positive carbon of the C=O, producing an intermediate magnesium salt. Acid hydrolysis of the magnesium salt produces an alcohol. The following examples show the versatility of this method. For simplicity, the intermediate is not shown. The oxygen atom of the carbonyl group becomes an OH, and the R group from the Grignard reagent attaches to the carbonyl carbon atom.

For primary (1°) alcohols

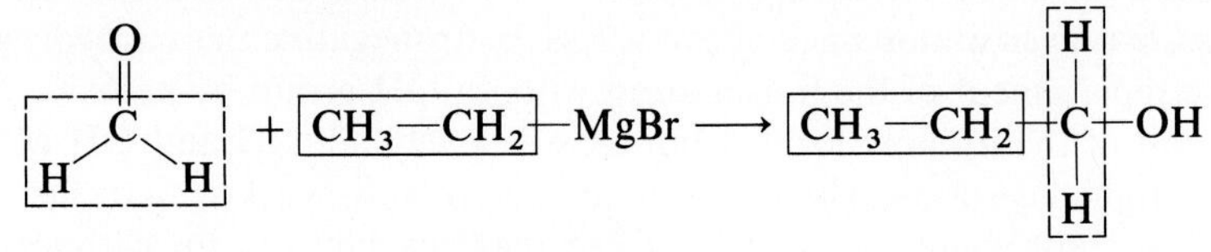

| Formaldehyde | Grignard reagent | A 1° alcohol |

For secondary (2°) alcohols

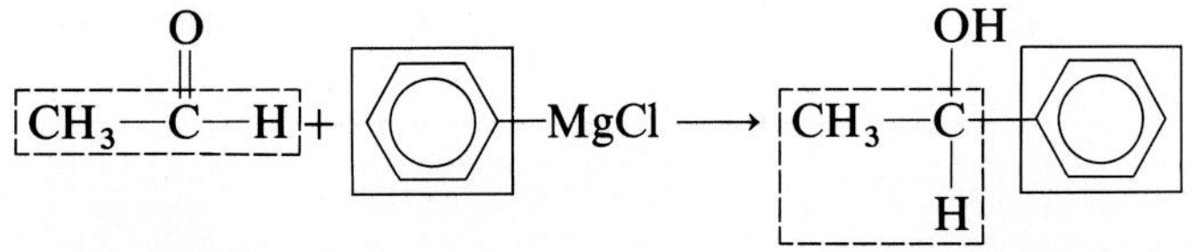

| An aldehyde other than formaldehyde | Grignard reagent | A 2° alcohol |

For tertiary (3°) alcohols

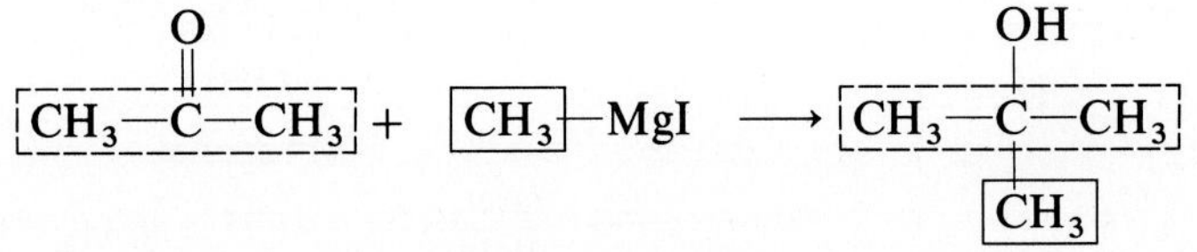

| A ketone | Grignard reagent | A 3° alcohol |

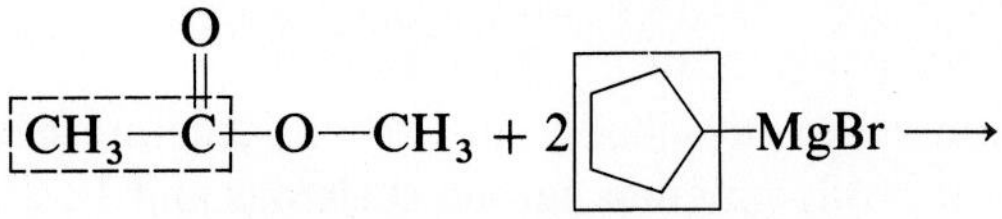

An ester   Grignard reagent

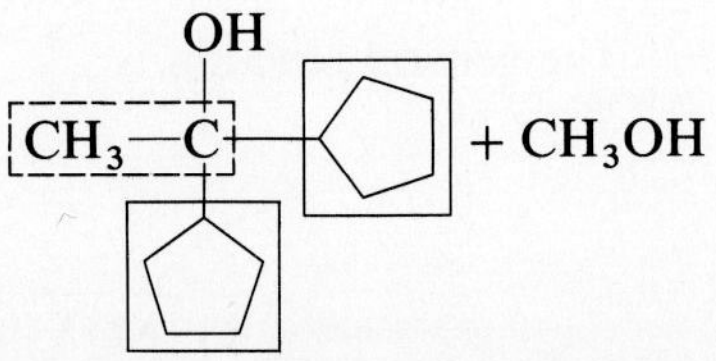

A 3° alcohol

As shown by the above equations, if we want to prepare a 1° alcohol, we treat formaldehyde with whatever Grignard reagent will give the particular alcohol desired. To prepare a secondary alcohol we use any combination of Grignard reagent and aldehyde (there may be more than one combination) that will give the correct carbon structure with the —OH in the right position. To prepare tertiary alcohols, we use either a ketone or an ester. When an ester is used, 2 moles of Grignard reagent are needed and we always get two of the Grignard reagent R groups in the 3° alcohol. The ketone approach allows all three groups to be different (or the same, if desired). The use of aldehydes and ketones to produce alcohols is discussed further in Chapter 8.

Ethyl and isopropyl alcohols can be prepared commercially by adding water across the double bond of alkenes under heat and pressure. Methyl alcohol is produced commercially by the catalyst-promoted reaction of carbon monoxide with hydrogen. In the laboratory, alcohols can be prepared by adding the elements of water across the double bond of alkenes using several different reagents, depending on the desired product. Alcohols can also be prepared from alkyl halides and by reducing aldehydes and ketones. Alcohols with larger carbon skeletons can be formed by the reaction of an appropriate Grignard reagent with an aldehyde, a ketone, or an ester.

REACTIONS OF ALCOHOLS

The reactions of alcohols fall into two categories; those that involve the breaking of the O—H bond, and those in which the C—O bond is broken. We will first discuss those which involve the breaking of the O—H bond.

Alkoxide formation

The hydrogen atom bonded to the oxygen atom in the OH functional group is **slightly acidic**. It is less acidic than the hydrogen atoms in water molecules. While it does not ionize when added to water, it can be "pulled off" as H^+, in the presence of a strong base, or reduced to H_2 by an active metal such as sodium.

$$R—OH \xrightarrow{\text{base}} R—O^- + \text{Base}—H$$
$$R—OH \xrightarrow{\text{Na}} R—O^-Na^+ + \tfrac{1}{2}H_2$$

For example

$$2CH_3-CH_2-OH + 2Na \longrightarrow 2CH_3-CH_2O^-Na^+ + H_2$$

$$CH_3-\underset{\underset{CH_3}{|}}{\overset{\overset{CH_3}{|}}{C}}-OH + KNH_2 \longrightarrow CH_3-\underset{\underset{CH_3}{|}}{\overset{\overset{CH_3}{|}}{C}}-O^-K^+ + NH_3$$

The resulting **alkoxide ions** are very reactive and are used as strong bases or nucleophiles. They are especially useful in the preparation of ethers in the Williamson synthesis (see pages 155 and 238).

Ester formation

Alcohols react with carboxylic acids in the presence of an inorganic, strong acid catalyst to form esters, when heated.

$$\underset{\text{Carboxylic acid}}{R-\overset{\overset{O}{\|}}{C}-OH} + \underset{\text{Alcohol}}{R'-OH} \xrightarrow[\Delta]{H^+} \underset{\text{Ester}}{R-\overset{\overset{O}{\|}}{C}-O-R'} + H_2O$$

The formation of esters is dealt with more fully in Chapter 12, but several examples are given below. The R′O— group of the alcohol replaces the —OH of the carboxylic acid.

$$CH_3-\overset{\overset{O}{\|}}{C}-OH + CH_3-CH_2-OH \xrightarrow[\Delta]{H^+}$$

$$CH_3-\overset{\overset{O}{\|}}{C}-O-CH_2-CH_3 + H_2O$$

$$\bigcirc\!\!\!-\overset{\overset{O}{\|}}{C}-OH + CH_3-OH \xrightarrow[\Delta]{H^+} \bigcirc\!\!\!-\overset{\overset{O}{\|}}{C}-O-CH_3 + H_2O$$

$$CH_3-CH_2-\overset{\overset{O}{\|}}{C}-OH + CH_3-\underset{\underset{H}{|}}{\overset{\overset{CH_3}{|}}{C}}-OH \xrightarrow[\Delta]{H^+}$$

$$CH_3-CH_2-\overset{\overset{O}{\|}}{C}-O-\underset{\underset{H}{|}}{\overset{\overset{CH_3}{|}}{C}}-CH_3 + H_2O$$

A common example of ester formation is the production of pear oil, which is used as flavoring in foods.

$$CH_3-\overset{\overset{\displaystyle O}{\|}}{C}-OH + HO-CH_2-CH_2-\underset{\underset{\displaystyle CH_3}{|}}{CH}-CH_3 \xrightarrow[\Delta]{H^+}$$

Acetic acid   3-Methyl-1-butanol
                    (isoamyl alcohol)

$$CH_3-\overset{\overset{\displaystyle O}{\|}}{C}-O-CH_2-CH_2-\underset{\underset{\displaystyle CH_3}{|}}{CH}-CH_3$$

Pear oil
(isoamyl acetate)

Oxidation

Alcohols can be changed into carboxylic acids, aldehydes, or ketones by appropriate oxidizing agents.

For an aldehyde

$$R-CH_2-OH \xrightarrow[\text{pyridine}]{CrO_3} R-\overset{\overset{\displaystyle O}{\|}}{C}-H$$

1° Alcohol   Aldehyde

This set of reagents is used in the solvent dichloromethane and is frequently abbreviated as CrO_3 2 pyr/CH_2Cl_2. Pyridine (pyr) is a heterocyclic aromatic compound with the following structure:

For a carboxylic acid

$$R-CH_2-OH \xrightarrow[\text{KMnO}_4]{\overset{K_2Cr_2O_7}{\text{or}}} R-\overset{\overset{\displaystyle O}{\|}}{C}-OH$$

1° Alcohol   Carboxylic acid

For a ketone

$$R-\underset{\underset{\displaystyle}{}}{\overset{\overset{\displaystyle OH}{|}}{CH}}-R \xrightarrow{[O]} R-\overset{\overset{\displaystyle O}{\|}}{C}-R$$

2° Alcohol   Ketone

Here, [O] represents any appropriate oxidizing agent.

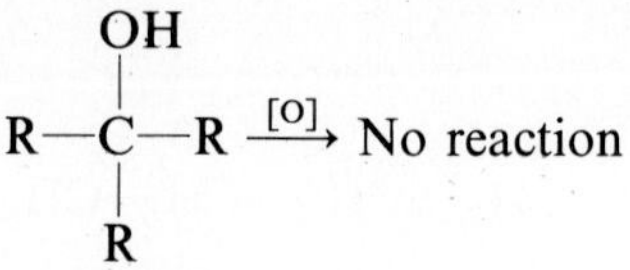

$$\underset{\underset{\displaystyle R}{|}}{\overset{\overset{\displaystyle OH}{|}}{R-C-R}} \xrightarrow{\text{[O]}} \text{No reaction}$$

3° Alcohol

For 1° alcohols, a mild oxidizing agent must be used if an aldehyde is desired. Chromium(VI) oxide (CrO_3) dissolved in pyridine and CH_2Cl_2 (an organic solvent) is a good reagent for this purpose. When a stronger oxidizing agent such as aqueous $K_2Cr_2O_7$ is used, a carboxylic acid is produced. Secondary alcohols can be converted to ketones by either reagent (among others, including $K_2Cr_2O_7/H_2SO_4$). Tertiary alcohols are not oxidized under normal conditions. Specific oxidizing reactions illustrating these general reactions are shown below. You should try to identify each aspect of the structures so that you can complete the reactions given at the end of the chapter. Ask yourself these questions: Is the starting alcohol 1°, 2°, or 3°? What functional group is produced?

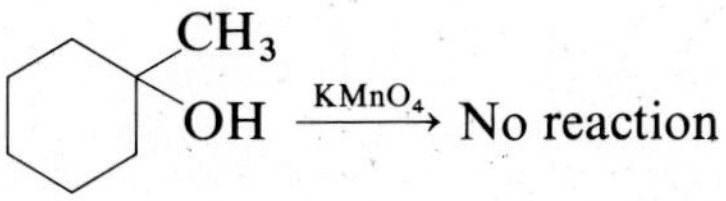

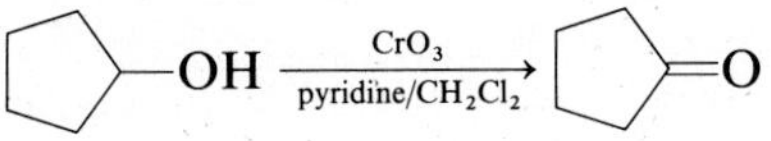

$$\text{(cyclohexane ring)}\underset{\displaystyle OH}{\overset{\displaystyle CH_3}{<}} \xrightarrow{\text{KMnO}_4} \text{No reaction}$$

$$\text{(cyclopentane ring)}-OH \xrightarrow[\text{pyridine/CH}_2\text{Cl}_2]{\text{CrO}_3} \text{(cyclopentanone)}=O$$

$$CH_3-CH_2OH \xrightarrow{\text{K}_2\text{Cr}_2\text{O}_7} CH_3-\overset{\overset{\displaystyle O}{\|}}{C}-OH$$

$$CH_3-CH_2-CH_2OH \xrightarrow[\text{pyridine/CH}_2\text{Cl}_2]{\text{CrO}_3} CH_3-CH_2-\overset{\overset{\displaystyle O}{\|}}{C}-H$$

Production of alkyl halides

We will now cover two reactions of alcohols that involve the breaking of the C—O bond. The —OH group can be replaced by a halogen atom by using one of several reagents. We covered this reaction of alcohols in Chapter 5, but we will review it here.

$$R-OH \xrightarrow[\text{or HX}]{\text{PX}_3} R-X$$

Examples of this reaction are as follows:

$$CH_3-CH_2-OH + PBr_3 \longrightarrow CH_3-CH_2-Br$$

$ZnCl_2$ dissolved in concentrated HCl is called the Lucas reagent.

Dehydration

As discussed in Chapter 6, alkenes can be produced by dehydration of alcohols. If there is more than one possibility, the most highly substituted alkene is produced in the highest yield (just as in dehydrohalogenation of alkyl halides—see page 163). Since this reaction follows a carbocation mechanism, rearrangement to produce a more stable carbocation may also occur. The general reaction is given here, followed by the mechanism and several examples. The mechanism of each example is shown so that the various possibilities in product structure can be considered.

The general mechanism is

Examples are as follows:

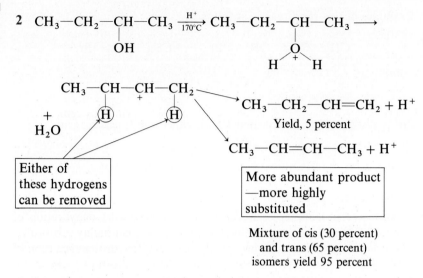

In studying such reactions, you should write out the mechanism in order to predict the products correctly. **Do not attempt to do this in your head when you are first learning this material**. After reaching the carbocation stage, ask yourself whether rearrangement can produce a more stable carbocation. In the reaction below, a 2° carbocation can be converted to a 3° carbocation by moving a hydrogen atom with its electron (this is called a **hydride ion shift**). After this rearrangement, ask yourself whether there is more than one location from which a hydrogen atom on an adjacent carbon atom can be removed. If so, draw the structures of both products and then choose the more stable one (more highly substituted) as the product. For example

$$CH_3—\underset{\underset{H}{|}}{\overset{\overset{CH}{|}}{C}}—\underset{\underset{OH}{|}}{CH}—CH_3 \xrightarrow{H^+} CH_3—\underset{\underset{H}{|}}{\overset{\overset{CH_3}{|}}{C}}—CH—CH_3$$

The thought process for this procedure is summarized in the following stepwise list:

1 **Protonate** the hydroxyl oxygen atom of the alcohol molecule.

2 Remove a water molecule and form a carbocation with the positive charge on the carbon atom which previously held the hydroxyl group.

3 Consider the possibility of **rearranging** the carbocation to produce a more stable species. If it can be done, write the structure of the more stable carbocation.

4 Write the structures of **all alkenes** that can be formed by removing an H^+ from all carbon atoms adjacent to the positive charge on the most stable carbocation written in step 3.

5 Write the structure of the **most highly substituted alkene** as the dominant product of the reaction.

Alcohols are subject to dehydration to form alkenes. Primary alcohols can be oxidized to aldehydes or carboxylic acids, depending upon the conditions, while secondary alcohols can be oxidized to ketones. Alcohols react with carboxylic acids to form esters and can have the hydroxyl hydrogen atom removed by a strong base or an alkali metal to form alkoxide ions. Alkyl halides can also be formed from alcohols by the use of PCl_3 or the Lucas reagent.

REACTION SUMMARY FLOW DIAGRAM FOR ALCOHOLS

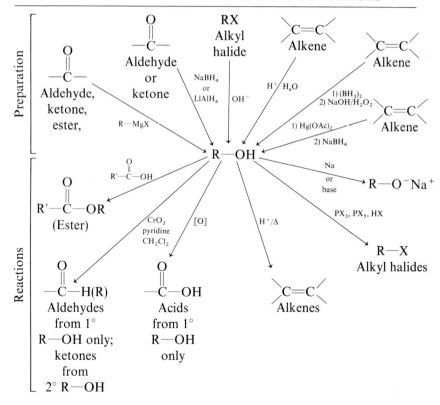

ETHERS

The ether functional group consists of an oxygen bonded to two alkyl or aromatic (aryl) groups.

$$R—O—R'$$

The alkyl groups may or may not be the same. As shown in Table 7-1, ethers are somewhat soluble in water, although usually only slightly so, and form a separate layer when they are mixed with water (see Figure 7-5). This is the physical basis for many separations carried out in the laboratory. When a mixture of two materials such as isopropyl alcohol and 1-chloropropane is added to such a system, the alcohol will dissolve primarily in the water layer and the alkyl halide, being less polar and having no hydrogen bonding ability, will dissolve in the ether layer. The two layers can then be separated by opening and closing the stopcock. Once the layers are separated, the alkyl halide and alcohol can be isolated by distillation.

Nomenclature

Ethers are named in the **classical system** by writing the names of the two alkyl groups followed by the word *ether*.

$$CH_3—CH_2—O—CH_3$$

Ethyl   Methyl

Methyl ethyl ether

$$CH_3—CH_2—O—CH_2—CH_3$$

Ethyl

Diethyl ether or ethyl ether

$$\text{Cyclohexyl}—O—CH_3$$

Cyclohexyl   Methyl

Methyl cyclohexyl ether

For more complex ethers, the same system is used as for substituted alkanes. The **alkoxy** group is treated as a substituent. The last example above could, thus, be called methoxycyclohexane. Another example follows:

Hexane

$$CH_3—CH_2—CH_2—CH_2—CH—CH_3$$
$$O—CH_2—CH_3$$

Ethoxy

2-Ethoxyhexane

Preparation of ethers

A good general method of forming ethers is the Williamson synthesis discussed in Chapter 5.

$$\text{R—OH} \xrightarrow{\text{Na}} \text{R—O}^- \xrightarrow{\text{R}'-\text{X}} \text{R—O—R}'$$

One of the R groups comes from an alcohol which has been changed into the nucleophilic alkoxide ion. The other R group is from an alkyl halide (preferably a 1° one). This reaction proceeds by an S_N2 mechanism (see Chapter 5). For example:

$$\text{CH}_3\text{—OH} \xrightarrow{\text{Na}} \text{CH}_3\text{—O}^- \xrightarrow{\text{CH}_3-\text{CH}_2-\text{CH}_2-\text{CH}_2-\text{Br}}$$
$$\text{CH}_3\text{—O—CH}_2\text{—CH}_2\text{—CH}_2\text{—CH}_3$$

Simple symmetrical ethers can be prepared by intermolecular (bimolecular) dehydration of certain 1° alcohols. For methyl alcohol

$$\text{CH}_3\text{—}\overline{\text{OH + H}}\text{O—CH}_3 \xrightarrow[\Delta]{\text{H}^+} \text{CH}_3\text{—O—CH}_3 + \text{H}_2\text{O}$$

For higher alcohols, internal dehydration to form alkenes usually happens preferentially, but sometimes the conditions can be adjusted to form ethers instead. For example

$$2\text{CH}_3\text{—CH}_2\text{—OH} \xrightarrow[\text{H}_2\text{SO}_4]{140°\text{C}} \text{CH}_3\text{—CH}_2\text{—O—CH}_2\text{—CH}_3$$

Reactions of ethers

Ethers are relatively **unreactive** and are frequently used as solvents. They are not easily converted to other functional groups by treatment with strong bases, reducing agents or most strong acids. They are flammable and will burn to produce CO_2 and water. They also react with two of the hydrogen halides (HBr and HI) to split into alkyl halides and alcohols. The alcohol is converted to an alkyl halide by additional hydrogen halide.

$$\text{R—O—R}' \xrightarrow{\text{HX}} \text{R—OH} + \text{R}'\text{—X}$$
$$\downarrow \text{HX}$$
$$\text{R—X} + \text{H}_2\text{O}$$

In other words, if 2 moles of HX are used for 1 mole of ether, the alcohol produced in the first step will be further changed to an alkyl halide. A specific example is the reaction of diethyl ether with hydrogen bromide.

$$CH_3-CH_2-O-CH_2-CH_3 \xrightarrow{\text{1HBr}}$$

$$\downarrow \text{2HBr} \qquad\qquad CH_3-CH_2-Br + CH_3-CH_2-OH$$

$$2CH_3-CH_2-Br + H_2O$$

Ethers are usually prepared by reacting a 1° alkyl halide with an alkoxide ion (Williamson ether synthesis) or by bimolecular dehydration of 1° alcohols. Ethers are generally unreactive, but are cleaved with HX.

REACTION SUMMARY FLOW DIAGRAM—ETHERS

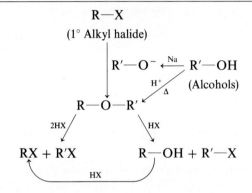

$$R-X$$
(1° Alkyl halide)

$$R'-O^- \xleftarrow{\text{Na}} R'-OH$$

$$\text{(Alcohols)}$$

$$R-O-R'$$

$$RX + R'X \qquad\qquad R-OH + R'-X$$

Commercially useful ethers

Diethyl ether and the cyclic ethers shown below are used as solvents in laboratory and industrial applications. Ethers, especially the low molecular weight ethers such as diethyl ether, are hazardous because they have a low flash point, burn violently, and sometimes form explosive peroxides when exposed to air.

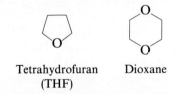

Tetrahydrofuran   Dioxane
(THF)

Diisopropyl ether has sometimes been used as a general anesthetic in the past, but it has been replaced by cyclopropane, sodium pentothol, and a number of safer and more effective anesthetics. The ether functional group is also found in eugenol—the essential component in oil of cloves. A nonionic polyether emulsifying agent commonly found in cosmetics is shown below. It is used to form creams from mixtures of water and oil, which are normally immiscible. The sex attractant for the gypsy moth is a cyclic ether (called an epoxide; see page 241).

$$CH_2\!=\!CH\!-\!CH_2\!-\!\text{⟨benzene ring⟩}\!-\!OH$$
$$O\!-\!CH_3$$

Eugenol

$$CH_3\!-\!(CH_2)_8\!-\!\text{⟨benzene ring⟩}\!-\!O\!-\!(CH_2\!-\!CH_2\!-\!O)_{\overline{x}}\,CH_2\!-\!CH_3$$

Long poly ether chain

Nonionic surfactant
(emulsifier)

$$\begin{array}{c} CH_3 \\ | \\ CH_3\!-\!O\!-\!C\!-\!CH_3 \\ | \\ CH_3 \end{array}$$

Methyl *tert*-butyl ether (MTBE)
(gasoline octane enhancer)

$$CH_3\!-\!CH\!-\!(CH_2)_4\!\overbrace{CH\!-\!CH}^{O}\!(CH_2)_4\!-\!CH_3$$
$$\underset{CH_3}{|}$$

Epoxide group

Gypsy moth
sex pheromone

FIGURE 7-6

The Gypsy moth whose
sex pheromone structure is
shown above. These
insects do severe damage
to trees in the northeastern
United States. Specimen
from the collection of the
University of Kentucky
Entomology Department.
(*Dr. Paul Freytag.*)

Another interesting type of ether is shown below. It is called 18-crown-6 ether. The term *crown* is used because the molecule, if viewed from the side, resembles a king's crown with the oxygen atoms forming the points. It is cyclic and has 18 atoms in the cycle, 6 of which are oxygens. It has the unique property of coordinating with potassium ions and making potassium salts soluble in alkanes or other nonpolar solvents in which they are normally not soluble. Thus, to oxidize cyclohexanol with $KMnO_4$, a small amount of 18-crown-6 ether can be added to solublize the $KMnO_4$ and facilitate the reaction.

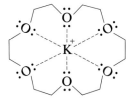

18-Crown-6
ether

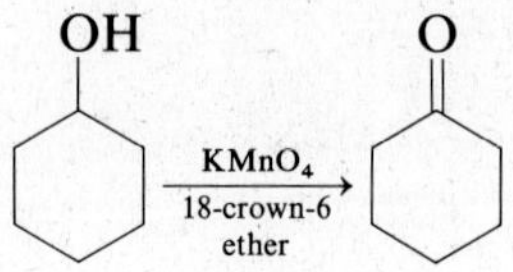

Epoxides

Three-membered cyclic ethers are called epoxides (or oxiranes) and are useful as intermediates in chemical synthesis. Epoxides are much more reactive than ordinary ethers because of the strained three-membered ring structure.

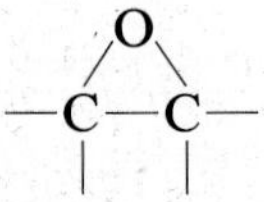

Epoxide group

Epoxides readily react with nucleophilic reagents which open the unstable ring. The following are examples:

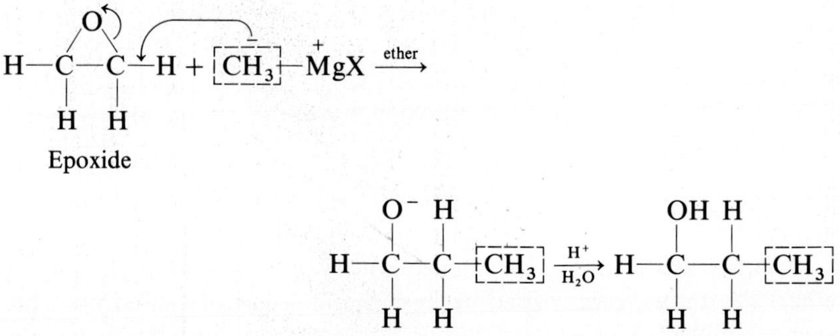

Epoxide

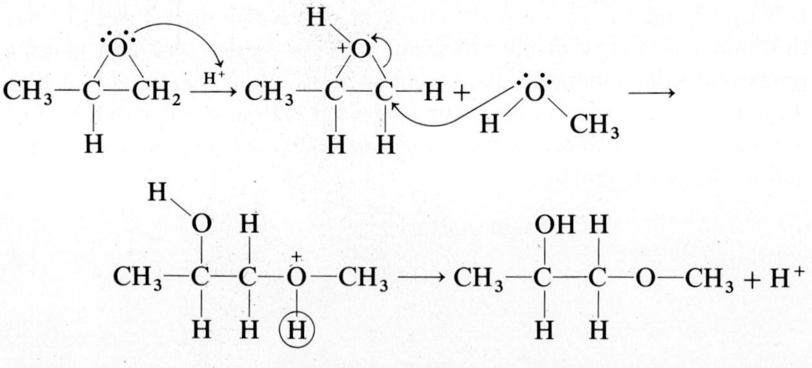

The most common consumer product involving epoxides is a strong, two-component glue. The following is the structure of the monomer component.

The polymerizing agent is 1,4-diaminocyclohexane (a nucleophile).

The following polymerization reaction occurs slowly when the two components (from two separate tubes) are mixed:

Hardened expoxide glue

SUMMARY

1   Physical properties of a substance are the result of its molecular structure. **Hydrogen bonding** and **polarity** both cause alcohols to have higher boiling points and water solubilities than do most compounds with similar molecular weights. In general, for compounds in all functional group classes, as molecular weight increases, boiling point increases and water solubility decreases.

2   **Alcohols** are **named** in the IUPAC system by designating the longest carbon chain containing the —OH group along with the names and positions of any substituents, giving the position of the —OH group, and adding the ending -ol. In the classical method of nomenclature, we use the name of the alkyl group attached to the —OH group, plus the word *alcohol*. Common names are also used for commercially important alcohols.

3   Ethyl alcohol is produced for beverage purposes by **fermentation** of various grains. The fermentation mixtures may be **distilled** to increase the alcohol content. The proof designation is a means of indicating the alcohol content of the beverage. Sometimes ethanol is deliberately **denatured** by

toxic or unpalatable materials to render it undrinkable and therefore nontaxable.

4   Several alcohols are **prepared** industrially by hydration of the appropriate alkene, while methyl alcohol is prepared by the catalytic reaction of CO and H_2. In the laboratory, alcohols are prepared by reduction of aldehydes and ketones, by hydration of alkenes, and by allowing Grignard reagents to react with aldehydes, ketones, and esters.

5   Alcohols can be changed into a number of other compounds including alkoxide salts, esters, aldehydes or ketones, carboxylic acids, alkenes, and alkyl halides.

6   **Ethers** are **named** by using the names of alkyl groups attached to the oxygen atom and adding the word *ether*; they are also named as alkoxy-substituted compounds.

7   Ethers are **prepared** by the Williamson ether synthesis, or, in a few cases, by the bimolecular dehydration of alcohols.

8   Ethers are notably **unreactive** except that they undergo cleavage to alkyl halides and alcohols when treated with HBr or HI.

9   **Epoxides** are three-membered cyclic ethers that are, unlike other ethers, reactive toward a number of reagents which open the epoxide ring. Epoxides are used commercially to prepare glue.

KEY TERMS

Alcohol	Epoxide	Oxidation
Alkoxide ion	Ester	Oxirane
Azeotrope	Fermentation	Rearrangement of
Carbinol	Grain alcohol	carbocations
Crown ether	Grignard reagent	Williamson synthesis
Denatured	Hydrogen bonding	Wood alcohol

SKILL PRACTICE PROBLEMS

1   What feature about the structure of ethers indicates that they do not form hydrogen bonds with other ether molecules?

2   Draw the structures of these compounds:

    (*a*) Menthol   (*b*) Isobutyl alcohol

    (*c*) Cyclohexyl alcohol   (*d*) 2,3-Dimethyl-4-octanol

    (*e*) Phenyl ethyl ether   (*f*) Di-tert-butyl ether

    (*g*) THF   (*h*) Cyclobutanol

    (*i*) 3-Methyl-3-chloro-2-pentanol   (*j*) Wood alcohol

3 Name each structure below.

(a) $HO-CH_2-CH_2-OH$ Give IUPAC and classical **names**.

(b)

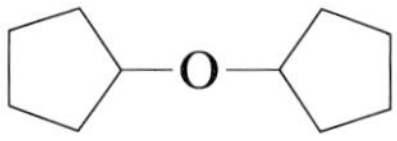

(c) $CH_3-CH_2-\underset{\underset{\displaystyle OH}{|}}{CH}-CH_3$ Give IUPAC and classical names.

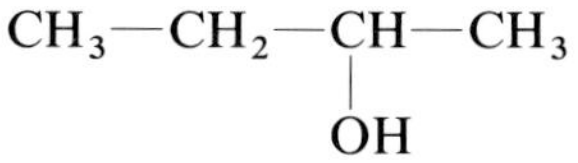

(d)

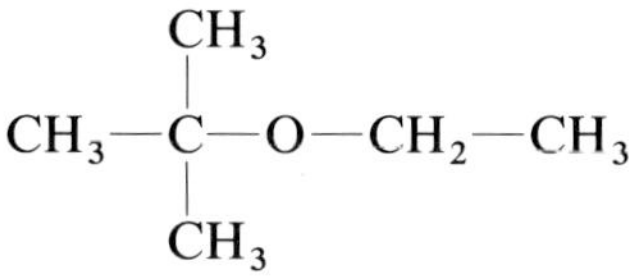

$$CH_3-\underset{\underset{\displaystyle CH_3}{|}}{\overset{\overset{\displaystyle CH_3}{|}}{C}}-O-CH_2-CH_3$$ Give IUPAC and classical names.

(e)

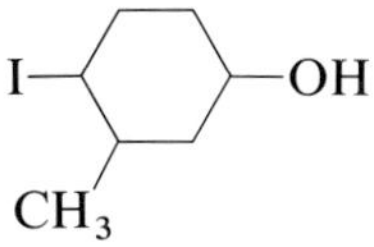

(f) $CH_3-CH_2-\underset{\underset{\displaystyle OH}{|}}{CH}-CH_2-CH_3$

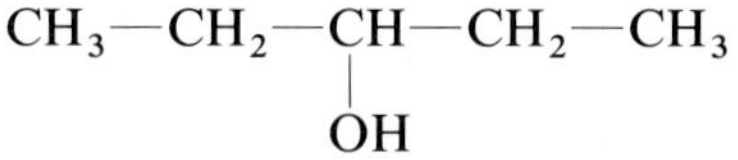

(g)

$$CH_3-CH_2-\underset{\underset{\displaystyle \triangle}{|}}{\overset{\overset{\displaystyle OH}{|}}{C}}-CH_3$$

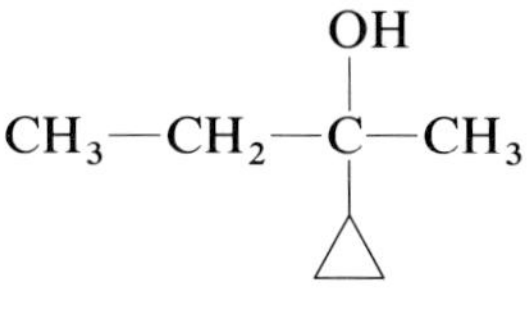

(h)

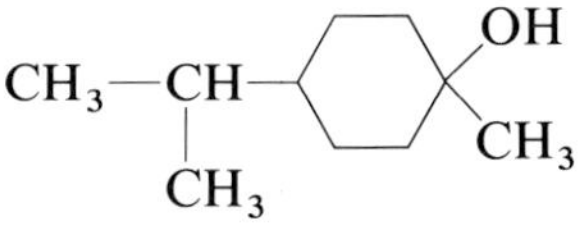

4 Complete these reactions.

(a)

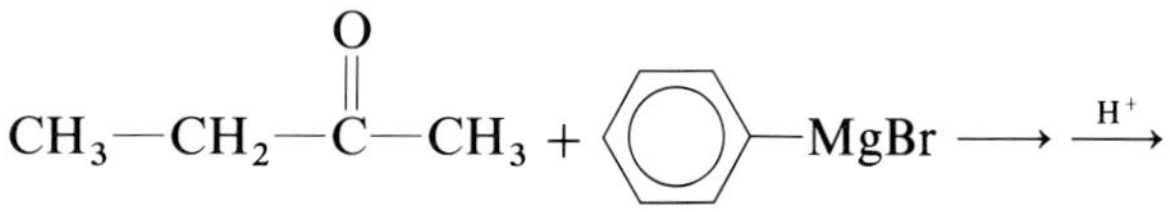

$$CH_3-CH_2-\overset{\overset{\displaystyle O}{||}}{C}-CH_3 + \text{⟨○⟩}-MgBr \longrightarrow \xrightarrow{H^+}$$

(b) $CO + 2H_2 \xrightarrow[\substack{300°C, \\ \text{pressure}}]{\text{ZnO, Cr}_2\text{O}_3}$

(c) $CH_3-O-CH_3 + 2HBr \longrightarrow$

(d) $CH_3-\underset{\underset{\displaystyle CH_3}{|}}{C}=CH-CH_3 + (BH_3)_2 \longrightarrow \xrightarrow{\text{NaOH/H}_2\text{O}_2}$

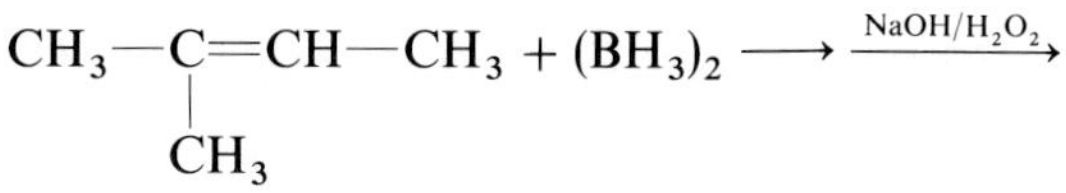

(e) $+ NaBH_4 \longrightarrow$

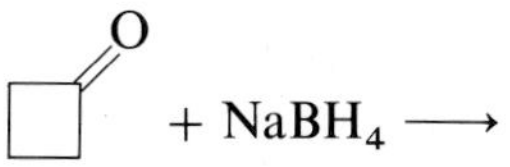

5 Complete these reactions.

(a) [cyclohexyl]—OH + PBr$_3$ $\longrightarrow$

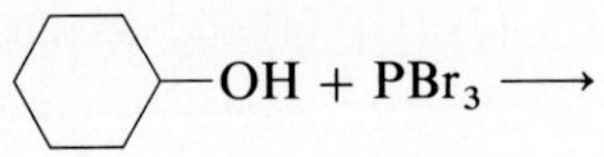

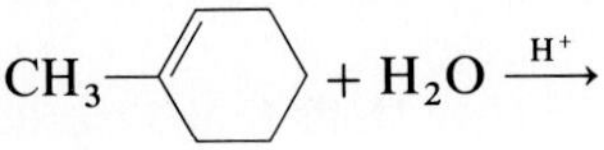

(b) CH$_3$—[cyclohexene] + H$_2$O $\xrightarrow{\text{H}^+}$

(c) CH$_3$—O—[cyclopentyl] + NaOH $\longrightarrow$

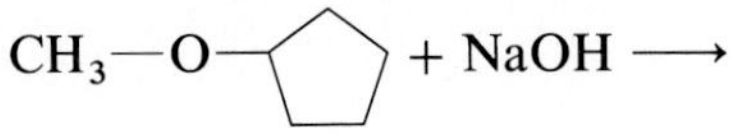

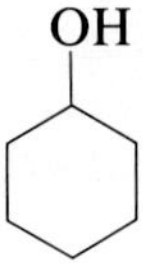

(d)

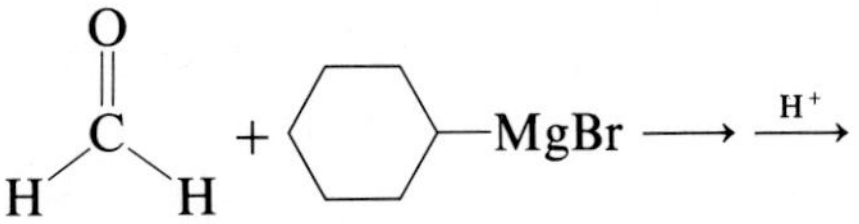

$$\underset{H}{\overset{O}{\underset{\|}{C}}}\underset{H}{}$$
+ [cyclohexyl]—MgBr $\longrightarrow$ $\xrightarrow{\text{H}^+}$

(e) CH$_3$—CH—CH$_3$ $\xrightarrow[\Delta]{\text{H}^+}$
        |
        OH

(f)

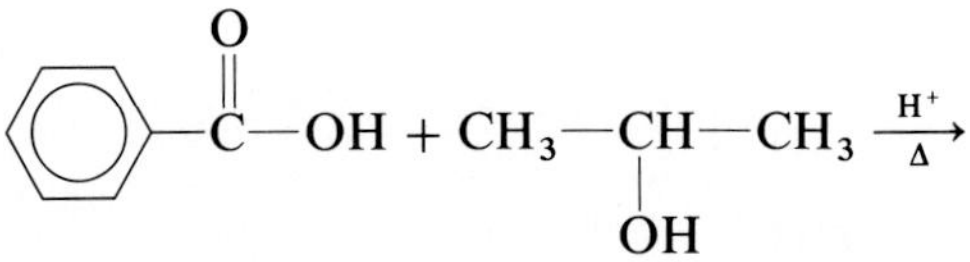

[benzene]—$\overset{O}{\overset{\|}{C}}$—OH + CH$_3$—CH—CH$_3$ $\xrightarrow[\Delta]{\text{H}^+}$
                                              |
                                              OH

6 Show how to prepare [cyclohexanol with OH] from [cyclohexene].

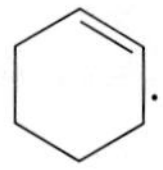

7 Show how to prepare CH$_3$—CH$_2$—O—$\overset{\overset{\displaystyle CH_3}{|}}{\underset{\underset{\displaystyle CH_3}{|}}{C}}$—CH$_3$ from CH$_3$—CH$_2$—OH and *tert*-butyl alcohol.

8 Design a synthesis for CH$_3$—CH$_2$—CH$_2$—OH from

CH$_3$—CH$_2$—Br and H—$\overset{O}{\overset{\|}{C}}$—H.

9 Design a synthesis for [cyclopentanone] from [cyclopentene].

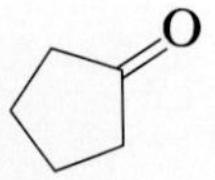

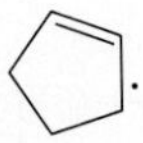

10 If an alcoholic beverage has 18% alcohol, what is its proof designation?

11 From what you learned in Chapter 3 about branching and physical properties, which would you expect would have a lower boiling point—*n*-butyl or *tert*-butyl alcohol?

12 Define the following terms.

(a) Alkoxide ion   (b) Williamson synthesis
(c) Denatured alcohol   (d) Dehydration
(e) Anti-Markovnikov orientation   (f) Epoxide
(g) Destructive distillation

13 From the six structures given below, choose one (or more) that fits the description given.

(a) The alcohol that can be oxidized to

(b) The compound that is not an alcohol
(c) The alcohol(s) that cannot be oxidized
(d) Cyclopentanol
(e) Primary alcohol(s)
(f) The alcohol that can be prepared from CH_3MgBr and formaldehyde
(g) Trimethylcarbinol (tert-butyl alcohol)
(h) Proprietary solvent
(i) The compound with the lowest boiling point
(j) The compound that can be prepared from a Grignard reagent and an ester

(1) ⬡—OH   (2) ⬠—OH

(3) CH_3CH_2OH (4) cyclohexane with CH_3 and OH

(5) $CH_3—\underset{\underset{CH_3}{|}}{\overset{\overset{OH}{|}}{C}}—CH_3$ (6) CH_3OH

14 Which of the following alcohols would produce the most stable carbocation after loss of water from the protonated alcohol?

⬡—OH   cyclohexane with OH and CH_3 $CH_3—\underset{\underset{OH}{|}}{CH}—CH_3$ $CH_3—CH_2—CH_2—OH$

15 Which of the choices in equation 14 would initially form a carbocation which would rearrange?

16 Which of the choices in question 14 would form the most highly substituted alkene upon acid catalyzed dehydration?

17 What carbohydrate source is used to produce vodka? What are the two basic steps involved in vodka production?

18 Draw the structure of 15-crown-5 ether.

REVIEW QUESTIONS

19 Name the following compound:

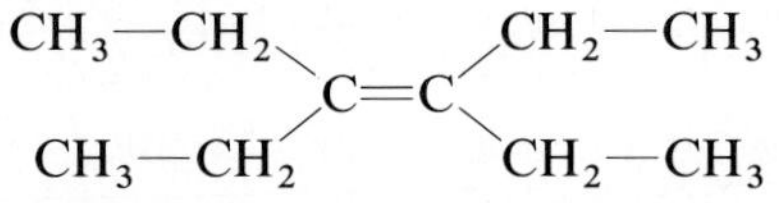

$$CH_3-CH_2 \searrow C=C \nearrow CH_2-CH_3$$
$$CH_3-CH_2 \nearrow \qquad \searrow CH_2-CH_3$$

20 Which of the following is the strongest nucleophile?

(a) $H_2\ddot{O}:$ (b) SH^-

(c) $CH_3\ddot{O}H$ (d) OH^-

21 Write the structure of the polymeric material used to make plastic wrap.

22 Write the steps in the mechanism of the following reaction:

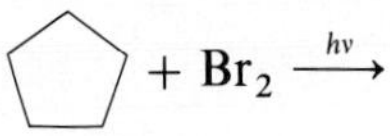

$$\bigcirc + Br_2 \xrightarrow{h\nu}$$

23 Define the terms **meso** and **chiral**.

PHEROMONES AND ALLELOPATHIC COMPOUNDS

ALLELOPATHIC CHEMICALS

It has been known since before 1940 that some plants give off chemical substances which inhibit the growth of other kinds of plants growing nearby. This phenomenon is called **allelopathy**. Allelopathic chemicals can be given off by roots, leaves, or decaying plant matter and may be water soluble or volatile. Allelopathic chemicals cause problems for gardeners and farmers who find it difficult or impossible to grow certain plants near other plants. For example, raspberries and tomatoes will not grow near a black walnut tree (*Juglones nigra*). See Figure C-1. The walnut tree apparently exerts its effect by emitting a substance called juglone.

FIGURE C-1

The black walnut tree produces juglone, which inhibits the growth of certain other plants.

Juglone

The current interest in allelopathy is caused by a more beneficial application of allelopathic chemicals. Plants can be grown to produce chemicals which control weeds, thus reducing need for herbicides of a more toxic nature. Sorghum, for example, releases dhurrin (see below) when it dies. Dhurrin prevents the growth of certain weed plants, while other plants such as beans can be grown in its presence.

Dhurrin

Some rather simple organic materials, such as acetic acid, are produced by decaying organic matter and help to prevent germination of certain seeds.

Much work needs to be done in this area. Allelopathic chemicals need to be isolated from plants and their structures determined. Biological testing of the effects of these materials is also necessary, but there is considerable hope that this area of study will have a positive impact on agriculture and the environment.

PHEROMONES

Another naturally occurring class of compounds, called **pheromones**, has great potential in agriculture and environmental control. Pheromones are chemicals given off by some species of insects to communicate information to other individuals of the same species. One example is the **sex pheromone**. This is a substance emitted by the female of the species to attract the male during mating season (or vice versa in some species). These materials can be placed in traps into which the insects of the attracted sex are drawn. The trapped insects cannot escape and can be destroyed in environmentally safe ways. With few insects of that sex left, breeding essentially ceases and the insect population is greatly reduced.

Since no toxic material is used, this approach is environmentally more desirable than is the use of toxic pesticides. This is also a very selective method. Further research is needed, however to discover pheromones for each of the species we may want to control.

As an example, consider the control of **bark beetles** in Scandinavia. A mixture of the three compounds shown below, used in trace amounts, causes the migrating beetles to enter special devices and to be trapped there.

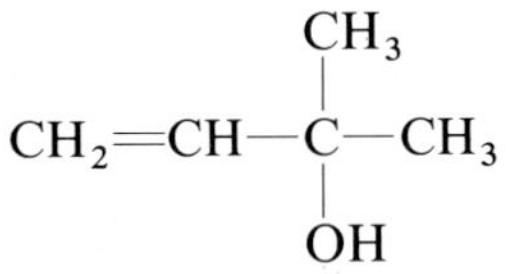

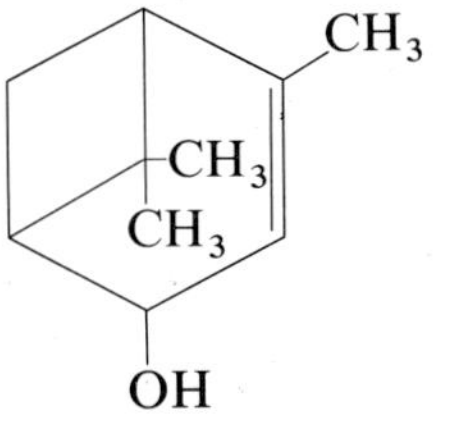

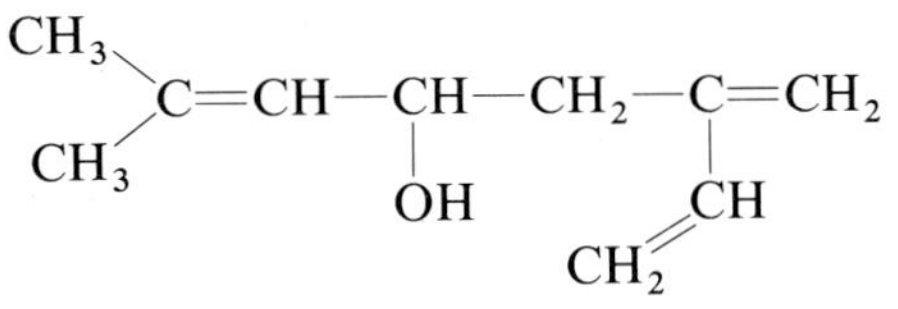

All three compounds have to be present. Note that all three are alcohols and alkenes, which are common functional groups in pheromones, and that they represent a range of complexity. These materials have to be produced synthetically, since they are found only in trace amounts in nature. By their use, a great deal of economic loss in the lumber industry is being prevented without introduction of toxins into the environment and without harm to other insect life or interference with the mating cycles of other species.

For the **boll weevil**, the sex attractant pheromones are a combination of the four compounds shown below:[1]

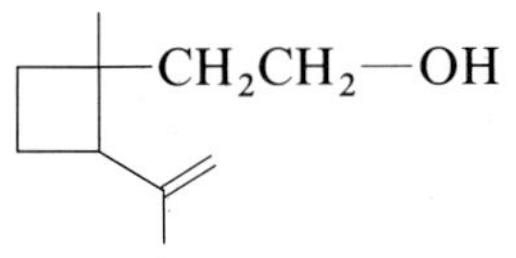

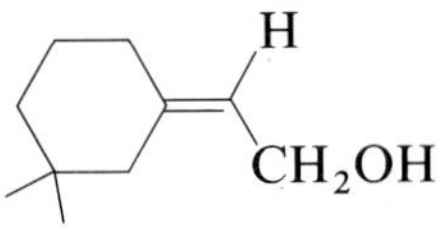

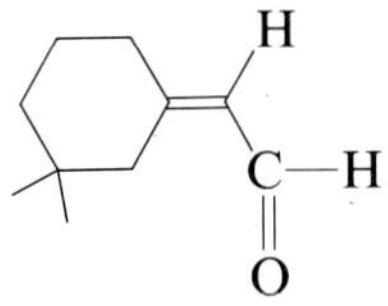

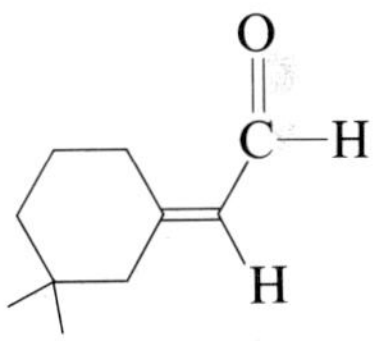

The **North American cockroach** also reacts to a natural sex attractant pheromone.[2]

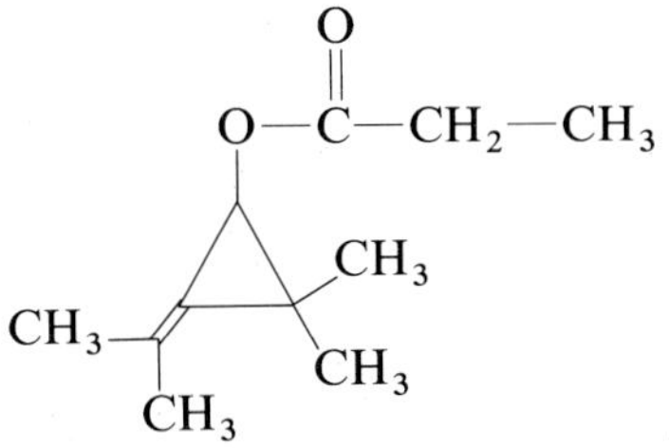

[1] Beroza, *Chemicals Controlling Insect Behavior*, Academic Press, 1970, p. 48
[2] Hartley and West, *Chemicals for Pest Control*, Pergamon Press, 1969, p. 100.

The above materials are **natural** pheromones. When the natural one for a given species cannot be found, other compounds are tested to see if they might attract the species into a trap. Such an **artificial** pheromone is shown below. It is called Siglure and is used for the **Mediterranean fruit fly**.[3]

In addition to sex pheromones, there are pheromones produced for many other purposes. These include trail-marking signals, swarming signals, territory-marking signals and alarm signals. The term *pheromone* refers to intraspecies communication only; other chemicals are used to send defense signals (repellants) and other messages to other species with which a given organism interacts. When chemicals are used for interspecies communication, they are not referred to as pheromones; however, the principle of chemically based information transfer is the same.

Several repellants found in ants are shown below.[4] These can be used in agriculture, as well as by campers and hikers to repel troublesome insects (see Figure C-2).

FIGURE C-2

Insect repellants use the pheromone principle.

Citronellal

Citronellol

Perillen

Farnesol

[3] Hartley and West, *Chemicals for Pest Control*, Pergamon Press, 1969, p. 101.
[4] Beroza, *Chemicals Controlling Insect Behavior*, Academic Press, 1970, p. 101.

CHAPTER 8

ALDEHYDES AND KETONES

LEARNING GOALS

1 To learn the naming systems for aldehydes and ketones

2 To examine the structures of commercially important aldehydes and ketones

3 To learn several methods of preparing aldehydes and ketones

4 To learn a few of the numerous reactions of aldehydes and ketones

5 To understand the concept of blocking functional groups during synthetic sequences

Aldehydes and ketones are chemically quite similar and, except where noted, undergo similar reactions. These two classes of compounds are characterized by the presence of a carbon-oxygen double bond, often called the **carbonyl group**. Since their chemistry is quite similar, they will be covered together throughout this chapter.

$$\begin{array}{c} O \\ \| \\ R—C—H \end{array}$$

Aldehyde

$$\begin{array}{c} O \\ \| \\ R—C—R' \end{array}$$

Ketone

In aldehydes, the carbon atom of the carbonyl group has at least one hydrogen atom attached, while ketones have the carbonyl carbon atom bonded to two other carbon atoms. Because of the greater electronegativity of oxygen, the carbonyl group is polar, with the oxygen end possessing a partial negative charge and the carbon end a partial positive charge. The carbonyl group is more polar than the C—O single bond.

$$120° \quad \begin{array}{c} O\ \delta^- \\ \| \\ C\ \delta^+ \end{array}$$

The polarity of the carbonyl group is responsible for many of the reactions of aldehydes and ketones and for making these compounds more soluble in water than the corresponding alkanes or ethers of similar structure. The carbonyl group is planar trigonal in geometry, with average bond angles of approximately 120°.

Figure 8-1 shows the orbital drawing of the carbonyl group. Notice the pi bond and thus the sp^2 hybridization of both the C and O atoms.

Most low molecular weight aldehydes and ketones are colorless liquids at room temperature. Formaldehyde, which has one carbon atom, is a gas and is used as a 40% solution in water for most purposes (this solution is trade named Formalin). The higher molecular weight compounds are solids.

Most lower molecular weight aldehydes have pungent, unpleasant odors, while lower molecular weight ketones have distinct but pleasant smells.

NOMENCLATURE

Aldehydes are named in the IUPAC system by using a base name indicating the longest chain of carbon atoms plus the ending *al*. The

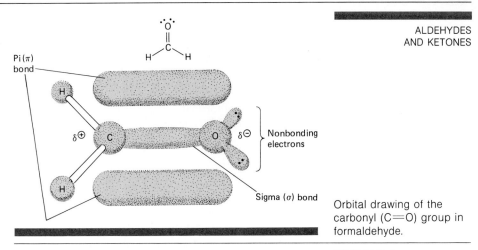

Orbital drawing of the
carbonyl (C=O) group in
formaldehyde.

FIGURE 8-1

carbon atoms are numbered **beginning at the aldehyde end**. Any substituents also are named and their positions on the longest carbon chain indicated. The IUPAC name therefore is made up of

$$\boxed{\text{Substituent groups}} + \boxed{\text{base name}} + \boxed{\text{-al}}$$

In the classical system we use a base name derived from the classical name of the corresponding carboxylic acid (i.e., the acid with the same carbon structure) which indicates the number of carbon atoms. This name is followed by the ending *-aldehyde* (not a separate word). Substituent positions are indicated by Greek letters beginning at the **carbon atom next to the aldehyde functional group**. The following table gives the classical base names used for aldehydes (and carboxylic acids).

NUMBER OF CARBON ATOMS	BASE NAME
1	form-
2	acet-
3	propion-
4	butyr-
5	valer-
6	capro-

Here are some examples showing how to write names of aldehydes. Classical names are in parentheses.

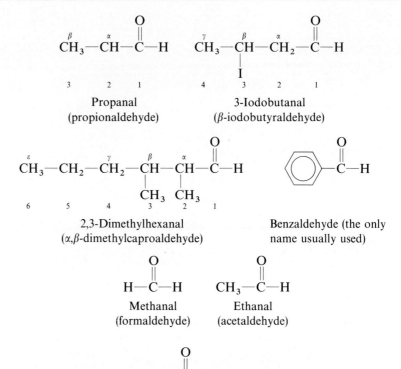

In the IUPAC system, the

$$\underset{\text{O}}{\overset{\text{O}}{\parallel}}$$

—C—H group may be referred to as *carbaldehyde* or as *the formyl group* when it is a substituent in complex molecules in which a different functional group dictates the ending of the name. Examples of these somewhat unusual approaches to naming are as follows:

Cyclohexanecarbaldehyde
or
cyclohexylmethanal

3-formylbenzoic acid

The IUPAC names for aldehydes are constructed by using the base name indicating the longest sequence of carbon atoms, along with the ending *-al* and giving the nature and position of any substituents. Numbering begins at the carbonyl carbon atom. In the classical system, the classical base name (derived from carboxylic acid classical names) is used along with the ending *-aldehyde*. Any substituents are given, and their positions are designated by sequential Greek letters beginning with alpha (α) at the carbon atom adjacent to the carbonyl group.

Molecular models of
acetone (left) and
acetaldehyde.

FIGURE 8-2

Ketones are named in the IUPAC system by using the base name for the longest carbon sequence plus the ending -*one*. Unlike aldehydes, whose functional group is always on the end of the molecule, ketones may have the carbonyl functional group in any of several positions, and we therefore must indicate this position. Carbon atoms are numbered so as to give the carbonyl carbon atom the lowest possible number. Names for ketones are therefore written using the formula:

$$\boxed{\text{Substituent groups}} + \boxed{\text{position of C}=\text{O}} + \boxed{\text{base name}} + \boxed{\text{-one}}$$

The classical method of nomenclature indicates the name of the two alkyl groups attached to the C=O and ends with the separate word *ketone*. This naming system is given in parentheses in the examples below. For the first two compounds, a common name is also given.

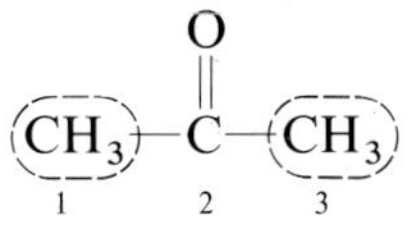

Propanone
(dimethyl ketone)
(acetone)

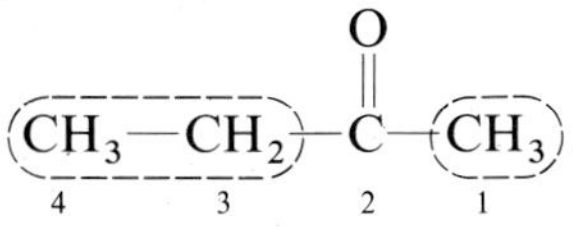

Butanone
(methyl ethyl ketone)
(MEK)

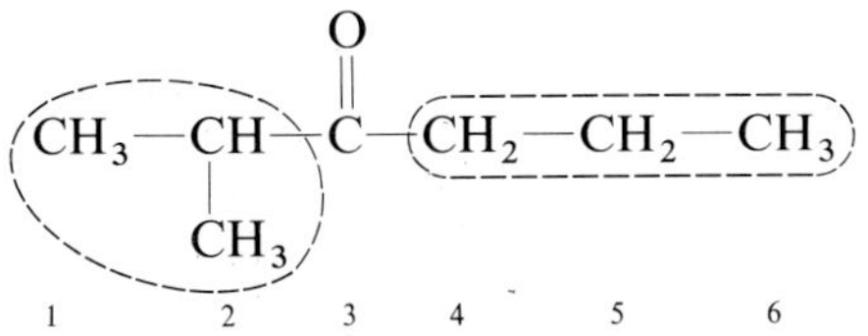

2-Methyl-3-hexanone
(*n*-propyl isopropyl ketone)

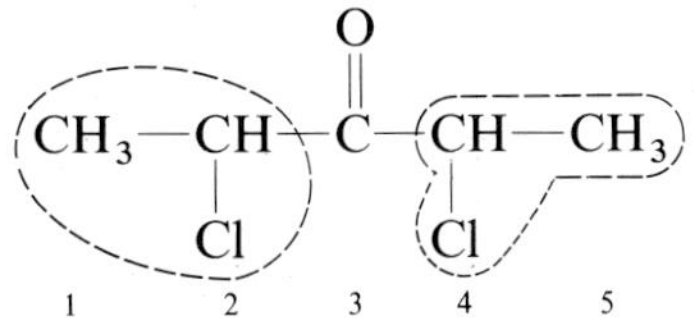

2,4-Dichloro-3-pentanone
(α,α'-dichlorodiethyl ketone)

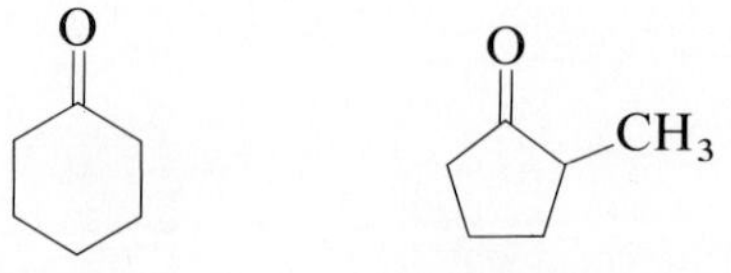

Cyclohexanone   2-Methylcyclopentanone

Ketones are named in the IUPAC system by using a base name indicating the number of carbon atoms in the longest sequence which contains the carbonyl group and the ending *-one*. The position of the carbonyl group and any substituents are also given. Classical names for ketones contain the word *ketone* preceded by the names of the two alkyl groups attached to the carbonyl carbon atom.

PROGRAMMED LEARNING UNIT: NAMING ALDEHYDES AND KETONES

Problems

1 Name the following compounds:

(a)

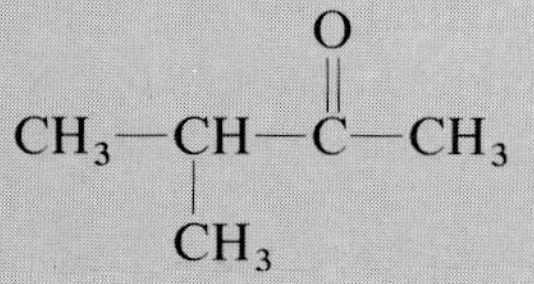

(b)

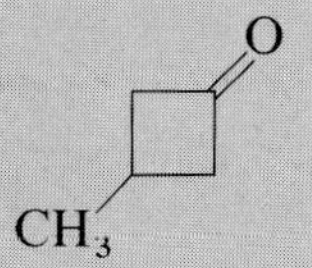

(c)

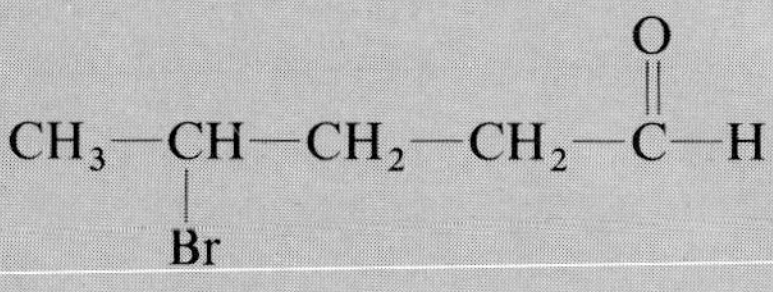

(d)

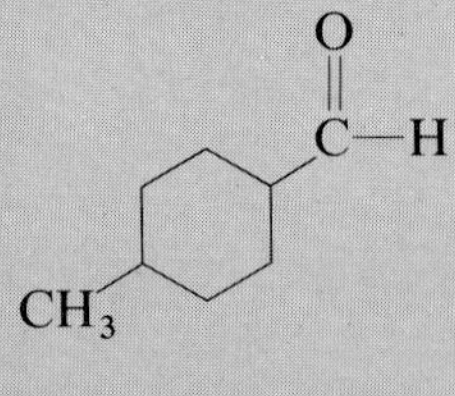

2 Draw the molecular structures indicated by the following names:
(a) α-Methylvaleraldehyde
(b) 2,2-Diiodo-3-hexanone
(c) 3-Ethylcyclobutanecarbaldehyde
(d) di-*n*-Propyl ketone

Solutions

1 (*a*) 3-Methyl-2-butanone or methyl isopropyl ketone
  (*b*) 3-Methylcyclobutanone
  (*c*) 4-Bromopentanal or γ-bromovaleraldehyde
  (*d*) 4-Methylformylcyclohexane, or
    4-methylcyclohexylcarbaldehyde, or
    4-methylcyclohexylmethanal

2 (*a*)

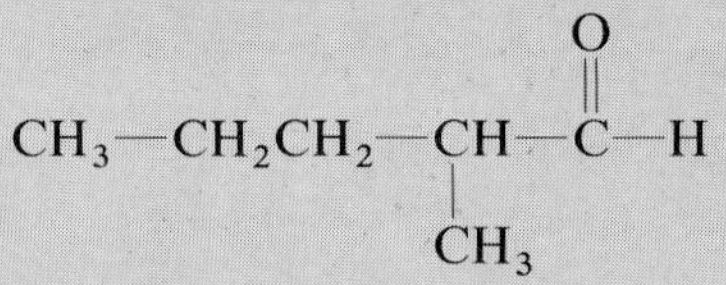

$$CH_3-CH_2CH_2-\underset{\underset{CH_3}{|}}{CH}-\overset{\overset{O}{\|}}{C}-H$$

(*b*)

$$CH_3-CH_2-CH_2-\overset{\overset{O}{\|}}{C}-\underset{\underset{I}{|}}{\overset{\overset{I}{|}}{C}}-CH_3$$

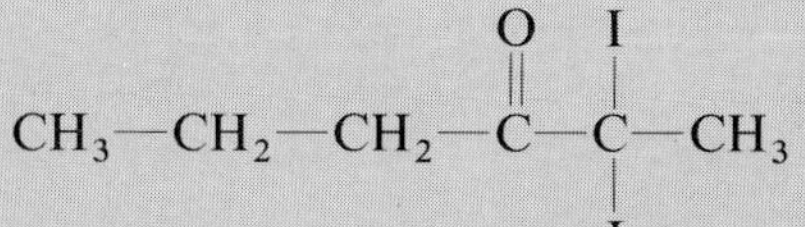

(*c*) CH_3—CH_2

$$\overset{\overset{O}{\|}}{\square}-C-H$$

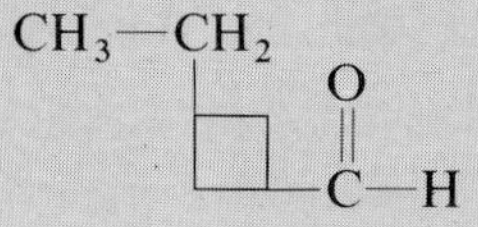

(*d*)

$$CH_3-CH_2-CH_2-\overset{\overset{O}{\|}}{C}-CH_2-CH_2-CH_3$$

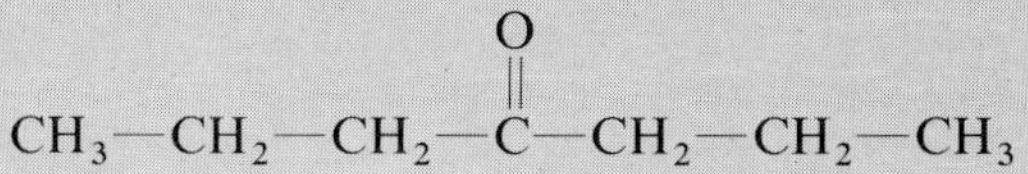

Some **commercially** or **biologically useful** aldehydes and ketones are shown below. Acetone and methyl ethyl ketone (MEK), whose structures have already been given, are used as solvents in the laboratory as well as in consumer products. Acetone is in fingernail polish remover, and MEK is in glues for making models. Benzaldehyde (see page 256) is found in flavorings. Formaldehyde is used to preserve biological specimens and is the active material in embalming fluid. Others are

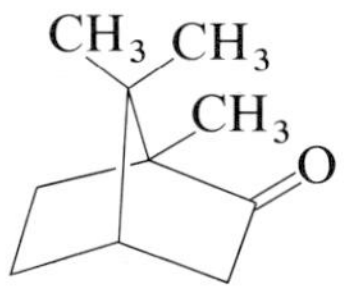

Camphor
(topical decongestant)

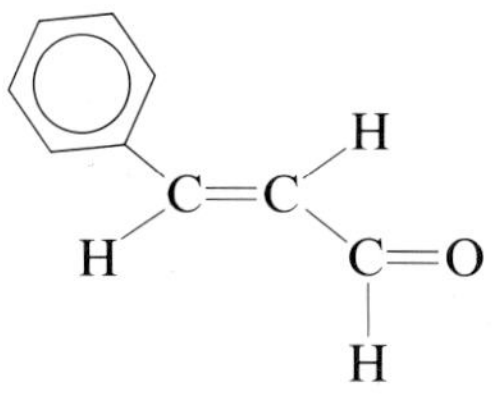

trans-Cinnamaldehyde
(cinnamon flavor)

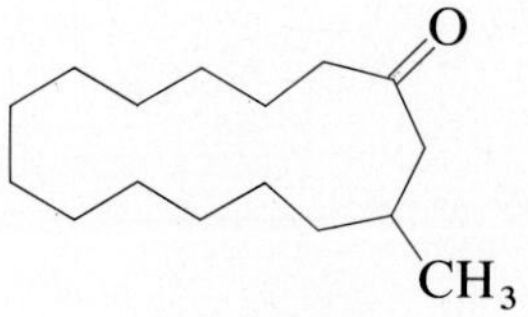

Muscone
(musk odor—perfumes)

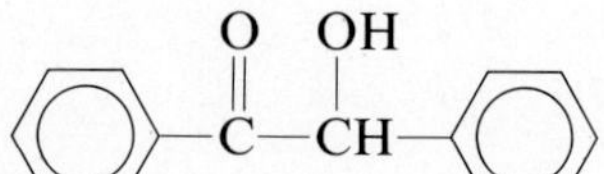

Benzoin
(topical disinfectant medication)

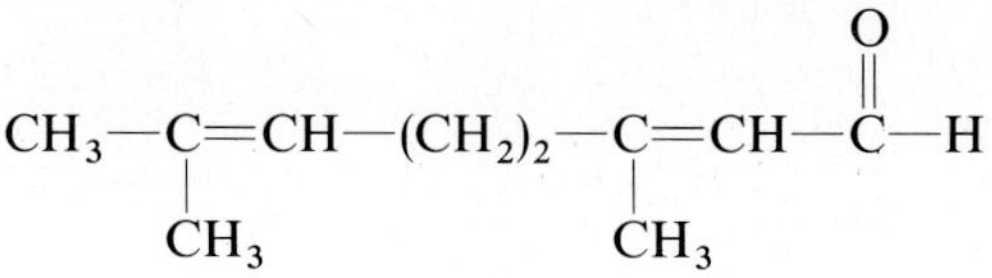

$$CH_3-C=CH-(CH_2)_2-C=CH-\overset{\displaystyle O}{\overset{\displaystyle \|}{C}}-H$$
$$\underset{CH_3}{|}\underset{CH_3}{|}$$

Citral
(odor and flavor of lemon)

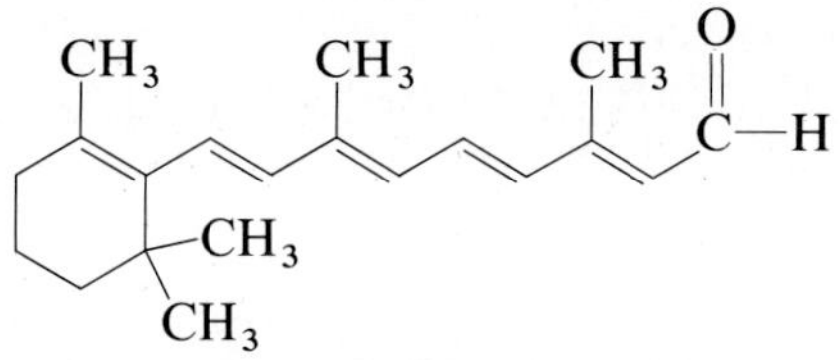

Retinal
(a light-active chemical involved in mammalian vision)

PREPARATION OF ALDEHYDES AND KETONES

Oxidation of alcohols

Aldehydes can be prepared by **oxidation** of 1° alcohols. Since the aldehydes are very easily oxidized further to carboxylic acids (see page 268) it is essential to use mild conditions when synthesizing aldehydes to prevent further oxidation. Chromium(VI) oxide with pyridine dissolved in CH_2Cl_2 at room temperature is one of the best reagents for this purpose. Potassium permanganate ($KMnO_4$), another common oxidizing agent, will not work when preparing aldehydes; as shown below, it will further oxidize the initially formed aldehyde to a carboxylic acid.

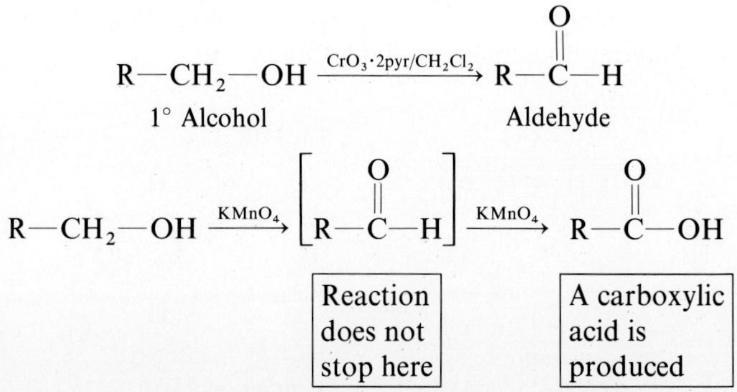

$$R-CH_2-OH \xrightarrow{\;CrO_3\cdot2pyr/CH_2Cl_2\;} R-\overset{\displaystyle O}{\overset{\displaystyle \|}{C}}-H$$

1° Alcohol $\qquad\qquad\qquad\qquad$ Aldehyde

$$R-CH_2-OH \xrightarrow{KMnO_4} \left[R-\overset{\displaystyle O}{\overset{\displaystyle \|}{C}}-H\right] \xrightarrow{KMnO_4} R-\overset{\displaystyle O}{\overset{\displaystyle \|}{C}}-OH$$

Reaction does not stop here	A carboxylic acid is produced

This frog specimen is
preserved with
formaldehyde.

FIGURE 8-3

Secondary (2°) alcohols can also be **oxidized**, in this case to ketones. Since ketones cannot be further oxidized easily, many oxidizing agents can be used. The symbol [O] is used to mean any oxidizing agent. Common oxidizing agents are CrO_3 (chromic oxide), $K_2Cr_2O_7$ (potassium dichromate), $KMnO_4$ (potassium permanganate), Ag_2O (silver oxide) and H_2O_2 (hydrogen peroxide).

$$
\underset{\text{2° Alcohol}}{R-\overset{\overset{\displaystyle OH}{|}}{C}H-R} \xrightarrow{\text{[O]}} \underset{\text{Ketone}}{R-\overset{\overset{\displaystyle O}{\|}}{C}-R}
$$

Tertiary (3°) alcohols cannot be oxidized under normal reaction conditions.

$$
R-\overset{\overset{\displaystyle OH}{|}}{\underset{\underset{\displaystyle R}{|}}{C}}-R \xrightarrow{\text{[O]}} \text{no reaction}
$$

Examples of alcohol oxidation are as follows:

$$
\underset{\text{2° Alcohol}}{\text{⬡—OH}} \xrightarrow{K_2Cr_2O_7} \underset{\text{Ketone}}{\text{⬡=O}}
$$

$$\underset{\text{1° Alcohol}}{\bigcirc\!\!-CH_2OH} \xrightarrow{\text{CrO}_3 \cdot \text{2pyr/CH}_2\text{Cl}_2} \underset{\text{Aldehyde}}{\bigcirc\!\!-\overset{\overset{\displaystyle O}{\|}}{C}\!\!-H}$$

$$\underset{\underset{\displaystyle CH_3}{|}}{CH_3\!\!-\!CH\!\!-\!CH_2\!\!-\!OH} \xrightarrow{\text{KMnO}_4} \underset{\underset{\displaystyle CH_3}{|}}{CH_3\!\!-\!CH\!\!-\!\overset{\overset{\displaystyle O}{\|}}{C}\!\!-OH}$$

1° alcohol   An acid—**not** the desired product

$$\underset{\underset{\displaystyle CH_3}{|}}{\overset{\overset{\displaystyle OH}{|}}{CH_3\!\!-\!C\!\!-\!CH_3}} \xrightarrow{\text{KMnO}_4} \text{no reaction}$$

3° Alcohol

Preparation from acyl halides

Acyl halides are derivatives of carboxylic acids in which the —OH group has been replaced with a halogen, most commonly chlorine. See Chapter 13 for the method of preparing acyl halides. The acyl halide, once prepared, can be reduced using LiAlH(*t*-BuO)$_3$ (lithium tri-*tert*-butoxyaluminum hydride) to produce aldehydes, or reacted with dialkyl cadmium to produce ketones with larger carbon skeletons. The dialkyl cadmium is composed of two alkyl groups bonded to a cadmium atom, R$_2$Cd.

The general reaction scheme is

$$R\!\!-\!\!\overset{\overset{\displaystyle O}{\|}}{C}\!\!-OH \xrightarrow{\text{SOCl}_2} \underset{\text{Acyl halide}}{R\!\!-\!\!\overset{\overset{\displaystyle O}{\|}}{C}\!\!-Cl}$$

$$\xrightarrow{\text{LiAlH}(t\text{-BuO})_3} \underset{\text{Aldehyde}}{R\!\!-\!\!\overset{\overset{\displaystyle O}{\|}}{C}\!\!-H}$$

$$\xrightarrow{\text{R}'_2\text{Cd}} \underset{\substack{\text{Ketone with} \\ \text{more carbons}}}{R\!\!-\!\!\overset{\overset{\displaystyle O}{\|}}{C}\!\!-R' + CdCl_2}$$

Specific examples are

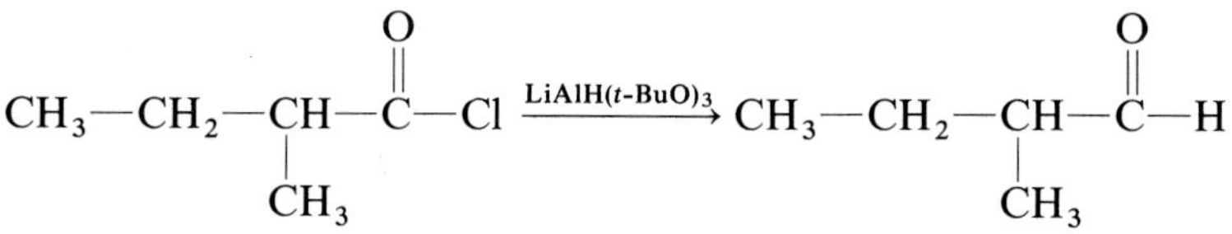

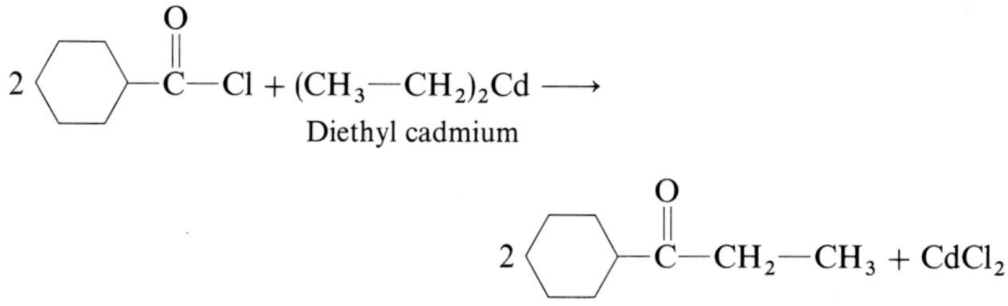

$$CH_3-CH_2-\underset{\underset{CH_3}{|}}{CH}-\overset{\overset{O}{\parallel}}{C}-Cl \xrightarrow{\text{LiAlH}(t\text{-BuO})_3} CH_3-CH_2-\underset{\underset{CH_3}{|}}{CH}-\overset{\overset{O}{\parallel}}{C}-H$$

2 ⬡—$\overset{\overset{O}{\parallel}}{C}$—Cl + $(CH_3-CH_2)_2Cd \longrightarrow$
  Diethyl cadmium

2 ⬡—$\overset{\overset{O}{\parallel}}{C}$—$CH_2-CH_3 + CdCl_2$

In Chapter 6 the ozonolysis of alkenes was discussed. You may recall that this produced aldehydes and ketones, as in the example below. For a fuller explanation refer back to page 187.

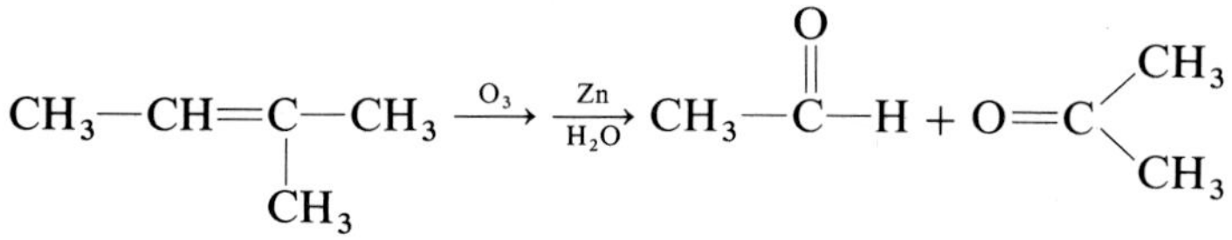

$$CH_3-CH=\underset{\underset{CH_3}{|}}{C}-CH_3 \xrightarrow[\text{H}_2\text{O}]{\text{O}_3 \quad \text{Zn}} CH_3-\overset{\overset{O}{\parallel}}{C}-H + O=C\overset{\diagup CH_3}{\diagdown CH_3}$$

Aldehydes are prepared by mild oxidation of 1° alcohols or by reduction of acyl halides. Ketones are prepared by oxidation of 2° alcohols or by reaction of dialkyl cadmium with acyl halides.

REACTIONS OF ALDEHYDES AND KETONES

Reaction with alcohols

In the presence of a mineral acid, 1 mole of aldehyde or ketone reacts with 1 or 2 moles of alcohol. The schemes and the general name for each product are shown below.

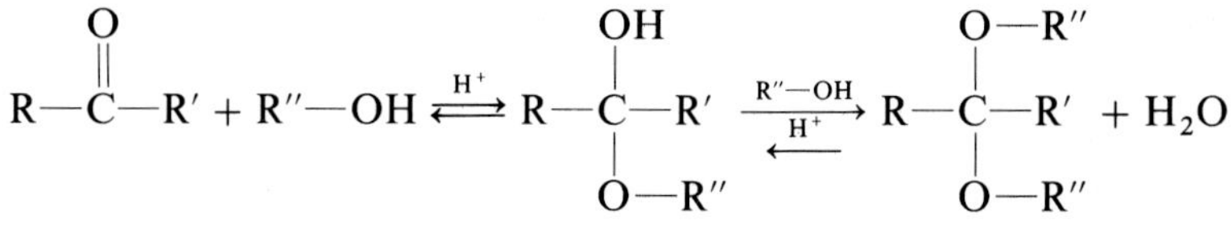

$$R-\overset{\overset{O}{\parallel}}{C}-R' + R''-OH \rightleftharpoons R-\underset{\underset{O-R''}{|}}{\overset{\overset{OH}{|}}{C}}-R' \underset{H^+}{\overset{R''-OH}{\rightleftharpoons}} R-\underset{\underset{O-R''}{|}}{\overset{\overset{O-R''}{|}}{C}}-R' + H_2O$$

Ketone   Hemiketal[1]   Ketal
          (unstable)

---

[1] While most hemiketals and hemiacetals are unstable, certain carbohydrate molecules are stable examples of these structures. See Chapter 14.

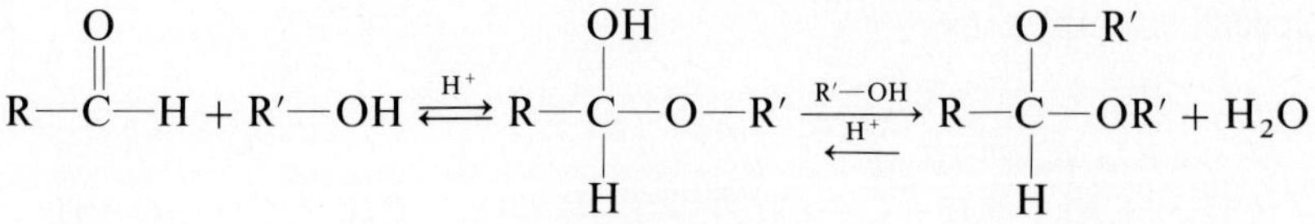

$$R-\overset{\overset{\displaystyle O}{\|}}{C}-H + R'-OH \underset{\longleftarrow}{\overset{H^+}{\rightleftharpoons}} R-\overset{\overset{\displaystyle OH}{|}}{\underset{\underset{\displaystyle H}{|}}{C}}-O-R' \underset{H^+}{\overset{R'-OH}{\longrightarrow}} R-\overset{\overset{\displaystyle O-R'}{|}}{\underset{\underset{\displaystyle H}{|}}{C}}-OR' + H_2O$$

Aldehyde   Hemiacetal[1]   Acetal
                           (unstable)

If you start with a carbonyl compound, a catalytic amount of a strong acid, and an excess of alcohol, the equilibrium will shift to the right, forming the ketal or acetal. On the other hand, if you start with a ketal or acetal, a catalytic amount of a strong acid, and lots of water and then warm this mixture above the boiling point of the alcohol, the equilibrium shifts to the left, forming the carbonyl compound.

Examples are as follows:

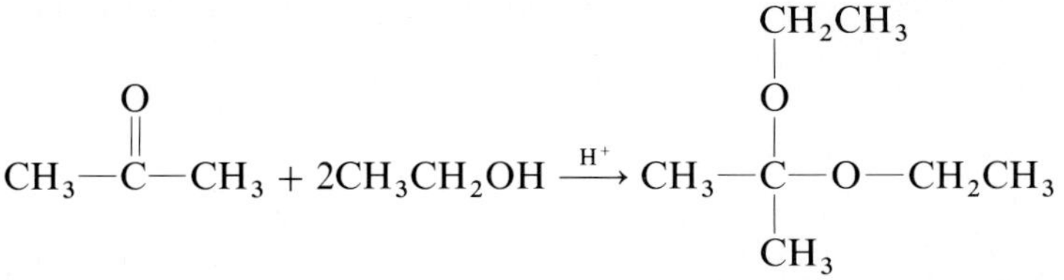

$$CH_3-\overset{\overset{\displaystyle O}{\|}}{C}-CH_3 + 2CH_3CH_2OH \overset{H^+}{\longrightarrow} CH_3-\overset{\overset{\displaystyle CH_2CH_3}{\overset{\displaystyle |}{\overset{\displaystyle O}{|}}}}{\underset{\underset{\displaystyle CH_3}{|}}{C}}-O-CH_2CH_3$$

The diethyl ketal of acetone

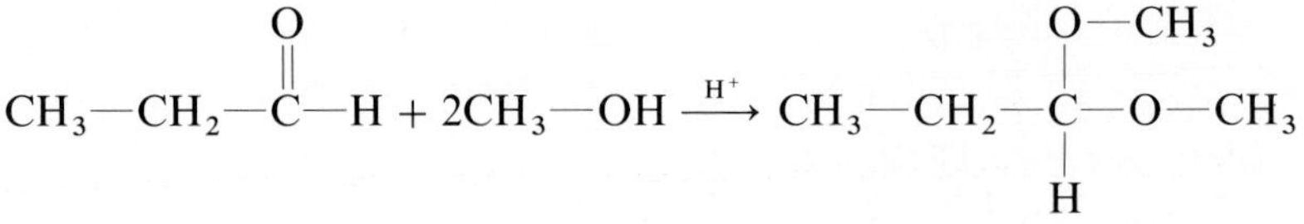

$$CH_3-CH_2-\overset{\overset{\displaystyle O}{\|}}{C}-H + 2CH_3-OH \overset{H^+}{\longrightarrow} CH_3-CH_2-\overset{\overset{\displaystyle O-CH_3}{|}}{\underset{\underset{\displaystyle H}{|}}{C}}-O-CH_3$$

The dimethyl acetal of propanal

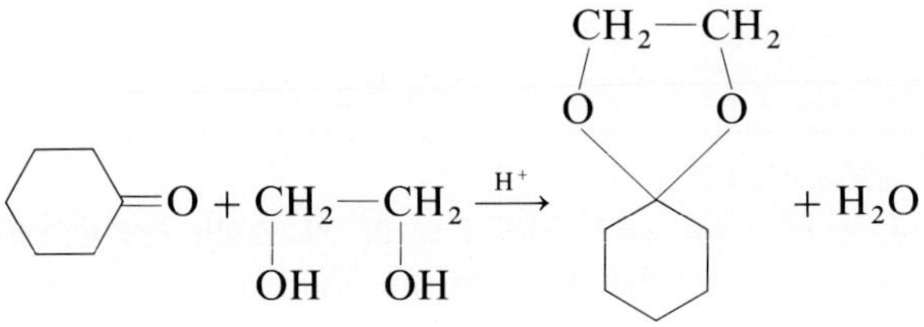

In the last example, both —OH groups used to form the ketal of cyclohexanone are in the same alcohol molecule (ethylene glycol; 1,2-ethanediol) and, thus, the ketal is cyclic.

Ketals and acetals (which have relatively unreactive ether groups) are used to **protect** (or **block**) the C=O group from unwanted reaction during a multistep synthesis. Consider part of the synthesis of hydrocortisone in Figure 8-4. The first structure shown (A) has two ketone groups, and the

----

[1] While most hemiketals and hemiacetals are unstable, certain carbohydrate molecules are stable examples of these structures. See Chapter 14.

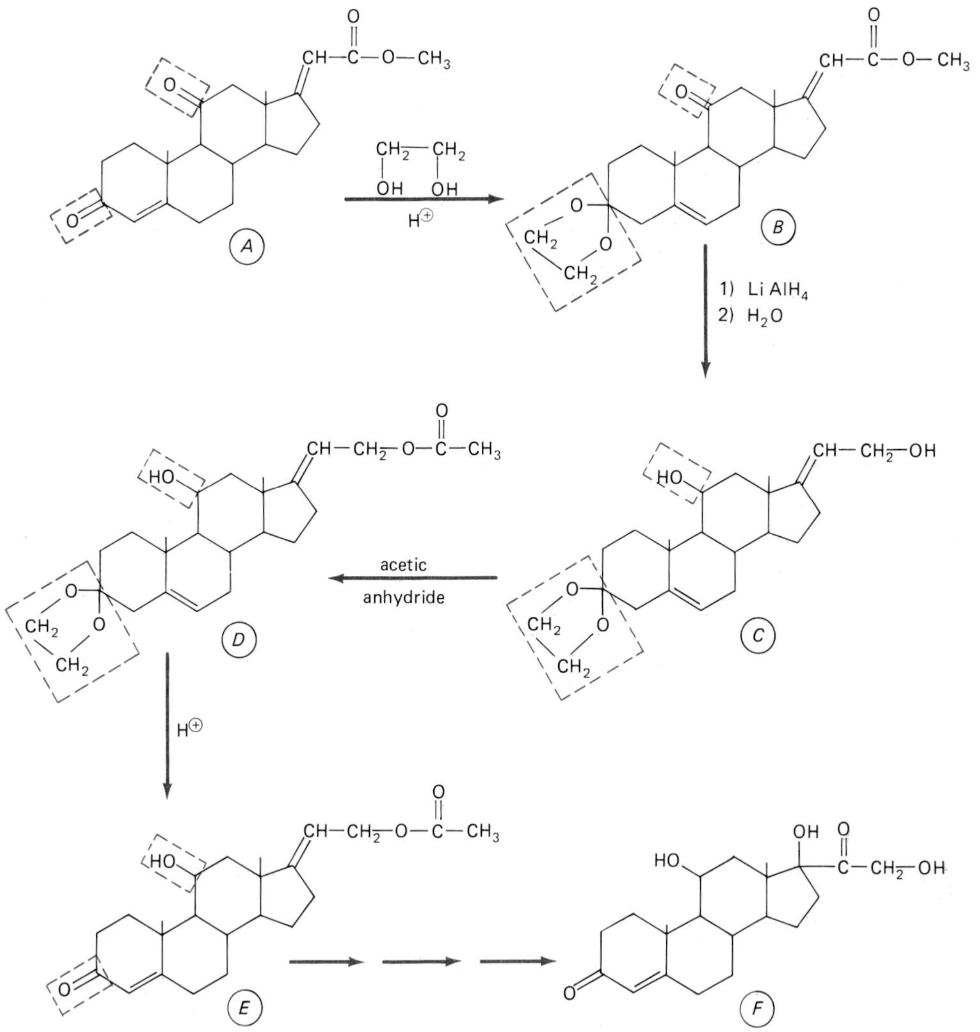

FIGURE 8-4

Part of the reaction
sequence used to
synthesize hydrocortisone.

final product has only one of those ketone groups reduced to an alcohol.
A reducing agent used on (A) would normally reduce both ketone groups—
indeed, the one we want to leave unchanged would be reduced most easily,
because it is less sterically hindered. To solve this problem, 1 mole of (A)
is allowed to react with 1 mole of ethylene glycol (1,2-ethanediol) to form
the ketal at the least sterically hindered ketone to form (B). The left ketone
group is now said to be **blocked** or rendered unreactive to reducing agents
and other chemical reagents which react with ketones. Now the remaining
ketone group can be reduced to an alcohol group with LiAlH$_4$ to give
(C) (see next section). Note that the LiAlH$_4$ also reduced the side chain
ester to an alcohol, but did not reduce the side chain alkene functional

group. After the desired reaction on the side chain to give (D), the blocking group is removed by adding acid to produce (E). Several more steps are needed to change other parts of the molecule to the final medically useful compound—hydrocortisone (F), used to treat arthritis, rheumatism, and other inflammatory conditions.

Another use of ketal formation is seen in the synthesis of guanadrel, a hypotensive (tension-lowering) drug. Here, the final product is a cyclic ketal.

Guanadrel

(Some of the details of this and the previous synthesis are omitted for the sake of emphasizing the part or parts being used for illustration.)

Reduction

Aldehydes and ketones can be **reduced** to 1° and 2° alcohols, respectively. Hydrogen gas and a catalyst will work, but in the laboratory such a reaction is cumbersome since gases require special equipment and skill. Mixed metal hydrides such as $NaBH_4$ or $LiAlH_4$ are much easier to use. Sometimes the symbol [H] is used to mean **any reducing agent**, such as H_2, $LiAlH_4$, or $NaBH_4$.

For example[2]

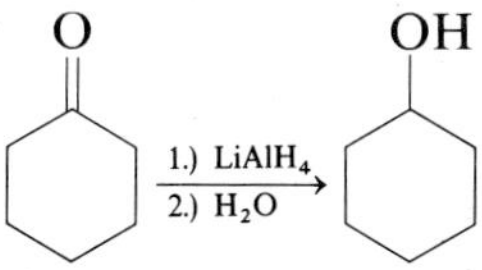
O
OH
1.) LiAlH4
2.) H2O

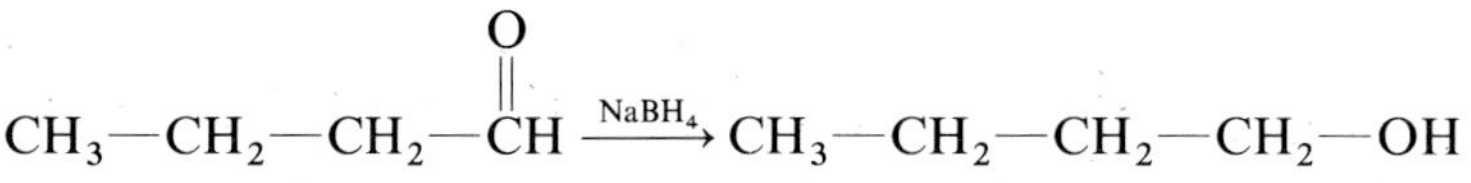
O
CH3—CH2—CH2—CH
NaBH4
CH3—CH2—CH2—CH2—OH

$NaBH_4$ may be used in water or alcohol; $LiAlH_4$ must be used in ether.

We can **reduce** carbonyl compounds all the way **to alkanes** by using one of the two reagents shown below.

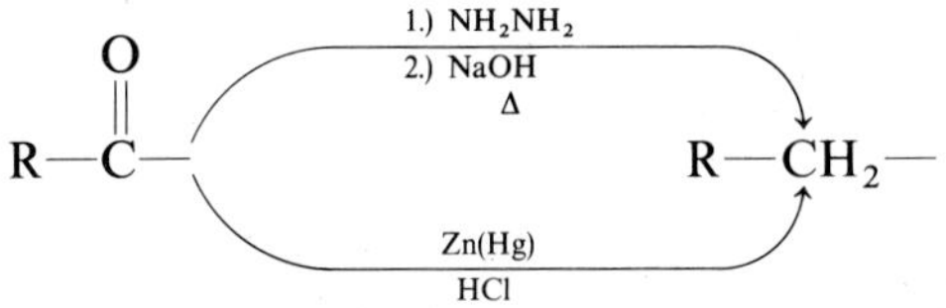
1.) NH2NH2
2.) NaOH
Δ
O
R—C—
R—CH2—
Zn(Hg)
HCl

Wolff-Kishner reduction

Clemmensen reduction

Either synthetic procedure can be used for most compounds, but if another part of the molecule is sensitive to acid, the Wolff-Kishner reaction using hydrazine and base is the one of choice. If the material is base sensitive, the Clemmensen reduction works better since it uses HCl and zinc amalgam (an amalgam is a solution of another metal in mercury). For example

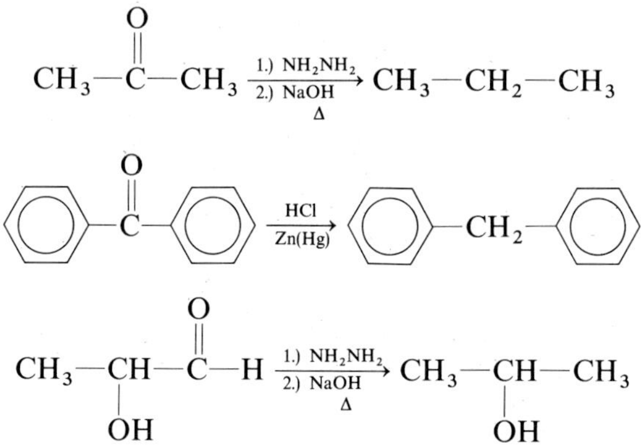
O
CH3—C—CH3
1.) NH2NH2
2.) NaOH
Δ
CH3—CH2—CH3
O
C
HCl
Zn(Hg)
CH2
O
CH3—CH—C—H
OH
1.) NH2NH2
2.) NaOH
Δ
CH3—CH—CH3
OH

[2] Recall that the notation used with the arrow means that the two reagents are used **in sequence**.

Acid would cause dehydration of the alcohol, so the Wolff-Kishner procedure is best for the last example above.

$$\underset{\text{CH}_2\text{Cl}}{\overset{\overset{\displaystyle O}{\overset{\|}{C}-CH_3}}{\bigcirc}} \xrightarrow[\text{HCl}]{\text{Zn(Hg)}} \underset{\text{CH}_2\text{Cl}}{\overset{CH_2-CH_3}{\bigcirc}}$$

Here base would cause the Cl to be replaced by an S_N2 reaction; therefore the acidic Clemmensen reduction is best.

Oxidation

While ketones cannot be further oxidized easily, aldehydes are easily **oxidized** to carboxylic acids with a variety of strong or weak oxidizing agents. Remember that the symbol [O] means any oxidizing agent, including $KMnO_4$, $K_2Cr_2O_7$, $CrO_3 \cdot 2pyr/CH_2Cl_2$, Ag_2O, or H_2O_2. This reaction was covered earlier in Chapter 7 (page 233) and on page 260 in this chapter. The general reactions are

$$R-\overset{\overset{\displaystyle O}{\|}}{C}-R \xrightarrow{[O]} \text{no reaction}$$

$$R-\overset{\overset{\displaystyle O}{\|}}{C}-H \xrightarrow{[O]} R-\overset{\overset{\displaystyle O}{\|}}{C}-OH$$

Specific examples are

$$\overset{\displaystyle O}{\bigcirc} \xrightarrow{K_2Cr_2O_7} \text{no reaction}$$

$$\bigcirc-\overset{\overset{\displaystyle O}{\|}}{C}-H \xrightarrow{KMnO_4} \bigcirc-\overset{\overset{\displaystyle O}{\|}}{C}-OH$$

$$CH_3-CH_2-\overset{\overset{\displaystyle O}{\|}}{C}-H \xrightarrow{Ag_2O} CH_3-CH_2-\overset{\overset{\displaystyle O}{\|}}{C}-OH$$

Aldehydes and ketones can be converted to acetals and ketals, respectively, by allowing 1 mole to react with 2 moles of alcohol or with 1 mole of a diol. Aldehydes and ketones can be reduced to 1° and 2° alcohols, respectively, by any one of several reducing agents. Both aldehydes and ketones can be reduced to alkanes by the Clemmensen or Wolff-Kishner methods. Aldehydes can be oxidized to carboxylic acids, while ketones are not easily oxidized.

Reaction with substituted ammonia compounds

Reactions that are useful in identifying aldehydes and ketones involve the use of substituted ammonia compounds. The general reaction is

$$\begin{array}{c}R \\ R' \end{array}\!\!C=O + \begin{array}{c}H \\ H \end{array}\!\!N-Z \longrightarrow \begin{array}{c}R \\ R' \end{array}\!\!C=N-Z + H_2O$$

The carbonyl carbon atom becomes doubly bonded to the nitrogen atom that originally had the two hydrogen atoms. A molecule of water is split out. The organic product is usually a solid, the melting point of which can be determined. Unknown aldehydes and ketones, which are usually liquids, can be identified by comparing the experimentally determined melting points of their derivatives (solids) with data found in tables. The three most commonly used substituted ammonia compounds are shown below reacting with representative carbonyl compounds. The 2,4-dinitrophenylhydrazine is especially useful because the solid which forms is a bright yellow or orange or red. These characteristic colors give the chemist a quick visual indication that an aldehyde or ketone is present.

$$\begin{array}{c}CH_3 \\ CH_3 \end{array}\!\!C=O + H_2N-OH \longrightarrow \begin{array}{c}CH_3 \\ CH_3 \end{array}\!\!C=N-OH + H_2O$$

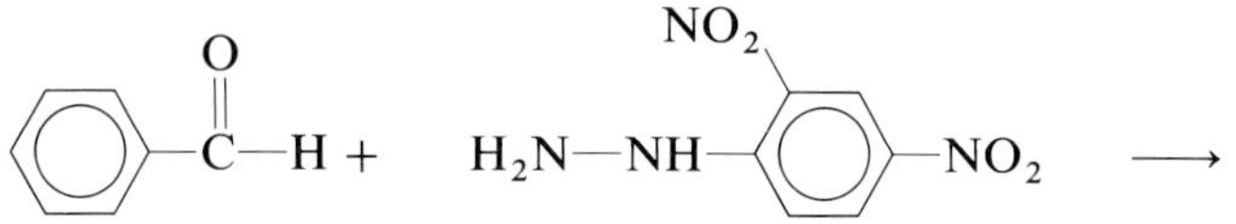

Hydroxylamine   An oxime

2,4-Dinitrophenylhydrazine (2,4-DNP)

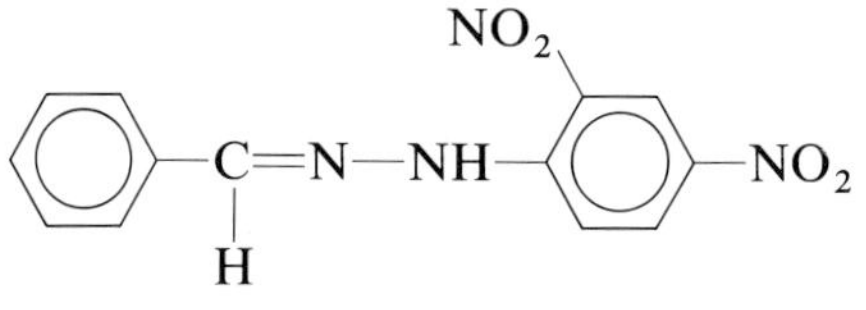

A 2,4-dinitrophenylhydrazone

$$CH_3-CH-\overset{\overset{\displaystyle O}{\|}}{C}-CH_3 + H_2N-NH-\overset{\overset{\displaystyle O}{\|}}{C}-NH_2 \longrightarrow$$
$$\underset{CH_3}{|}$$

Semicarbazide

$$CH_3-CH-C=N-NH-\overset{\overset{\displaystyle O}{\|}}{C}-NH_2$$
$$\underset{CH_3}{|} \ \underset{CH_3}{|}$$

A semicarbazone

Table 8-1 shows the melting points of the derivatives of a number of aldehydes and ketones. If, for example, a chemist has an unknown compound which, upon reaction with 2,4-DNP, produces a bright orange precipitate with a melting point of 256°C, it is most likely cinnamaldehyde or 4-bromobenzaldehyde. If a further experiment shows the oxime of the unknown to melt at 110°C, then the compound in question is 4-bromobenzaldehyde. Since virtually all aldehydes and ketones have known derivatives, they can be positively identified by preparing one or more derivatives and consulting complete melting point tables.

Halogenation

Aldehydes and ketones react with halogens (Cl_2, Br_2, I_2) in the presence

TABLE 8-1 MELTING POINTS

COMPOUND	MELTING POINT OF DNP DERIVATIVE, °C	MELTING POINT OF OXIME DERIVATIVE, °C	MELTING POINT OF SEMICARBAZONE DERIVATIVE, °C
Acetaldehyde	168	47	163
Pentanal	107	52	(oil)
Propanal	149	40	89
Cinnamaldehyde	255	64	215
Benzaldehyde	237	35	222
4-Bromobenzaldehyde	257	111	228
Acetone	126	59	190
Cyclopentanone	122	149	209
2-Pentanone	144	58	111
3-Pentanone	156	69	138
Benzophenone	238	142	164

of acid or base, or with hypohalite ions to form α-halogen substituted compounds, as follows:

$$R-\overset{\overset{\displaystyle O}{\|}}{C}-CH- \xrightarrow[\text{H}^+\text{ or OH}]{X_2} R-\overset{\overset{\displaystyle O}{\|}}{C}-\overset{\overset{\displaystyle X}{|}}{C}-$$

Examples are

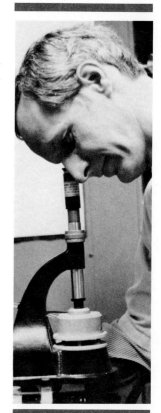

FIGURE 8-5

Melting-point apparatus, used to determine the melting point of solid materials in order to identify substances or estimate their purity.

(cyclohexanone) + Br$_2$ $\xrightarrow{\text{H}^+}$ (2-bromocyclohexanone) + HBr

$$\overset{\overset{\displaystyle O}{\|}}{\text{C}6H_5-C}-CH_3 \xrightarrow[\text{(sodium hypochlorite)}]{\text{NaOCl}} \overset{\overset{\displaystyle O}{\|}}{C_6H_5-C}-CH_2Cl$$

$$CH_3-CH_2-\overset{\overset{\displaystyle O}{\|}}{C}-CH_2-CH_3 \xrightarrow[\text{(sodium hypobromite)}]{\text{NaOBr}} CH_3-CH_2-\overset{\overset{\displaystyle O}{\|}}{C}-\overset{\overset{\displaystyle}{\underset{\underset{\displaystyle Br}{|}}{CH}}}-CH_3$$

In the special case of a **methyl ketone** and excess halogen, trihalogenation occurs on the methyl group only followed by the loss of the halogenated methyl group. This is called the **haloform reaction**.

$$CH_3-CH_2-\overset{\overset{\displaystyle O}{\|}}{C}-CH_3 \xrightarrow[\text{NaOH}]{\text{excess I}_2} CH_3-CH_2-\overset{\overset{\displaystyle O}{\|}}{C}-O^-\underset{Na^+}{} + \underset{\text{Iodoform}}{CHI_3}$$

Here the trihalomethane is formed along with a carboxylate anion. When iodine is used, the product is **iodoform**, a yellow solid with a characteristic odor and a melting point of 119°C. The observation of a precipitate when a carbonyl compound is treated with excess iodine in base indicates that a methyl ketone is present.

Addition reactions

The pi bond between the C and O in carbonyl compounds allows a number of materials to add across this bond.

$$\overset{\overset{\displaystyle O}{\|}}{C} + \overset{\overset{\displaystyle X}{|}}{Y} \longrightarrow -\overset{\overset{\displaystyle O-X}{|}}{C}-Y$$

The formation of hemiacetals and hemiketals already discussed falls in this category.

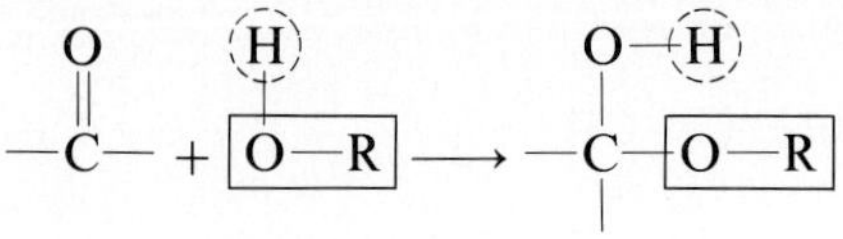

$$-\overset{\overset{O}{\|}}{C}- + \boxed{O-R} \longrightarrow -\overset{O-H}{\underset{|}{C}}-\boxed{O-R}$$

Most of the addition reactions are nucleophilic, and since the carbon atom carries a partial positive charge, the nucleophile first attaches itself to this carbon atom. A typical addition reaction involves the cyanide ion adding to benzaldehyde, as shown below.

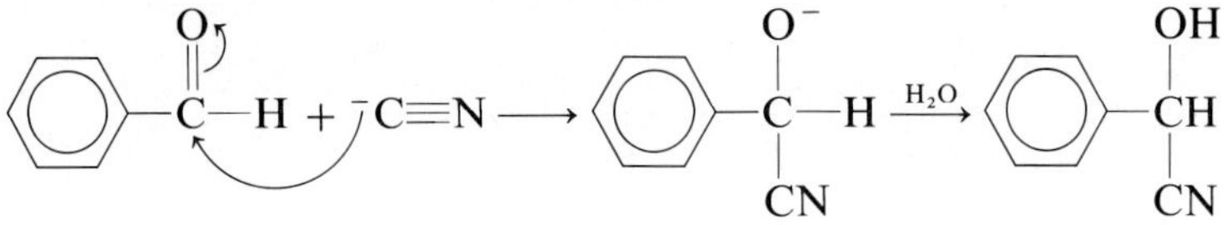

The $-O^-$ ion removes an $-H^+$ from the water used as solvent to become an $-OH$ group. The **nitrile**, as organic cyanide compounds are called, can be hydrolyzed to produce a carboxylic acid.

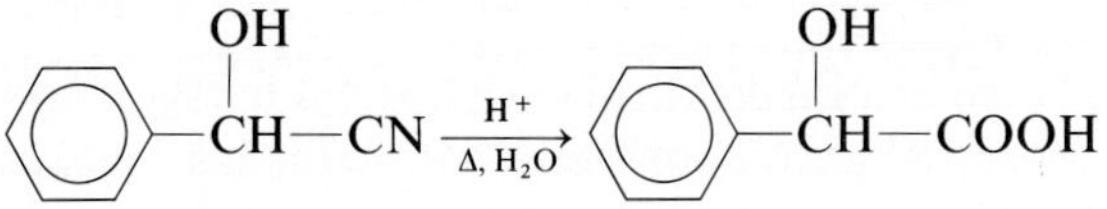

An example of this reaction is shown below in the synthesis of the analgesic called ibuprofen. This is the active ingredient in the pain relievers Advil and Motrin and other over-the-counter medications. See Figure 8-6.

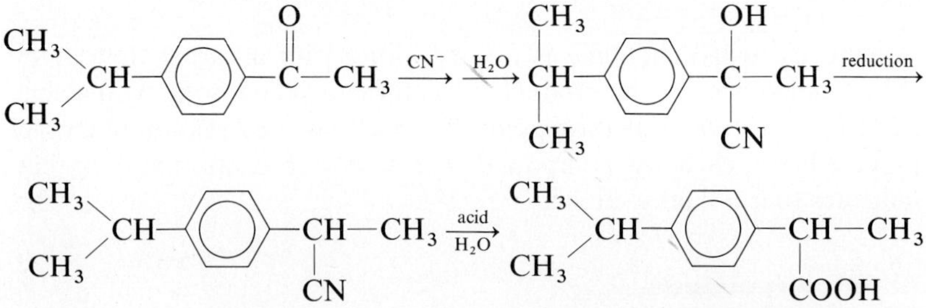

Ibuprofen

Other nucleophilic additions include the addition of Grignard reagents to both aldehydes and ketones. Several examples are shown below as a review of the formation of alcohols covered in Chapter 7 (see page 229). The final product, after hydrolysis, is shown in each case.

$$R-\overset{\displaystyle O}{\underset{\displaystyle\diagdown}{C}} + R'-MgX \longrightarrow \longrightarrow R-\overset{\displaystyle OH}{\underset{\displaystyle |}{C}}-R'$$

Examples are

$$\underset{\text{Formaldehyde}}{H-\overset{\displaystyle O}{\overset{\displaystyle ||}{C}}-H} + \boxed{\bigpentagon}-MgBr \xrightarrow{} \xrightarrow{H^+} \boxed{\bigpentagon}-\overset{\displaystyle H}{\underset{\displaystyle H}{\overset{\displaystyle |}{\underset{\displaystyle |}{C}}}}-OH$$

Formaldehyde   1° Alcohol

$$\underset{\text{Other aldehyde}}{CH_3-\overset{\displaystyle O}{\overset{\displaystyle ||}{C}}-H} + \boxed{CH_3-CH_2}-MgCl \longrightarrow \xrightarrow{H^+} CH_3-\overset{\displaystyle OH}{\underset{\displaystyle H}{\overset{\displaystyle |}{\underset{\displaystyle |}{C}}}}\boxed{CH_2-CH_3}$$

Other aldehyde   2° Alcohol

$$\underset{\text{Ketone}}{CH_3-\overset{\displaystyle O}{\overset{\displaystyle ||}{C}}-\bighexagon} + \boxed{CH_3-CH_2-CH_2}-MgI \longrightarrow \xrightarrow{H^+}$$

Ketone

$$CH_3-\overset{\displaystyle OH}{\underset{\displaystyle \bighexagon}{\overset{\displaystyle |}{C}}}\boxed{CH_2-CH_2-CH_3}$$

3° Alcohol

FIGURE 8-6

One of the many over-the-
counter medications
containing Ibuprofen.

All of these reactions allow the construction of larger carbon chains. The Grignard reagent allows the synthesis of virtually any alcohol. Formaldehyde always produces a 1° alcohol when reacted with a Grignard reagent. Similarly, other aldehydes always give 2° alcohols, and ketones give 3° alcohols.

Aldol condensation

For those aldehydes with an alpha hydrogen (a hydrogen atom on the carbon atom adjacent to the carbonyl group), a coupling reaction occurs when the compound is treated with a water solution of NaOH. This is an important way of linking molecules together to build larger carbon skeletons. To illustrate this reaction consider what happens when two molecules of acetaldehyde react with each other:

$$2CH_3-\overset{\overset{\displaystyle O}{\|}}{C}-H \xrightarrow{OH^-} CH_3-\overset{\overset{\displaystyle OH}{|}}{CH}-CH_2-\overset{\overset{\displaystyle O}{\|}}{C}-H \longrightarrow$$

$$CH_3-CH=CH-\overset{\overset{\displaystyle O}{\|}}{C}-H + H_2O$$

In the reaction above, during the first step, a β-hydroxy aldehyde is formed. The common name of this particular compound is aldol, and all similar reactions are therefore called **aldol condensations**. Such β-hydroxy compounds frequently dehydrate to produce α,β-unsaturated aldehydes. The net result is the formation of a molecule with twice as many carbon atoms as the starting aldehyde.

The general mechanism of the aldol condensation is as follows:

Two resonance forms

1 The OH^- pulls off an α hydrogen (from the α carbon, C^*) in a small fraction of the molecules. The α H is slightly acidic because of the resonance stabilization of the resulting anion.

2 The resulting anion acts as a nucleophile and attacks the $C=O$ of another molecule of the aldehyde, forming a new C—C bond.

3 The resulting O^- picks up an H^+ from water, regenerating the OH^- catalyst.

4 The β-hydroxyaldehyde may lose water from the α and β positions to form an α,β-unsaturated carbonyl compound. This step usually occurs spontaneously, although heat is indicated in the equation above.

The overall result is that the carbonyl carbon of one molecule becomes doubly bonded to the α carbon of the other molecule. The boxes drawn above in the final product show the parts which come from each molecule. Examples follow.

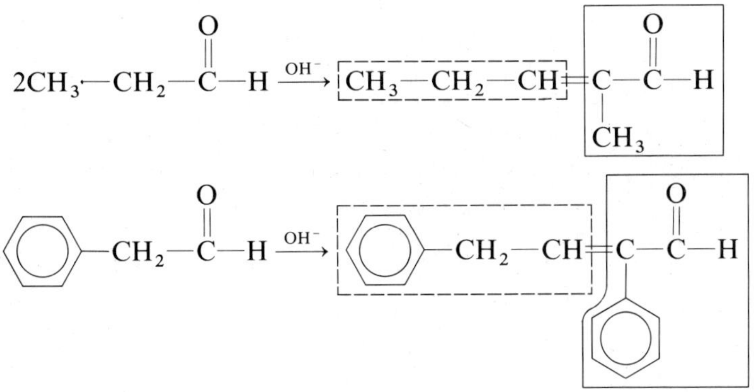

After the α,β-unsaturated aldehyde has been formed, the aldehyde or alkene parts of the molecule can be altered as desired to produce a large number of materials with new carbon skeletons. For example:

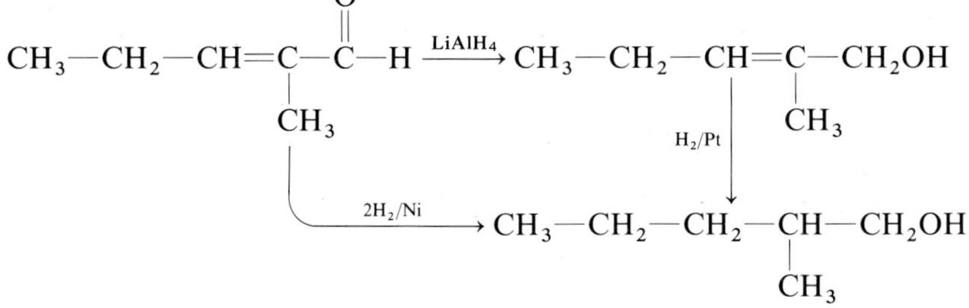

Wittig reaction

Aldehydes and ketones react with a class of compounds called phosphorus

ylides to produce a larger carbon skeleton alkene. The ylides are first prepared from trialkyl phosphines and alkyl halides, in the presence of a strong base such as butyllithium (LiC_4H_9).

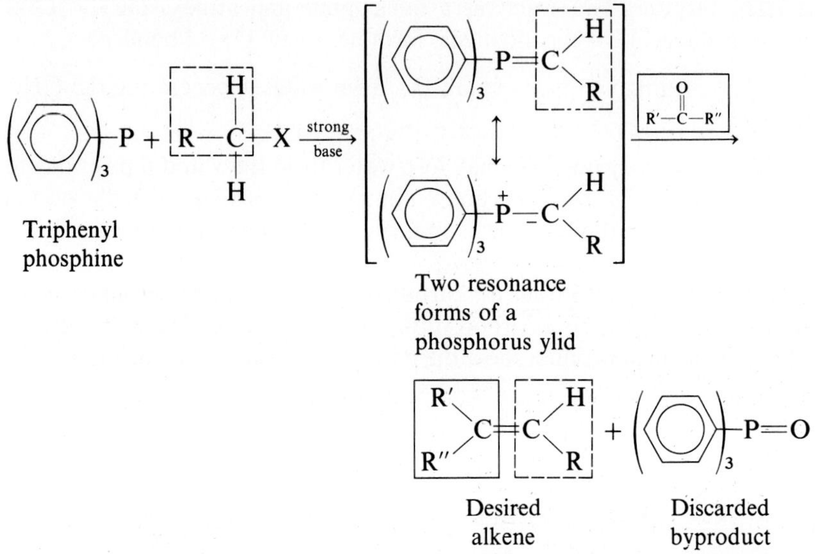

Triphenyl
phosphine

Two resonance
forms of a
phosphorus ylid

Desired
alkene

Discarded
byproduct

Note that the final alkene is composed of the carbon portion from the alkyl halide and the carbon portion of the aldehyde or ketone (note outlined areas). The two carbon atoms which are now doubly bonded to each other in the alkene are those which were previously bonded to the oxygen atom (in the $C=O$ of the aldehyde or ketone) and halogen atom (in the $R-X$).

For example

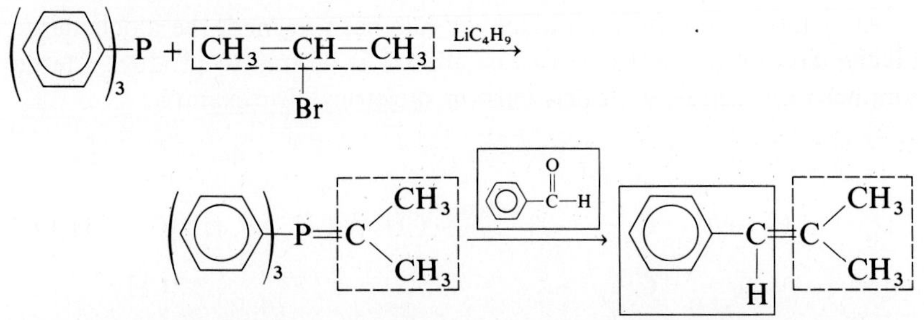

Aldehydes and ketones can be converted to solid derivatives for purposes of identification. Both functional groups are halogenated preferentially at the alpha (α) position under acid or base catalysis. Methyl ketones form iodoform when they react with aqueous I_2/OH^-. This serves to give evidence about ketone structure. Aqueous cyanide ion will add to the carbonyl group of aldehydes or ketones to produce nitriles, which can be converted to carboxylic acids having one more carbon atom than the original compound had. Alcohols can be prepared by adding Grignard reagents to aldehydes or ketones. The aldol condensation and the Witting reaction can be used to build larger carbon chains.

REACTION SUMMARY FLOW DIAGRAM—PREPARATION AND REACTIONS OF ALDEHYDES AND KETONES

Aldehydes only   Ketone only

$$R-\overset{\overset{\displaystyle O}{\|}}{C}-Cl \qquad R-\overset{\overset{\displaystyle O}{\|}}{C}-Cl$$

$$\underset{R}{\overset{R}{>}}C=C\underset{R}{\overset{R}{<}} \qquad \text{(See Chapter 6)}$$

LiAlH(t-BuO)₃   (R')₂Cd   O₃

$$\left(\text{⬡}\right)_3-P=C\underset{R'''}{\overset{R''}{<}} \qquad \underset{R}{\overset{R'}{>}}C=C\underset{R'''}{\overset{R''}{<}}$$

[O] (Aldehyde only) $$R-\overset{\overset{\displaystyle O}{\|}}{C}-R'$$ [H]   —2R"OH—

$$R-COOH$$

Z⁻   Z—NH₂   X₂ H⁺ or OH⁻

$$R-\overset{\overset{\displaystyle OH}{\,}}{\underset{\underset{\displaystyle H}{\,}}{C}}-R'$$

$$R-\overset{\overset{\displaystyle OH}{\,}}{\underset{\underset{\displaystyle Z^*}{\,}}{C}}-R' \qquad R-\overset{\overset{\displaystyle O}{\|}}{\underset{\underset{\displaystyle X}{\,}}{C}}-R'$$

1.) (N₂H₄/2) OH⁻ or Zn(Hg) HCl

$$R-\overset{\overset{\displaystyle N}{\|}}{\underset{\underset{\displaystyle Z}{\,}}{C}}-R'$$

$$R-\overset{\overset{\displaystyle O-R''}{\,}}{\underset{\underset{\displaystyle R'}{\,}}{C}}-OR''$$

$$R-CH_2-R'$$

SUMMARY

1   In the IUPAC system, **aldehyde names** end in -*al* and ketone names end in -*one*, and include the longest carbon chain designation along with names and locants of any substituents. Classical aldehyde names use base names derived from classical carboxylic acid names plus the suffix -*aldehyde*, while classical **ketone names** include the names of the two alkyl groups attached to the carbonyl group, followed by the word *ketone*.

2   Aldehydes and ketones can be **prepared** by oxidation of 1° and 2°

---

* $Z^- = CN^-$, $-\overset{\,}{\underset{\,}{\overset{-}{C}}}-\overset{\overset{\displaystyle O}{\|}}{C}-H$, $R^- - \overset{+}{M}gX$

Note: Here R' stands for an alkyl or aryl group or a hydrogen atom. R" and R''' are other such groups.

alcohols, respectively. Ketones can be prepared by the reaction of acyl halides with dialkyl cadmium, while reduction of acyl halides produces aldehydes. Ozonolysis of alkenes also produces aldehydes and/or ketones.

3 Aldehydes and ketones **react** with 1 or 2 moles of alcohol per mole to produce useful products or protecting groups. Aldehydes and ketones can be reduced to 1° and 2° alcohols, respectively, with the proper reducing agent, or they can be reduced to alkanes with Clemmensen or Wolff-Kishner reagents. Aldehydes are easily oxidized to carboxylic acids. For purposes of identification, carbonyl compounds can be converted into derivatives whose melting points serve as identifying data. Halogenation occurs selectively at the alpha position; in the case of methyl ketones, CHI_3 (iodoform) is formed under base-catalyzed conditions. Aldehydes and ketones add cyanide ions to produce nitriles (which can be changed into carboxylic acids) and add Grignard reagents to produce alcohols. Larger carbon chains can be built by the aldol condensation or by the Wittig reaction.

KEY TERMS

Acetal	Dialkyl cadmium	Nitrile
Aldol condensation	2,4-DNP	Oxidation
Amalgam	Hemiacetal	Oxime
Blocking a functional group	Hemiketal	Reduction
	Hydrazone	Semicarbazone
Carbonyl group	Iodoform	Wolff-Kishner reduction
Clemmensen reduction	Ketal	
Derivative		

SKILL PRACTICE PROBLEMS

Name these compounds:

1

$$CH_3-CH_2-\overset{\overset{\displaystyle O}{\|}}{C}-CH_2-CH_2-CH_3$$

2

$$CH_3\underset{\underset{\displaystyle Cl}{|}}{CH}-\overset{\overset{\displaystyle O}{\|}}{C}-\underset{\underset{\displaystyle CH_3}{|}}{CH}-CH_3$$

3

$$CH_3-\overset{\overset{\displaystyle O}{\|}}{C}-H$$

4 △=O

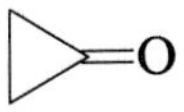

5
$$CH_3-\underset{\underset{CH_3}{|}}{\overset{\overset{CH_3}{|}}{C}}-CH_2-\overset{\overset{O}{||}}{C}-H$$

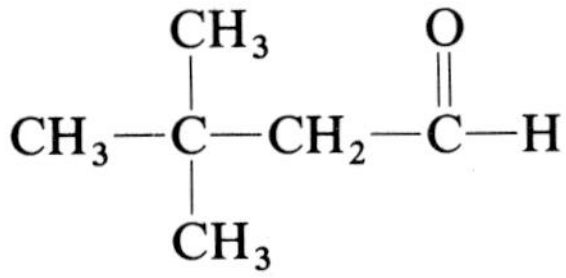

6
$$CH_3-\boxed{}-\overset{\overset{O}{||}}{C}-H$$
$$\underset{Br}{|}$$

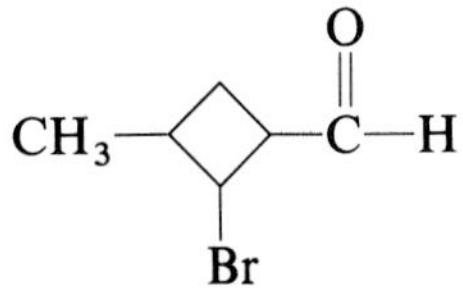

Draw structures of the following compounds:

7   Cinnamaldehyde   8   3,3-Dimethylformylcyclohexane
9   2,2-Dichloropentanal   10 4-Ethylcyclohexanone
11 Camphor   12 Di-*n*-butyl ketone
13 3-Hexanone

Complete the following reactions:

14
$$\overset{O}{\underset{\bigcirc}{||}} + CH_3-MgBr \longrightarrow$$

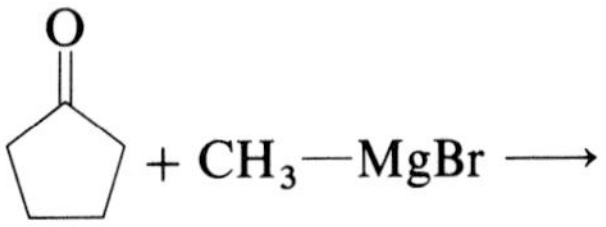

15
$$CH_3-\overset{\overset{O}{||}}{C}-H + KMnO_4 \longrightarrow$$

16
$$\overset{O}{\underset{\bigcirc}{||}} + CrO_3 \cdot 2pyr/CH_2Cl_2 \longrightarrow$$

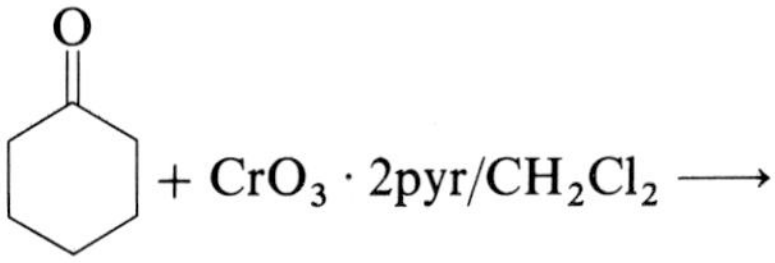

17
$$CH_3-CH_2-\overset{\overset{O}{||}}{C}-Cl + (CH_3)_2Cd \longrightarrow$$

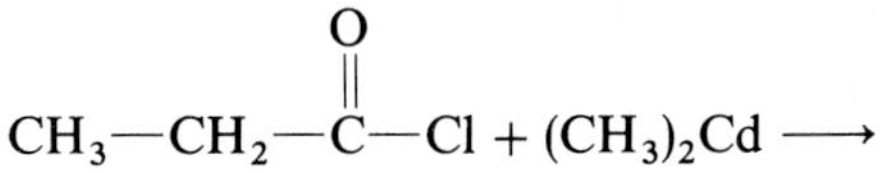

18
$$CH_3-\overset{\overset{O}{||}}{C}-H + H_2N-NH-\overset{\overset{NO_2}{}}{\bigcirc}-NO_2 \longrightarrow$$

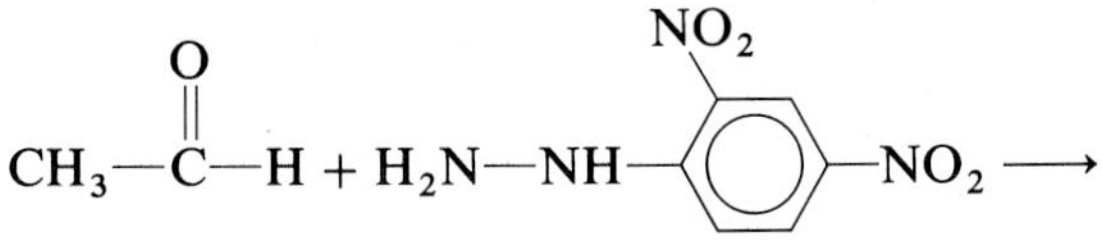

19
$$CH_3CH_2CH_2-\overset{\overset{O}{||}}{C}-H \overset{OH^-}{\longrightarrow}$$

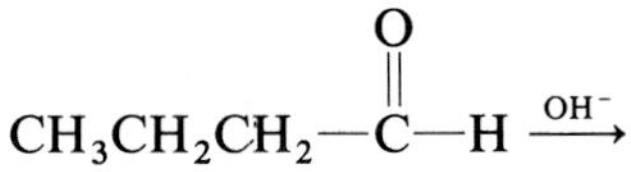

20
$$\bigcirc-OH + K_2Cr_2O_7 \longrightarrow$$

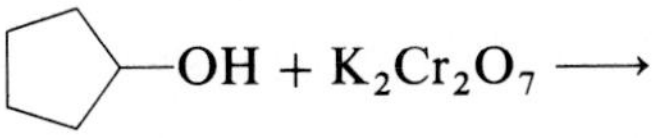

21

$$CH_3-CH_2-CH_2-\overset{\overset{\displaystyle O}{\|}}{C}-H + CH_3-CH_2-MgCl \longrightarrow$$

22    $CH_3-CH_2-CH_2OH \xrightarrow{CrO_3 \cdot 2pyr/CH_2Cl_2}$

23

$$CH_3-CH_2-\overset{\overset{\displaystyle O}{\|}}{C}-CH_3 + LiAlH_4 \longrightarrow$$

24   From the data in Table 8-1, what are the possible identities of an unknown if its oxime derivative melts at 54 to 56°C? (Melting point data are accurate to $\pm 3°C$.)

25   If the unknown in problem 24 has a 2,4-DNP derivative with a melting point of 124 to 125°C, what is the unknown?

26   Plan a synthesis of cyclohexanone from cyclohexane and any inorganic reagents. You may need to use reactions from previous chapters.

27   Plan a synthesis of $CH_3-CH_2-\overset{\overset{\displaystyle OH}{|}}{CH}-\overset{\overset{\displaystyle O}{\|}}{C}-OH$ from 1-propanol and any inorganic materials.

28   Plan a synthesis of diethyl ketone from n-propyl alcohol, 1-bromo-ethane and any inorganic reagents.

29   What is the common use or occurrence for:
(a)   benzoin   (b)   citral
(c)   retinal

30   What is(are) the purpose(s) of the following processes?
(a)   Forming a 2, 4-DNP derivative
(b)   Blocking a carbonyl by formation of a ketal
(c)   Carrying out an aldol condensation
(d)   Using $CrO_3 \cdot 2$ pyr/CH_2Cl_2 instead of $KMnO_4$ during the oxidation of 1-butanol to produce butanal.

31   Why would Clemmensen reduction not work as well as Wolff-Kishner reduction for this conversion?

32   What is the general empirical formula for an acyclic aldehyde? How does the general formula for an acyclic ketone differ from that of aldehydes?

33   Write the mechanism for the reaction in problem 19.

34   Draw the resonance forms of the anion which results from pulling an α-H from the aldehyde in the first step of the mechanism you wrote in answering problem 33.

35 Which of the following compounds would give a precipitate when added to a solution of I_2 and OH^- (i.e., which one(s) would give a positive iodoform test)?

(a)

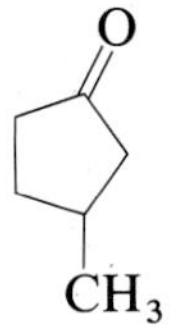

(b)

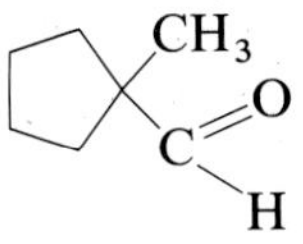

(c)

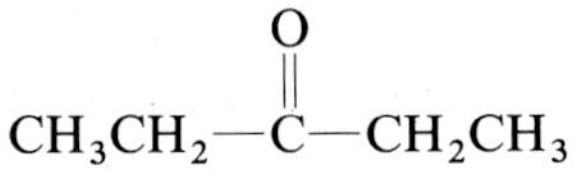

$$CH_3CH_2-\overset{\overset{\displaystyle O}{\|}}{C}-CH_2CH_3$$

(d)

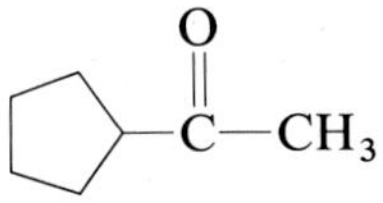

36 Which of the compounds in problem 35 would be oxidized to a carboxylic acid by $KMnO_4$?

37 What would be the product of the following sequence involving the Wittig reaction?

$$\left(\text{\hexagon}\right)_3 P + CH_3-CH_2-CH_2-Cl \xrightarrow{\text{base}} CH_3CH_2CH_2\overset{\overset{\displaystyle O}{\|}}{C}-H \longrightarrow$$

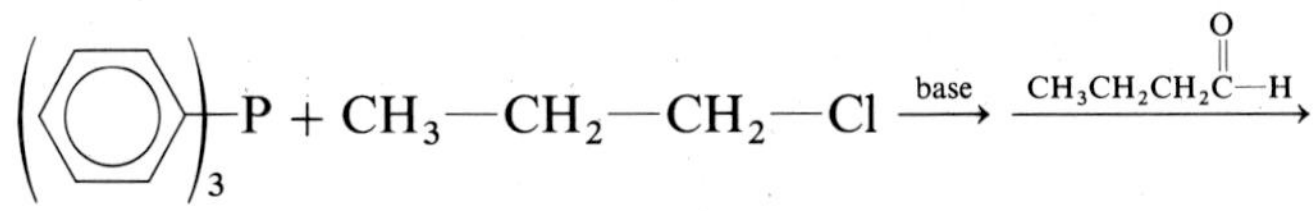

38 What alkyl halide and what aldehyde or ketone would you use to produce the following alkene using the Wittig reaction?

$$\text{\hexagon}=CH-CH_3$$

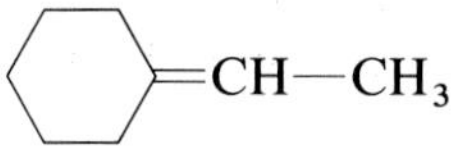

REVIEW QUESTIONS

39 Name this compound by the IUPAC system.

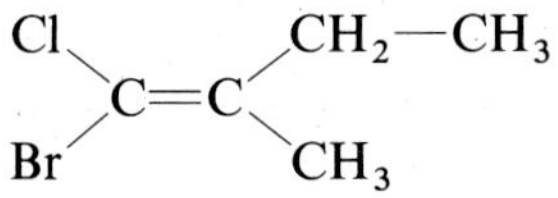

$$\underset{Br}{\overset{Cl}{>}}C=C\underset{CH_3}{\overset{CH_2-CH_3}{<}}$$

40 What is the product of methylcyclohexane reacting with Br_2 with light?

41 Give the general reaction for the Williamson ether synthesis.

42 What reagent will convert cyclohexene to cis-1,2-cyclohexanediol?

43 Give the absolute configuration at the chiral center of the following compound:

$$
\begin{array}{c}
CH_3 \\
| \\
H-C-Cl \\
| \\
CH_2 \\
| \\
CH_3
\end{array}
$$

44 What would the product be if the alkene shown in problem 38 were reacted with H_2/Pt? What would you obtain if the alkene in problem 38 were subjected to ozonolysis?

CHAPTER 9

AROMATIC COMPOUNDS

LEARNING GOALS

1 To learn the nomenclature systems for aromatic compounds, especially those of substituted benzenes

2 To understand the concept of aromaticity and to be able to determine whether or not a species is aromatic

3 To learn the reactions of benzene and its derivatives along with methods of preparation

4 To examine the molecular structures of some commercially important aromatic compounds and understand the synthetic procedures leading to selected commercial materials

In chapter 6, we studied alkenes and alkynes, both of which are classified as unsaturated hydrocarbons. In this chapter, we again encounter unsaturated compounds; we will study materials with a special kind of unsaturation—the **aromatic** compounds.

Aromatic compounds are those which can be recognized quickly as having a cyclic structure and alternating double and single bonds around the ring. Since most of these are substituted benzenes, we will concentrate in this chapter on benzene, while considering the more complex compounds in a few instances. It should be noted that the term *aromatic* has nothing to do with the compound's odor.

REPRESENTATION OF AROMATIC FORMULAS

Benzene itself is commonly represented in two ways as follows:

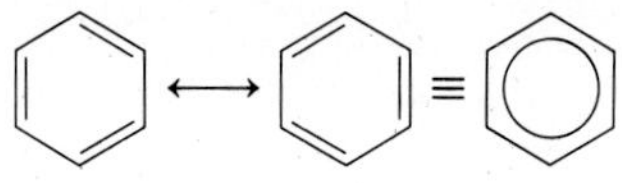

(a) (b)

There are six pi electrons, or the equivalent of three double bonds in the benzene ring. However, since there is a **delocalization** of these electrons (this is discussed more fully later in the chapter) method (a) is misleading. A circle is frequently inscribed within the ring to indicate this delocalization, and in the case of benzene the circle represents six pi electrons distributed equally around the ring. For those aromatic compounds with several rings, such as naphthalene, the inscribed circles simply mean a delocalization of electrons; there are not necessarily six electrons per ring. Both rings have six pi electrons available, but since one pair of electrons is common to both rings, there are only ten pi electrons in a naphthalene molecule.

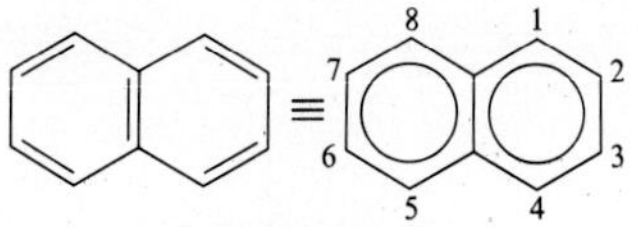

Naphthalene

In this text, we will use circles rather than alternating double and single bonds to indicate aromaticity in most formulas.

In this text, aromatic compounds are usually represented as polygons with inscribed circles. This indicates a delocalized group of pi electrons (usually six) available to each ring.

NOMENCLATURE

In addition to benzene and naphthalene, which are shown above, two other aromatic hydrocarbons are shown below and are numbered as indicated.

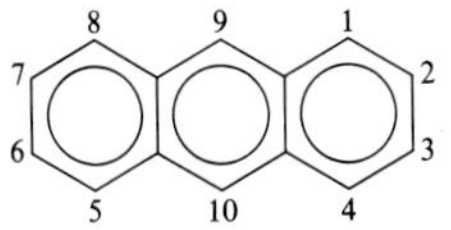

Anthracene 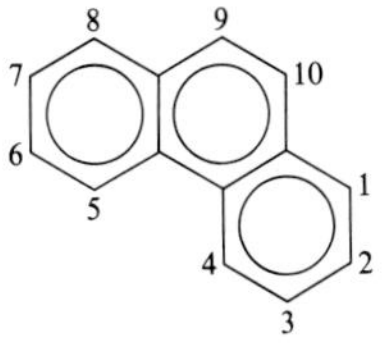   Phenanthrene

In the IUPAC system, substituent groups are named and numbered as in other cyclic compounds. The standard numbering systems are shown above for particular aromatic systems. Other polycyclic aromatic systems have their own numbering systems. Examples follow which illustrate aromatic nomenclature.

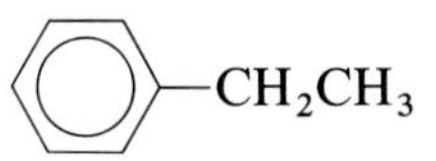

Ethylbenzene 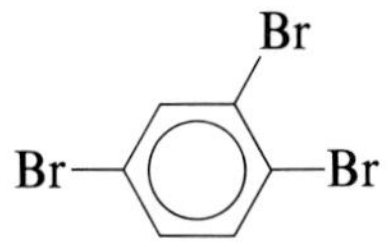   1,2,4-Tribromobenzene 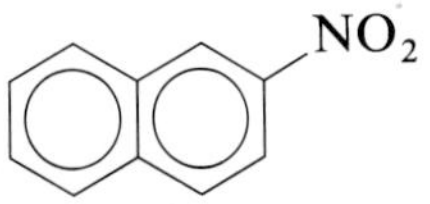   2-Nitronaphthalene

For disubstituted benzenes (*only* **two substituents**), a classical system is still in common use. If X and Y represent any two substituents, the following prefixes are used to show the position relationship of the groups to each other.

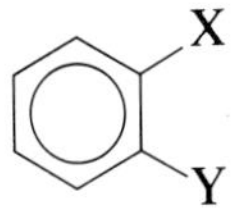

ortho- (*o-*) 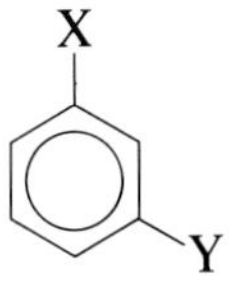   *meta-* (*m-*) 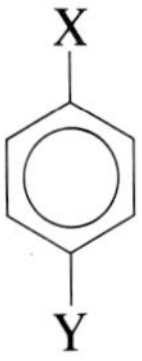   *para-* (*p-*)

When the two groups are on adjacent carbon atoms, the compound is called ortho. When the two groups are separated by one carbon atom, the compound is meta, and when they are opposite each other, the compound is para. For example

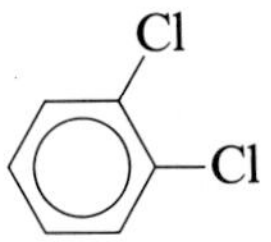

1,2-Dichlorobenzene
(*o*-Dichlorobenzene or
ortho-dichlorobenzene)

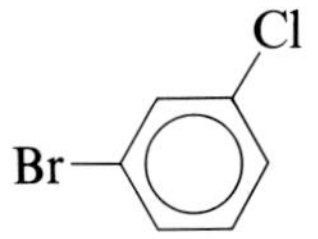

1-Bromo-3-chlorobenzene
(*m*-Bromochlorobenzene or
meta-bromochlorobenzene)

1,4-Dinitrobenzene
(*p*-Dinitrobenzene or
para-dinitrobenzene)

Several monosubstituted benzenes (those with only one group attached) have special names used in all systems. They are as follows.

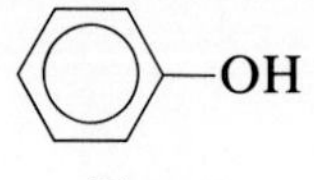

Phenol 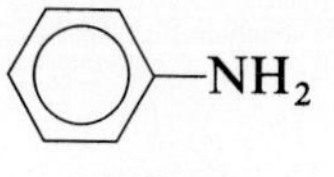   Aniline 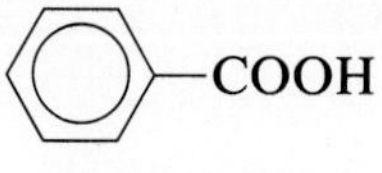   Benzoic acid 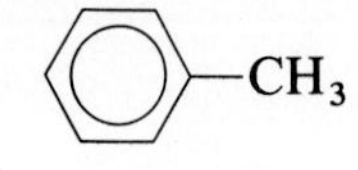   Toluene

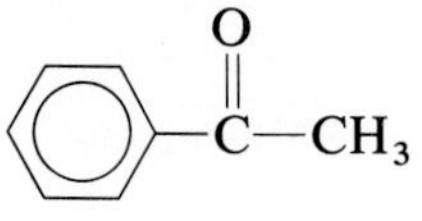

Acetophenone 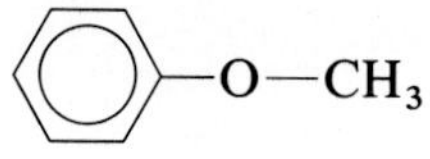   Anisole

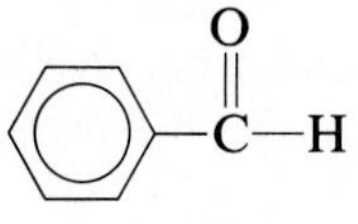

Benzaldehyde 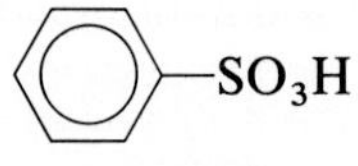   Benzenesulfonic acid

When these groups are found in a complex molecule, the compound is named as a derivative of the above names. For example

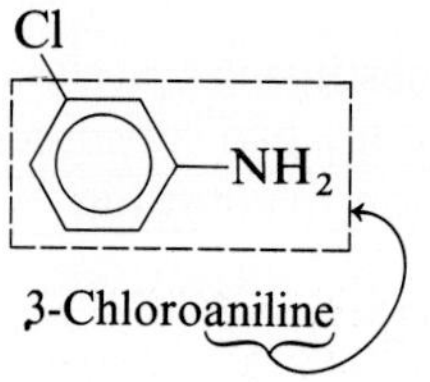

3-Chloroaniline 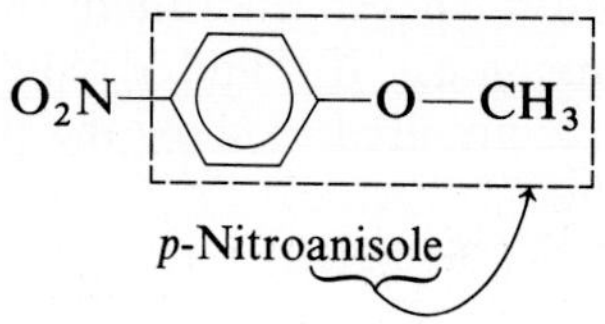   p-Nitroanisole

Other common names are shown below.

p-Xylene   Cumene   Styrene
(1,4-Dimethylbenzene)   (Isopropylbenzene)   (Vinylbenzene)

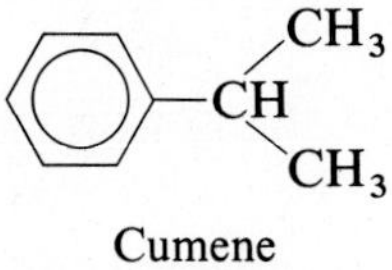

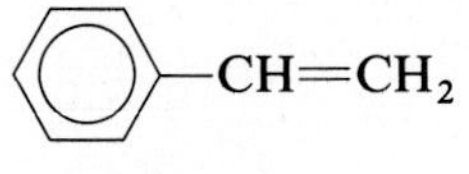

For other aromatic compounds and all but disubstituted benzenes, the following examples further illustrate the IUPAC system.

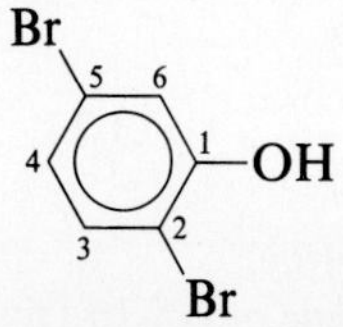

2,5-Dibromophenol 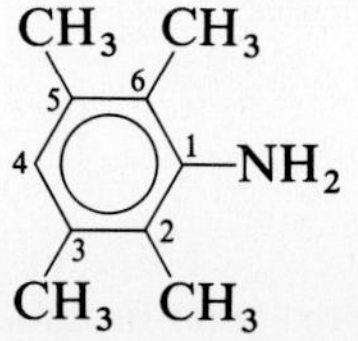   2,3,5,6-Tetramethylaniline

$CH_3CH_2CH_2$ COOH

CH_3

CH_2CH_3

2-Methyl-4-ethyl-6-
propylbenzoic acid

Br

Bromobenzene

CH_3

NO_2

1-Methyl-4-nitronaphthalene

Cl

O_2N Br

3-Bromo-5-chloronitrobenzene

Aromatic compounds are named in the IUPAC system by indicating the base name of the ring system along with any substituents and their positions. Several substituted benzenes have special names which should be learned and used as the base name of compounds containing them. For disubstituted benzenes, the prefixes *ortho-*, *meta-*, and *para-* are used to indicate the positions of the two groups relative to each other.

COMMERCIAL AROMATIC COMPOUNDS

So many products contain compounds with the benzene ring that it would be impossible to list them all. Several are shown as illustrations.

FIGURE 9-1

(a) One of the many food products containing butylated hydroxyanisole (BHA); (b) The label showing BHA is a constituent of the product.

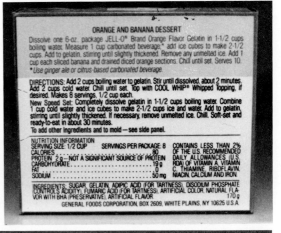

Hexachlorophene
(disinfectant)

p-Cresol
(creosote formerly used as a wood
preservative. Now prohibited for
environmental reasons)

Butylated hydroxytoluene
(BHT—food antioxidant)

Butylated hydroxyanisole
(BHA—food antioxidant. See Figure 9–1)

Naphthalene
(mothballs)

p-dichlorobenzene
(mothballs and "air freshener")

AROMATICITY

Benzene, which we have already classified as an aromatic compound, has some unique properties that are representative of a phenomenon shown by other compounds and charged intermediates. Aromaticity, when present, imparts **unusual stability** to a molecule or reactive intermediate. We, therefore, need to expand our definition of the term *aromatic* from a structural one to one that reflects chemical properties as well.

For example, benzene is quite unreactive compared to alkenes. As shown in Chapter 3, alkenes easily react with hydrogen and a catalyst (H_2/Pt) to produce alkanes, and in Chapter 6 many reactions of alkenes were presented. Benzene, on the other hand, is quite **unreactive** toward most of the reagents used with alkenes; when reaction does occur, benzene requires much stronger conditions to react, such as high temperature and pressure. One such example of the latter case is catalytic hydrogenation. Cyclohexene reacts with H_2 easily when a metal catalyst is present, but benzene will react with H_2 only under extreme conditions.

The heat energy given off when a material reacts (ΔH of the reaction) can sometimes be used to measure its stability. Consider the hydrogenation of three cyclic "alkenes" below. The ΔH values (in kilocalories per mole, kcal/mol) can be used as a measure of the stability of the original "alkene." When several compounds form the same product on hydrogenation, the energy given off during the reaction can be used as a measure of the difference in the original internal energy content.

$$\Delta H_1 = 28.5 \text{ kcal/mol}$$

$$\Delta H_2 = 55.0 \text{ kcal/mol}$$

$$\Delta H_3 = 49.5 \text{ kcal/mol}$$

All other things being equal, we might expect that 2 moles of H_2 reacting with two double bonds would give off twice as much heat as would 1 mole. Similarly, 3 moles should produce three times as much heat. Figure 9-2 shows graphically how the expected values compare with the experimental ones.

Since all three reactions produce the same product, the amount of energy given off during the reaction indicates the relative energies of the reactants prior to the reaction. This situation can be compared to having several people parachute from airplanes at various altitudes and landing at the same spot. The distance each has fallen is a measure of the starting altitude, since the finish level is the same in all cases. In Figure 9-2, the actual values are shown as ΔH_1, ΔH_2, and ΔH_3 for the three reactions we are considering. The expected values, based on multiples of ΔH_1, are also shown. The ΔH_2 value is nearly what we would expect, but the heat of hydrogenation for benzene is 36 kcal/mol less than predicted. This means that benzene must be 36 kcal/mol **more stable** (less reactive) than it would be if it were composed of three C=C units in cyclic form. This difference is called the **resonance energy**.

We explain this unusual stability by the fact that the pi electrons in the double bonds of benzene are completely delocalized. This means that they are not arranged so as to form alternating double and single bonds

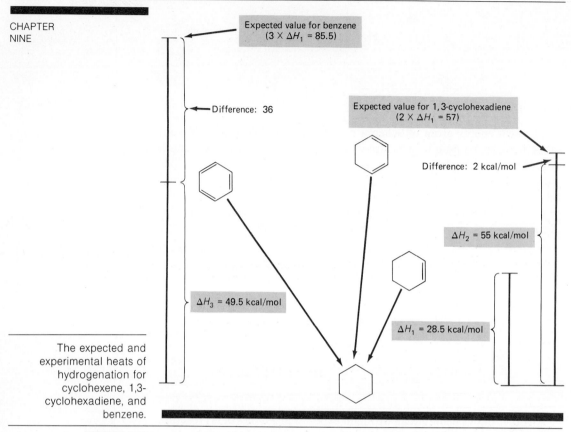

The expected and
experimental heats of
hydrogenation for
cyclohexene, 1,3-
cyclohexadiene, and
benzene.

FIGURE 9-2

around the ring but are equally distributed in two doughnut-shaped
clouds of electron density shown in Figure 9-3.

This delocalization of electrons is the reason why we represent a benzene
molecule with a circle in the carbon ring rather than with alternating
double and single bonds, as discussed at the beginning of the chapter.

Chemists have discovered that certain cyclic reactive intermediates such
as free radicals and charged species can also be aromatic. When they are,
they have an increased stability over what would otherwise be expected,
and the charged species can sometimes actually be isolated as salts. How
can we predict whether or not a compound will be aromatic? To be aromatic, that is, to have extensive pi electron delocalization, the four conditions shown in Table 9-1 (page 292) must be met.

If a compound is expected to exhibit aromatic character, it must be
cyclic, planar, have a continuous cloud of pi electrons, and have any one
of a limited number of pi electrons. The last requirement is called Huckel's
rule, and the numbers of pi electrons which will allow a compound to be
aromatic are 2, 6, 10, 14, etc. (counting by fours).

The following examples illustrate these rules:

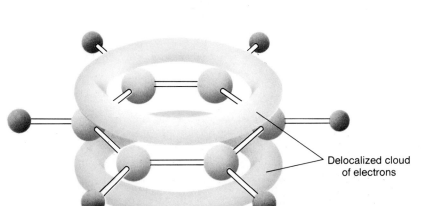

Carbon   Hydrogen

Delocalized cloud
of electrons

Molecular model of
benzene. Note the rings of
pi electron density above
and below the ring of
carbon atoms.

FIGURE 9-3

COMPOUND	CONDITIONS	

This compound is not aromatic.
1 It is cyclic
2 It is planar
3 One atom is sp^3 hybridized, therefore the closed ring of electrons could not form.
4 It has six pi electrons—(2 + 2 + 2; a Huckel number)

This compound is not aromatic
1 It is cyclic
2 It is planar
3 It as a p orbital at each atom
4 It has four pi electrons (2 + 2; not a Huckel number)

This compound is aromatic
1 It is cyclic
2 It is planar
3 All atoms are sp^2 hybridized (p orbital at each atom)
4 It has two pi electrons (2 + 0; a Huckel number)

A cyclic compound is aromatic (i.e., especially stable and containing a delocalized cloud of pi electrons) if it meets four conditions. While benzene, naphthalene, and other hydrocarbons along with their derivatives are the most commonly encountered aromatic materials, the stabilities of reactive intermediates can also be greatly enhanced by aromaticity.

TABLE 9-1

CONDITIONS FOR AROMATICITY	CONDITION	OPERATIONAL CHARACTERISTICS
	1 The compound must be cyclic	Carbons (or O, N, S) must be in a cyclic arrangement
	2 The compound must have planar molecules	All 3- to 7-membered rings that meet the other three conditions will be planar
	3 There must be a p orbital at each atom in the ring	One of the following must be observed at *each* atom in the cycle: double bond pair of unbonded electrons free radical cation anion
	4 The molecules must have $(4n + 2)$ π ring electrons (Huckel's rule). If $n = 0$, then $4n + 2 = 2$ 1 6 2 10 3 14 etc.	The total π electrons are counted as follows: $C{=}C$ 2 $Z{:}^{*}$ 2 $C{\cdot}$ 1 C^{+} 0 C^{-} 2

* Z represents a hetero atom, such as N or O, which has an unbonded pair of electrons.

PREPARATION OF SUBSTITUTED BENZENES

There are few ways to prepare aromatic rings from nonaromatic ones. Here we will limit our coverage to the formation of substituted benzenes from substituted cyclohexanes. Either cyclohexane itself or substituted cyclohexanes can be changed into their aromatic equivalents by removing six hydrogen atoms under vigorous catalytic conditions, as follows:

For example

GENERAL REACTIONS OF BENZENE AND ITS DERIVATIVES

Hydrogenation

As already mentioned, benzene is unusually stable because of its pi electron delocalization. This means that benzene will undergo few of the reactions that are typical of alkenes. Even when reactions similar to those of alkenes do occur they require much stronger reaction conditions. Benzene and its derivatives (substituted benzenes) can be hydrogenated to produce the corresponding cyclohexanes. This is just the reverse of the change accomplished by the reaction given in the previous section. The reaction below takes place at 100 atmospheres (100 atm) of pressure.

$$\text{C}_6\text{H}_5\text{—R} + 3\text{H}_2 \xrightarrow[\text{Ni}]{100°\text{C, 100 atm}} \text{R—C}_6\text{H}_{11}$$

This reaction has to be carried out in a high pressure reaction vessel like that shown in Figure 9-4.

The aromatic compound and catalyst are placed in a thick-walled steel vessel, and the line from a tank of compressed H_2 is hooked up. The H_2 pressure is adjusted to 1400 lb/in² (100 atm) or more, and the heating unit surrounding the vessel is adjusted to give 100°C. This reaction is run for several hours while the pressure vessel is rocked mechanically to stir the contents.

Examples of this reaction type are

$$\text{C}_6\text{H}_5\text{—CH}_3 + 3\text{H}_2 \xrightarrow[\text{Ni}]{100°\text{C, 100 atm}} \text{C}_6\text{H}_{11}\text{—CH}_3$$

Toluene · Methylcyclohexane

$$\text{(}m\text{-Diethylbenzene)} + 3\text{H}_2 \xrightarrow[\text{Ni}]{100°\text{C, 100 atm}} \text{1,3-Diethylcyclohexane}$$

m-Diethylbenzene · 1,3-Diethylcyclohexane

$$\text{C}_6\text{H}_5\text{—OH} + 3\text{H}_2 \xrightarrow[\text{Ni}]{100°\text{C, 100 atm}} \text{C}_6\text{H}_{11}\text{—OH}$$

Phenol · Cyclohexanol

Side chain halogenation

When an alkyl benzene is subjected to free radical halogenation conditions, side chain hydrogen atoms on the carbon atom next to the aromatic ring are the most reactive. These are called **benzylic** hydrogen atoms, and they are even more reactive than are tertiary hydrogen atoms.

FIGURE 9-4

Vessel used for high-temperature–high-pressure hydrogenation reactions.

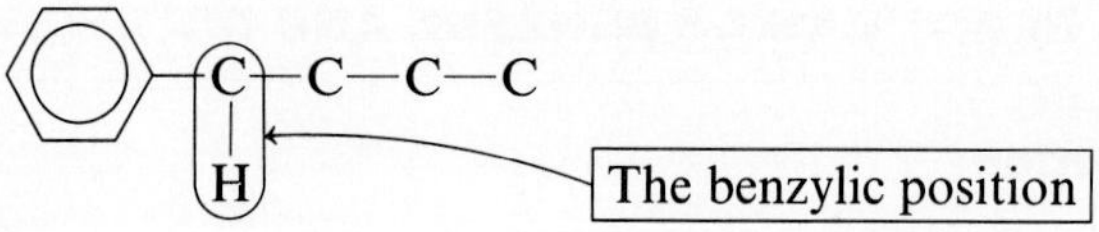

The benzylic position

For example

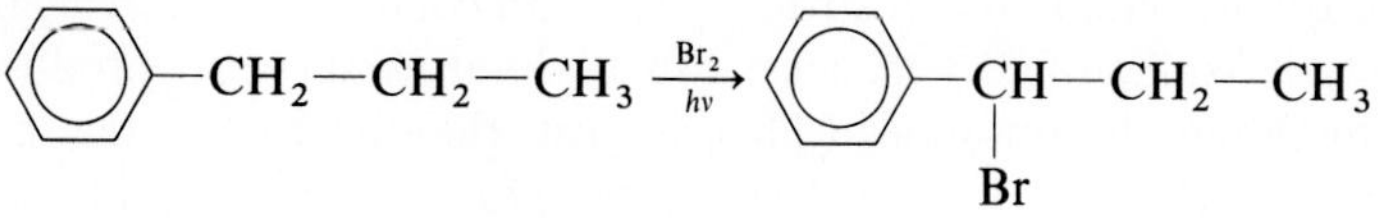

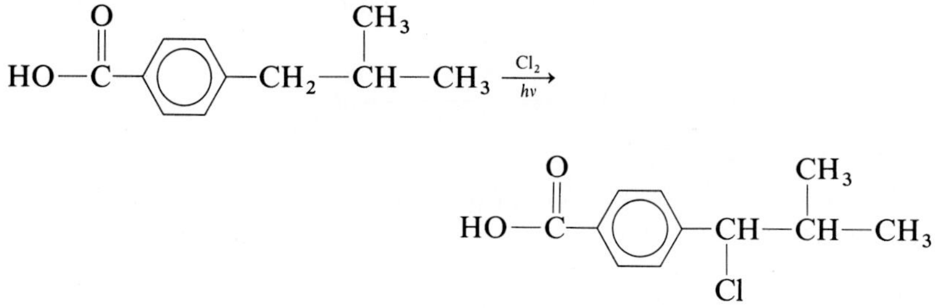

The reason why the benzylic position is so reactive is that the intermediate free radical is **resonance-stabilized**—the free radical character can be distributed over the benzene ring rather than localized on the benzylic carbon atom. Delocalization causes increased stability in this case just as it does in carbocations. See Chapter 3 for a review of the mechanism of free radical halogenation. For example:

$$Cl_2 \xrightarrow{hv} 2Cl \cdot$$

Resonance-stabilized
free radical

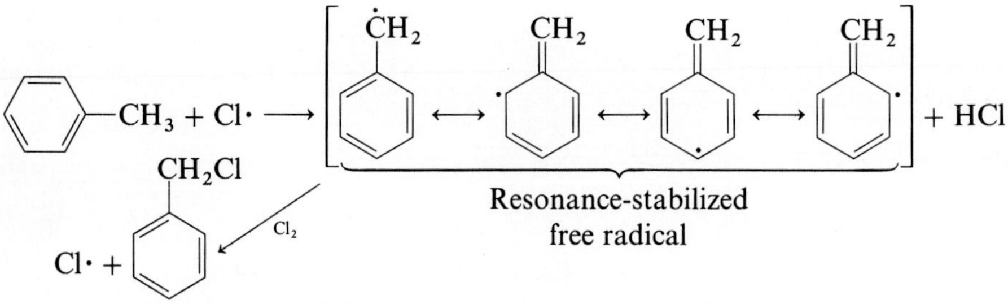

Side chain oxidation

If an alkyl group is attached to an aromatic ring and there is at least one α (benzylic) hydrogen atom, then an excess of a very strong oxidizing agent such as hot concentrated $KMnO_4$ will convert a side chain of any size into a carboxyl group as shown in the examples below.

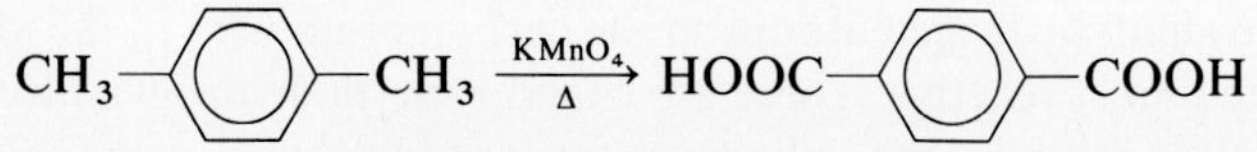

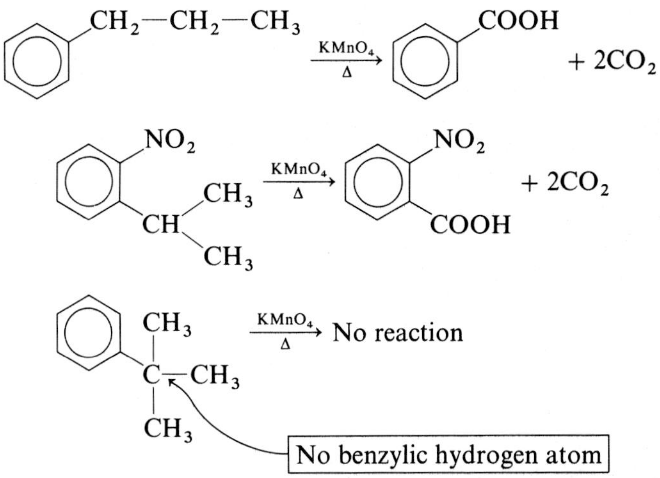

This reaction makes it possible to introduce an acid functional group onto an aromatic ring in a synthesis problem.

Benzene and its derivatives can be changed to the corresponding cyclohexanes by hydrogenation. The side chains of alkyl benzenes can be oxidized to carboxylic acid groups or selectively halogenated at the benzylic position.

ELECTROPHILIC AROMATIC SUBSTITUTION

The most useful reaction of benzene is the substitution of one or more hydrogen atoms by an electrophilic group. Many commercial products are synthesized by using this type of reaction. Many groups can be placed on a benzene ring, and some of them can be changed into other functional groups after placement on the ring. The general reaction may be represented as follows:

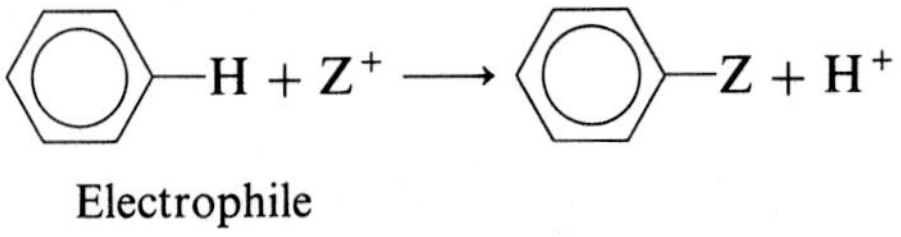

Electrophile

Five of the most common electrophilic reagents that can be used, along with an example of each, are shown below.

NAME	REAGENTS	GROUP ADDED
Nitration	HNO_3/H_2SO_4	$-NO_2$ Nitro

$$\text{benzene} + HNO_3 \xrightarrow{H_2SO_4} \text{C}_6\text{H}_5-NO_2$$

NAME	REAGENTS	GROUP ADDED
Sulfonation	$H_2SO_4 \cdot SO_3$ Oleum	$-SO_3H$ Sulfonic acid

$$CH_3-\text{C}_6H_4 + H_2SO_4 \cdot SO_3 \longrightarrow CH_3-\text{C}_6H_4-SO_3H$$

NAME	REAGENTS	GROUP ADDED
Friedel-Crafts alkylation	$RX/AlCl_3$	$-R$

NAME	REAGENTS	GROUP ADDED
Friedel-Crafts acylation	$R-\overset{O}{\underset{\|\|}{C}}-X/AlCl_3$	$-\overset{O}{\underset{\|\|}{C}}-R$

NAME	REAGENTS	GROUP ADDED
Halogenation (Cl_2, Br_2 only)	X_2/Fe	$-X$

$$\text{benzene} + Br_2 \xrightarrow{Fe} \text{C}_6H_5-Br$$

The following three reactions are frequently used to change groups on an aromatic ring into other functional groups.

Reduction of side chain carbonyl

Example

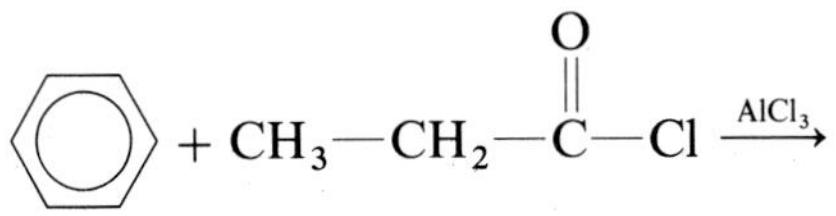

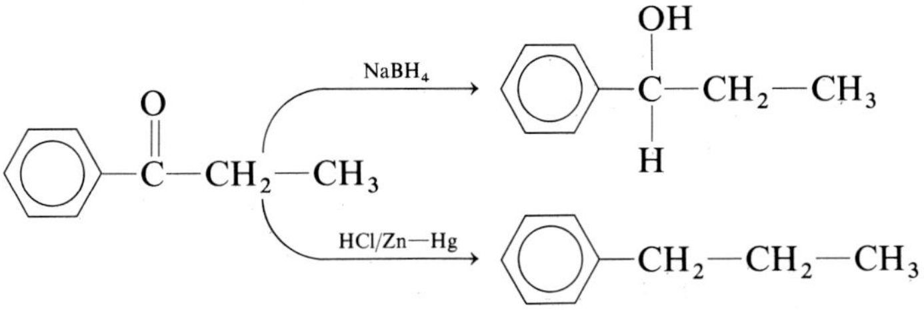

Reduction of nitro group

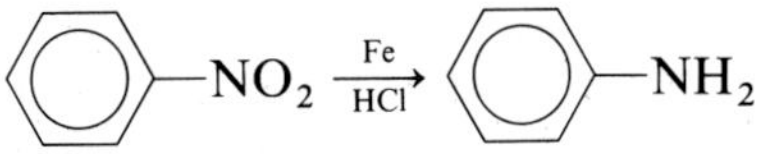

Example

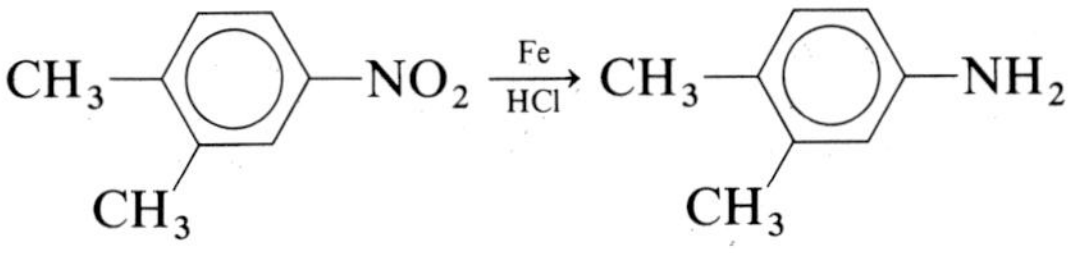

Diazotization and subsequent modification

The —NH$_2$ group can be changed into a very reactive species called a **diazonium salt**.

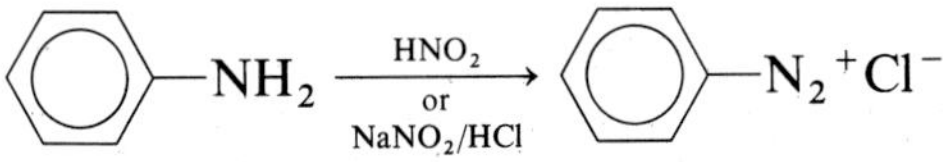

Diazonium salt

The diazonium salt can then be treated with any one of several reagents to produce other functional groups. In many cases, reaction with a diazonium salt is the only way that a particular functional group can be placed on a benzene ring. (In the scheme below, G stands for an activating group.)

The treatment of a diazonium salt with copper(I) salts is called the **Sandmeyer reaction**, and replaces the N_2^+ with a Cl, Br or CN group. KI and HBF_4 will replace N_2^+ with I or F, respectively. **Iodine** and **fluorine** cannot be introduced by direct halogenation, so this is the preferred method of preparing aromatic iodides and fluorides.

The **COOH** group can be produced from hydrolysis of the nitrile group (CN) or by carbonation of the Grignard reagent (see Chapter 12 for carbonation of Grignard reagents). **Phenols** are most conveniently produced in the laboratory by the reaction of diazonium salts with water.

The N_2^+ group (and thus NH_2 or NO_2 groups) can be **removed** by hypophosphorous acid (H_3PO_2), which replaces the N_2^+ group with a hydrogen atom. Finally, the diazonium salts can be allowed to react with other activated aromatic compounds to produce "azo" dyes. As noted, the letter G in the scheme stands for an activating group (see page 303 for a definition and examples). Dyes can be prepared in many colors, the exact color depending on the nature of the other groups on both aromatic rings.

The HNO_2 (nitrous acid) used to produce the $-N_2^+$ group is unstable and must be produced in situ (within the reaction vessel) by the reaction of HCl with $NaNO_2$. In a chemical equation, it can be expressed by either of the ways shown in the examples below.

or

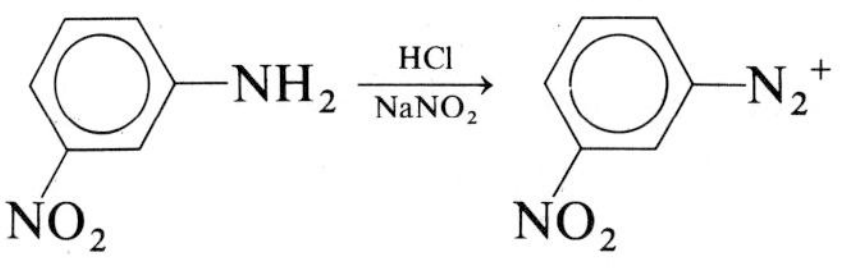

Some examples of the use of diazonium salts in syntheses follow:

a)

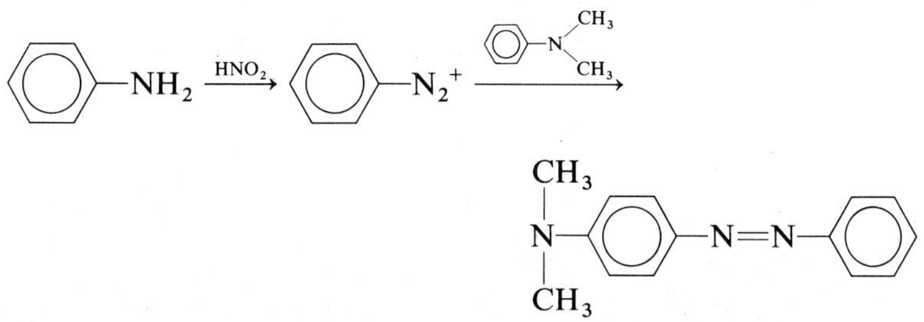

Yellow dye
(butter yellow)[1]

b)

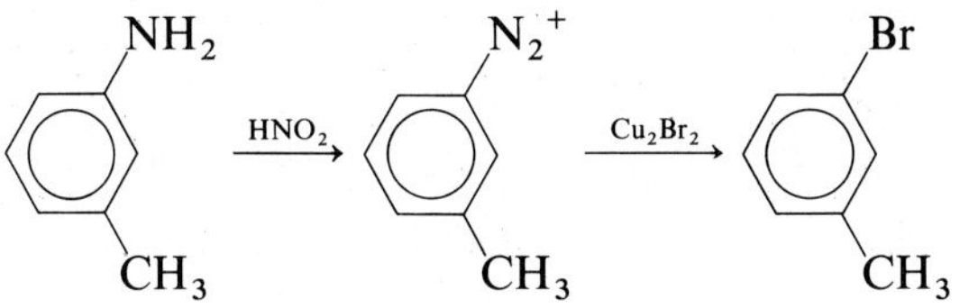

c)

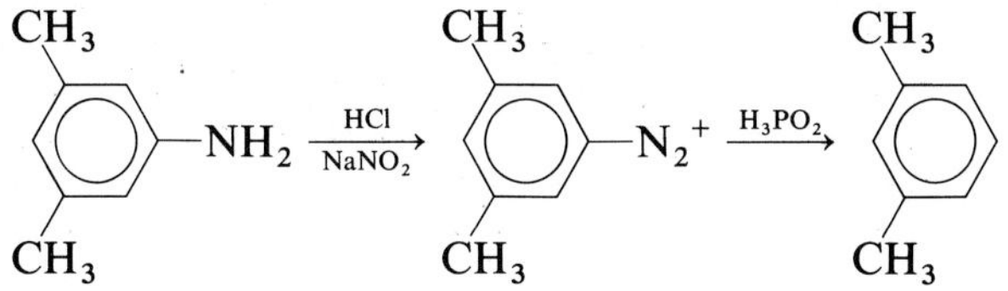

d)

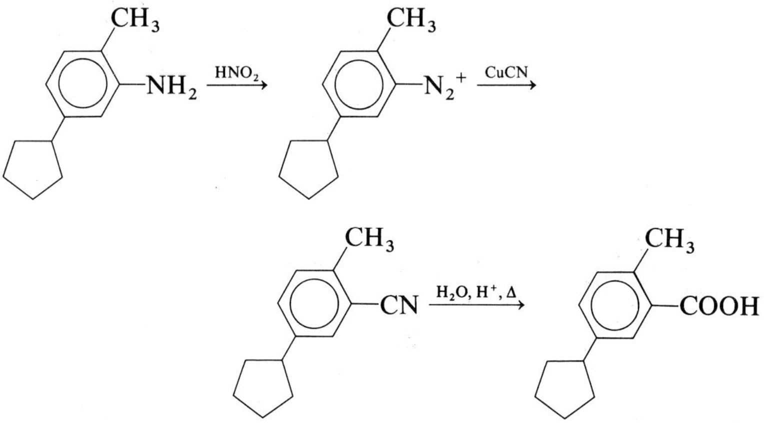

---

[1] Butter yellow is no longer used because of suspected carcinogenicity.

Commercial preparations using electrophilic substitution

A dye Methyl orange can be produced by the reaction of the diazonium salt shown below with dimethylaniline. Other substituent groups attached produce other colors.

$$HO_3S-\text{<benzene ring>}-NH_2 \xrightarrow{Na_2CO_3}$$

$$Na^+\bar{O}_3S-\text{<benzene ring>}-NH_2 \xrightarrow[NaNO_2]{HCl} \boxed{\begin{array}{c} Na^+ \\ \bar{O}_3S-\text{<benzene ring>}-N_2{}^+ \end{array}}$$

$$\bar{O}_3S-\text{<benzene ring>}-N_2{}^+ + \text{<benzene ring>}-N\begin{array}{c} CH_3 \\ CH_3 \end{array} \longrightarrow$$
$$Na^+$$

$$\boxed{\begin{array}{c} Na^+ \\ \bar{O}_3S-\text{<benzene ring>} \end{array}}-N=N-\text{<benzene ring>}-N\begin{array}{c} CH_3 \\ CH_3 \end{array}$$

Methyl orange

A polymer Some of the familiar polystyrene (see Figure 9-5) is produced by Friedel-Crafts acylation (using the anhydride instead of the acid chloride) followed by reduction, acid catalyzed dehydration (using KHSO$_4$ as the acid) and polymerization (see page 194). Most styrene produced today is made by a less expensive method involving the dehydrogenation of ethylbenzene.

$$\text{<benzene ring>} + \begin{array}{c} CH_3-C\overset{O}{\diagup}\diagdown_{O} \\ CH_3-C\diagdown_{O} \end{array} \xrightarrow{AlCl_3} \text{<benzene ring>}-\overset{\overset{O}{\|}}{C}-CH_3 \xrightarrow{NaBH_4} \text{<benzene ring>}-\overset{OH}{\underset{H}{C}}-CH_3 \xrightarrow[\Delta]{KHSO_4}$$

$$\text{<benzene ring>}-CH=CH_2 \xrightarrow{peroxide} \text{<benzene ring>}-(\text{CH}-CH_2)_x$$
Styrene   Polystyrene

A medicine Here, the first two reactions are standard reactions which have already been covered. The third step causes blocking of the —NH$_2$

FIGURE 9-5

This drinking cup is made of polystyrene foam.

300

group so that it will not react with the chlorosulfonic acid in the next step. After the NH_3 has reacted with the SO_2Cl group to produce the SO_2NH_2, the blocking amide group is changed back to the desired —NH_2 group. The product is sulfanilamide, one of the sulfa drugs. These were the first widely used antibiotics and are still used for some microbial infections.

Electrophilic substitution reactions allow us to introduce any one of several groups onto a benzene ring. Some of these groups can subsequently be converted to other functional groups if desired.

Mechanism for electrophilic aromatic substitution

The following is the accepted two-step mechanism by which all electrophilic aromatic substitution reactions occur. The different electrophilic species (Z^+) are generated by the various reagents, but a positive species always becomes attached to the benzene ring to produce a carbocation. This carbocation (shown in brackets below) is **resonance stabilized**. It subsequently loses a proton(H^+) to return to the aromatic state. We show the individual double bonds in benzene for "electron bookkeeping" purposes—there is actually complete delocalization, as you will remember.

The following two examples illustrate the mechanism of electrophilic substitution including formation of the electrophilic species (Z^+). For halogenation

Generation of electrophile
$$\begin{cases} 3Cl_2 + 2Fe \longrightarrow 2FeCl_3 \\ FeCl_3 + Cl_2 \longrightarrow FeCl_4^- + \quad Cl^+ \\ \qquad\qquad\qquad\qquad\qquad \text{Electrophile} \end{cases}$$

For Friedel-Crafts acylation

Generation of electrophile
$$\begin{cases} \underset{\text{Electrophile}}{CH_3-\overset{\displaystyle O}{\overset{\|}{C}}-Cl + AlCl_3 \longrightarrow AlCl_4^- + CH_3-\overset{\displaystyle O}{\overset{\|}{C}}{}^+} \end{cases}$$

Activation and directing effects

When a substituted benzene reacts with one of the reagents used to put a new group on the ring, the substituent already on the ring determines **where** the new group will go and also the **rate** of the reaction. The reagents determine **what** the new group will be.

| This controls **where** Z will go and the ease of substitution | This is the **new group** to be placed on the ring |

Of the possible Y groups, all can be classified into three categories. Those categories and commonly encountered members of each will now be discussed.

Activators, ortho-para directors   These groups cause the reaction to go faster than it would with unsubstituted benzene, and they cause the new group to be substituted **ortho** and **para** to the group already in place (two products are produced). The terms strong, moderate, and mild refer to the degree to which the reaction rate is enhanced relative to that of benzene itself.

STRONG	MODERATE	MILD
$-\overset{..}{\underset{..}{N}}H_2$	$-\overset{..}{\underset{..}{O}}-\overset{\overset{\textstyle O}{\|}}{C}-R$	$-R$
$-\overset{..}{\underset{..}{O}}H$	$-\underset{H}{\overset{..}{N}}-\overset{\overset{\textstyle O}{\|}}{C}-R$	⬡

Deactivators, meta directors   These groups cause the reactions to go more slowly than they would with benzene and cause the entering groups to go to the **meta** position relative to the group already in place.

STRONG	MODERATE
$-NO_2$	$-\overset{\overset{\textstyle O}{\|}}{C}-R$
$-NH_3{}^+$	$-\overset{\overset{\textstyle O}{\|}}{C}-O-R$
	$-SO_3H$

Deactivators, ortho-para directors   Only halogen atoms show this effect.

Examples of directing and activating effects

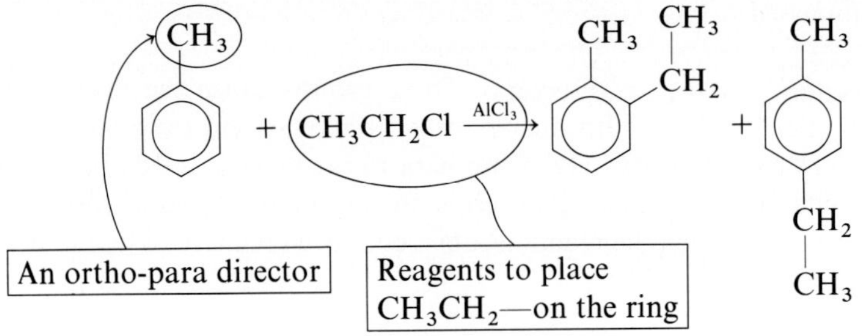

An ortho-para director

Reagents to place
CH_3CH_2—on the ring

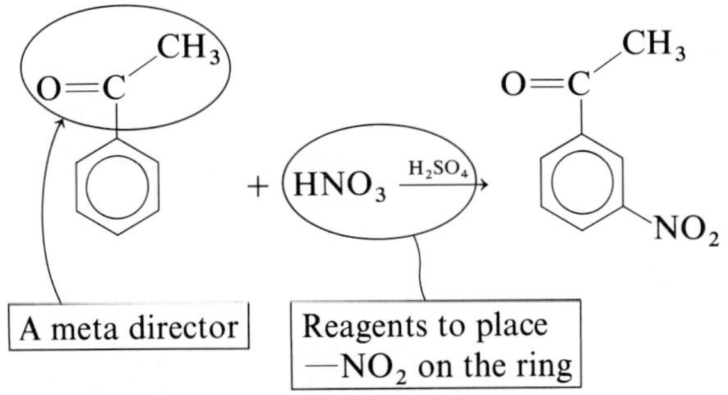

A meta director

Reagents to place
—NO_2 on the ring

Explanation of directing effects

Why should different groups show different directing and activation effects?
The answer can best be presented by showing the resonance-stabilized
intermediates produced when each type of group is present. If we draw
the resonance forms resulting from electrophilic attack on the various
positions of substituted benzenes, certain intermediate aromatic cations
will be seen to be more stable than others.

When a given compound is capable of undergoing two or more different
reaction pathways with a particular reagent, it will usually take the reaction path in which the most stable intermediate species is produced. Below
are shown the resonance forms of the species resulting from ortho, para,
and meta attack by an electrophile (X^+) on

Phenol, where the OH group is a strongly activating ortho-para director
Toluene, where the methyl group is a mildly activating ortho-para director
Nitrobenzene, where the nitro group is a strongly deactivating meta
director

1 Considering ortho, para, and meta attack on phenol, with ortho attack,
the possibilities are as follows:

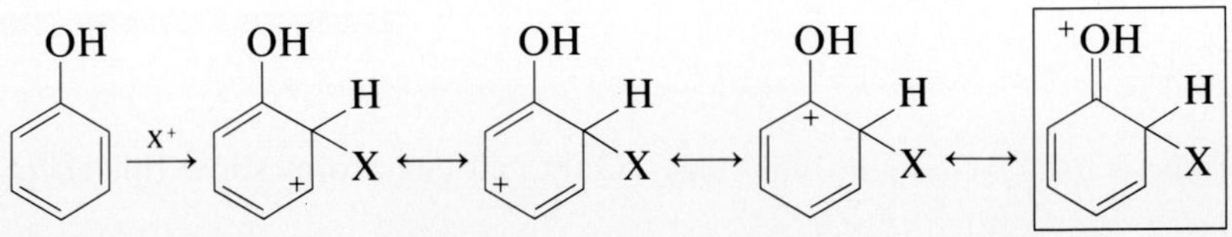

With para attack, the possibilities are as follows:

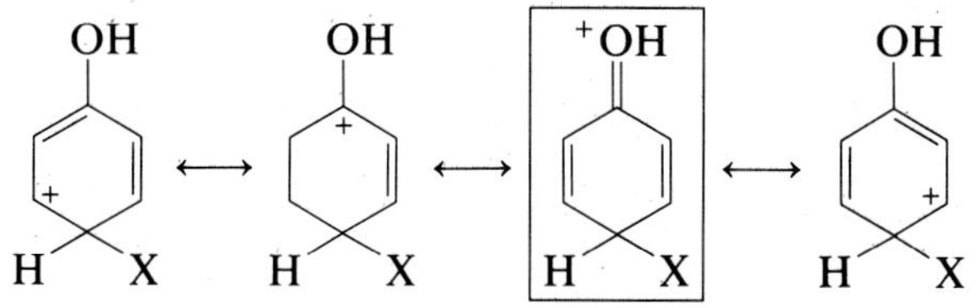

With meta attack, the possibilities are as follows:

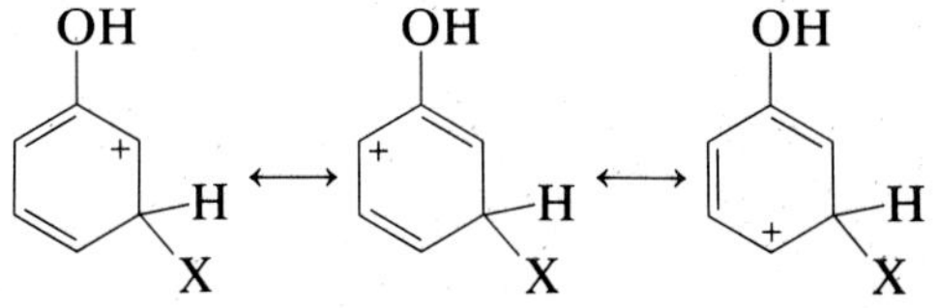

Both ortho and para attacks produce species that have more resonance forms than do species from meta attack, and one of them (outlined) is especially stable (all atoms have octets of electrons). Thus, the oxygen atom can hold a positive charge more easily than a carbon atom. Thus, ortho and para attacks produce an intermediate that is **more stable** than that which would be produced with unsubstituted benzene (see page 301). The reaction goes faster than it would with benzene because the activation energy leading to the more stable intermediate is lower. The ortho-para attack produces the most stable form and so is preferred over the meta attack. All the strong and moderate activators have an electronegative atom with an unbonded pair of electrons next to the aromatic ring. These electrons can be used to share with the ring and produce a resonance form with the positive charge on that electronegative atom (such as O or N). This cause for enhanced reaction rates is called **activation by resonance**.

2   Considering ortho, meta, and para attack on toluene, for ortho attack the possibilities are as follows:

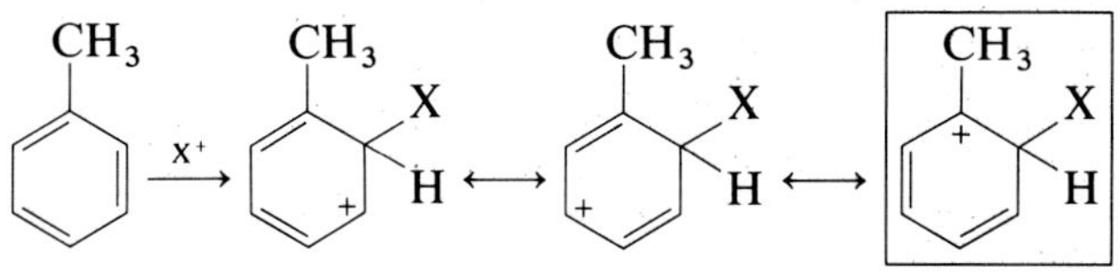

For para attack

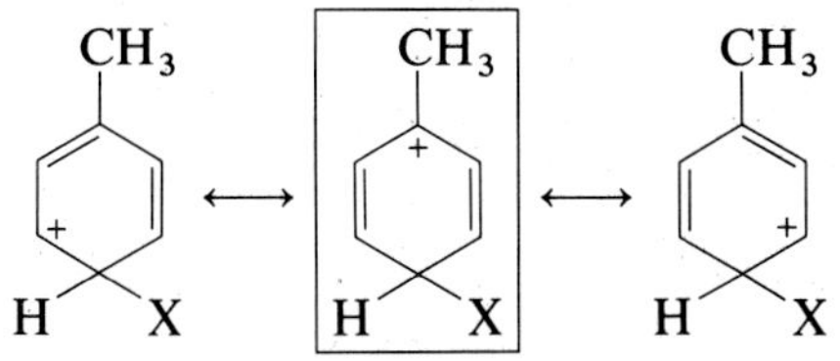

For meta attack

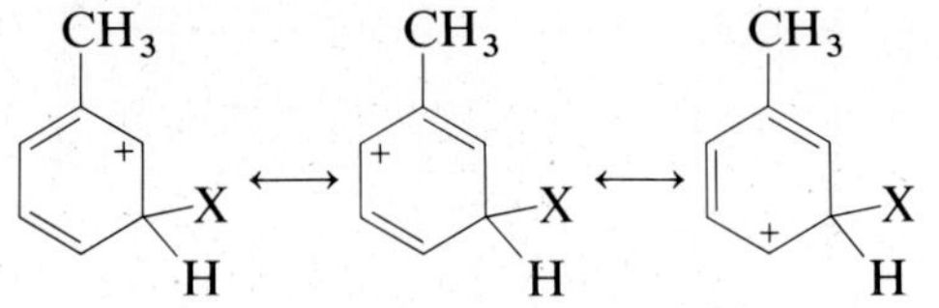

In this situation, both ortho and para attacks produce an intermediate that is more stable than that which would be produced by unsubstituted benzene. The outlined resonance forms have a 3° carbocation (see page 151), while the meta attack produces no such 3° cation. Here again, ortho-para attack produces a species which is a little more stable than would be produced by benzene itself, and toluene is therefore a little more reactive toward electrophilic substitution than is benzene. Again the ortho-para mode of attack is preferred over the meta mode because the species resulting from ortho-para attack is more stable. This phenomenon is called **activation by positive inductive effect**.

3   Considering ortho, meta, and para attack on nitrobenzene, for ortho attack the possibilities are as follows:

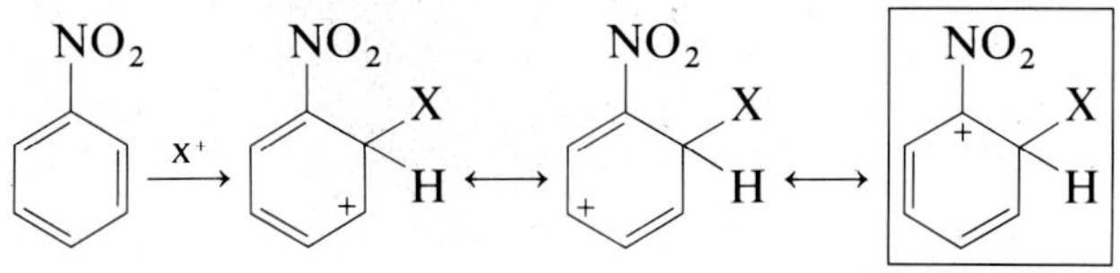

For para attack

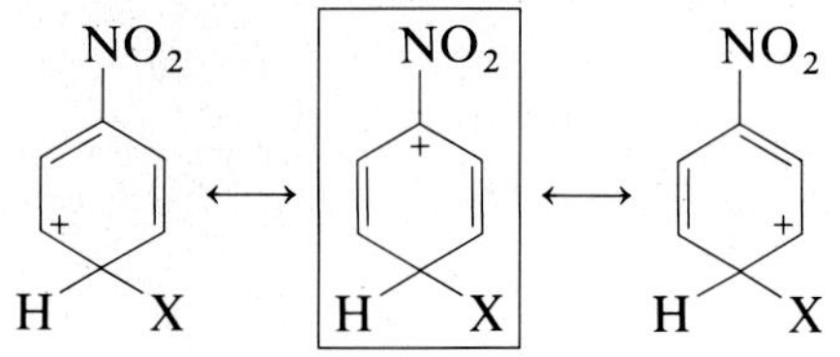

For meta attack

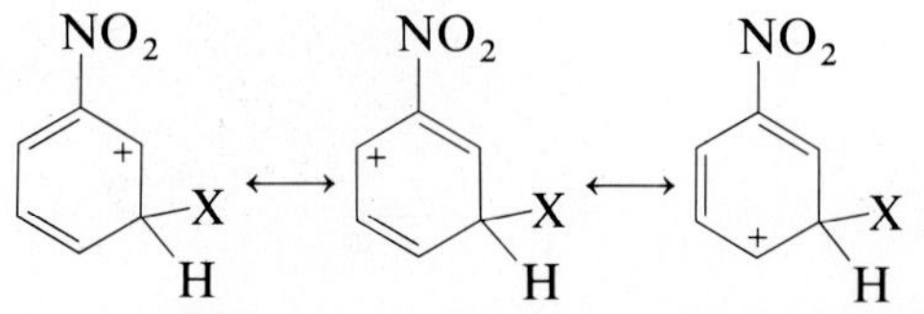

All deactivators, including the nitro group (—NO$_2$), have electron deficient atoms attached to the aromatic ring. These atoms tend to pull electron density from the aromatic ring, as is the case for the circled resonance forms above. This makes these resonance forms especially **unstable**. Thus, the meta attack is favored over ortho-para attack. Nitrobenzene is less reactive than benzene because the —NO$_2$ group pulls electron density from the aromatic ring, causing the electrophile to be attracted less than it would be toward unsubstituted benzene. This is called **deactivation by negative inductive effect**.

Electrophilic aromatic substitution reactions occur by a two-step mechanism involving a resonance-stabilized intermediate. Different substituent groups on benzene cause different activating and directing effects toward an incoming group for electrophilic reactions. These effects can be explained by considering the stabilities of the intermediate carbocation formed after initial attack at the various positions.

REACTION SUMMARY FLOW
DIAGRAM—AROMATIC COMPOUNDS

PHENOLS

Phenols are compounds in which an —OH is bonded directly to an aromatic ring. They are much more acidic than alcohols but not as acidic as carboxylic acids.

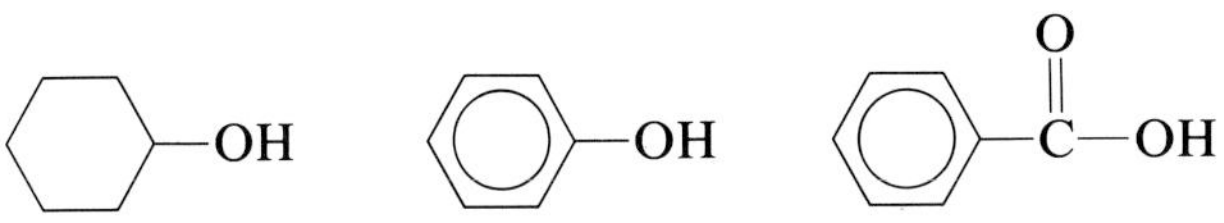

Cyclohexanol	Phenol	Benzoic acid
$K_a = 1 \times 10^{-16}$	$K_a = 1 \times 10^{-10}$	$K_a = 6 \times 10^{-5}$

Phenols act like alcohols in reactions involving the breaking of the O—H bond, such as alkoxide ion formation and ester formation. But, unlike alcohols, most phenols cannot be oxidized to carbonyl groups, nor can they be dehydrated. They notably act as weak acids and, thus, react with bases.

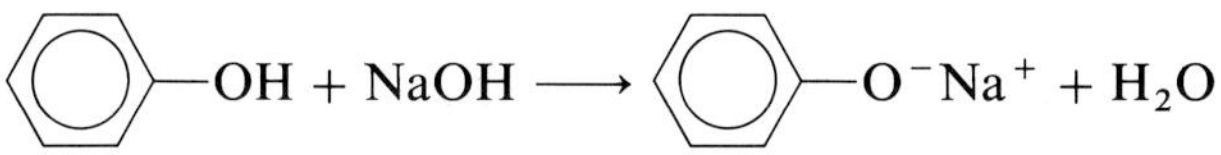

$$\text{C}_6\text{H}_5\text{—OH} + \text{NaOH} \longrightarrow \text{C}_6\text{H}_5\text{—O}^- \text{Na}^+ + \text{H}_2\text{O}$$

Phenoxide ion

The phenoxide ion can act as a nucleophile in the Williamson ether synthesis, as shown in the two examples below.

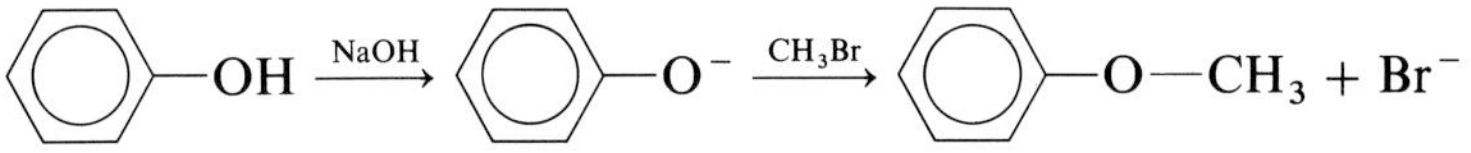

Anisole

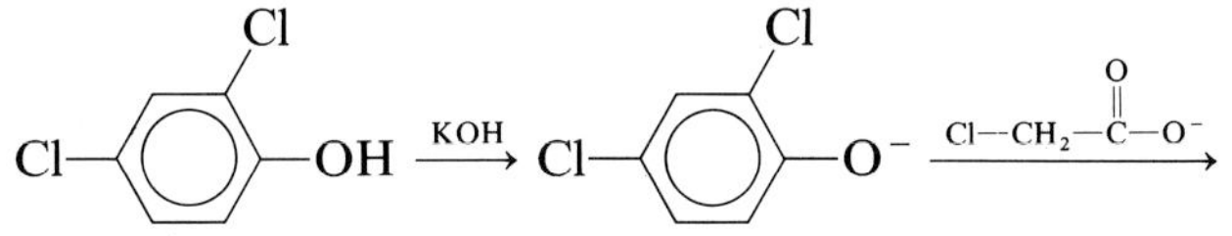

2,4-Dichlorophenol

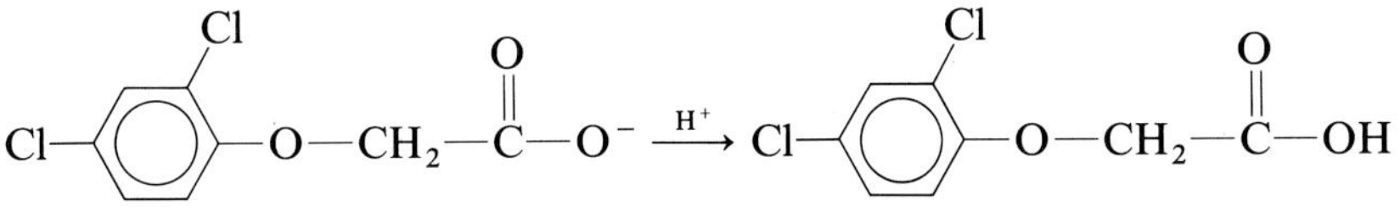

2,4-Dichlorophenoxyacetic acid
(2,4-D; a broadleaf herbicide)

Phenol itself is a strong bacteriocide in less than 1% solution, but if used in concentrated solutions it will cause severe skin burns. It is used in medical preparations (one is trade-named Camphophenique) and in industrial cleaning formulations. Substituted phenols (see below) are now used more commonly for cleaners and disinfectant products.

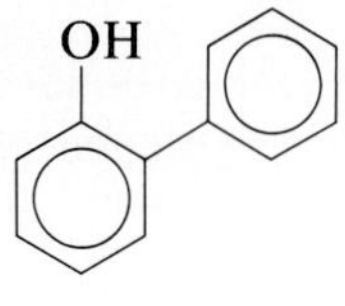

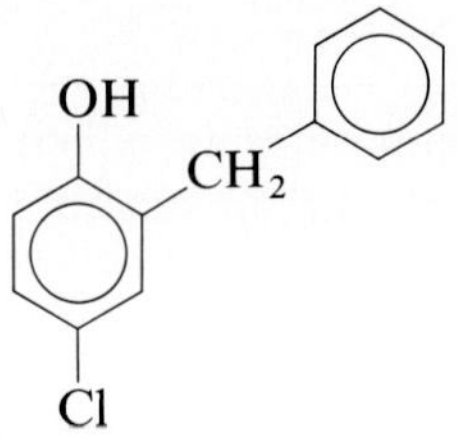

o-Phenylphenol   4-Chloro-2-benzylphenol
(both are ingredients in the cleaner trade-named Lysol)

Other phenols are used commercially as shown below. The structures of cresol, BHA, BHT, and hexachlorophene have already been given (see page 288).

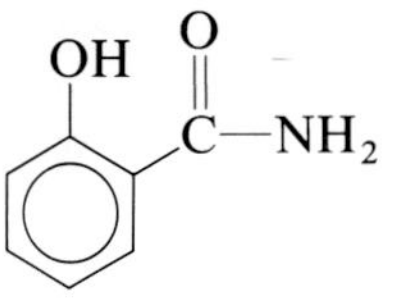

Salicylamide
(aspirin substitute)

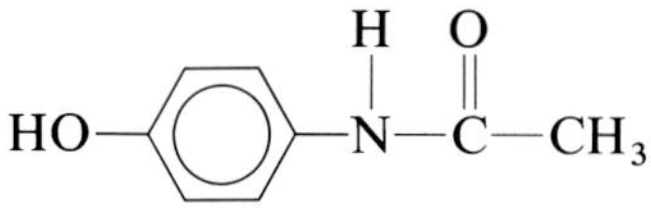

Acetaminophen
(in Tylenol and other analgesics)

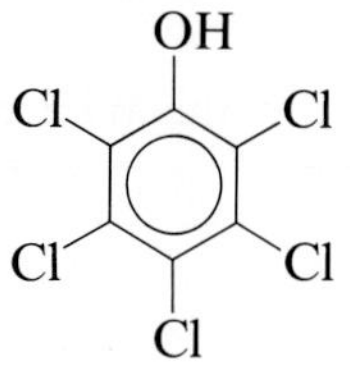

Pentachlorophenol
("penta" wood preserver)

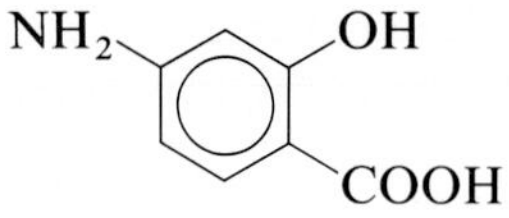

para-Aminosalicylic acid
(antibacterial drug)

SUMMARY

1 Aromatic rings are represented as alternating double and single bonds or as a **circle inscribed** in the ring of carbons.

2 Benzene derivatives (substituted benzenes) are named in the IUPAC system by choosing the **base name** (such as benzene, phenol, or toluene) and indicating other **substituent** groups present and their **positions**. For disubstituted benzenes the prefixes *ortho-*, *meta-*, and *para-* indicate the relative positions of the two groups.

3 Compounds that are aromatic must be cyclic, planar, and have a continuous cloud of pi electrons containing $4n + 2$ electrons. Aromatic molecules are especially **stable**—they have lower than expected heats of hydrogenation and are less reactive toward most reagents than are alkenes.

4 Benzenes can be prepared from cyclohexanes by catalytically removing three molecules of hydrogen (H_2).

5 The **reactions** of benzene and its derivatives include the hydrogenation of the ring, side chain oxidation, side chain halogenation, and the electrophilic aromatic substitution of nitro, sulfonic acid, alkyl, acyl, and halogen groups to the ring. The nitro group can subsequently be converted to an amino group, then the diazonium salt and, hence, to a number of other groups.

6 Various substituents already on the benzene ring cause electrophilic substitution reactions to proceed at a rate faster than the rate of the reaction of benzene itself (**activators**) or slower than that of benzene (**deactivators**); they also control the position of the new group being introduced.

7 **Phenols** are compounds in which an —OH group is bonded directly to the aromatic ring. They are somewhat acidic and are used commercially as disinfectants.

8 Many consumer products are aromatic. These include drugs, polymers, pesticides, dyes, and food and wood preservatives.

KEY TERMS

Activating substituent	Diazonium salt	Ortho
Acylation	Electrophilic	Para
Alkylation	substitution	Phenol
Aniline	Heat of	Resonance energy
Aromatic	hydrogenation	Sulfonation
Benzoic acid	Huckel's rule	Toluene
Deactivating	Meta	
substituent	Naphthalene	
	Nitration	

SKILL PRACTICE PROBLEMS

1 Which of the following species are aromatic? Why or why not?

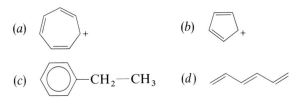

(a)   (b)   (c) —CH$_2$—CH$_3$ (d)

2 Name these compounds.

(a) 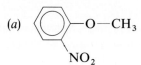 —O—CH$_3$

         NO$_2$

(b) NO$_2$— —NO$_2$

(c) CH$_2$CH$_3$

(d) CH$_3$

    Br   CH$_3$

(e) Br— —CH$_2$CH$_3$

(f)   Br

    HO   CH$_3$

3 Name these commercially useful materials.

(a) OH— —N—C—CH$_3$
               H O

(b) —OH

(c) Cl   Cl

   Cl— —OH

   Cl   Cl

(d)   Cl

Cl— —O—CH$_2$COOH

(e) HO— —O—CH$_3$
               CH$_3$
             C
       CH$_3$ CH$_3$

(f) Cl— —Cl

4 Draw structures for the following:
(a) 2-Nitro-3-cyclohexylphenol
(b) BHT
(c) o-Chlorobenzoic acid
(d) 2,4,6-Trinitrotoluene (TNT)
(e) 1,3,5-Triiodobenzene
(f) 2-Methylanthracene

5 Draw the molecular structure for each of the following materials.
(a) 2-Chloro-4-n-butyltoluene   (b) p-Methylaniline
(c) Anisole   (d) 1-Nitronaphthalene
(e) Hexachlorophene   (f) 1,2,3-trinitrobenzene

6 Complete these reactions.

(a)

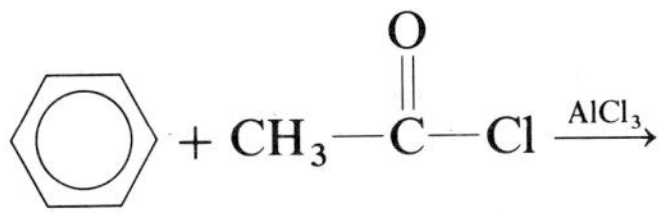

(b)

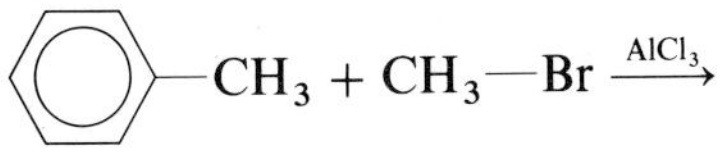

(c)

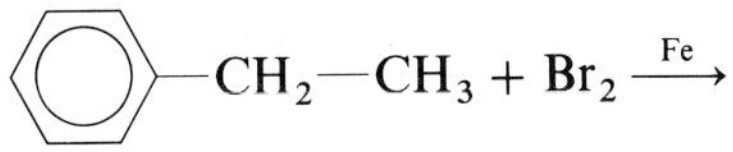

(d) CH$_3$

CH$_3$

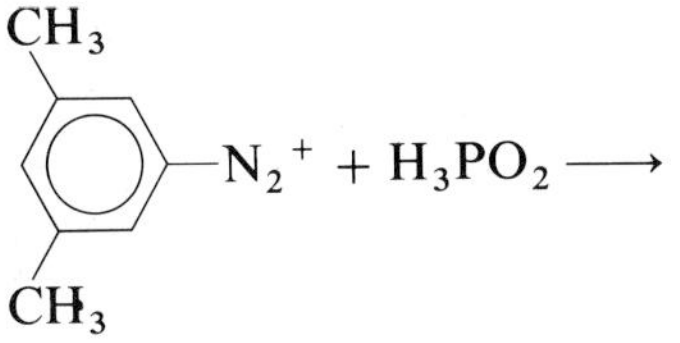

(e)

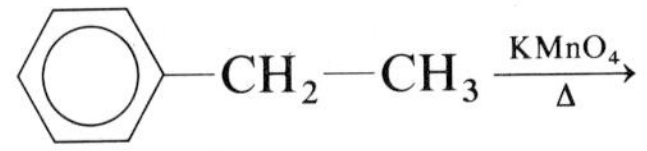

7 Give the organic products of these reactions:

(a)

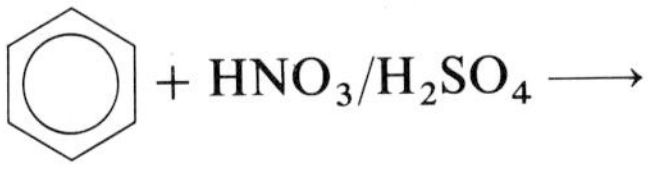

(b)

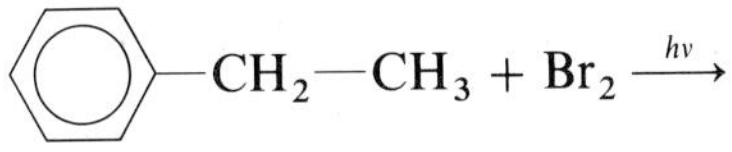

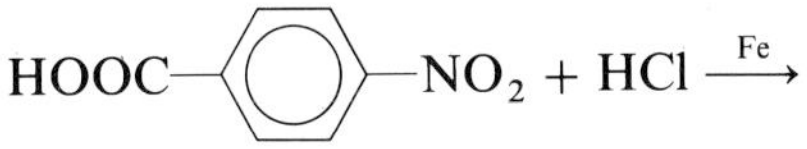

(c)

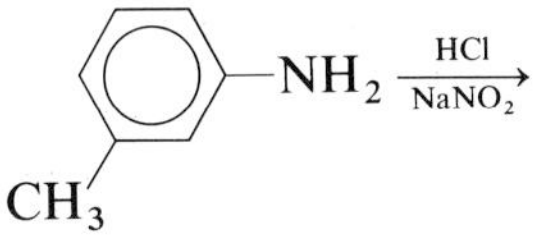

CH$_3$

(d) HOOC—

—NO$_2$ + HCl $\xrightarrow{\text{Fe}}$

(e) Br—

—N$_2{}^+$ + NaBF$_4$ ⟶

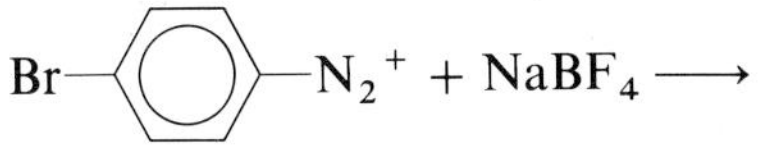

8 How would you synthesize *p*-iodotoluene from benzene?

9 Show how to prepare HOOC—

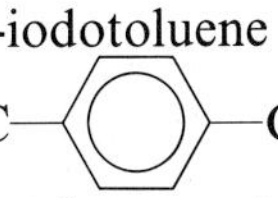

—COOH from toluene.

10 Propose a synthetic route from benzene to *m*-nitrobenzoic acid.

11 How would you prepare 2-*n*-propylnitrobenzene from benzene and propane?

12 If the heats of hydrogenation of 1-pentene and *trans*-2-pentene are 30 and 28 kcal/mol, respectively, which of the two compounds would be more stable? Is this consistent with what you learned about alkene stabilities in Chapter 6?

13 Define, using your own words, the following terms:
(a) Aromatic   (b) Side chain oxidation
(c) Electrophilic substitution (d) The benzylic position

14 Based on statistics alone, what would you expect the ratio of ortho to para product to be for those reactions involving an ortho-para director? What molecular structure factors would cause a deviation from the predicted ratio?

15 Why are phenols more acidic than alcohols? (Hint: Consider charge delocalization and analogy with the resonance forms drawn on page 305.)

16 From memory, list four groups that are activating toward electrophilic aromatic substitution. Repeat for two deactivating groups.

17 Which one of the following pairs would be the more reactive toward nitration?

(a)
or

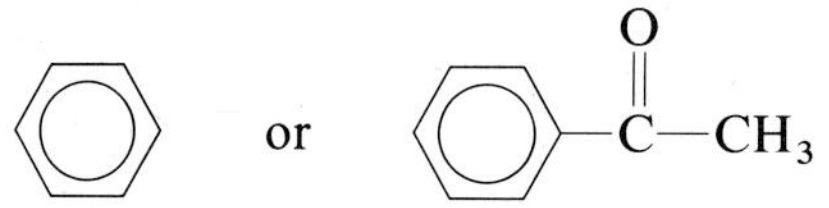

(b)
or

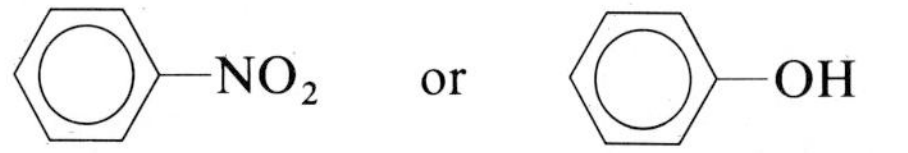

(c)
or

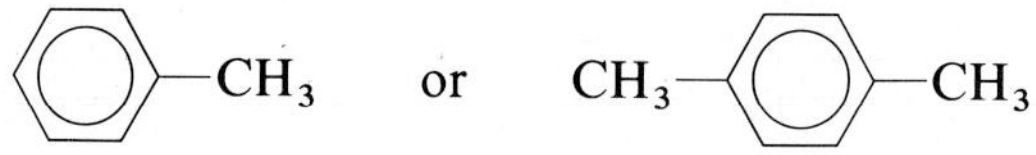

(d)
or

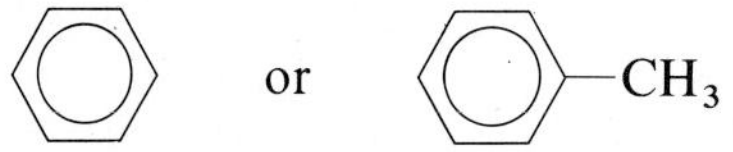

18 Under mild conditions (room temperature and low pressure) how many moles of H_2 would add to each of the following compounds?

(a)

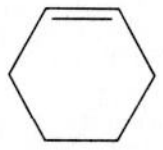

(b)

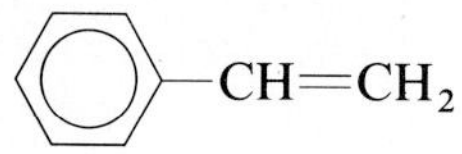

(c)

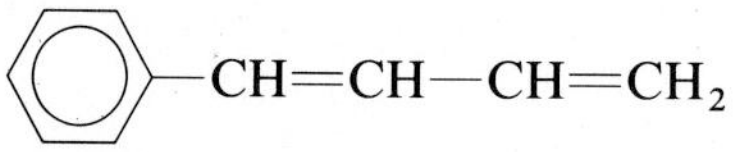

(d)

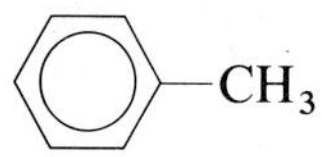

REVIEW QUESTIONS

19 Name the following compounds:

(a) $CH_3—CH—CH_2—CH_2—CH_3$
                |
               OH

(b)

$CH_3—CH_2—CH_2—\overset{\displaystyle O}{\overset{\displaystyle \|}{C}}—H$

(c)

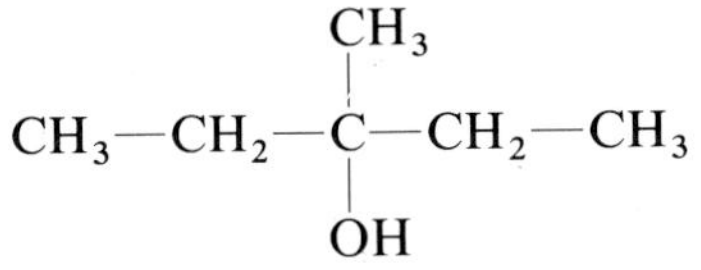

$$CH_3-CH_2-\overset{\overset{\displaystyle CH_3}{|}}{\underset{\underset{\displaystyle OH}{|}}{C}}-CH_2-CH_3$$

(d)

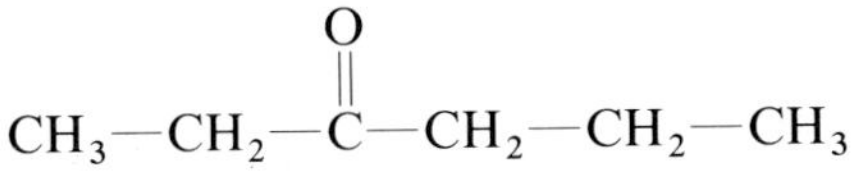

$$CH_3-CH_2-\overset{\overset{\displaystyle O}{||}}{C}-CH_2-CH_2-CH_3$$

(e) 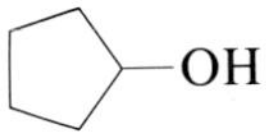 ⬠—OH

20 List three names for CH_3OH.

21 What is the volume percent of ethanol in a beverage with a 180 proof designation?

22 Give the structures of acetone and diethyl ketone.

23 Which of the following compounds would give a positive iodoform test—cyclohexanone, acetone, di-*n*-propyl ketone and 2-pentanone?

CARCINOGENIC AROMATIC COMPOUNDS

Carcinogenic materials are those which **cause cancer** in humans or test animals. Many cancers are thought to be caused by chemical substances, and there is concern over identifying those materials which are dangerous and minimizing human exposure to them.

Table D-1 lists the known human carcinogenic (cancer-causing) materials. Notice that many of them are aromatic.

Frequently a small change in molecular structure can produce a dramatic change in physiological properties such as medicinal, toxic, or carcinogenic potential. For example: 1-naphthylamine is not carcinogenic, while 2-naphthylamine is a powerful carcinogen. We can, thus, draw **no conclusions** about cancer-causing potential (or other physiological properties) by analogy with the properties of compounds with similar structure or similar functional groups. Each compound must be tested for its cancer-causing potential. This is true even for homologs and positional isomers.

An especially potent carcinogen which is frequently encountered is **benzpyrene**.

TABLE D-1

SUMMARY OF KNOWN HUMAN CARCINOGENS	MATERIAL	FORMULA
	Asbestos	Complex inorganic silicates
	Acrylonitrile	$CH_2{=}CH{-}C{\equiv}N$
	Benzidine	
	Chloromethyl ether	$CH_3{-}O{-}CH_2Cl$
	Chloronaphthalene	
	Epichlorohydrin	
	Benzpyrene	

MATERIAL	FORMULA

Diethylstilbesterol

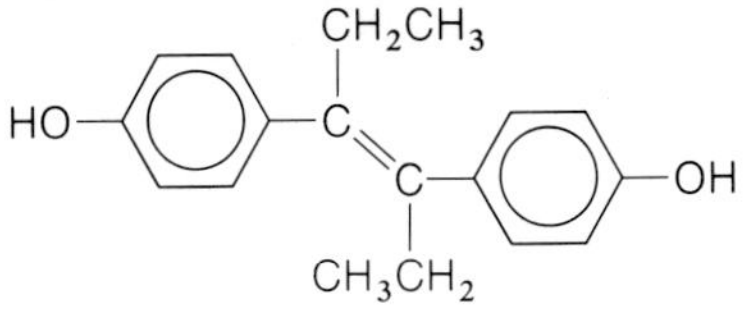

Benzene

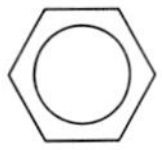

2-Naphthylamine
(β-naphthylamine;
2-aminonaphthylene)

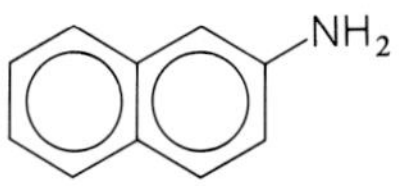

Phenytoin
(Dilantin)*

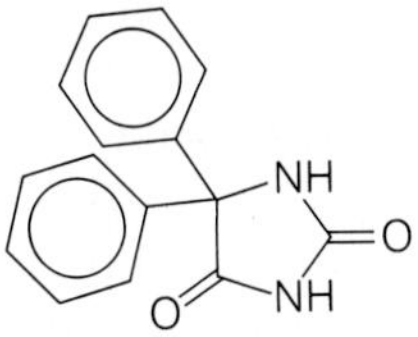

Vinyl chloride

$CH_2{=}CHCl$

Ethylene oxide

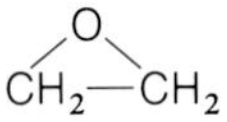

p-Phenylaniline

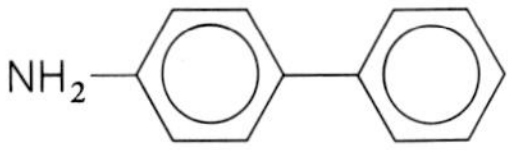

Cyclophosphamide

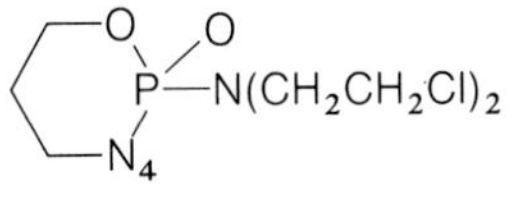

Chloramphenicol

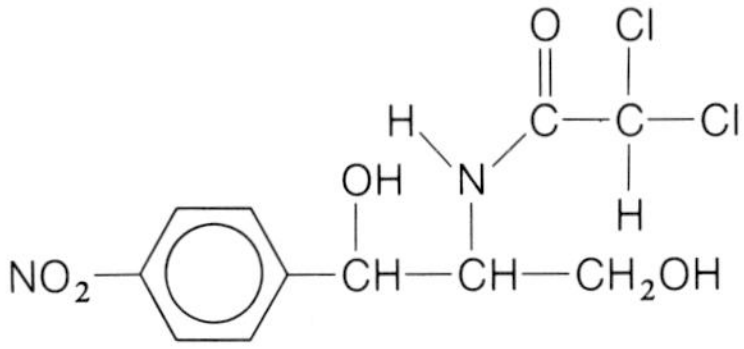

Phenylalanine mustard

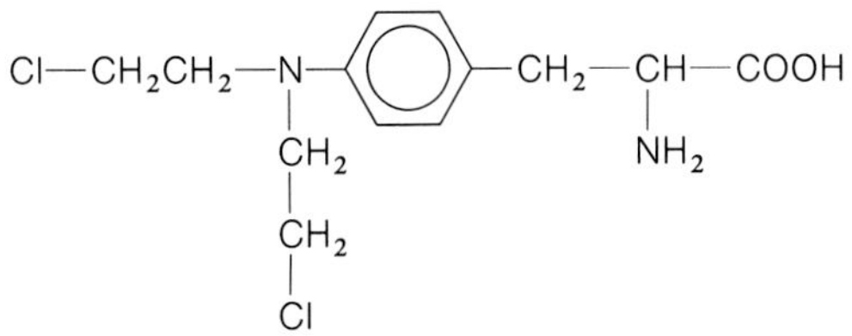

**Some inorganic chromium
and nickel compounds**

* Still used as an anticonvulsant because of excellent medicinal properties

Benzpyrene

It forms when many organic materials burn. The most dangerous source is **tobacco smoke**, where it is a major component in "tar," but it also occurs in wood and leaf smoke and in meat that is charcoal cooked to the point of charring on the outside. Figure D-1 briefly outlines some aspects of current thinking on the subject of cancer caused by benzpyrene.

A cigarette yields 5 to 20 milligrams (mg) of tar. Certain enzymes (ENZ_1) in the body convert benzpyrene to the alcohol-epoxide shown in Figure D-1. Compound II is the "primary carcinogen"—the material that actually changes the DNA.[1] The mutant (abnormal) DNA causes the cells to grow in a grotesque and rapid manner, and a malignant tumor results.

There is another enzyme (ENZ_2) that can destroy compound II and prevent it from initiating cancer (see Figure D-1). Current evidence suggests that it is the relative amounts of these two enzymes that determine whether cancer will actually occur in a person who smokes. The hypothesis is that if a person has large amounts of ENZ_1 and little of ENZ_2, much

---

[1] Deoxyribonucleic acid—the material in the cell that controls cell function and heredity (see Chapter 17).

FIGURE D-1

Schematic diagram showing current thought about the production of cancer by benzpyrene.

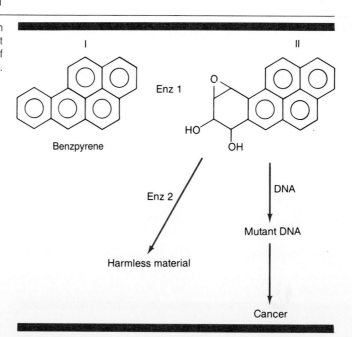

more compound II is formed than is destroyed, and a high level of compound II remains to react with DNA. If a person, apparently because of hereditary factors, has about equal amounts of ENZ_1 and ENZ_2—which means that compound II is destroyed about as fast as it is formed—the chance of cancer is smaller. This is the best explanation to date for the observation that some people who smoke do not get cancer, while others who smoke do. A series of studies have shown that about 45 percent of the population have a favorable enzyme ratio and are at low risk. Another 45 percent have about 15 times as much ENZ_1 as ENZ_2 and have a significant risk of getting cancer if they smoke. The remaining 10 percent have 30 times as much of ENZ_1 as ENZ_2 and are at high risk. Chemical tests for ENZ_1 levels are available only for research purposes at this time, and they are not very reliable.

One way to estimate your probable level is to consider the smoking habits of, and cancer incidence in, your older relatives. But this is not much more than a guess. The only way to eliminate the risk of smoke-induced cancer is to avoid smoking.

CHAPTER 10

CHEMICAL SYNTHESIS

LEARNING GOALS

1 To help organize the numerous reactions already learned into useful categories for use in answering individual reaction questions and in working synthesis problems

2 To aid in developing strategies for working synthesis problems. The reasoning used here will be similar to that used by organic chemists who do chemical synthesis

3 To further develop problem-solving skills which are needed not only in chemistry but in most other fields also

In Chapter 2, we examined the important role of synthetic processes in producing new materials. In the subsequent chapters, we have, at times, given chemical equations for the reactions or sequence of reactions used to produce commercial materials.

In this chapter, we will "take a rest" from learning new reactions and concepts and instead work to develop skills in **organizing** and **recalling** reactions, and actually **proposing reaction sequences** that could be used to change one material into another. You will play the role of a chemist in designing a series of reactions which will produce the desired material.

We will not concern ourselves with the technical aspects of reactions, such as the temperature, the concentrations of reactants, or what solvents to use. Neither will we worry about purification of the desired material or its percent yield; we will only concern ourselves with being able to connect reactions that are real and which could conceivably produce the desired material. At those times when one method gives only one product and another gives a mixture, it is preferable to choose the former in order to avoid separation steps.

SYNTHESIS PROCESSES

In this section we will organize the reactions we have learned into categories according to what is to be accomplished. Basically, organic chemists are interested in accomplishing one of the following tasks:

1   Building carbon frameworks

2   Introducing a functional group into an alkane or aromatic compound

3   Eliminating functional groups to produce alkanes

4   Changing the nature of a functional group

Building carbon structures

The following table lists ways to build the desired carbon skeleton using reactions we have already covered.

CHANGE DESIRED	METHODS		SPECIAL CHARACTERISTICS
1 Adding one carbon at a time	(a)	$R—MgX + \underset{H \quad H}{\overset{O}{\overset{\|}{C}}}$ (see Chapters 7 & 8)	Produces only 1° alcohols
	(b)	$R—X + CN^- \longrightarrow R—CN \longrightarrow R—COOH$	Produces only nitriles or acids
	(c)	$R—MgX + CO_2$	Adds COOH

CHANGE DESIRED	METHODS	SPECIAL CHARACTERISTICS
2 Linking two large carbon chains	(a) Wurtz reaction $2RX \xrightarrow{Na} R—R$	Forms only symmetrical alkanes (which are unreactive)
	(b) Lithium dialkyl copper (Corey-House reaction) $R—X \xrightarrow{Li} \xrightarrow{Cu_2X_2} \xrightarrow{R—X} R—R$ (see Chapter 3)	Alkanes are produced (unreactive)
	(c) Wittig reaction 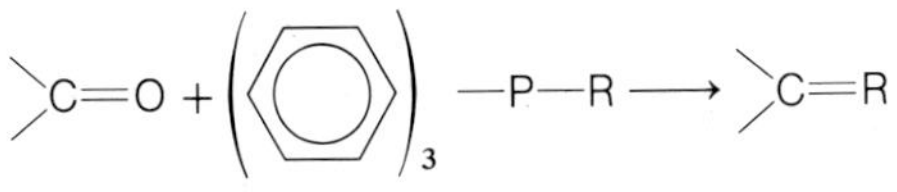 $\bigg\rangle C{=}O + \Big(\langle\!\langle\bigcirc\rangle\!\rangle\Big)_3 —P—R \longrightarrow \bigg\rangle C{=}R$ (see Chapter 8)	Produces alkenes (which are versatile)
	(d) Aldol condensation (see Chapter 8)	Produces α,β unsaturated aldehydes and ketones (which are synthetically versatile)
	(e) $R—X + R'—C{\equiv}C^- \longrightarrow R—C{=}C—R'$ (see Chapter 6)	The alkynes produced are easily converted to many functional groups
	(f) R—MgX + aldehyde (or ketone or esters) $\longrightarrow$ 2° or 3° alcohols (see Chapters 7 & 8)	Virtually limitless structural possibilities
	(g) Friedel-Craft alkylation & acylation (see Chapter 9)	Links aromatic and aliphatic segments

Introducing functional groups

We have studied only one way to introduce functional groups into the relatively inert alkane compounds. This is free radical **halogenation**. Combustion and cracking are not useful in synthesis, and halogenation is one of the few other reactions of alkanes. For synthesis, **bromination** is usually the best halogenation reaction because it is more selective than chlorination and allows us to place the bromine selectively on a 2° or 3° carbon (see Chapters 3 & 5).

$$Br_2 + R—H \xrightarrow{h\nu} R—Br + HBr$$
$$\searrow \text{Many other functional groups}$$

A functional group can be introduced on an aromatic ring by **nitration** as shown below. Once introduced, the nitro group can be changed to the amino group which can, in turn, be converted into a number of other groups via the diazonium salt.

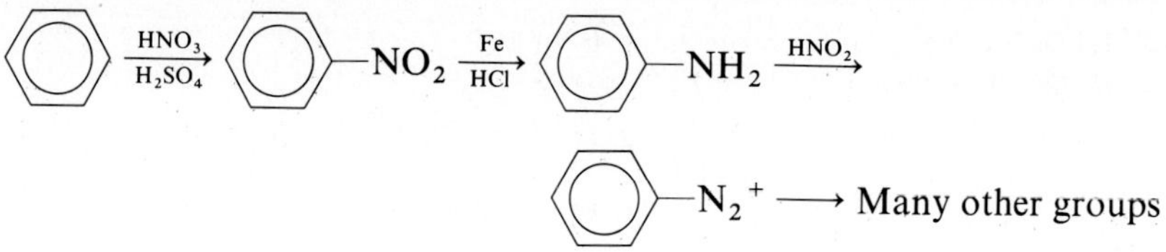

Eliminating functional groups

We have studied several ways of eliminating functional groups from various starting materials.

1 From alcohols

$$R\!-\!OH \xrightarrow{H^+} \text{alkenes} \xrightarrow[Pt]{H_2} \text{alkanes}$$

2 From alkenes or alkynes

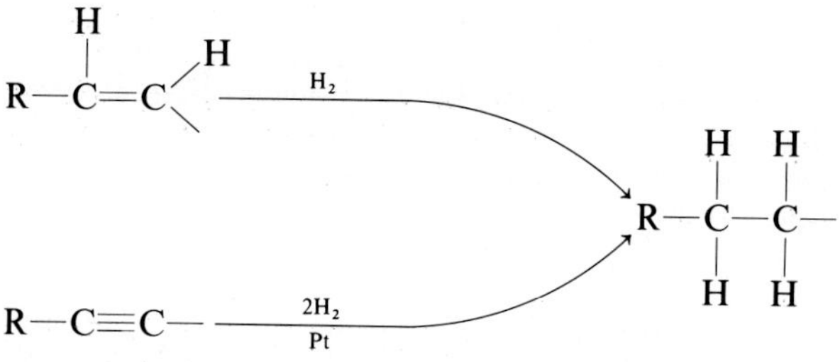

3 From alkyl halides

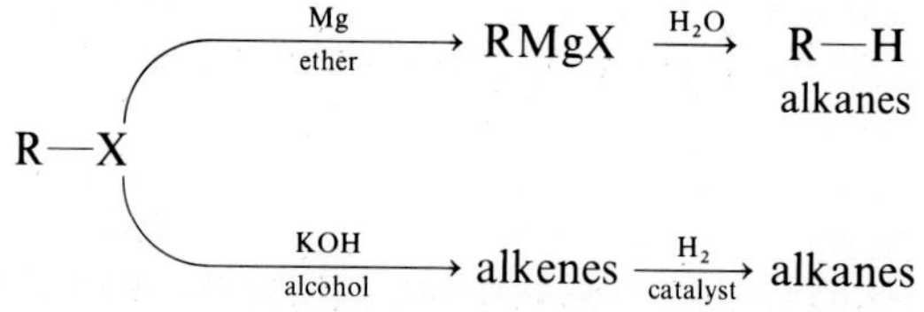

4 From aldehydes or ketones

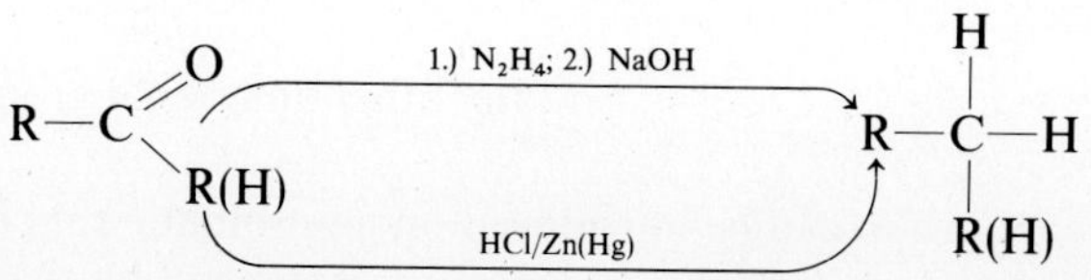

Changing functional groups

This area is too large to cover in detail in an outline. The possibilities include most of the reactions you have been learning and applying. Below are listed some commonly used reaction sequences that should be kept in mind. For a given synthesis only part of each may be needed, however.

1

$$R—H \xrightarrow[hv]{Br_2} R—Br \xrightarrow[H_2O]{NaOH} R—OH \xrightarrow{[O]} R—\overset{\overset{\textstyle O}{\|}}{C}— \xrightarrow{[O]}$$

$$R—\overset{\overset{\textstyle O}{\|}}{C}—OH \xrightarrow{R'—OH} R—\overset{\overset{\textstyle O}{\|}}{C}—O—R'$$

2 $R—H \xrightarrow[hv]{Br_2} R—Br \xrightarrow[H_2O]{NaOH} R—OH$

$$\Big\downarrow H^+/\Delta$$

$$\xrightarrow[alcohol]{KOH} R'—\overset{|}{C}=C\big\langle$$

3

$$R—\overset{\overset{\textstyle O}{\|}}{C}—OH \xrightarrow[{[H]}]{} R—C\overset{\diagup O}{\diagdown H} \xrightarrow{[H]} R—CH_2—OH$$

4

$$R—C{=}C\big\langle$$

$$\xrightarrow{HBr} R—\overset{\overset{\textstyle H}{|}}{C}—\overset{|}{C}— \;\; Br$$

$$\xrightarrow{HBr/peroxide} R—\overset{\overset{\textstyle H}{|}}{C}—\overset{|}{C}—Br$$

$$\xrightarrow[H^+]{H_2O} R—\overset{\overset{\textstyle H}{|}}{C}—\overset{|}{C}— \;\; OH$$

$$\xrightarrow[NaOH/H_2O_2]{B_2H_6} R—\overset{\overset{\textstyle H}{|}}{C}—\overset{|}{C}—OH$$

Note: Remember that [O] and [H] stand for oxidizing and reducing agents, respectively.

STRATEGY FOR SOLVING SYNTHESIS PROBLEMS

General problem solving techniques

The following three general methods are frequently used by good problem solvers in all areas of academics—and in life situations in general. They should all three be kept in mind for synthesis problems. After a brief presentation of the method, we will illustrate how it can be used for solving organic chemistry synthesis problems.

1 Put in writing the various aspects of the problem. What are you trying to accomplish? Your mind often works better when facts and organization are written down than when they are kept "in your head."

2 Think broadly at the beginning. Even consider seemingly impossible solutions. They may be possible after all, or they may lead to a solution that is possible.

3 Use trial and error. Do something! Even if you start out with nonsense, it will get you moving; you cannot steer a parked car! When there are a limited number of possibilities, write them **all** out and evaluate each one.

If you reach an impasse, leave the problem and return to it later.

Approaching synthesis problems

While you will most likely work out your own problem-solving approach, consider the following three basic techniques:

1 A logical approach

2 Working forward and backward

3 A trial-and-error solution

We will illustrate these approaches in solutions to the following problem:

Starting with butane and methyl alcohol, show how to prepare *sec*-butyl methyl ether.

A logical approach **Write** the structures of the starting materials and desired products, and indicate the changes that must come about. This is the most logical approach, and the one that should always be attempted. **Make a list** of the changes you must bring about and several possible orders of accomplishing them. Then write out reactions to accomplish each. Finally, string them together to give the entire sequence. Let's follow this approach in solving the above problem.

1 Write structures and indicate reactions.[1]

---

[1] Three reaction arrows are used in this text to designate a series of reactions—not necessarily three reactions.

$$\begin{array}{c} CH_3CH_2CH_2CH_3 \\ \text{and} \\ CH_3-OH \end{array} \longrightarrow \longrightarrow \longrightarrow \underset{\displaystyle \overset{|}{CH_3}}{CH_3-CH_2-CH}-O-CH_3$$

Starting materials   Desired product

2 Consider desired changes. We are preparing an ether, so the Williamson ether synthesis (using an alkyl halide and alkoxide ion) will be needed. Since the alkoxide is prepared from an alcohol, there will be very little change in the CH_3OH. We will have to convert the butane into an alkyl halide. Since we start with an alcohol, we must first convert it to alkoxide and then follow this by reaction with the proper alkyl halide.

3 Write the sequence.

$$CH_3-OH \xrightarrow{Na} CH_3O^- \xrightarrow[\underset{Br}{CH_3-CH-CH_2-CH_3}]{} CH_3-CH_2-\underset{\displaystyle \underset{CH_3}{|}}{CH}-O-CH_3$$

The alkyl halide needed in this synthesis is 2-bromobutane. We can produce alkyl halides in several ways, but since we have an alkane as the starting material, let us try direct halogenation as follows:

$$CH_3-CH_2-CH_2-CH_3 + Br_2 \xrightarrow{h\nu} CH_3-\underset{\displaystyle \underset{Br}{|}}{CH}-CH_2-CH_3$$

We could now use the 2-bromobutane just produced to react with the methoxide ion to form the ether we want. The Williamson reaction works best when the alkyl halide is 1°, however (see page 238), so this will not be a very good method.

Working forward and backward Work from both ends of the problem. Perhaps you can think of one step that will change the starting material into a compound that will open up a number of possibilities. You may also think of a compound that can be easily changed into the compound you are trying to prepare. Go ahead and write down both of these steps. This makes the gap between starting material and final product two steps shorter and will increase the chances of the solution becoming apparent. You can try to work one step further in both directions, and thus continue until the connection is made. To demonstrate this approach, let's continue with the same problem.

1 First, we brominate the butane (**work forward**),

$$CH_3CH_2CH_2CH_3 \xrightarrow[h\nu]{Br_2} CH_3-CH_2-\underset{\displaystyle \underset{Br}{|}}{CH}-CH_3$$

2 Next, **working backward**, we might observe that two sets of reagents will produce the desired ether, thus:

$$CH_3-CH_2-\underset{\underset{Br}{|}}{CH}-CH_3 + CH_3O^- \qquad CH_3Cl + CH_3-CH_2-\underset{\underset{O^-}{|}}{CH}-CH_3$$

$$CH_3-CH_2-\underset{\underset{O-CH_3}{|}}{CH}-CH_3$$

We should observe that the reaction on the right involves the attack of a nucleophile on a methyl halide, while the one on the left involves the attack of a nucleophile on a 2° alkyl halide. In Chapter 7 it was pointed out that secondary alkyl halides do not work well for the Williamson ether synthesis. Therefore, the reaction on the right above is the one of choice.

3 We next consider how to prepare the chloromethane and *sec*-butoxide ion. Let's **work backward** one more step:

$$CH_3-CH_2-\underset{\underset{OH}{|}}{CH}-CH_3 \xrightarrow{Na} CH_3-CH_2\underset{\underset{O^-}{|}}{CH}-CH_3$$

and

$$CH_3OH \xrightarrow{PCl_3} CH_3Cl$$

4 We are already back to methanol, which is one of our starting materials. The 2-butanol can be prepared from the 2-bromobutane which we obtained in step 1 as follows:

$$CH_3-CH_2-\underset{\underset{Br}{|}}{CH}-CH_3 \xrightarrow[\text{alcohol}]{KOH}$$

$$CH_3-CH=CH-CH_3 \xrightarrow[H^+/\Delta]{H_2O} CH_3-CH_2-\underset{\underset{OH}{|}}{CH}-CH_3$$

or

$$CH_3-CH_2-\underset{\underset{Br}{|}}{CH}-CH_3 \xrightarrow[H_2O]{NaOH} CH_3-CH_2-\underset{\underset{OH}{|}}{CH}-CH_3$$

5 Putting all this together

$$CH_3CH_2-CH-CH_3$$

$$CH_3OH \xrightarrow{PCl_3} CH_3Cl \longrightarrow \quad \overset{|}{OCH_3}$$

$$CH_3CH_2CH_2CH_3 \xrightarrow[hv]{Br_2} CH_3CH_2-\underset{\underset{Br}{|}}{C}HCH_3 \xrightarrow[H_2O]{NaOH}$$

$$CH_3CH_2\underset{\underset{OH}{|}}{C}HCH_3 \xrightarrow{Na} CH_3CH_2\underset{\underset{O^-}{|}}{C}HCH_3$$

A trial-and-error solution Make changes in the starting material in several directions somewhat randomly until one of them appears to be leading in the right direction. A trial-and-error solution of the synthesis problem might take the following form:

1 $CH_3-CH_2-CH_2-CH_3 \xrightarrow[hv]{Br_2}$ $CH_3-CH_2-\underset{\underset{Br}{|}}{C}H-CH_3$

$\xrightarrow{Mg/ether}$ $CH_3-CH_2-\underset{\underset{MgBr}{|}}{C}H-CH_3$

$\xrightarrow[\text{KOH/alcohol}]{}$ $CH_3-CH=CH-CH_3$

$\xrightarrow[H_2O]{NaOH}$

$CH_3-CH_2-\underset{\underset{OH}{|}}{C}H-CH_3$

2 $CH_3OH \xrightarrow{Na} CH_3O^-$

$\downarrow [O]$ $\searrow PCl_3$

$\underset{H}{\overset{O}{\underset{\|}{C}}} \quad CH_3Cl$

$\overset{}{OH}$

3 After writing these probabilities down, we notice that the two materials circled could be used to produce the desired product using Williamson synthesis.

$$CH_3O^- + CH_3CH_2\underset{\underset{Br}{|}}{C}HCH_3 \longrightarrow CH_3CH_2\underset{\underset{O}{|}}{C}HCH_3$$
$$\qquad\qquad\qquad\qquad\qquad\qquad\qquad\qquad\qquad CH_3$$

Alternatively, we may use the materials in the dotted rectangles as follows:

$$\underset{\overset{|}{OH}}{CH_3—CH_2—CH—CH_3} \xrightarrow{Na} \underset{\overset{|}{O^-}}{CH_3—CH_2—CH—CH_3} \xrightarrow{CH_3Cl}$$

$$\underset{\overset{|}{O}}{\underset{\overset{|}{CH_3}}{CH_3—CH_2—CH—CH_3}}$$

The latter approach would work better, since the alkyl halide is methyl rather than 2°.

Putting it together

All skills take **practice** and the more you practice synthesis problems, the easier they will become. Some problems are much more difficult conceptually than others or are longer and therefore more difficult to put together. Do not become discouraged if you have trouble at first. Try the problems at the end of this chapter after studying the few examples that follow.

Keep in mind that you cannot put together reactions that you do not know. **It is essential to have learned all of the individual reactions before you work synthesis problems.**

SOLVING SYNTHESIS PROBLEMS

Worked example

Convert 2-bromopropane into 1-bromopropane.

1 Write out the structures.

$$\underset{\overset{|}{Br}}{CH_3CHCH_3} \longrightarrow \longrightarrow \longrightarrow CH_3—CH_2CH_2—Br$$

2 Changes: The bromine atom is to be moved over by one carbon atom.

3 We can sometimes reverse the orientation of a bromine by the peroxide effect when HBr reacts with an alkene. Therefore, let us start by forming an alkene.

4 Write out a possible sequence.

$$CH_3CHCH_3 \xrightarrow[\text{alcohol}]{\text{KOH}} CH_3CH=CH_2 \xrightarrow[\text{peroxide}]{\text{HBr}} CH_3CH_2CH_2-Br$$
$$|$$
$$Br$$

Worked example

Starting with coal, water, and limestone, show how to produce 1-butanol. You may use any inorganic reagents, but you must show how to prepare all organic materials from these three materials.

1 Write out the structures.

$$C, H_2O, CaCO_3 \longrightarrow \longrightarrow \longrightarrow CH_3CH_2CH_2CH_2OH$$

2 Changes:
   (*a*) Inorganic compounds to be changed to organic
   (*b*) Carbons to be linked together

3 Whenever we start with these materials, we first convert them to acetylene. This is one of only two reactions we have learned that allow us to convert inorganic materials into organic compounds (the other reaction is the conversion of carbon monoxide and hydrogen into methyl alcohol).

$$Coal \xrightarrow{\Delta\Delta} \underset{\text{Coke}}{C} \xrightarrow[\Delta\Delta]{CaCO_3} CaC_2 \xrightarrow{H_2O} \underset{\text{Acetylene}}{H-C\equiv C-H}$$

When we have a terminal alkyne, we should think of converting it to the anion and then reacting this anion with the appropriate alkyl halide. To get four carbons, we need to link the acetylene to an **ethyl** halide, such as chloroethane.

$$H-C\equiv C-H \xrightarrow{Na} H-C\equiv C^- \xrightarrow{CH_3CH_2Cl} H-C\equiv C-CH_2CH_3$$

The ethyl chloride could be prepared from the acetylene by adding 1 mole of H_2, followed by 1 mole of HCl.

$$H-C\equiv C-H \xrightarrow[\substack{\text{Lindlar's} \\ \text{catalyst}}]{H_2} H_2C=CH_2 \xrightarrow{HCl} CH_3-CH_2-Cl$$

Next we need to change our alkyne functional group into an alcohol. One way would be to change it into an alkene, followed by anti-Markovnikov addition of water.

$$H-C\equiv C-CH_2-CH_3 \xrightarrow[\text{Lindlar's catalyst}]{H_2}$$

$$H_2C=CH-CH_2-CH_3 \xrightarrow[\text{NaOH}]{(BH_3)_2, \; H_2O_2}$$

$$HO-CH_2-CH_2-CH_2-CH_3$$

Worked example

Using ethene as your only organic material, along with any needed inorganic reagents, show how to synthesize 3-hexanone.

1 Structures:

$$CH_2=CH_2 \longrightarrow \longrightarrow \longrightarrow CH_3CH_2CH_2-\overset{\overset{\textstyle O}{\|}}{C}-CH_2CH_3$$

2 Changes: We have to link three of the original two carbon units together and then introduce a ketone functional group.

3 We could prepare acetylene from the ethene and then prepare ethyl chloride as follows:

$$CH_3CH_2Cl \xleftarrow{HCl} CH_2=CH_2 \xrightarrow{Cl_2}$$

$$\underset{\displaystyle \overset{|}{Cl} \quad \overset{|}{Cl}}{CH_2-CH_2} \xrightarrow{2NaNH_2} H-C\equiv C-H$$

The acetylene could be converted to the anion, which could be allowed to react with the ethyl chloride.

$$H-C\equiv C-H \xrightarrow{Na} H-C\equiv C^- \xrightarrow{CH_3CH_2Cl} H-C\equiv C-CH_2CH_3$$

Repeating this sequence at the other end of the triple bond gives the desired number of carbon atoms.

$$H-C\equiv C-CH_2CH_3 \xrightarrow{Na} {}^-C\equiv C-CH_2CH_3 \xrightarrow{CH_3CH_2Cl}$$

$$CH_3CH_2-C\equiv C-CH_2CH_3$$

Reducing the alkyne to an alkene followed by the addition of H_2O/H^+ will produce an alcohol. Oxidation will then produce the desired ketone.

$$CH_3CH_2C{\equiv}CCH_2CH_3 \xrightarrow[\substack{\text{Lindlar's}\\\text{catalyst}}]{H_2} CH_3CH_2\overset{\overset{\displaystyle H}{|}}{C}{=}\overset{\overset{\displaystyle H}{|}}{C}CH_2CH_3$$

$$\Big\downarrow \text{H}_2\text{O/H}^+$$

$$CH_3CH_2CH_2\overset{\overset{\displaystyle O}{||}}{C}CH_2CH_3 \xleftarrow{\text{KMnO}_4} CH_3CH_2CH_2\underset{\underset{\displaystyle OH}{|}}{C}HCH_2CH_3$$

SUMMARY

1 Synthesis problem solving involves the choosing of a sequence of chemical reactions from among those reactions you have learned that will accomplish the change(s) in molecular structure required.

2 There are **four categories** of molecular structural changes into which we divide all possible tasks. It is helpful to **organize** the reactions you know into these categories for reference in solving synthesis problems.

3 By applying standard problem-solving techniques, synthesis problems can be worked with greater ease.

4 Individual reactions must be learned before synthesis problems can be solved.

5 **Practice** will help in developing skill in solving chemical synthesis problems.

SKILL PRACTICE PROBLEMS

1 Show how to prepare iodocyclopentane from cyclopentane as your only carbon-containing material. You may use any inorganic reagents you wish.

2 How would you prepare antifreeze (ethylene glycol—see page 222) from ethane?

3 Starting with 1-butanol, show how to prepare 2-ethyl-1-hexanol.

4 How would you prepare banana flavor from 1-chloropentane and ethyl alcohol? It has the formula $CH_3{-}\overset{\overset{\displaystyle O}{||}}{C}{-}O{-}(CH_2)_4{-}CH_3$.

5 Starting with any compounds with five or fewer carbons, show how to synthesize 2-hexanol.

6 Using acetylene and propane, show how to prepare pentane.

7 Use cyclohexane and 1-butyne to produce 2-cyclohexyl-2-butanol.

8 Synthesize ⬠=O from cyclopentane as your only organic material.

9 Prepare 1,6-dichlorohexane from cyclohexane.

10 Convert acetone into hexane.

11 Using reactions we have seen thus far, show how to change coal into natural gas (methane).

12 How would you convert methane into dimethyl ether?

13 Show how to bring about the following conversion:

14 Show how to change 1-pentanol into 1-butanol.

15 Show how to prepare iodobenzene from benzene and any needed inorganic reagents.

16 How would you synthesize *p*-aminobenzoic acid from toluene?

CHAPTER 11

MOLECULAR SPECTROSCOPY

LEARNING GOALS

1 To understand the nature of electro-magnetic radiation

2 To understand the mechanisms by which molecules absorb electromag-netic radiation in the infrared and radio frequency regions of the spectrum

3 To develop skill in interpreting infra-red and nuclear magnetic resonance spectra

4 To gain general familiarity with ultraviolet spectroscopy and mass spectroscopy

5 To understand how organic chem-ists use molecular spectroscopy to de-termine molecular structure

Molecular structure is a major theme in chemistry, and it is especially important in organic chemistry. It has occupied the majority of our discussions in this text. Have you ever wondered how chemists determine the molecular structures of new reaction products or new materials isolated from natural sources? How do research chemists know what they have produced? The most convenient and reliable method is called **molecular spectroscopy.** This involves the interaction of **electromagnetic radiation** with the molecules of the material in question. Before considering the several types of spectroscopy, we shall take a look at the electromagnetic radiation spectrum and briefly explain the nature of light itself.

INTRODUCTION TO SPECTROSCOPY

For most purposes, light can be thought of as a traveling electrical field alternating from positive to negative values. In other words, it consists of waves of positiveness and negativeness (**not** positive and negative particles) moving through space. Human beings experience light and color when the retina, optic nerve, and brain receptors respond to these oscillations of charge. Light can be characterized by two of its properties: wavelength, symbolized by the Greek letter lambda (λ); and frequency, symbolized by the Greek letter nu (v). All light, regardless of its color, travels through space at a constant speed of 186,000 miles per second (mi/s). This is equal to 300,000,000 meters (m) or 300,000 kilometers (km) per second. The

FIGURE 11-1

Water waves.

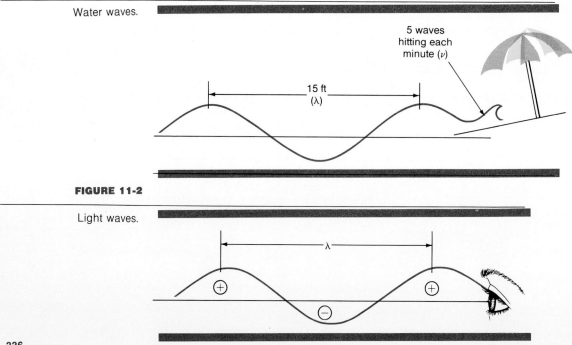

FIGURE 11-2

Light waves.

wavelength (λ) is the **distance** between crests of waves, and the frequency is the **number of times** each second a new wave moves past a fixed point (or hits the optic nerve).

In order to understand this better, let's take a brief look at waves in water. Figure 11-1 shows a beach. The distance between wave crests is 15 feet, which would be the wavelength (λ). The waves are coming to the beach at a rate of 5 each minute, which is the frequency (v) of the waves. Figure 11-2 illustrates this same idea for waves of light. At one instant, a wave of positiveness is interacting with the eye of the observer. At the next instant, a wave of negativeness comes into the eye. The wavelength (λ) is shown as the distance between crests, and the frequency is the number of waves that hit the eye per unit of time (usually each second).

Each color of the visible spectrum (i.e., the colors we can see) has its own wavelength and frequency. Since all colors travel at the same speed, if the wavelength is greater, then the frequency must be smaller, and vice versa. As an illustration, consider two people walking side by side. If one takes large steps and the other small, in order for them to walk at the same speed, the one with the shorter steps must walk more quickly (with a higher frequency) than the other. Likewise, if a given kind of light has shorter distances between waves (lower λ) than another kind of light, then it must have more waves per second (higher v) for their speeds to be the same. As shown in Figure 11-3, red light has a greater λ and lower v than blue light, which has a shorter λ and higher v. The red light (with a long wavelength) is hitting the eye at a relatively low frequency. The blue light (with a shorter wavelength) is hitting with a higher frequency. Color, then, is the human optical system's response to different frequencies of light. When one looks at a red sweater, the light coming from it hits the eye at low frequency and the brain interprets that as "red." Each color in the

FIGURE 11-3

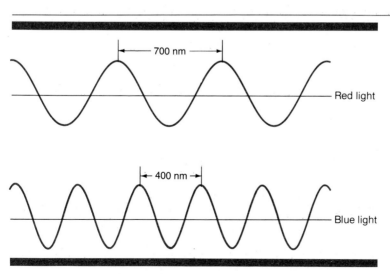

Difference in wavelength between red and blue light.

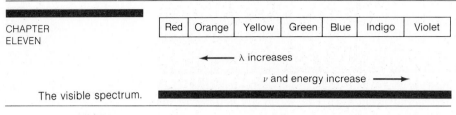

Red	Orange	Yellow	Green	Blue	Indigo	Violet

$\longleftarrow \lambda$ increases

v and energy increase $\longrightarrow$

The visible spectrum.

FIGURE 11-4

spectrum, which is shown in Figure 11-4, has its own λ and v. As one goes toward the violet end, the λ becomes shorter and the v higher.

Another concept that is of considerable importance is the **energy** of various colors. It can be shown that violet light has more energy per photon[1] than red light has. As the frequency increases, so does the energy of that light.

Visible light is part of a larger spectrum called the **electromagnetic radiation spectrum**. There are wavelengths shorter than the wavelength of violet light and others longer than that red light. Human beings cannot see these kinds of radiation but they do exist and can interact with matter and cause various responses, even though the human retina is not sensitive to them. Figure 11-5 shows the entire electromagnetic radiation spectrum, along with the changes in wavelength, frequency, and energy within it.

Some useful relationships between the speed of light (C), wavelength (λ), frequency (v), and the energy per photon (E) are given below. Planck's constant [$h = 6.63 \times 10^{-34}$ joule $\cdot$ seconds (J $\cdot$ s)] allows us to calculate the energy if the frequency or wavelength is known. Notice that energy is proportional to frequency (Equation 1) and inversely proportional to wavelength (Equation 2).

Molecular spectroscopy involves the absorption of electromagnetic radiation by the material whose molecular structure we are attempting to determine. The relationship which describes the amount of radiation absorbed is **Beer's law**; it is shown as Equation 4 below. The absorption

---

[1] A photon is a quantity or quantum (package) of light. We have seen that light behaves as a wave, but it also behaves as particles called photons.

FIGURE 11-5

The entire electromagnetic radiation spectrum.

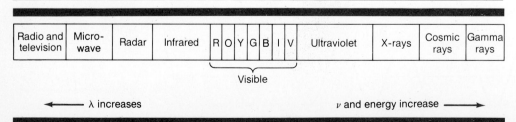

Radio and television	Micro-wave	Radar	Infrared	R	O	Y	G	B	I	V	Ultraviolet	X-rays	Cosmic rays	Gamma rays

Visible

$\longleftarrow \lambda$ increases $\qquad v$ and energy increase $\longrightarrow$

(*A*) is proportional to the inherent absorbing ability of the substance (ε; molar absorptivity or extinction coefficient), the concentration of the absorbing compound (*c*) and the distance the radiation is traveling through the sample (*l*).

$$E = hv \qquad (1)$$

$$E = hC/\lambda \qquad (2)$$

$$C = \lambda v \qquad (3)$$

$$A = \varepsilon(c)l \qquad (4)$$

Molecular spectroscopy is used to determine molecular structure and involves the interaction of matter with electromagnetic radiation. Different regions of the radiation spectrum have different wavelengths, frequencies, and energies.

INFRARED (IR) SPECTROSCOPY

One of the oldest forms of spectroscopy uses the **infrared region** of the electromagnetic radiation spectrum. We have already described light in terms of waves. In order to understand IR spectroscopy, we must first consider the motion of atoms in molecules. In Chapter 1 we described molecules as dynamic structures. The covalently bonded atoms vibrate in various ways rather than being stationary, as our drawings and models erroneously suggest. The two most common motions involved are stretching and bending.

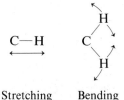

Stretching   Bending

In **stretching**, the bond length alternately gets longer and shorter (much like a yo-yo), and in **bending**, the bond angle alternates between larger and smaller values (much like a pair of scissors opening and closing).

Each of these vibration modes has a **natural frequency** of motion. This natural frequency is determined by the **mass** of the atoms bonded and the **strength** of the bond. The larger masses have a lower frequency (they are slower) and the stronger bonds have higher frequency (they have faster vibrations). This is illustrated in Figure 11-6.

Situation 1 shows a small weight attached to a large, loose spring. It would bounce with a certain frequency—say, 50 per minute (50/min). Situation 2 has the same spring, but a larger mass. The natural rate of motion would be less (perhaps 25/min). In the third situation, we see a strong, tight spring with the same large mass as in the second drawing.

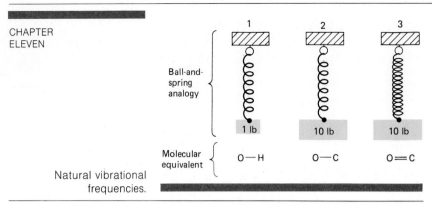

Ball-and-spring analogy

1 lb   10 lb   10 lb

Molecular equivalent

O—H   O—C   O=C

Natural vibrational frequencies.

FIGURE 11-6

This would have a higher frequency than is true in Situation 2 (perhaps 40/min).

For real molecules, or covalent bonds within larger molecules, the natural frequency follows the same trends. The O—H bond has a higher frequency of vibration than the O—C bond has since the average mass of the atoms is less for OH (both have single bonds). The O=C bond has a higher frequency than the O—C bond has since the bond is stronger (the masses are the same here).

Organic molecules absorb infrared "light," or radiation, as follows. When a frequency of IR radiation is synchronized with a natural vibration frequency of the molecule, reinforcement of the vibration can occur; that is, when IR radiation is absorbed, the molecule begins to vibrate with a greater amplitude (but with the same frequency), and thus the molecule has gained energy. This means that energy has been transferred from the radiation to the molecule, and that the molecule has absorbed electromagnetic radiation. Only **polar covalent** bonds absorb IR radiation (nonpolar and ionic bonds do not absorb). This absorption is shown in Figure 11-7 for the bending mode of the CO_2 molecule.

Since each type of bond has a unique combination of atomic mass and bond strength, each has a unique natural vibration frequency and will absorb a characteristic wavelength of IR radiation.

Compounds containing polar covalent bonds absorb electromagnetic radiation in the infrared (IR) region of the spectrum. Each type of bond will absorb IR radiation of a unique wavelength.

The spectrum

If we build an instrument in such a way as to allow a sample of unknown material to be held in position while the various wavelengths of the IR region shine on it in turn, we can find which wavelengths are absorbed and which are not. This scan can be plotted on a graph and is called the **infrared spectrum** of the material. A spectrum is a plot of absorbance

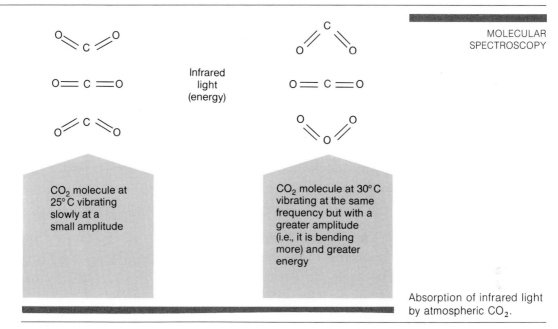

Absorption of infrared light
by atmospheric CO_2.

FIGURE 11-7

versus wavelength, frequency, or some other energy-related quantity. A
typical IR spectrum is shown in Figure 11-8.

By learning which frequencies are absorbed by the bonds of each functional group, a chemist can identify the functional groups present in a
material from its IR spectrum. Most of the spectral features (peaks; absorbances) which allow us to readily identify functional groups are found
in the left part of the spectrum. This is sometimes called the **functional
group region** of the spectrum. These absorbances are listed in Table 11-1.
The right-hand portion of the spectrum is more complex, and each peak
is not readily identified with a particular part of the molecule. The entire
spectral pattern is unique for a given compound, however. No two compounds have exactly the same pattern, and thus, the IR spectrum can be
used to identify a compound much as a **fingerprint** is used to identify a
person. If an unknown substance has the same IR spectrum as a known
sample of phenobarbital, for example, then the unknown substance is also
phenobarbital.

You will notice from Table 11-1 that some functional groups absorb
at several places because of different bonds within the group or different
modes of vibration of a given bond. Alcohols, for example, have both
O—H and C—O bonds, which absorb at 3400 and about 1150 to
1050 cm^{-1}, respectively.[2] It is even possible to differentiate between 1°,

---

[2] For IR spectra, we usually plot the reciprocal of the wavelength, which is proportional to
frequency. This is given in units of cm^{-1}; it is called the **wave number**.

TABLE 11-1

INFRARED ABSORBANCES OF COMMON FUNCTIONAL GROUPS			ABSORBANCES*	
	NAME	STRUCTURE	WAVE NUMBER, cm^{-1}	BOND
	Alkane	C—H	1370 (w)	CH_3
			1470 (m)	CH_2, CH_3
			2900 (s)	C—H
	Ketone		1710 (s)	C=O
	Aldehyde		1725 (s)	C=O
			2700 (w)	C—H
	Ester		1200 (s)	C—O
			1750 (s)	C=O
	Amide		1690 (s)	C=O
			3400 (m)	N—H
	Ether	R—O—R	1200 (s)	C—O
	Alcohol	R—O—H	1050 (s)	1° C—O
			1100 (s)	2° C—O
			1150 (s)	3° C—O
			3400 (s)	O—H
	Aromatic		1900 (w)	Overtones
			3050 (w)	C—H
	Alkene		1650 (m)	C=C
			3100 (w)	C—H
	Alkyne	—C≡C—H	2100 (w)	C≡C
			3300 (w)	C—H
	Amine		1600 (m)	N—H
			3400 (m)	N—H

* Relative lengths of peaks are indicated as (s), strong; (m), moderate; (w), weak.

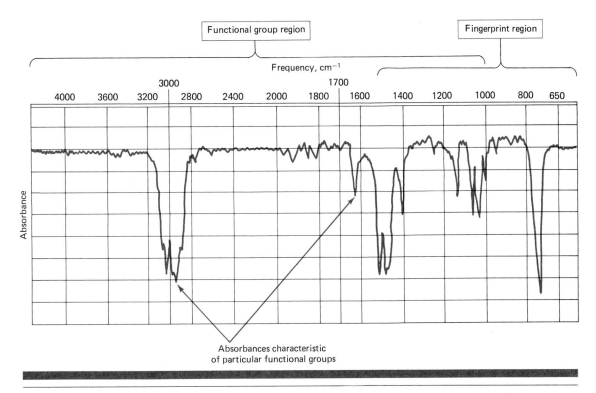

Functional group region

Fingerprint region

Frequency, cm⁻¹

Absorbances characteristic
of particular functional groups

FIGURE 11-8

Typical infrared spectrum.

2°, and 3° alcohols on the basis of the exact position of the C—O absorbance in the spectrum. Figure 11-9 shows the spectra of ethyl and isopropyl alcohols, along with the assignments taken from Table 11-1.

The infrared (IR) spectrum of a compound is a plot of absorbance versus wavenumber. From the positions of the various absorbances (peaks) we can determine the functional groups in molecules of a compound and/or positively identify a compound if its IR spectrum is already known.

Spectral interpretation

The steps used by a chemist to find information about molecular structure from the IR spectrum are as follows:

1 Obtain a spectrum of the material on an IR spectrophotometer (see Figure 11–10).

2 Using information from tables (or memory) and absorbances from the functional group region of the spectrum, identify the functional groups present.

3 Compare this spectrum with those of known compounds (i.e., ones

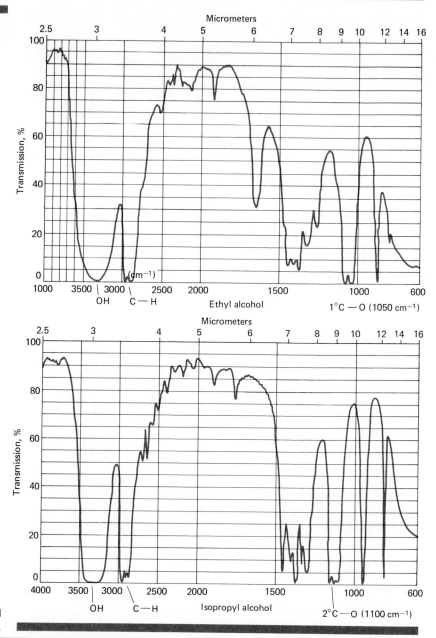

Infrared spectra of ethyl
and isopropyl alcohols.

FIGURE 11-9

whose IR spectra have been published in a catalog). Or obtain a known
sample of a suspected material and actually run its spectrum for comparison.

The following brief Programmed Learning Unit will allow you to
develop the skill of spectral interpretation.

An infrared
spectrophotometer.

FIGURE 11-10

INTERPRETING INFRARED SPECTRA

Worked example

List the bonds found in the material whose IR spectrum is shown in Figure 11-11.

1 After learning the positions of the common bonds shown in Table 11-1, observe major absorbances in the spectrum at 3400, 2900, 1470, and 1100 cm^{-1}.

2 Correlate these with the table data as follows:
3400 cm^{-1} —OH
2900 cm^{-1} —C—H
1470 cm^{-1} —CH$_2$ and/or —CH$_3$
1370   No peak, therefore no —CH$_3$
1100 cm^{-1} C—O of 2° alcohols

3 This must be a cyclic (no —CH$_3$), 2° alcohol such as cyclopentanol or cyclohexanol.

Worked example

From the choices below, choose the one whose IR spectrum is shown in Figure 11-12.

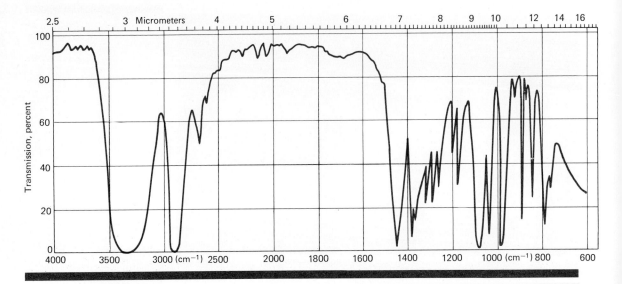

FIGURE 11-11

Infrared spectrum of
unknown compound.

FIGURE 11-12

Infrared spectrum of
unknown compound.

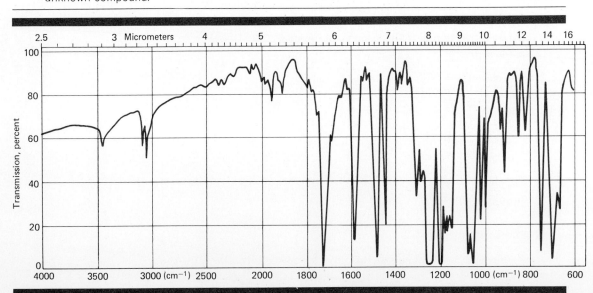

(a)

(b)

(c)

(d)

1 Observe peaks at the following positions (in cm^{-1}) and correlate.

3050   C—H of aromatic or alkene
2900   aliphatic C—H (none present)
1900   aromatic ring
1750   C=O of esters
1200   C—O of esters or ethers
1470   CH$_2$ (none present)
1370   CH$_3$ (none present)

2 Choice (a) is the only one that matches. Choice (a) has no CH$_3$; (b) is an amide and would have a C=O at 1690 cm^{-1}; (d) is an ether with no C=O. Choices (c), (b), and (d) would have C—H at 2900 and 1400 cm^{-1}.

At this point, it should be obvious that you need to know the data in Table 11-1. To aid you in becoming familiar with this information and to give a pictorial view of where each functional group shows up, the following exercise is recommended. Figure 11-13 shows a blank spectrum. Using colored pencils or markers, draw peaks on the spectrum for each functional group. For example, for aldehydes, place a short green peak at 2700 cm^{-1} and a long green one at 1725 cm^{-1}. For amides, put a moderate yellow peak at 3400 cm^{-1} and a large yellow one at 1690 cm^{-1}. This should help you to gain a useful perspective on what may seem a complex mass of data.

Problems

Determine the functional groups contained in the compound shown in Figure 11-14. Work on this and make a decision **before** looking at the solution below.

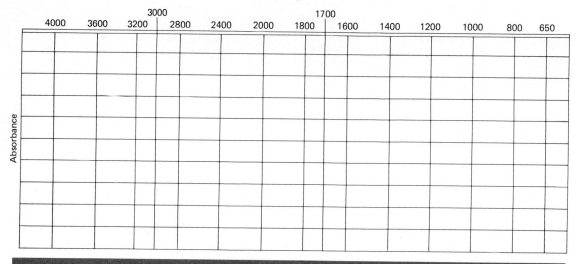

Frequency, cm⁻¹

FIGURE 11-13

Blank infrared spectrum. The student should
indicate the location of absorbances of common
functional groups from Table 11-1

FIGURE 11-14

Infrared spectrum of
unknown compound.

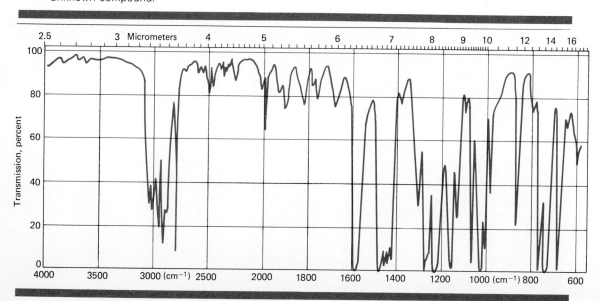

Solution

1   Observe absorbances at
      3050 cm^{-1} aromatic C—H
      2900 cm^{-1} C—H of alkyl groups
      1900 cm^{-1} aromatic ring
      1470 cm^{-1} CH_2/CH_3
      1370 cm^{-1} CH_3
      1200 cm^{-1} C—O of ether or ester

2   Since there is no peak at 1750 cm^{-1}, this is not an ester. It must
be an ether.

3   It must be an ether with both alkane and aromatic parts.

Problem

From the list below choose the compound whose IR spectrum is
shown in Figure 11-15.

(a)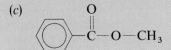

(b)

$$CH_3—\overset{\overset{\textstyle O}{\|}}{C}—CH_2CH_3$$

(c)

$$\overset{\overset{\textstyle O}{\|}}{\underset{}{}}—C—O—CH_3$$

(d) $CH_3—CH_2—NH_2$

Solution

1   Peaks come at
      2900 cm^{-1} C—H of alkyl groups
      1750 cm^{-1} C=O of ketones
      1470 cm^{-1} CH_2/CH_3
      1370 cm^{-1} CH_3

2   This is, therefore, a ketone with CH_3 groups. Choice (b), alone,
matches this description.

3   Choice (a) has no CH_3; (c) would have peaks at 3050 and
1900 cm^{-1} (aromatic) and one at 1200 cm^{-1} (C—O); choice (d)
would have a peak at 3400 cm^{-1} and none at 1725 cm^{-1}.

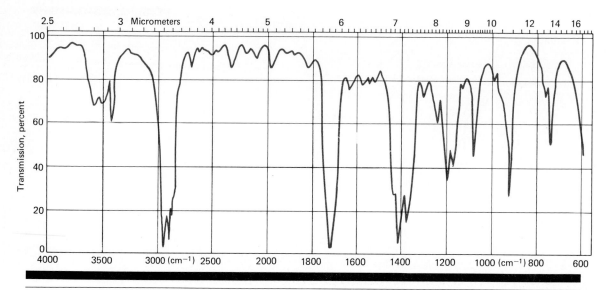

FIGURE 11-15

Infrared spectrum of
unknown compound.

NUCLEAR MAGNETIC RESONANCE
(NMR) SPECTROSCOPY

NMR is certainly one of the most powerful tools the chemist has for elucidating molecular structure. In this type of spectroscopy, the compound is placed in a **magnetic field**, and exposed to electromagnetic radiation in the **radio frequency** (RF) region. As the scan of this region is performed, the **hydrogen atoms** in various parts of the molecule absorb energy at different wavelengths. Under the correct conditions other atoms can also absorb RF energy, but here we will limit our coverage to hydrogen absorbance, because this is the most useful type of NMR spectroscopy.

The nucleus of a hydrogen atom is a single proton. It is physically spinning, and because it is charged, it is a tiny magnet with its own axis. In the absence of an external magnetic field, the spins of the protons are randomly oriented; but when placed near a magnet, they line up in one of two ways, as shown in Figure 11-16. These orientations are called **spin states**. The spins with the magnetic moments (arrows) pointing up in the drawing have slightly lower energy than those with arrows pointing down (those spinning in the opposite direction). It so happens that the energy difference between the two spin states is the same as the energy of a photon of RF radiation. When RF radiation "shines" on the sample containing hydrogen atoms in a magnetic field, the protons in the lower energy spin states (up arrow) absorb the energy of the RF radiation and flip over to the higher energy state (down arrow). Thus, the sample has absorbed the RF energy. We can therefore use the absorbance of RF energy by a compound which has been placed in a magnetic field to detect the presence of hydrogen atoms.

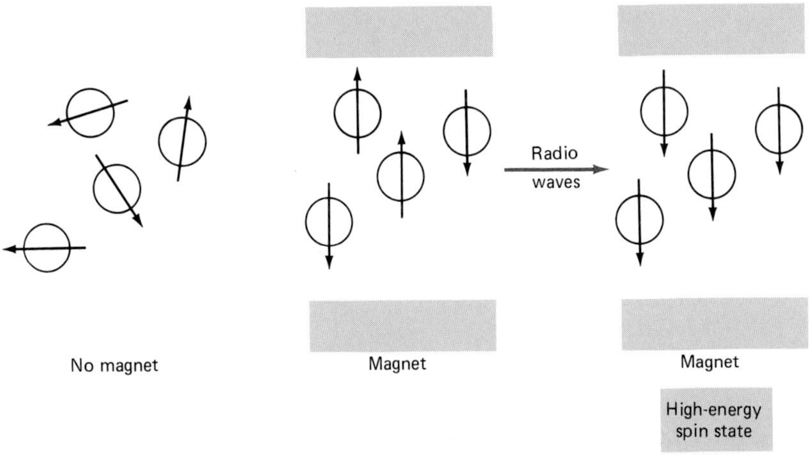

Radio
waves →

No magnet   Magnet   Magnet

High-energy
spin state

Behavior of protons in a
magnetic field.

FIGURE 11-16

Each hydrogen atom in a molecule can be in a slightly different environment, however. Some are on CH_3 groups, some are near oxygen or chlorine atoms, others are near double bonds or aromatic rings. These subtle differences in electronic environment are enough to change the energy between the spin states and thus change the exact RF range that will be absorbed.

The NMR spectrum of a compound arises from the absorbance of RF radiation in the presence of a magnetic field. We can use NMR to distinguish between hydrogen atoms in different environments within a molecule.

The NMR spectrum

When we scan the RF range, certain frequencies are absorbed by the hydrogen atoms in the molecules, depending on the environment of the various hydrogen atoms present. By knowing at what point of the spectrum each type of hydrogen atom absorbs radiation, we can deduce something about the molecular structure. Figure 11-17 shows a typical NMR spectrum and indicates the absorbances due to three types of hydrogen atoms. These are at δ equal to 1.0, 3.5, and 4.6 on the **chemical shift scale**. The chemical shift scale is divided into parts per million (ppm) of the RF range used. When this scale increases from right to left, we call it the **delta scale** (δ), which usually goes from 0 to 10 ppm. Certain terms such as upfield (to right) and downfield (to left) are also shown in Figure 11-17. Note that the peaks go up from the bottom of the spectrum in NMR rather than down from the top, as in IR. This is drawn this way by tradition only.

Figure 11-18 shows an NMR instrument.

There are three features of an NMR spectrum that give useful information. These are shown in Table 11-2.

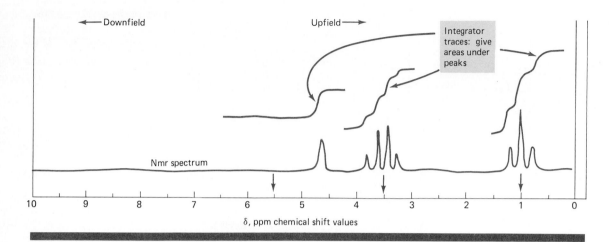

←— Downfield   Upfield —→   Integrator traces: give areas under peaks

Nmr spectrum

δ, ppm chemical shift values
10   9   8   7   6   5   4   3   2   1   0

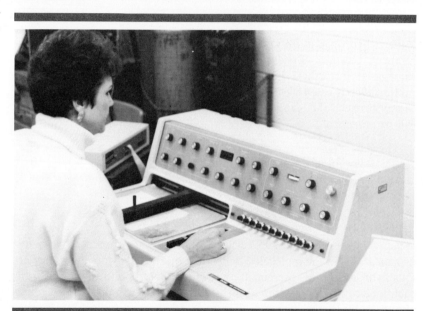

TABLE 11-2

NMR SPECTRAL FEATURES AND THEIR USEFULNESS

FEATURE	INFORMATION
Position on scale	Type of hydrogen
Size (area) of absorbance	Relative number of hydrogen atoms of each type
Multiplicity (pattern) of absorbance	Number of hydrogen atoms of other types nearby

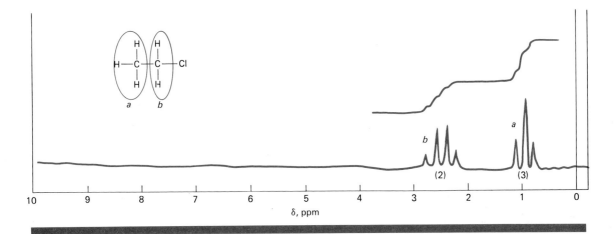

FIGURE 11-19

NMR spectrum of
1-chloroethane.

To illustrate these three features, we will consider the spectrum of 1-chloroethane (Figure 11-19). First note the **position of each peak on the scale**. This is called the **chemical shift value**. The (*a*) protons (CH_3) come at 1.0, which indicates that they are not near an electronegative atom, while the (*b*) protons (CH_2) appear at about 2.5 on the scale. The common chemical shift values should be learned just as the absorbance values for IR should be. The more important ones are given in Table 11-3.

Second, the size or **area of the peak** indicates the relative number of hydrogen atoms of each type. This is shown on the typical spectrum by numbers under each absorbance; they are determined by the integrator trace running above the peaks. The rise in the line is proportional to the number of each type of hydrogen atom. In Figure 11-19, the relative numbers are 3:2 (i.e, there are three hydrogen atoms of the CH_3 type and two of the CH_2 type).

Finally we come to the pattern of the absorbance, usually called its **multiplicity**. Notice in Figure 11-19 that the CH_3 absorbance (at 1.0 ppm) is a **triplet** (triple peak) while the absorbance at 2.5 ppm is a **quartet** (four peaks). These patterns tell us how many hydrogen atoms are on adjacent carbon atoms. There is always one more peak in the pattern than there are hydrogen atoms on the adjacent carbon atoms.

NAME OF PATTERN	NUMBER OF PEAKS	NUMBER OF H ATOMS ON ADJACENT C
Singlet	1	0
Doublet	2	1
Triplet	3	2
Quartet	4	3
———	$x + 1$	x

Thus if we observe a singlet peak, we know that there are no hydrogen atoms on the atoms next to the one whose absorbance is being registered. In Figure 11-19, if we consider the methyl absorbance, a triplet is observed.

TABLE 11-3

SELECTED NUCLEAR MAGNETIC RESONANCE (NMR) CHEMICAL SHIFT VALUES

TYPE NAME	STRUCTURE	CHEMICAL SHIFT*, (δ), ppm
Methyl	$-CH_3$ (1°)	0.9
Methylene	$-CH_2-$ (2°)	1.2
Methyne	$-\overset{\displaystyle \vert}{\underset{\displaystyle \vert}{C}}-H$ (3°)	1.5
Allylic	$C=C-\overset{\displaystyle \vert}{C}-$ ⒽH	1.7–2.2
Benzylic	⟨◯⟩$-\overset{\displaystyle \vert}{C}-$ ⒽH	2.2–3.0
Alpha to electronegative atoms	Ⓗ $-\overset{\displaystyle \vert}{\underset{\displaystyle \vert}{C}}-X$ X = O, N, F, Cl, Br, I	2–4
Alcohol	$-O-$Ⓗ	2–5
Alpha to carbonyl groups	Ⓗ O $-\overset{\displaystyle \vert}{\underset{\displaystyle \vert}{C}}-\overset{\displaystyle \Vert}{C}-$	2
Vinyl	$\diagdown C=C \diagup$ Ⓗ	5–6
Aromatic	⟨◯⟩$-$Ⓗ	6.5–8
Aldehyde	O $\Vert$ $-C-$Ⓗ	9–10
Carboxylic acid	O $\Vert$ $-C-O-$Ⓗ	10–12

* Note: If a halogen atom is on an adjacent carbon, move the absorbance higher by 0.5 ppm for each halogen present. A halogen directly attached to the same carbon shifts the position of the absorbance by about 2.0 ppm

This means there must be two hydrogen atoms on the next carbon atom. This is indeed the case.

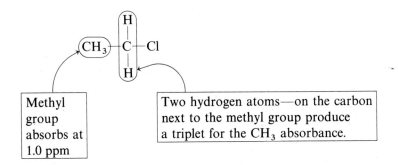

Similarly, the CH_2 peak is a quartet because there are three hydrogen atoms "next door."

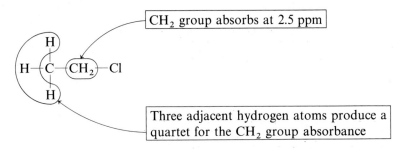

The following steps are used to draw the NMR spectrum we would expect for a given molecule. Once these steps are mastered, the same features are used in reverse to find the molecular structure from the NMR spectrum of an unknown compound. By practicing the examples used in the Programmed Learning Unit that follows, you will develop skill in drawing spectra. You will then be asked to interpret spectra in order to determine molecular structures.

Steps in drawing NMR spectra

1 Write out the complete **molecular structure** of the molecule.

2 **Draw loops** around hydrogen atoms of an equivalent nature within the molecule. Observe the relative number of hydrogen atoms of each type.

3 Determine from Table 11-3 (or memory), the approximate **chemical shift** of each.

4 **Draw a blank spectrum with the chemical shift scale** and place arrows or dots at the position for each type of hydrogen atom.

5 Determine the **multiplicity** of each absorbance.

(a) Focus on one type of hydrogen atom at a time.
(b) Observe the number of equivalent hydrogen atoms on adjacent carbon atoms.
(c) Assign the multiplicity of the absorbance on which we are focusing; it will be one more than the number of hydrogen atoms on adjacent carbon atoms.
(d) Repeat steps 5(a) to 5(c), for each type of hydrogen atom identified in step 2.

6 Draw the spectrum with a signal of the proper size (from step 2), at the proper place (from step 3), and of the correct multiplicity (from step 5).

PROGRAMMED LEARNING UNIT: DRAWING NMR SPECTRA

Worked example

Draw the NMR spectrum of dimethyl ether.

1

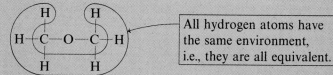

All hydrogen atoms have the same environment, i.e., they are all equivalent.

2 From Table 11-3, the chemical shift value would come somewhere between 2 and 4 ppm (H—C—X type).

3

$$\delta, \text{ppm}$$

4 There are no hydrogen atoms "next door," therefore the absorbance would be a singlet.

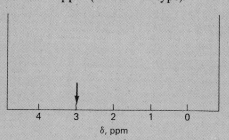

$$CH_3\text{—}O\text{—}CH_3$$

This oxygen atom is adjacent to the carbon atoms to which the hydrogen atoms are attached. There are no hydrogen atoms attached to it.

5

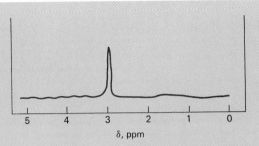

δ, ppm

Worked example

Draw the NMR spectrum of 1,2,2-trichloropropane.

1 Write the molecular formula.

$$\begin{array}{c c c}
\text{H} & \text{Cl} & \text{H} \\
| & | & | \\
\text{H}-\text{C}-\text{C}-\text{C}-\text{H} \\
| & | & | \\
\text{H} & \text{Cl} & \text{Cl}
\end{array}$$

2 Draw outlines around each group of equivalent hydrogen atoms.

$$\begin{array}{c c c}
\text{H} & \text{Cl} & \text{H} \\
| & | & | \\
\text{H}-\text{C}-\text{C}-\text{C}-\text{H} \\
| & | & | \\
\text{H} & \text{Cl} & \text{Cl}
\end{array}$$

| (a) Three H's of the methyl type | (b) Two H's of the CH_2—X type |

3 The (a) type would be methyl; the peak would come at 0.9 ppm (see Table 11-3). Because there are two chlorine atoms adjacent, move the absorbance by $2 \times 0.5 = 1.0$. This gives 1.9 ppm as the position of the peak for these hydrogen atoms. The (b) hydrogen atoms are of the H—C—X type and the peak would come between 2 and 4 ppm. Taking the midrange of 3.0 and adding $2 \times 0.5 = 1.0$ (owing to the Cl atoms adjacent) we get a value of 4.0 ppm for these hydrogen atoms.

4 Draw a scale and indicate the position due to each type of band.

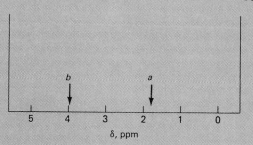

5 The carbon atom adjacent to both types has no hydrogen atoms. Therefore both signals (absorbances) will be singlets.

6 Draw the spectrum. The peak for (b) should be two-thirds as large as that for (a).

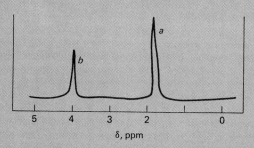

Worked example

Draw the NMR spectrum of 2-chloro-2-methyl butane.

1

```
                H
             H—C—H
             H)      H) H)
       H—C—C—C—C—H
             H) Cl (H) H)
       (a)                 (c)
                 (b)
```

2 (a) CH_3 with a Cl adjacent: $0.9 + 0.5 = 1.4$ ppm
   (b) CH_2 with a Cl adjacent: $1.2 + 0.5 = 1.7$ ppm
   (c) CH_3: 0.9 ppm

3

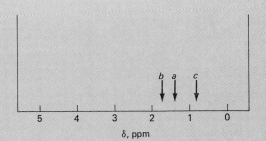

4 Type (*a*) has no hydrogen atoms adjacent: singlet
Type (*b*) has three hydrogen atoms on an adjacent atom: quartet
Type (*c*) has 2 hydrogen atoms next door: triplet

5

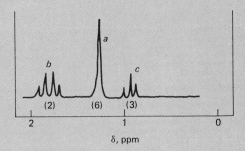

Worked example

Draw the NMR spectrum of 1-phenyl-1-bromoethane.

1

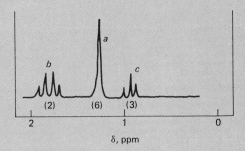

2 (*a*) Aromatic: 7.0 ppm (approximate midrange)
  (*b*) Benzylic with a halogen atom directly attached: 2.5 + 2.0 =
4.5 ppm

Note Since ranges are given in Table 11-3, these values are only
estimates good to ±0.5 ppm.
  (*c*) Methyl with halogen next door: 0.9 + 0.5 = 1.4 ppm

3

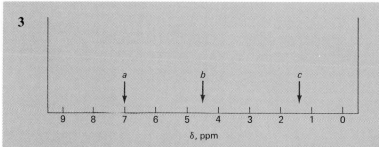

4 Type (*a*) has only nearly equivalent hydrogen atoms next door (i.e., each aromatic hydrogen atom has another aromatic hydrogen atom next door): singlet

Note Identical types of hydrogen atoms on adjacent atoms do not cause an increase in multiplicity.
Type (*b*) has three hydrogen atoms next door: quartet
Type (*c*) has one hydrogen atom next door: doublet

5.

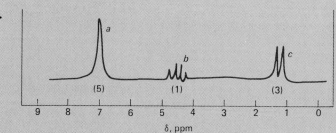

Worked example

Draw the NMR spectrum of 3-bromobutanal.

1

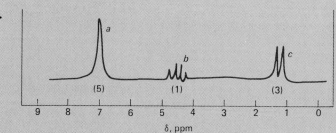

2 (*a*)   Methyl group with a bromine atom adjacent: $0.9 + 0.5 = 1.4$ ppm
(*b*)   H—C—X group: 3.0 ppm
(*c*)   Alpha to C=O with a bromine atom adjacent: $2.0 + 0.5 = 2.5$ ppm
(*d*)   Aldehyde: 9.5 ppm

3

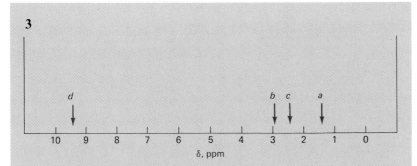

4 (*a*)   One hydrogen atom adjacent: doublet
(*b*)   Three adjacent hydrogen atoms in one direction, indicating a quartet; two hydrogen atoms of a different type adjacent in the other direction, indicating a triplet

Note   When a given hydrogen atom has more than one type of hydrogen atom on adjacent carbon atoms, calculate each one independently and then multiply. In this case, $4 \times 3 = 12$. When such a high multiplicity results, it is called a **complex multiplet** and is drawn as a broad, low "sawtooth" pattern.
(*c*)   One hydrogen atom of one type on one side and one hydrogen atom of a different type on the other; two doublets.
(*d*)   Two hydrogen atoms adjacent: triplet

5

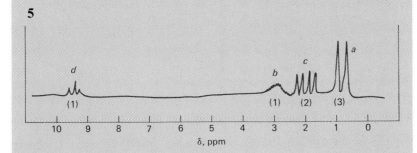

Problems

1   Draw the NMR spectrum for $CH_3 - \overset{\displaystyle O}{\overset{\|}{C}} - O - CH_2 - CH_3$ on the graph below. Be sure to try this before looking at the answer on page 363.

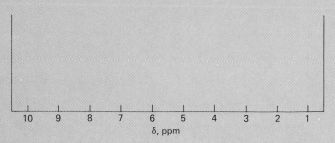

2 Draw the NMR spectrum for the following compound:

$$\underset{H}{\overset{H}{\diagdown}}C=C\underset{CH_3}{\overset{CH_3}{\diagup}}$$

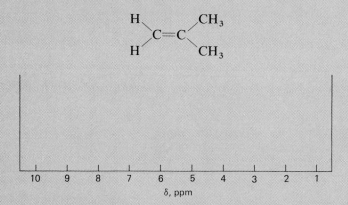

3 Draw the NMR spectrum for 2-methylpropanal.

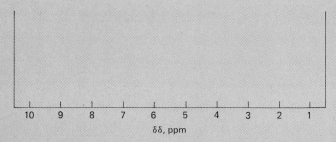

Answers

1

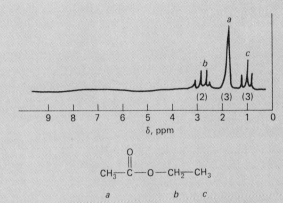

(a) Alpha to C=O with no adjacent hydrogen atoms: singlet
(b) —CH$_2$—O— with three adjacent hydrogen atoms: quartet
(c) CH$_3$ with two adjacent hydrogen atoms: triplet

2

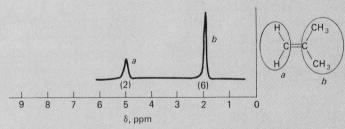

(a) Vinyl with no adjacent hydrogen atoms: singlet
(b) Allylic with no adjacent hydrogen atoms: singlet

3

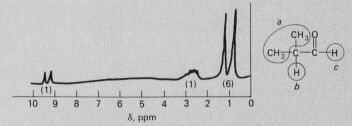

(a) Methyl groups with one hydrogen atom adjacent: doublet
(b) Alpha to C=O with six adjacent hydrogen atoms in one
     direction (indicating seven peaks) and one adjacent in the
     other direction (causing a double +): 2 × 7 = 14, therefore a
     complex multiplet
(c) Aldehyde with one hydrogen atom on adjacent carbon:
     doublet

ULTRAVIOLET (UV) SPECTROSCOPY

There are two other types of spectroscopy commonly used by organic chemists with which you should be familiar. They are ultraviolet spectroscopy (UV) and mass spectroscopy (MS). In this text, we will not give an in-depth presentation or attempt skill development in spectral interpretation for these two areas, but you should be familiar with the principles involved and the kinds of information that can be gained from each.

In **ultraviolet spectroscopy** we measure the absorbance in the ultraviolet region of the electromagnetic radiation spectrum [200 to 400 nanometers (nm)] by organic molecules. Compounds which absorb UV "light," or radiation, are those which contain pi bonds (C=C or C=O groups). The absorption is accomplished by **electronic transitions** within the molecules. For molecules with pi bonds, the energy difference between the ground state (normal structure) and the excited electronic state (an electron in a higher energy orbital) is the same as the energy of photons of UV light. UV light causes an electron within the molecule to be promoted to the excited state, thus transferring the energy of the radiation to the molecule.

We obtain a UV spectrum by scanning the 200 to 400 nm region of the spectrum and observing the wavelengths that are absorbed. The spectrum usually consists of a single broad absorbance, the position of which indicates the pi bond arrangement in the molecule. The more double bonds there are in **conjugation**, the higher the wavelength at which the compound absorbs. The term *in conjugation* means that the double bonds are separated from each other by one, and only one, single bond. Table 11-4

TABLE 11-4

SELECTED ULTRAVIOLET (UV) ABSORBANCE VALUES	STRUCTURE	UV MAXIMUM ABSORBANCE nm
	$H_2C{=}CH_2$	165
		217
		253
		256
		219
		249
	Ethanol	No absorbance*
	Hexane	No absorbance*

* No π bonds.

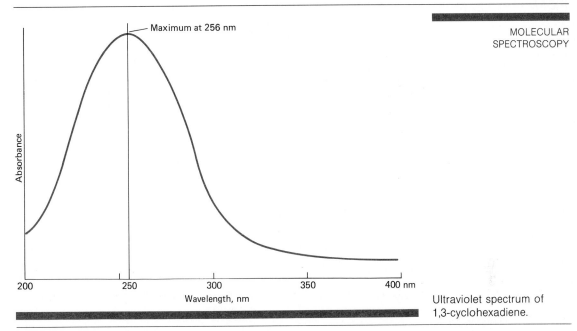

Ultraviolet spectrum of
1,3-cyclohexadiene.

FIGURE 11-20

shows typical structures along with their maximum absorbance values, and Figure 11-20 shows the UV spectrum of 1,3-cyclohexadiene.

From Table 11-4, it can be observed that each additional conjugated double bond contained in the molecule causes the absorbance value to increase by about 30 nm. Also notice that those compounds with no double bonds do not absorb UV radiation.

If a molecule has seven or more conjugated double bonds, the absorbance region is above 400 nm, which is in the visible region of the spectrum (400 to 700 nm). This causes the material to be colored, since certain colors are selectively absorbed.

Ultraviolet spectroscopy allows a chemist to determine the number of conjugated carbon-carbon and carbon-oxygen double bonds in a molecule. The spectrum arises from electronic transitions.

MASS SPECTROSCOPY (MS)

The mass spectrum of a compound arises from subjecting molecules of that compound to a **high energy electron beam**. This causes a molecule to break up into fragments characteristic of its structure. We then measure the **mass** of the intact molecule and each of its fragments, along with the relative **abundance** of each. This is the only type of spectroscopy that does not involve the absorption of electromagnetic radiation. Figure 11-21 shows a mass spectrum and indicates the useful features it contains.

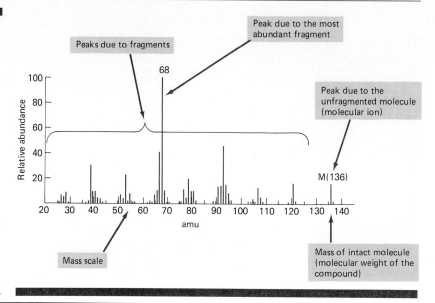

Peaks due to fragments

Peak due to the most
abundant fragment

Peak due to the
unfragmented molecule
(molecular ion)

Mass scale

Mass of intact molecule
(molecular weight of the
compound)

Typical mass spectrum.

FIGURE 11-21

There are 3 kinds of information an organic chemist can obtain from the mass spectrum of a compound:

1 **Molecular weight** of the compound.

2 Masses of the **fragments.** This information gives clues concerning the structural features of the molecule. A mass of 77 atomic mass units (amu) could indicate that a phenyl group is present; if there is a mass 15 amu less than the molecular weight of the molecule, a methyl group may have been present before fragmentation took place.

3 The entire mass spectrum constitutes a **fingerprint** of the compound in question. Each material has its own unique fragmentation pattern because of its unique molecular structure. So, like the IR spectrum, the mass spectrum serves as a positive identification of a substance.

> Mass spectroscopy involves the measurement of the masses of molecules and their fragments. The molecular weight, the identity of some of the component parts of the molecules, and a positive identification of the substance can all be obtained from the mass spectrum.

SOLVING STRUCTURE PROBLEMS

Finding the molecular structure of a newly prepared or isolated substance presents a considerable challenge, both intellectually and experimentally. Some clues can be gathered from knowledge of the reactions that produced the substance, from chemical reactions the substance undergoes which give known compounds, or from chemical tests that give colors or other indications of the presence of certain functional groups. In the last several decades, researchers have relied more and more heavily on spectroscopic data, especially IR and NMR data, for determining molecular structures.

Ultraviolet (UV) spectroscopy can sometimes be used to gain information about the presence or absence of double bonds in a molecule and, if present, the number of double bonds in conjugation. Mass spectroscopy (MS) can give the molecular weight of a compound and information about fragments in the molecule, as well as a fingerprint pattern unique to each compound. Analysis of a typical set of data is shown in the next sections.

Data on an unknown compound

Composition   contains only C, H, and O

Molecular weight   60 amu

IR data (cm^{-1}) 2900
1400
1370
1200

NMR data $(\delta$ ppm)   3.5 quartet (2H)
3.0 singlet (3H)
1.0 triplet (3H)

Interpreting the IR Data

First, the IR absorbances, in cm^{-1}, are examined to identify the functional groups.

2900   CH of alkyl groups

1470 CH_2, CH_3

1370 CH_3

1200   ether or ester

Since there is no $C=O$ (1750 cm^{-1}) or OH (3400 cm^{-1}), we can eliminate esters, alcohols, ketones, and aldehydes and conclude that this compound must be an ether.

Interpreting the NMR data

The NMR data can be interpreted to find the carbon structures in the molecule from the hydrogen atom arrangements observed. The singlet at 3.0 ppm, because it has three hydrogen atoms and is a singlet, must be a CH_3 with no hydrogen atoms next door. The quartet must be CH_2 with three hydrogen atoms next door, and the triplet must be a CH_3 group with two hydrogen atoms on an adjacent carbon atom.

Determining the structure of the unknown compound

Once this kind of analysis has been done, creative reasoning must be used to find a structure consistent with the data. Sometimes trial and error works well here; draw some structures and then modify them rather than wait until your mind can put it all together correctly. In the example given above we can draw the parts we have identified.

CH_3- no hydrogen atoms adjacent

$-O-$

CH_3- two hydrogen atoms adjacent

$-CH_2-$ three hydrogen atoms adjacent

We notice at this point that the CH_3 and CH_2 might be bonded together to form an ethyl group.

$$CH_3-CH_2-$$

Since an ether has to have two alkyl groups, it seems only logical, from what we have so far, that one must be a methyl group and one an ethyl group. We arrive at the following structure for our previously unknown compound:

$$CH_3-O-CH_2-CH_3$$

We can go back to check the correctness of this structure. All the data are indeed consistent with the structure we have proposed. The ultimate proof, however, is to get an authentic sample of methyl ethyl ether (or synthesize it if necessary) and run an IR spectrum. If it matches the IR spectrum of our unknown material in every respect, then we have proven that our unknown is methyl ethyl ether.

SUMMARY

1 Electromagnetic radiation is best thought of as **waves** of electrical charge. Different regions of the spectrum are characterized by different **wavelengths**, **frequencies**, and **energies**. Electromagnetic radiation can also be thought of as "packages" of light energy called **photons**.

2 Substances containing **polar covalent bonds** absorb **infrared (IR) radiation** when the frequency of the radiation correlates with the natural vibrational frequency of bonded atoms within the molecules of that substance.

3 Different functional groups absorb IR radiation at different positions on the spectrum, giving a plot of absorbance versus wavenumber. By examining the IR spectrum of a material, and by learning the wavelength at which each type of bond absorbs, a chemist can determine which **functional groups** are **present** in molecules of that material. Each compound has a unique IR spectrum which constitutes a positive **fingerprint** identification of that compound.

4   In the presence of a magnetic field, hydrogen atoms assume one of two possible spin states. Absorption of radiation in the radio frequency region of the spectrum causes a transition to the higher energy spin state. Different **electronic environments** cause different hydrogen atoms to absorb radiation of different frequencies. The absorbed frequencies are shown on the **nuclear magnetic resonance (NMR)** spectrum of that compound.

5   By examining the NMR spectrum of a substance, we can determine the number of different **types of hydrogen** atoms present (from the number of peaks or absorbances seen) and the **relative number** of atoms of each type (from the relative sizes of the peaks). The pattern (multiplicity) of the peaks gives us information about the number of hydrogen atoms on **adjacent atoms**. From these NMR spectral data, we can determine the structure of those parts of the molecule which contain hydrogen atoms, especially the alkyl portions.

6   Molecules that contain **double bonds** absorb **ultraviolet (UV) radiation**. The more double bonds in conjugation, the longer the wavelength of the light that is absorbed. From the position of the maximum absorbance on the spectrum, a chemist can determine the number of double bonds present.

7   **Mass spectroscopy (MS)** is used to find the **molecular weight** of a substance; it also gives information about **molecular fragments**. The mass spectrum serves as a **fingerprint identification** of each material.

8   By using a combination of several types of spectroscopy, we can determine the molecular structure of new materials and prove the identity of known materials.

KEY TERMS

Absorbance

Chemical shift

Conjugation

Doublet

Electronic transition

Electromagnetic radiation

Fingerprint

Frequency

Infrared (IR) spectroscopy

Mass spectroscopy (MS)

Molecular fragments

Molecular spectroscopy

Multiplicity of nuclear magnetic resonance (NMR) peaks

Natural frequency of vibration

Nuclear magnetic resonance (NMR) spectroscopy

Photon

Quartet

Radio frequency (RF)

Singlet

Spectrum

Spin states

Triplet

Ultraviolet (UV)
spectroscopy

Wavelength

Wave number

SKILL PRACTICE PROBLEMS

1 What is the purpose of obtaining IR and/or NMR spectra of a compound?

2 Which has the higher natural frequency of each pair given below:
 (*a*) C—O or C—S   (*b*) C≡C or C≡N
 (*c*) C—C or C=C

3 From what you know about where each functional group absorbs, do those with higher natural frequencies generally absorb at higher or lower wave numbers (cm^{-1})?

4 From memory, give the IR absorbances (in cm^{-1}) of the following bonds:
 (*a*) OH   (*b*) NH
 (*c*) CH (three possible values)   (*d*) C—O
 (*e*) C=O

5 From memory, give the approximate NMR chemical shift values (in ppm) for the following types of protons:
 (*a*) —CH$_2$—Br
 (*b*) Vinyl
 (*c*) The alpha hydrogen atoms in acetone
 (*d*) Aromatic
 (*e*) Methyl
 (*f*) The protons in cyclohexane

6 Circle the equivalent protons in each structure shown.

 (*a*) CH$_3$—CH$_2$—N—CH$_2$—CH$_3$ (*b*)
                    |
                    CH$_3$

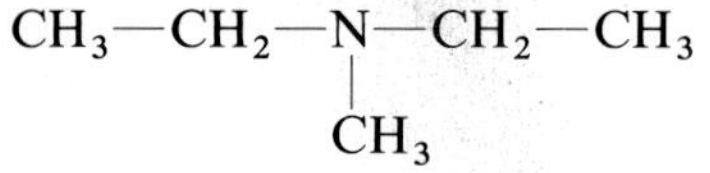

 (*c*)   CH$_3$
              |
       CH$_3$—C—CH$_2$—CH$_3$
              |
              CH$_3$

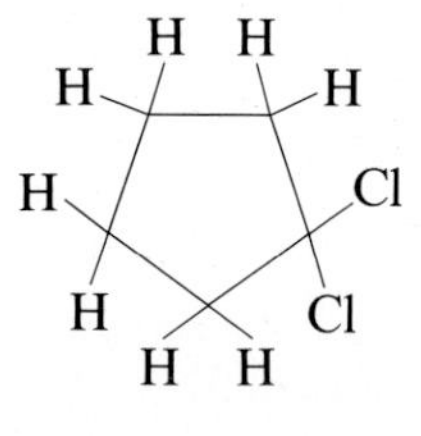

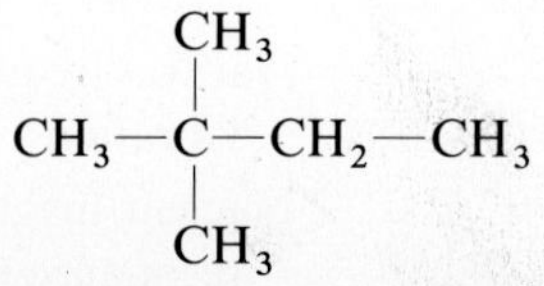

7 Sketch the NMR spectrum you would expect for each of the following compounds:

(a) t-Butyl benzene

(b) Isopropyl alcohol

(c)

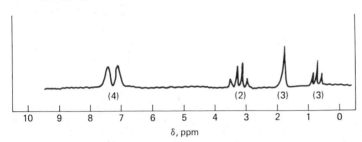

(d)

8 What molecular structure would you expect for a compound with formula $C_{10}H_{12}O_2$ and an NMR as shown below?

$$\delta, \text{ppm}$$

9 One method of detecting alcohol intoxication in a person is to use a specially designed IR spectrometer to measure the intensity of various absorbances caused by alcohol. What regions of the IR spectrum would be appropriate for use in such a device? See Figure 11-9.

10 Name the type of spectroscopy that would allow you to distinguish between each of the pairs shown below. Indicate what differences you would observe in the spectra.

(a)

(b) CH_3 CH_3

        and

(c) Cl CH_3—CH—CH_2

        CH_3—C—CH_3 and Cl Cl

        Cl

(d) CH_3

        CH_3—CH_2—CH_2—CH_2—OH and CH_3—C—CH_3

                                                OH

(e) CH_3CH_2—Cl   and CH_3CH_2—O—CH_2CH_3

11 A compound shows a strong peak at 1725 cm^{-1} along with peaks at 2900, 1470, and 1370 cm^{-1}. The NMR shows a singlet at 2.0, a triplet at 1.0, and a quartet at 2.5 ppm. Suggest a structure for this compound. The molecular weight is shown by mass spectroscopy to be 72 amu.

12 A compound shows peak at 3050, 2900, 1470, 1370, and 1200 cm^{-1}. The NMR spectrum has only a broad singlet at 7.2 and a singlet at 3.0 ppm. Propose a structure based on the formula $C_8H_{10}O_2$.

13 Which of the following compounds would absorb UV light of the longest wavelength?

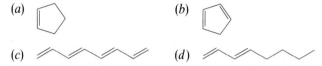

14 Using compounds in Table 11-4 for reference and the rule that each carbon-carbon double bond increases the absorbance value by about 30 nm, what position on the UV spectrum would you expect for the absorbance of the following compound?

15 List the three kinds of information we can get from the mass spectrum of a compound.

16 Give the structure of an alkane with a molecular weight of 84 amu which has a doublet at 0.9 ppm in the NMR spectrum (in addition to other absorbances).

17 Propose a structure for an alcohol with the molecular formula $C_5H_{12}O$, which has an IR absorbance at 1050 cm^{-1} and a singlet at 1.0 ppm in the NMR spectrum (in addition to other absorbances).

REVIEW QUESTIONS

18 Give the hybridization of the indicated atoms in the following structure.

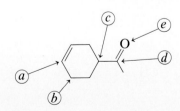

19 Give an example of a dehydration reaction of an alcohol. Indicate the correct reagent(s) and the structure of the product(s).

20 Complete these reactions:

(a) $\bigcirc\!\!-CH_3 \xrightarrow[hv]{Br_2}$

(b) $CH_3CH_2CH_2OH + Na \longrightarrow$

(c) $CH_3CH_2-O-CH_2-CH_3 \xrightarrow{Mg}$

(d)

$\bigcirc\!\!-\overset{\displaystyle O}{\overset{\|}{C}}-CH_3 + H_2NOH \longrightarrow$

21 Name the organic compound used as a reactant in question 20(d).

DETERMINING BLOOD ALCOHOL CONTENT

The abuse of alcoholic beverages causes many problems in society, including the problem of drunken driving. Driving while intoxicated has, for many years, caused about half (25,000) of the yearly highway fatalities in the United States. With stricter laws and with harsher penalties being imposed for drunken driving, it is hoped that the number of fatalities will decrease.

Alcohol is metabolized by liver enzymes, and while different people have different enzyme concentrations, most people metabolize ethanol at a rate of about 1 ounce (30 milliliters or mL) per hour. That is approximately the amount of alcohol in one can of beer, one glass of wine, or a 2-ounce "shot" of liquor. Usually, if not more than 1 ounce of alcohol is consumed each hour, no obvious physical or mental incapacity results. At a faster rate of consumption, however, intoxication gradually occurs. At a blood level of about 0.05 percent alcohol people become somewhat uninhibited, and at a level around 0.1 percent alcohol many people become noticeably intoxicated. The intoxication level does vary a great deal from person to person, however, depending on body chemistry and past drinking habits, among other factors. Some people may be unable to drive safely at the 0.08 percent level, while some may be safe drivers at 0.15 percent or even higher.

There are a number of field tests that can be used to determine intoxication. These tests are useful to police officers in enforcing drunken driving laws. A suspected drunk driver can be asked to perform any one of several simple physical tasks such as to walk a straight line. Failure to accomplish such a task indicates an alcohol level too high for safe driving. The officer may then want a more quantitative measure of blood alcohol in order to prove in a court of law that the driver is intoxicated. Most localities consider 0.1 percent or more of ethanol in the blood to constitute **legal drunkenness**, while some exact a stricter penalty if the ethanol level is above 0.15 percent. To determine if these levels have been reached or exceeded, several good analytical methods are available.

The first involves a device that rapidly and accurately measures alcohol in the breath of the suspect by using **spectroscopy**. Commonly used brands of breath analyzers are the Breathalyser and the Intoxalyser. When a person has alcohol in the blood, some of it evaporates into the lung air space. Thus, the breath contains alcohol in proportion to the amount of alcohol in the blood. The breath analyzer is a specially designed **infrared spectrometer** with two or more carefully calibrated settings in the 2900 cm^{-1} region of the spectrum. This is the most powerful C—H absorbing region. (See Table 11-1 and Figure 11-8.) Since ethyl alcohol has

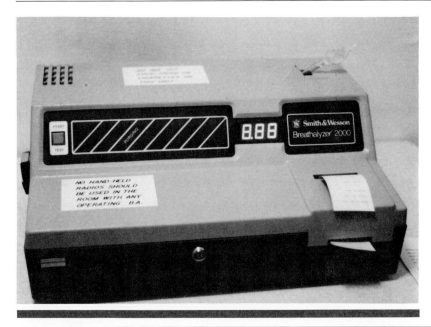

An alcohol breath-analysis device. Note the digital readout near the center of the instrument and the paper printout on the front right. The suspect blows into the tube on the upper right. (*Photo taken with permission of officer John Poland of the Georgetown, Kentucky, police department.*)

FIGURE E-1

C—H bonds, the more alcohol in the breath, the greater will be the absorbance in the 2900 cm^{-1} region. The breath analysis device measures the ratios of the absorbances, converts them into percent alcohol in the blood or breath, and displays them on a dial, or by a printed or digital readout. Figure E-1 shows a breath analyzer and its readout.

Spectroscopy is used not only to determine molecular structure and identify substances quantitatively, as discussed in Chapter 11, but also to help solve a social problem.

The second method used for alcohol blood analysis involves the collection of the breath sample in a small tube made of **indium** metal. The tube is sealed by **crimping** in four spots so that three chambers (or breath samples) of about $\frac{1}{4}$ mL each are sealed off. Indium is the most practical material for such a device since it is soft enough to allow a complete seal to be easily formed. The crimped tube is sent to a forensic laboratory for alcohol analysis by gas chromatography. Two of the chambers are used for duplicate analysis, while the third is kept for future reference or for analysis by an independent laboratory if the suspect so desires. Figure E-2 shows a police officer collecting a breath sample in an indium tube, and Figure E-3 shows a sample gas chromatographic analysis of the gas it contains. In this analysis, a laboratory standard sample equivalent to 0.160 percent blood alcohol is first run to check the accuracy of the instrument. Duplicate analysis of the indium crimp sample showed the suspect to have a blood alcohol level of 0.190 percent.

The third standard method of blood alcohol analysis involves the direct

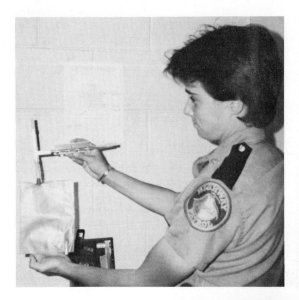

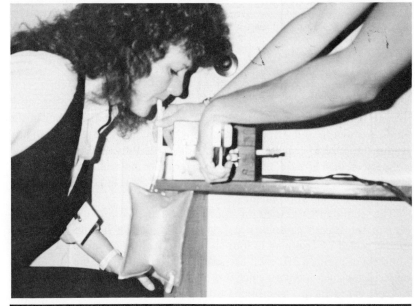

The indium tube test for blood alcohol. (*a*) Police officer holding the indium tube (in her right hand) along with the connecting tubes and overflow bag. (*b*) Indium tube being placed in the crimping apparatus. (*c*) Suspect blowing her breath into the apparatus. (*Photos courtesy of officer Diane Russo of the Florida Highway Patrol.*)

FIGURE E-2

withdrawal of blood by a medical technologist (at the "suggestion" of the police officer, of course). The blood sample is then sent to a laboratory where it is analyzed by gas chromatography. After dilution, the blood sample may be injected directly into a gas chromatographic instrument along with a calibration standard.

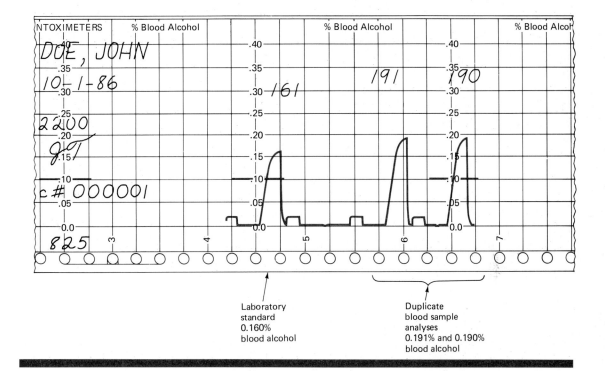

Laboratory
standard
0.160%
blood alcohol

Duplicate
blood sample
analyses
0.191% and 0.190%
blood alcohol

FIGURE E-3

Gas chromatographic
analysis of an indium tube
breath sample. (*This trace
was supplied by Mr. James
Tutsock of the Sarasota,
Florida, police department
breath analysis laboratory.*)

CHAPTER 12

CARBOXYLIC ACIDS AND THEIR DERIVATIVES

LEARNING GOALS

1 To develop skill in naming carboxylic acids, esters, amides, acyl halides, salts, and anhydrides

2 To understand the relationship between molecular structures of carboxylic acids and their relative acid strengths

3 To understand the methods of preparing carboxylic acids and the ways of converting them into esters, amides, acyl chlorides, and anhydrides

4 To learn the reactions of carboxylic acids, amides, and esters

5 To recognize the structures of carboxylic acids and those derivatives which are biologically active and encountered in consumer products, including synthetic fibers

In this chapter, we will study **carboxylic acids** and those functional group classes that are related to carboxylic acids. These related functional groups are called **derivatives** of carboxylic acids because they are usually prepared from them. The functional groups emphasized in this chapter are as follows:

$$
\begin{array}{ccc}
\overset{\displaystyle O}{\underset{\displaystyle}{R-C-OH}} & \overset{\displaystyle O}{\underset{\displaystyle}{R-C-O-R}} & \overset{\displaystyle O}{\underset{\displaystyle}{R-C-N}} \\
\text{Carboxylic} & \text{Esters} & \text{Amides} \\
\text{acids} & &
\end{array}
$$

Other related functional groups that will be referred to briefly are

$$
\begin{array}{ccc}
\overset{\displaystyle O}{\underset{\displaystyle}{R-C-Cl}} & \overset{\displaystyle O}{\underset{\displaystyle}{R-C-O^-}} & \overset{\displaystyle O\quad\quad O}{\underset{\displaystyle}{R-C-O-C-R}} \\
\text{Acid chlorides} & \text{Salts} & \text{Anhydrides} \\
\text{(acyl chlorides)} & &
\end{array}
$$

Since these six functional groups have many of the same structural features, you may have difficulty distinguishing one from another at first. Before proceeding, take some time to study the outlined boxes above and note the unique bonding features of each one.

CARBOXYLIC ACIDS

Carboxylic acids are called acids because they ionize, when placed in water, to produce an excess of H^+ ions. Acids are those materials which donate a proton (H^+) when added to water. This corresponds to the Arrhenius and Bronsted-Lowery definitions of acids. Table 12-1 summarizes the three definitions of acids and bases for your review.

TABLE 12-1

SUMMARY OF ACID AND BASE DEFINITIONS		ARRHENIUS DEFINITION	BRONSTED-LOWERY DEFINITION	LEWIS DEFINITION
	Acid	Proton (H^+) donor	Proton donor	Electron pair acceptor
	Base	Hydroxide ion (OH^-) donor	A compound which accepts a proton from an acid	Electron pair donor

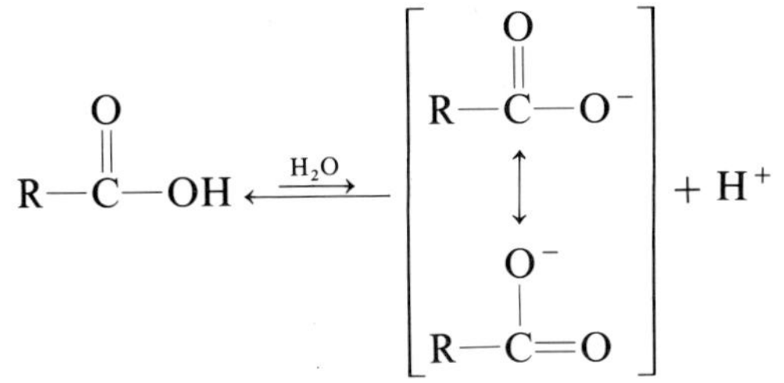

$$R—\overset{\displaystyle\overset{O}{\|}}{C}—OH \xrightleftharpoons{H_2O} \left[\begin{array}{c} R—\overset{\displaystyle\overset{O}{\|}}{C}—O^- \\ \updownarrow \\ \underset{R—C=O}{\overset{O^-}{\mid}} \end{array} \right] + H^+$$

While carboxylic acids are weak acids compared to the strong mineral acids such as HCl, HNO_3, and H_2SO_4, they are the most acidic of the common organic functional group classes. The **resonance stabilization** of the carboxylate anion (shown in brackets above) accounts for the relatively strong ionization ability of carboxylic acids. Remember that when a species has several resonance forms, it is more stable, and that a reaction tends to go more readily if the products are more stable.

Relative acidities

Some carboxylic acids are "stronger" than others. The stronger ones have a greater tendency to ionize and, thus, have a larger numerical value for the acidity constant (K_a). The K_a value of an acid is an expression of the equilibrium constant for the ionization reaction shown below. The larger the concentration of products relative to reactants at equilibrium, the larger the numerical value of the equilibrium constant. In this case, H^+ is a product, and so the K_a value indicates the tendency of the acid to give up H^+ ions when added to water.

$$R—COOH \xrightleftharpoons{H_2O} R—COO^- + H^+$$

$$K_a = \frac{[R-COO^-][H^+]}{[R-COOH]}$$

The strengths of acids are determined by the nature of the R group in the general formula above. Those R groups that withdraw electrons stabilize the anion even more and cause the acids to be stronger (have larger K_a values). Such electron-withdrawing groups contain electronegative atoms such as F, Cl, Br or I or functional groups that contain electronegative atoms, such as —OH, —NH_2, or —NO_2. The closer the electronegative atom is to the —COOH group, the more the acid is strengthened. It is also true that the greater the number of electronegative atoms present, the more acidic is the compound.

On the other hand, larger alkyl groups tend toward weaker acidity since they "feed" electrons toward the —COOH group and destabilize the —COO^-. These electronic (**inductive**) effects are shown in Figure 12-1.

These trends are illustrated by data in Table 12-2. You should look carefully at the correlation between K_a value and structure to confirm the trends discussed above. You will also notice that there are exceptions.

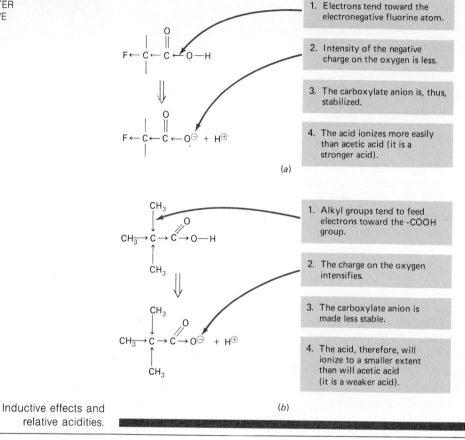

(a)

(b)

Inductive effects and relative acidities.

FIGURE 12-1

Carboxylic acids are considered weak acids but are the most acidic of the common organic compounds. Their relative acidities are determined by the nature of the substituents present. Large alkyl groups make the acids weaker, while electronegative atoms tend to increase acid strength.

Nomenclature

Acids are named in the IUPAC system by using the base name for the longest chain along with the ending *-oic acid*. Classical names are also used; the more common ones are shown below in parentheses.

$$H-\overset{\overset{\displaystyle O}{\|}}{C}-OH \qquad CH_3-\overset{\overset{\displaystyle O}{\|}}{C}-OH \qquad CH_3CH_2-\overset{\overset{\displaystyle O}{\|}}{C}-OH$$

Methanoic acid   Ethanoic acid   Propanoic acid
(formic acid)   (acetic acid)   (propionic acid)

$$CH_3CH_2CH_2\overset{\displaystyle O}{\overset{\|}{C}}-OH \qquad CH_3(CH_2)_3\overset{\displaystyle O}{\overset{\|}{C}}-OH$$

Butanoic acid   Pentanoic acid
(butyric acid)   (valeric acid)

$$CH_3(CH_2)_4\overset{\displaystyle O}{\overset{\|}{C}}-OH \qquad CH_3-(CH_2)_{16}\overset{\displaystyle O}{\overset{\|}{C}}-OH$$

Hexanoic acid   Octadecanoic acid
(caproic acid)   (stearic acid)

TABLE 12-2

ACIDITIES OF SELECTED
CARBOXYLIC ACIDS

STRUCTURE	K_a
CH_3COOH	1.8×10^{-5}
CH_3CH_2COOH	1.34×10^{-5}
$CH_3CH_2CH_2COOH$	1.5×10^{-5}
$CH_3-CH-COOH$ $\quad\quad\ \ \|$ $\quad\quad\ \ CH_3$	1.4×10^{-5}
$CH_3(CH_2)_6COOH$	1.28×10^{-5}
$Cl-CH_2COOH$	1.4×10^{-3}
$Cl_2CHCOOH$	3.3×10^{-2}
Cl_3CCOOH	2.0×10^{-1}
⬡—COOH	6.5×10^{-5}
Cl—⬡—COOH	1.0×10^{-4}
NO_2—⬡—COOH	3.9×10^{-4}
CH_3—⬡—COOH	4.3×10^{-5}
$HOOC-COOH$ (Ka_1)	5.9×10^{-2}
$CH_3-CH-COOH$ $\quad\quad\ \ \|$ $\quad\quad\ \ Cl$	1.5×10^{-3}
$Cl-CH_2-CH_2-COOH$	1.0×10^{-4}
$CH_3-CH-COOH$ $\quad\quad\ \ \|$ $\quad\quad\ \ NH_2$	4.6×10^{-3}

In the IUPAC system, substituent positions are indicated by numbers beginning with the COOH carbon atom as number 1. In the classical system, Greek letter designations are used. Names are shown below for two examples; again, the classical names are given in parentheses.

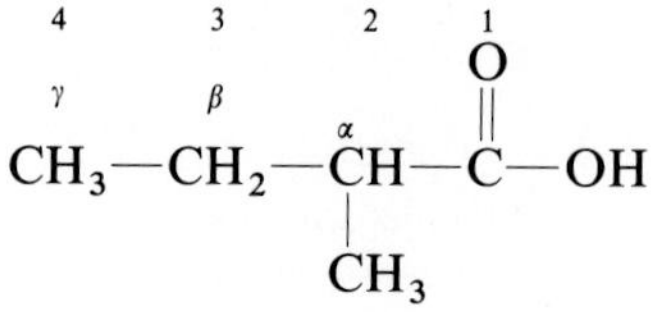

2-Methylbutanoic acid
(α-methyl butyric acid)

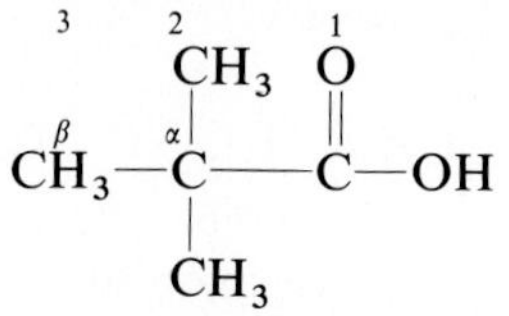

2,2-Dimethylpropanoic acid
(α,α-dimethylpropionic acid)

Cyclic acid compounds are named by using the name of the cyclic portion plus the words *carboxylic acid*.

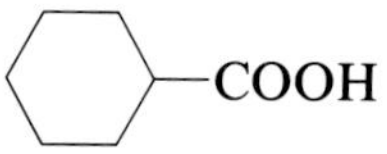

Cyclohexane carboxylic
acid

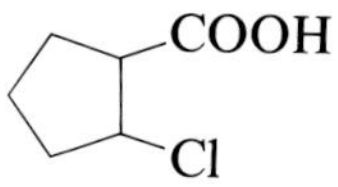

2-Chlorocyclopentane
carboxylic acid

Aromatic carboxylic acids are named much like other cyclic acids, as illustrated by the three examples that follow. The common names shown in parentheses are the ones actually used most frequently by chemists.

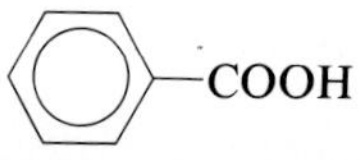

Benzene carboxylic
acid
(benzoic acid)

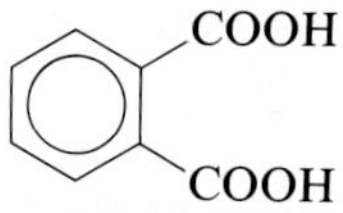

1,2-Benzene
dicarboxylic acid
(phthalic acid)

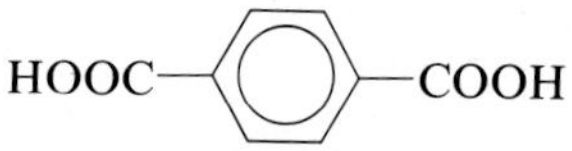

1,4-Benzene
dicarboxylic acid
(terephthalic acid)

Dicarboxylic open chain acids are named in the IUPAC system by using the base name for the longest chain plus the ending *-dioic acid*. There are also common names. Below are shown the common names for the six smallest dicarboxylic acids.

STRUCTURE	IUPAC NAME	COMMON NAME
$HO-\overset{O}{\overset{\|\|}{C}}-\overset{O}{\overset{\|\|}{C}}-OH$	Ethanedioic acid	Oxalic acid
$HOOC-CH_2-COOH$	Propanedioic acid	Malonic acid

STRUCTURE	IUPAC NAME	COMMON NAME
$HOOC(CH_2)_2COOH$	Butanedioic acid	Succinic acid
$HOOC(CH_2)_3COOH$	Pentanedioic acid	Glutaric acid
$HOOC(CH_2)_4COOH$	Hexanedioic acid	Adipic acid
$HOOC(CH_2)_5COOH$	Heptanedioic acid	Pimelic acid

The common names for dicarboxylic acids are more easily remembered by the sentence: "*Oh my, such good apple pie.*" The first letters of the words are the same as the first letters of the names of the first six dicarboxylic acids.

The most frequently encountered dicarboxylic acid is oxalic acid, which is quite toxic. It is found in the wilted leaves of the wild cherry tree (*Prunus serotina* Ehrh.) which, when ingested by cattle or other livestock, can cause death (see Figure 12-2). It is also formed in the body by enzymatic oxidation of accidentally ingested ethylene glycol (antifreeze), which is why antifreeze is toxic.

Oxalic acid can be purchased in solid form at drug and hardware stores. When dissolved in water, it can be used to remove iron rust and some ink stains from rugs, wood, clothing, and so forth.

Carboxylic acids are named systematically as alkanoic acids or classically by using conventionally accepted common names. Substituent

FIGURE 12-2

Wild cherry leaves contain oxalic acid when wilted.

locations are designated by numbers beginning at the carbonyl carbon atom or by Greek letters beginning with the alpha carbon atom adjacent to the carbonyl group. Dicarboxylic acids are named as alkanedioic acids and are given common names as well.

Occurrence and use of carboxylic acids

The following compounds containing the —COOH group are commercially useful or are otherwise of general or biological interest.

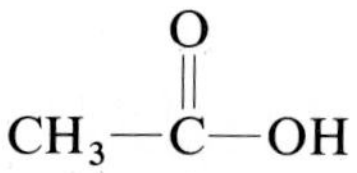

$$CH_3-\overset{\overset{\displaystyle O}{\|}}{C}-OH$$

Acetic acid
(5% solution
is vinegar)

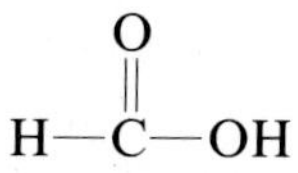

$$H-\overset{\overset{\displaystyle O}{\|}}{C}-OH$$

Formic acid
(stinging
agent in ant
bites)

COOH

Benzoic acid
(food and
beverage
preservative)

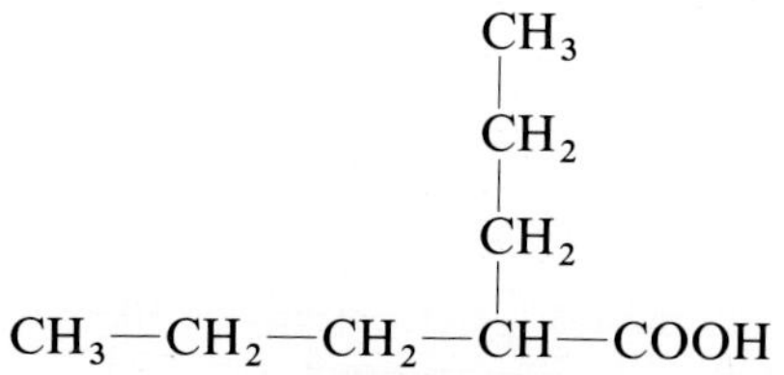

$$CH_3-CH_2-CH_2-\underset{\underset{\displaystyle COOH}{\overset{\displaystyle CH_3}{\overset{|}{\underset{|}{CH_2}}}}}{CH}$$

Valproic acid
(anticonvulsant medication for treatment
of epilepsy—trade name, Mylproin)

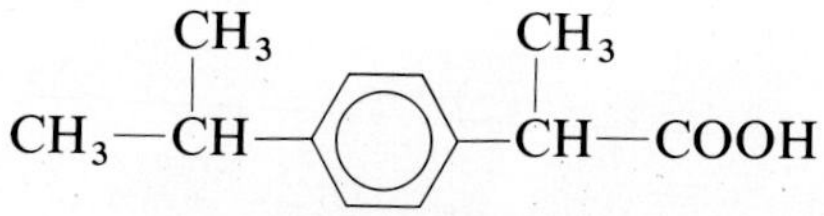

$$CH_3-\overset{\overset{\displaystyle CH_3}{|}}{CH}-\bigcirc-\overset{\overset{\displaystyle CH_3}{|}}{CH}-COOH$$

Ibuprofen
(analgesic medication
used in Motrin and Advil)

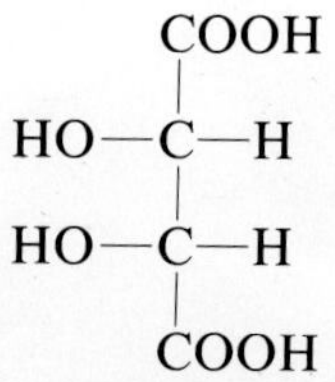

$$\begin{array}{c} COOH \\ | \\ HO-C-H \\ | \\ HO-C-H \\ | \\ COOH \end{array}$$

Tartaric acid
(cream of tartar—baking
powder component along
with $NaHCO_3$)

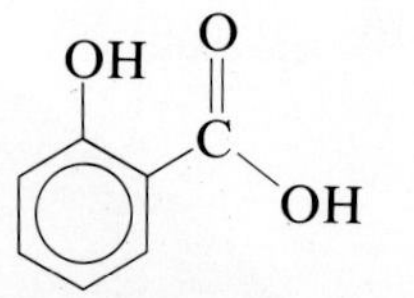

Salicyclic acid
(used to produce aspirin)

PREPARATION OF CARBOXYLIC ACIDS

Oxidation of aldehydes or 1° alcohols

As discussed in Chapter 8, strong oxidizing agents such as $KMnO_4$ will change primary alcohols to carboxylic acids. Aldehydes are even more easily oxidized to acids.

$$R{-}CH_2OH \quad \text{or} \quad R{-}\overset{\overset{\displaystyle O}{\|}}{C}{-}H \xrightarrow{[O]} R{-}\overset{\overset{\displaystyle O}{\|}}{C}{-}OH$$

Examples are

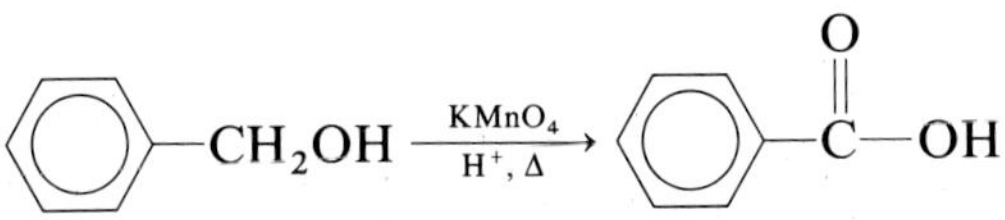

$$CH_3{-}\underset{\underset{\displaystyle CH_3}{|}}{CH}{-}\overset{\overset{\displaystyle O}{\|}}{C}{-}H \xrightarrow{\text{dil } KMnO_4} CH_3{-}\underset{\underset{\displaystyle CH_3}{|}}{CH}{-}\overset{\overset{\displaystyle O}{\|}}{C}{-}OH$$

Aromatic side chain oxidation

When a benzene ring has an alkyl side chain with an α-hydrogen, vigorous oxidizing conditions will convert this side chain to COOH regardless of the number of carbon atoms in the chain. (See page 294 for a fuller discussion.) The general reaction is

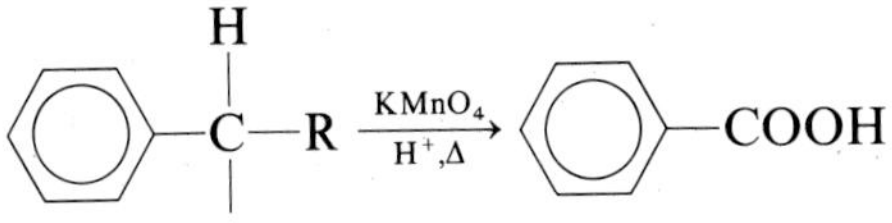

Examples are

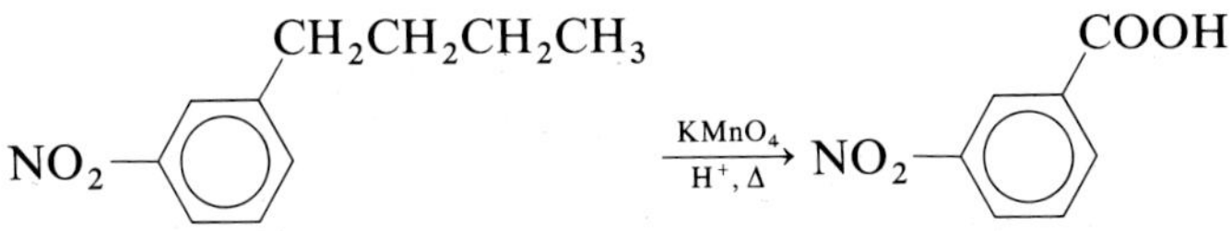

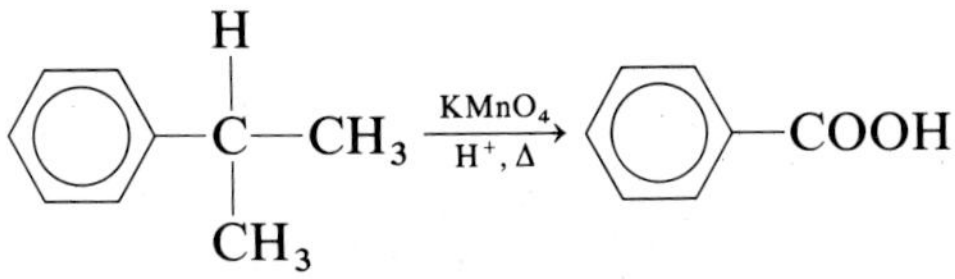

Malonic ester synthesis

One reaction sequence that is quite useful in **preparing carboxylic acids**
and in **building carbon skeletons** is called the **malonic ester synthesis**. It
begins with the alkylation of the diethyl ester of malonic acid (diethyl
malonate—sometimes simply called **malonic ester**) followed by decarboxylation. The general reaction for the first step is as follows:

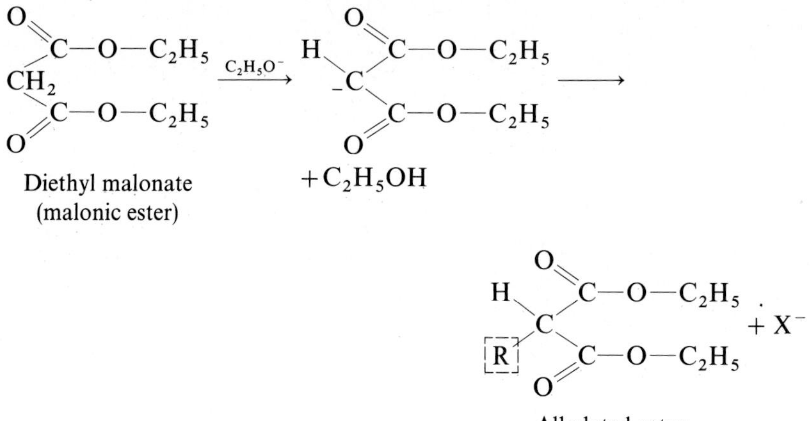

Diethyl malonate
(malonic ester)

$+C_2H_5OH$

Alkylated ester

A base $(C_2H_5O^-)$ is used to pull an H^+ from the alpha carbon atom
of the diethyl malonate. This produces a nucleophile which can substitute
on an alkyl halide (RX). The net result is the substitution of an R group
on the $-CH^-$ carbon atom. This reaction can be repeated to substitute
another R group if desired, as shown below for the general case.

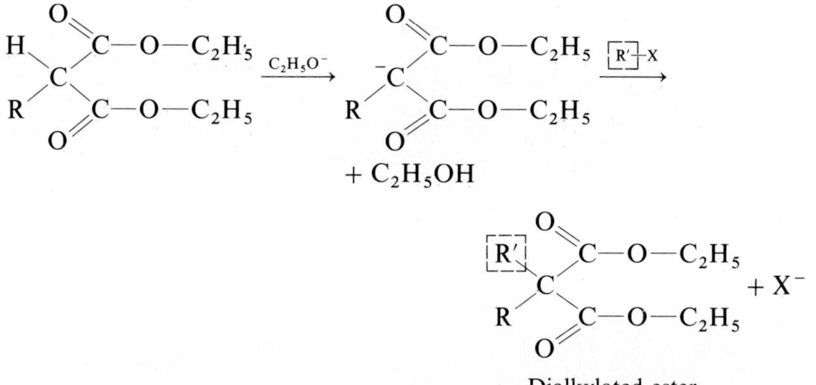

$+ C_2H_5OH$

Dialkylated ester

Once one or two R groups have been attached, the resulting alkylated
ester can be treated in several ways to produce other materials. The reaction we are interested in is the production of mono-carboxylic acids as
shown below.

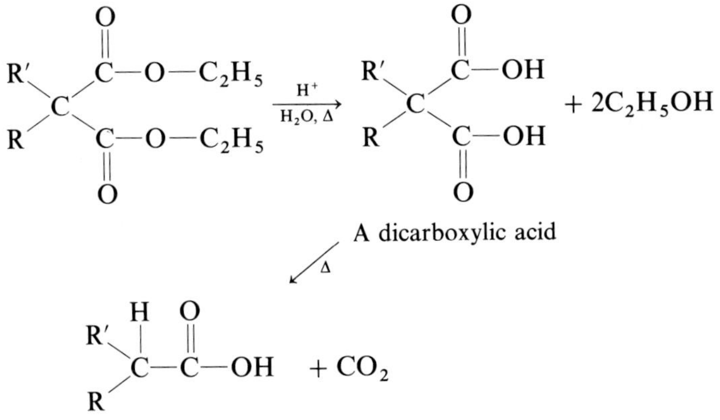

A dicarboxylic acid

A monocarboxylic acid

The alkylated or dialkylated ester is converted to the corresponding dicarboxylic acid by **hydrolysis** (see page 399 for a discussion of ester hydrolysis). When the dicarboxylic acid is heated, it easily loses one COOH group as a CO_2 molecule. This loss of a COOH group is called **decarboxylation**.

As an example of this type of synthesis of a carboxylic acid, consider the following synthetic route to valproic acid, the most recently marketed anticonvulsant medication (antiepileptic).

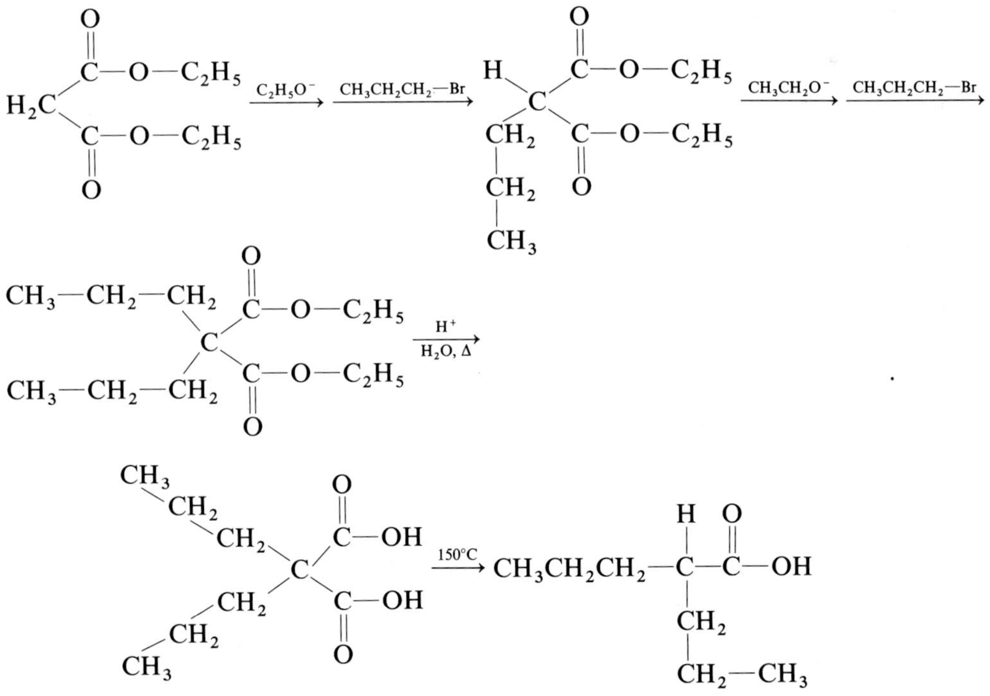

Valproic
acid

Carbonation of Grignard reagents

Carboxylic acids can be prepared by the reaction of a Grignard reagent (see Chapter 3) with carbon dioxide (CO_2), as shown by the following general equations:

$$R-X \xrightarrow[\text{ether}]{Mg} R-MgX \xrightarrow{CO_2} R-\overset{\displaystyle O}{\overset{\displaystyle \|}{C}}-O^- \xrightarrow[H_2O]{H^+} R-\overset{\displaystyle O}{\overset{\displaystyle \|}{C}}-OH + MgX_2$$

Grignard reagent ^+MgX

This reaction sequence allows us to form carboxylic acids that have **one more carbon atom per molecule** than the alkyl halide (or Grignard reagent). Examples of this process are given below.

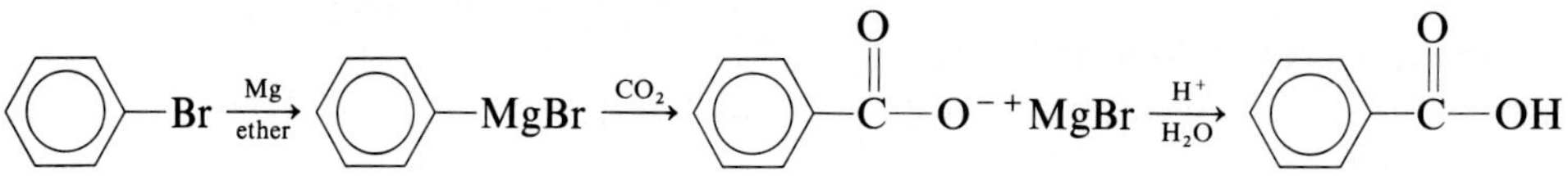

Benzoic acid

$$CH_3-CH_2-CH_2-Br \xrightarrow[\text{ether}]{Mg} CH_3CH_2CH_2-MgBr \xrightarrow[H_2O]{CO_2 \quad H^+} CH_3CH_2CH_2COOH$$

Butanoic acid

Carboxylic acids are prepared by oxidation of 1° alcohols or aldehydes, by vigorous oxidation of alkyl benzenes, or by carbonation of Grignard reagents. The malonic ester synthesis can be used to produce a carboxylic acid with a larger carbon skeleton than any of the starting materials.

CARBOXYLIC ACID ANHYDRIDES

Anhydrides (properly called carboxylic acid anhydrides) are prepared by removing a molecule of water from two molecules of a carboxylic acid and linking the acids together where the water splits out. This removal of water is called **dehydration** and is usually accomplished by simply heating the carboxylic acid, as shown below.

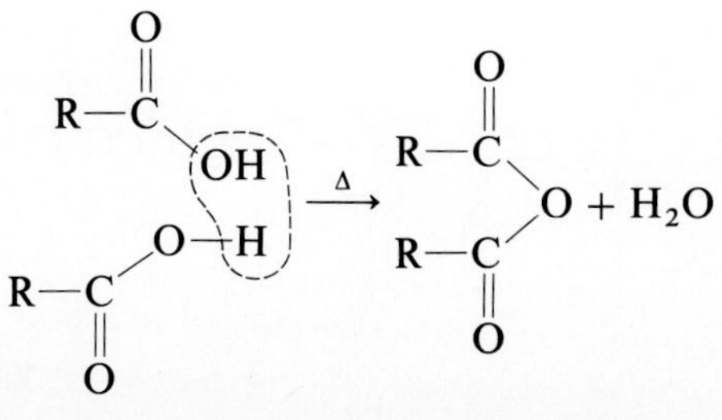

Anhydrides are more reactive toward most reagents than are the acids themselves. They are named by using the name of the acid plus the word *anhydride*. For example, when acetic acid is used, the resulting compound is called acetic anhydride. This and other examples are shown below.

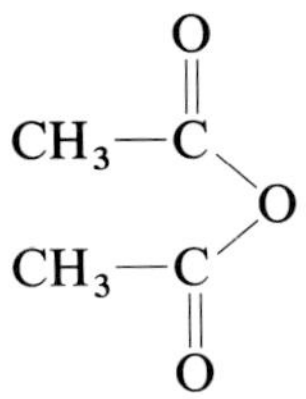

| Acetic anhydride or ethanoic anhydride | Propanoic anhydride | Phthalic anhydride |

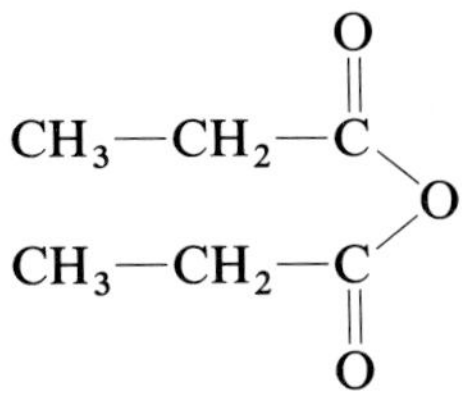

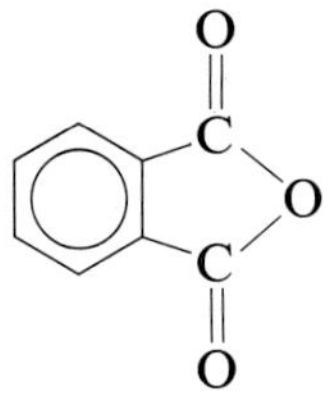

Anhydrides are dehydrated carboxylic acids; they are more reactive than the corresponding acids.

ACID HALIDES

We have already used **acid chlorides** (also called acyl chlorides), the most common type of acid halide, for several preparations in this text. Acid chlorides are more reactive than the corresponding acids and are prepared from them, as already mentioned (see page 262), by using $SOCl_2$.

$$R—\overset{\overset{\displaystyle O}{\|}}{C}—OH \xrightarrow{SOCl_2} R—\overset{\overset{\displaystyle O}{\|}}{C}—Cl + HCl + SO_2$$

Carboxylic acid   Acid chloride

Examples are

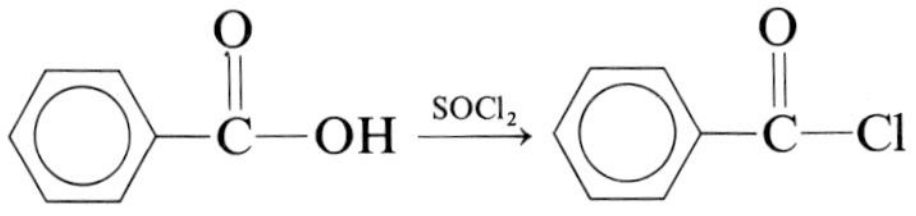

Benzoic acid   Benzoyl chloride

Acetic acid   Acetyl chloride
(ethanoic acid)   (ethanoyl chloride)

Acid chlorides are named by removing the ending-*ic acid* from the name of the acid from which they are derived (in either the IUPAC or classical system) and adding the ending-*yl chloride*. See the two examples above. Acid halides, like anhydrides, are used as chemically reactive intermediates, to produce other compounds; they are not used in consumer products nor are they found in nature.

Acid chlorides (acyl chlorides) are especially reactive derivatives of carboxylic acids, prepared from the latter by reaction with thionyl chloride.

ESTERS

Esters are produced by the reaction of a **carboxylic acid** and an **alcohol** by acid catalysis. They can also be prepared by heating alcohols with either acid chlorides or anhydrides. Examples are

$$CH_3-\overset{O}{\underset{\|}{C}}-OH + CH_3OH \xrightarrow{H^+} CH_3-\overset{O}{\underset{\|}{C}}-O-CH_3 + H_2O$$

Acetic acid   Methyl alcohol   Methyl acetate

Benzoyl chloride   *tert*-Butyl alcohol

tert-Butyl benzoate

$$CH_3-CH_2-\underset{\underset{Br}{|}}{CH}-\overset{O}{\underset{\|}{C}}-OH + CH_3CH_2OH \xrightarrow{H^+}$$

2-Bromobutanoic acid   Ethyl alcohol

$$CH_3CH_2\underset{\underset{Br}{|}}{CH}-\overset{O}{\underset{\|}{C}}-O-CH_2-CH_3 + H_2O$$

Ethyl 2-bromobutanoate

Esters are named as shown in Figure 12-3. The first part of an ester name is the name of the alkyl group from the alcohol used to produce the ester. This is the alkyl group attached to the oxygen atom in the ester. The second part of the ester name (beginning a new word) is the base name of the carboxylic acid from which the ester was prepared (i.e., the acid name minus

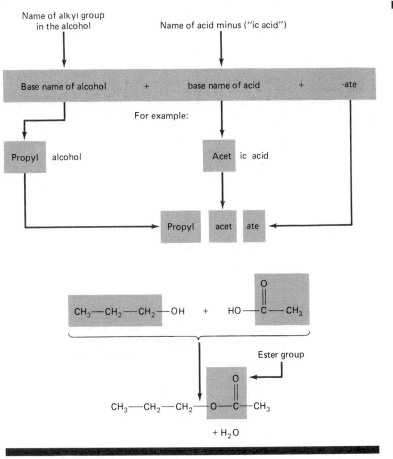

Name of alkyl group
in the alcohol

Name of acid minus ("ic acid")

| Base name of alcohol | + | base name of acid | + | -ate |

For example:

Propyl alcohol

Acet ic acid

Propyl acet ate

$$CH_3—CH_2—CH_2—OH \quad + \quad HO—\overset{\overset{\displaystyle O}{\|}}{C}—CH_3$$

Ester group

$$CH_3—CH_2—CH_2—O—\overset{\overset{\displaystyle O}{\|}}{C}—CH_3$$

$$+ H_2O$$

The method used to name
esters.

FIGURE 12-3

the ending -*ic acid*) plus the syllable -*ate*. The general form of the name is always **alkyl alkanoate**. Figure 12-3 illustrates this method for naming propyl acetate, which is derived from propyl alcohol and acetic acid. Also, note the names of the esters shown above.

Commercial esters

Esters are usually pleasant-smelling materials used in flavors and perfume. Table 12-3 shows some of the fruit flavors that are due to esters. Other commercial esters are shown below.

$$H_2N—\overset{}{\bigcirc}—\overset{\overset{\displaystyle O}{\|}}{C}—O—CH_2CH_3 \qquad CH_3—\overset{\overset{\displaystyle O}{\|}}{C}—O—CH_2—\bigcirc$$

Ethyl 4-aminobenzoate
(Benzocaine—topical
anesthetic)

Benzyl acetate
(oil of jasmine—perfume)

TABLE 12-3

ESTERS

NAME AND USE	ACID AND ALCOHOL USED TO PREPARE ESTER	STRUCTURE
Pentyl acetate Banana flavor	$CH_3-\overset{\overset{\text{O}}{\|}}{C}-OH + HO-(CH_2)_4-CH_3$	$CH_3-\overset{\overset{\text{O}}{\|}}{C}-O-(CH_2)_4-CH_3$
Octyl acetate Orange flavor	$CH_3-\overset{\overset{\text{O}}{\|}}{C}-OH + HO-(CH_2)_7-CH_3$	$CH_3-\overset{\overset{\text{O}}{\|}}{C}-O-(CH_2)_7-CH_3$
Methyl anthranilate Grape flavor	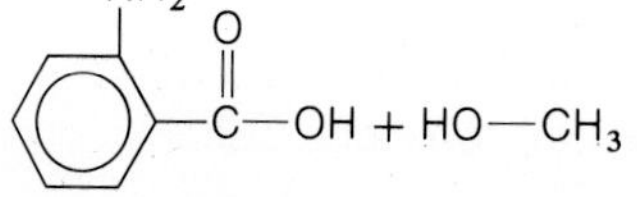 (benzene ring with NH_2)$-\overset{\overset{\text{O}}{\|}}{C}-OH + HO-CH_3$	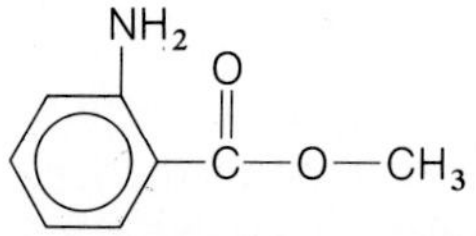 (benzene ring with NH_2)$-\overset{\overset{\text{O}}{\|}}{C}-O-CH_3$
Ethyl butyrate Pineapple flavor	$CH_3CH_2CH_2\overset{\overset{\text{O}}{\|}}{C}-OH + CH_3CH_2OH$	$CH_3CH_2CH_2\overset{\overset{\text{O}}{\|}}{C}-O-CH_2CH_3$
Isopentyl acetate Pear flavor	$CH_3-\overset{\overset{\text{O}}{\|}}{C}-OH + CH_3-\underset{\underset{CH_3}{\|}}{CH}-CH_2-CH_2OH$	$CH_3-\overset{\overset{\text{O}}{\|}}{C}-O-CH_2-CH_2-\underset{\underset{CH_3}{\|}}{CH}-CH_3$

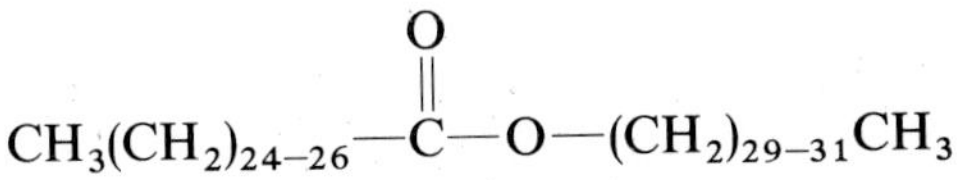

$$CH_3(CH_2)_{24-26}-\overset{\overset{\displaystyle O}{\|}}{C}-O-(CH_2)_{29-31}CH_3$$

Major component of
beeswax

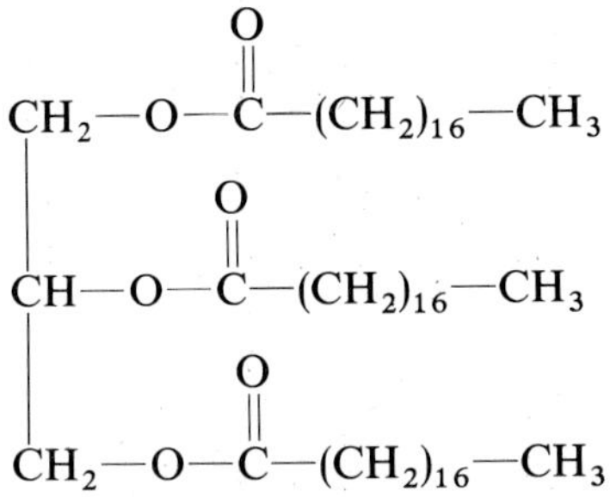

$$CH_2-O-\overset{\overset{\displaystyle O}{\|}}{C}-(CH_2)_{16}-CH_3$$

$$CH-O-\overset{\overset{\displaystyle O}{\|}}{C}-(CH_2)_{16}-CH_3$$

$$CH_2-O-\overset{\overset{\displaystyle O}{\|}}{C}-(CH_2)_{16}-CH_3$$

Component of lard and
solid vegetable shortening

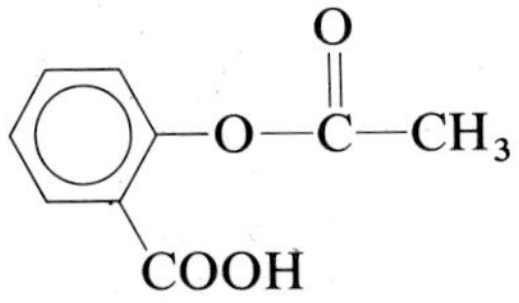

Acetyl salicylic acid
(aspirin—analgesic)

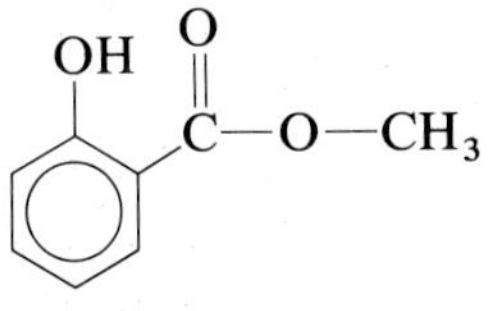

Methyl salicylate
(oil of wintergreen—
flavors and muscle rubs)

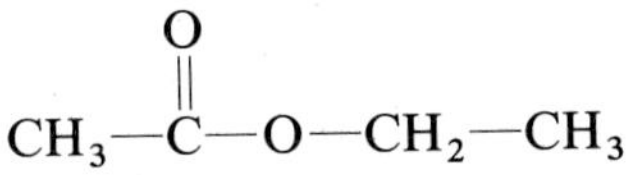

$$CH_3-\overset{\overset{\displaystyle O}{\|}}{C}-O-CH_2-CH_3$$

Ethyl acetate
(solvent, fingernail
polish remover)

Claisen condensation

Esters that have an **α-hydrogen** atom will undergo a condensation reaction when placed in the presence of a strong base such as ethoxide ion. The mechanism is shown below and is similar (in the first two steps) to the aldol condensation of aldehydes discussed in Chapter 8 (see page 274).

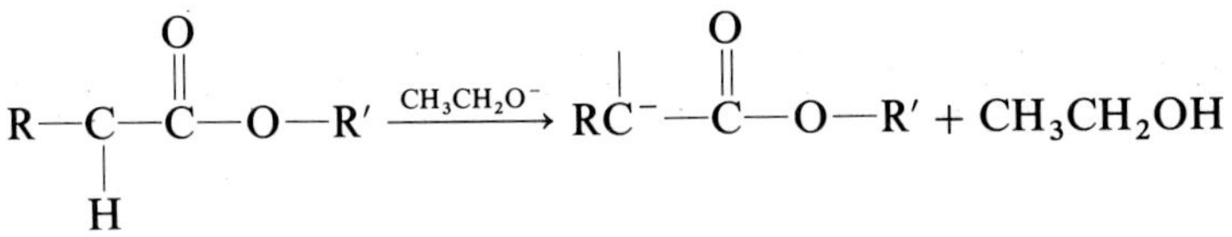

$$R-\overset{\overset{\displaystyle O}{\|}}{\underset{\underset{\displaystyle H}{|}}{C}}-C-O-R' \xrightarrow{CH_3CH_2O^-} R\overset{-}{\underset{\underset{}{|}}{C}}-\overset{\overset{\displaystyle O}{\|}}{C}-O-R' + CH_3CH_2OH$$

α Hydrogen

$$R-\overset{O}{\underset{|}{C}}-\overset{|}{\underset{|}{C}}-O-R' + R-\overset{O}{\underset{|}{C}}-\overset{|}{\underset{|}{C}}-O-R' \longrightarrow$$

$$R-\overset{O^-}{\underset{|}{C}}-\overset{|}{\underset{|}{C}}-\overset{O}{\underset{|}{C}}-\overset{||}{\underset{|}{C}}-OR' \longrightarrow R-\overset{O}{\underset{|}{C}}-\overset{||}{\underset{|}{C}}-\overset{O}{\underset{|}{C}}-\overset{||}{\underset{|}{C}}-O-R' + {}^-OR'$$

A β-keto ester

Thus, two molecules of ester have condensed to form a larger skeleton. The α-carbon atom of one molecule becomes bonded to the carboxyl carbon atom of the other molecule.

Examples are

$$2\ \mathrm{CH_3CH_2-C}\overset{O}{\underset{}{\|}}\mathrm{O-CH_2CH_3} \xrightarrow{\text{base}}$$

$$\mathrm{CH_3CH_2-C}\overset{O}{\underset{}{\|}}\mathrm{CH}\overset{O}{\underset{\underset{CH_3}{|}}{\|}}\mathrm{C-O-CH_2CH_3} + \mathrm{CH_3CH_2-O^-}$$

$$2\ \mathrm{CH_3-C}\overset{O}{\underset{}{\|}}\mathrm{O-CH_2CH_3} \xrightarrow{\text{base}}$$

$$\mathrm{CH_3-C}\overset{O}{\underset{}{\|}}\mathrm{CH_2-C}\overset{O}{\underset{}{\|}}\mathrm{O-CH_2CH_3} + \mathrm{CH_3CH_2-O^-}$$

$$2\ \mathrm{CH_3-CH-CH_2-C}\overset{CH_3\quad O}{\underset{}{|\quad\ \ \|}}\mathrm{O-CH_2CH_3} \xrightarrow{\text{base}}$$

$$\mathrm{CH_3-CH-CH_2-C}\overset{CH_3\quad O}{\underset{}{|\quad\ \ \|}}\mathrm{CH-C}\overset{O}{\underset{\underset{CH_3\ \ CH_3}{\underset{}{CH}}}{\|}}\mathrm{O-CH_2-CH_3} + \mathrm{CH_3CH_2-O^-}$$

$$2\ CH_3-\underset{\underset{CH_3}{|}}{\overset{\overset{CH_3}{|}}{C}}-C-O-CH_2CH_3 \xrightarrow{\text{base}} \text{no reaction}$$

No α hydrogen

Esters are prepared from carboxylic acids and alcohols and are named as alkyl alkanoates. Many fruit flavors are due to the presence of a small amount of an ester. The Claisen condensation reaction can be used to build larger carbon chains and produce β-keto esters.

SALTS

Acids react with hydroxide bases to produce a **salt** plus water. Salts of carboxylic acids are produced in the same way. Usually the base used is a strong base such as NaOH or KOH, and the sodium or potassium salt is produced. Salts of carboxylic acids are usually fairly soluble in water, while carboxylic acids that have more than four carbon atoms are themselves not soluble in water. Names for salts include the name of the metal or positive ion followed by the base name of the acid from which the salt was produced and then the ending *-ate*. Thus esters and salts have the same name structure. See the examples shown below. Figure 12-4 shows one of the commercial products containing a carboxylic acid salt.

FIGURE 12-4

A commercial product containing monosodium glutamate (MSG).

$$CH_3-COOH + KOH \longrightarrow CH_3-COO^-K^+ + H_2O$$

Acetic acid   Potassium acetate

$$\langle\!\!\bigcirc\!\!\rangle-COOH + NaOH \longrightarrow \langle\!\!\bigcirc\!\!\rangle-COO^-Na^+ + H_2O$$

Benzoic acid   Sodium benzoate
(retards spoilage
in foods and beverages)

$$HOOC-CH_2-CH_2-\underset{\underset{NH_2}{|}}{CH}-COOH \xrightarrow{\text{NaOH}}$$

Glutamic acid

$$HOOC-CH_2-CH_2-\underset{\underset{NH_2}{|}}{CH}-COO^-Na^+ + H_2O$$

Monosodium glutamate (MSG)
(food flavor enhancer)

Salts of carboxylic acids are prepared by the reaction of the acid with a strong base and are usually water soluble. They are named as metal alkanoates.

AMIDES

Amides are prepared by reacting ammonia or 1° or 2° amines with carboxylic acids, anhydrides, or acid chlorides. The latter react more quickly and give higher yields of product. The general reaction using an acid chloride is

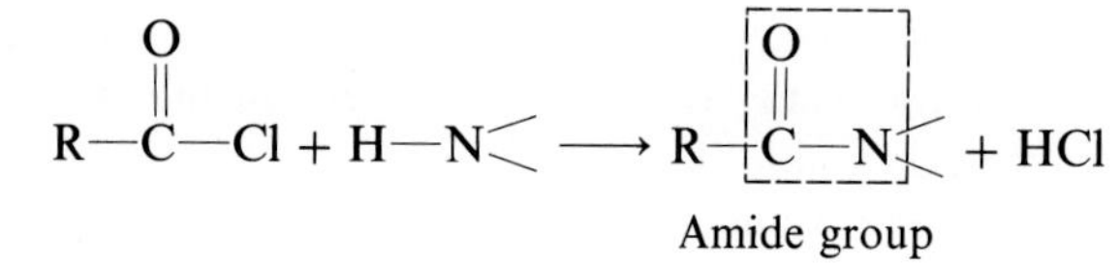

$$
\underset{}{R-\overset{\overset{\displaystyle O}{\|}}{C}-Cl} + H-N\!\!< \longrightarrow R-\overset{\overset{\displaystyle O}{\|}}{C}-N\!\!< + HCl
$$

Amide group

Examples are

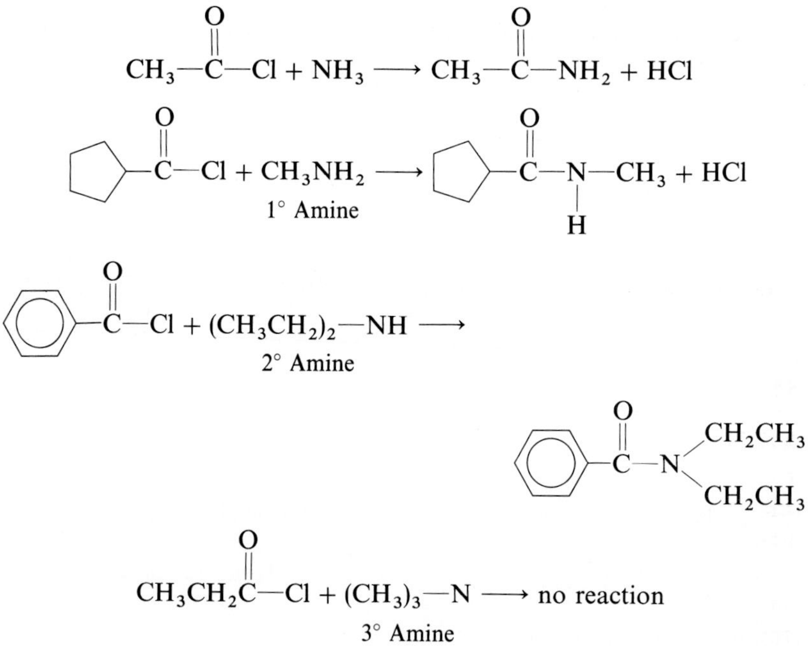

$$
CH_3-\overset{\overset{\displaystyle O}{\|}}{C}-Cl + NH_3 \longrightarrow CH_3-\overset{\overset{\displaystyle O}{\|}}{C}-NH_2 + HCl
$$

$$
\bigcirc\!\!-\overset{\overset{\displaystyle O}{\|}}{C}-Cl + CH_3NH_2 \longrightarrow \bigcirc\!\!-\overset{\overset{\displaystyle O}{\|}}{C}-\underset{\underset{\displaystyle H}{|}}{N}-CH_3 + HCl
$$

1° Amine

$$
\bigcirc\!\!-\overset{\overset{\displaystyle O}{\|}}{C}-Cl + (CH_3CH_2)_2-NH \longrightarrow
$$

2° Amine

$$
\bigcirc\!\!-\overset{\overset{\displaystyle O}{\|}}{C}-N\!\!<^{CH_2CH_3}_{CH_2CH_3}
$$

$$
CH_3CH_2\overset{\overset{\displaystyle O}{\|}}{C}-Cl + (CH_3)_3-N \longrightarrow \text{no reaction}
$$

3° Amine

Amides are named by using the base name of the acid (i.e., the acid name with the ending -oic acid omitted) followed by the ending -amide and preceded by any substituents. The positions for substituents are designated as shown below. The carbon chain is numbered as in carboxylic acids. If a substituent is attached to the nitrogen atom, however, the position indicator "N" is used to show its position. This position indicator is printed in italics.

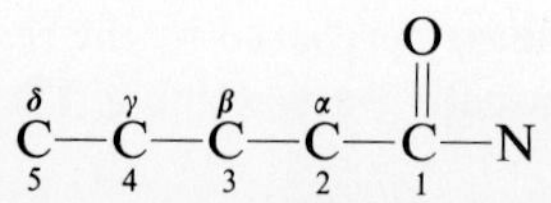

$$
\underset{5}{\overset{\delta}{C}}-\underset{4}{\overset{\gamma}{C}}-\underset{3}{\overset{\beta}{C}}-\underset{2}{\overset{\alpha}{C}}-\underset{1}{\overset{\overset{\displaystyle O}{\|}}{C}}-N
$$

Examples are

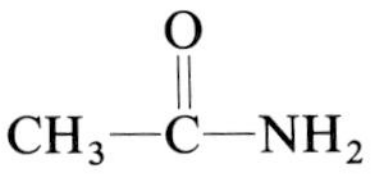

$$CH_3-\overset{\overset{\textstyle O}{\|}}{C}-NH_2 \qquad CH_3-CH_2-\overset{\overset{\textstyle O}{\|}}{C}-\underset{\underset{\textstyle H}{|}}{N}-\square$$

Acetamide
(ethanamide)

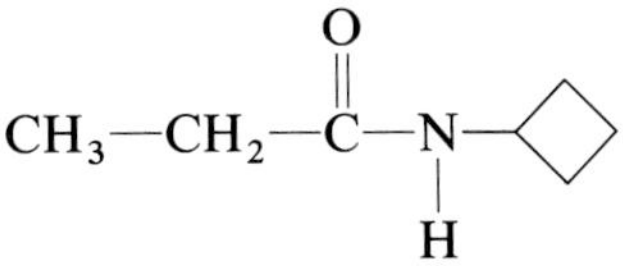

N-Cyclobutylpropanamide

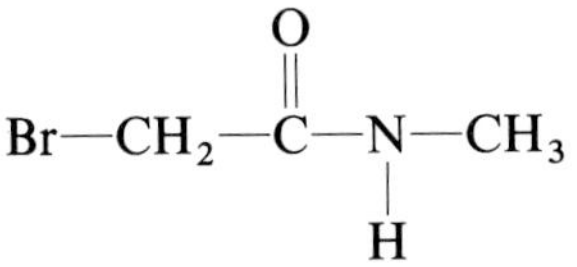

$$Br-CH_2-\overset{\overset{\textstyle O}{\|}}{C}-\underset{\underset{\textstyle H}{|}}{N}-CH_3 \qquad \bigcirc-\overset{\overset{\textstyle O}{\|}}{C}-\overset{\overset{\textstyle H}{|}}{N}-CH_3$$

α-Bromo-*N*-methylacetamide
or
2-Bromo-*N*-methylethanamide

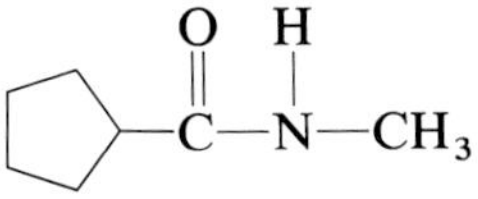

N-methylcyclopentancarboxamide

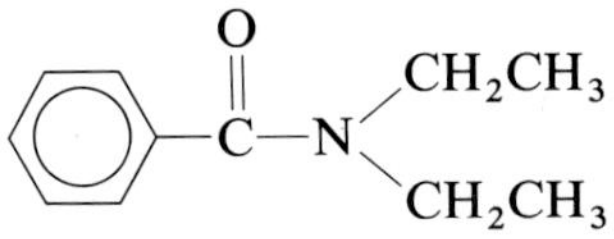

$$\bigcirc-\overset{\overset{\textstyle O}{\|}}{C}-N\overset{\diagup CH_2CH_3}{\diagdown CH_2CH_3}$$

N,N-diethylbenzamide

Amides are prepared from ammonia or a 1° or 2° amine reacting with an acyl chloride. Amides are named as carbon- or nitrogen-substituted alkanamides.

HYDROLYSIS OF CARBOXYLIC ACID DERIVATIVES

All of the derivatives of carboxylic acids can be changed back into the acid from which they were prepared by reaction with water. This process is called **hydrolysis** because the derivative molecule is split apart and a **water molecule is also split** and added to the two parts of the derivative molecule. Hydrolysis of esters and amides requires vigorous conditions, including an acid or base catalyst and heat, while anhydrides and acyl chlorides usually react spontaneously and rapidly with water under mild conditions. The general hydrolysis reactions are shown below and are followed by several examples.

Very fast $\quad R-\overset{\overset{\textstyle O}{\|}}{C}-Cl + H_2O \longrightarrow R-\overset{\overset{\textstyle O}{\|}}{C}-OH + HCl$

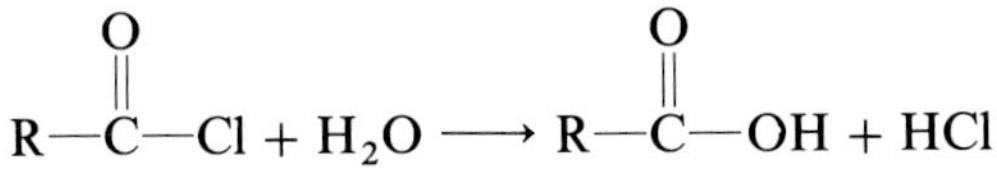

Fast $\quad \begin{matrix} R-\overset{\overset{\textstyle O}{\|}}{C} \\ \diagdown \\ R-\underset{\underset{\textstyle O}{\|}}{C} \end{matrix} O + H_2O \longrightarrow 2R-\overset{\overset{\textstyle O}{\|}}{C}-OH$

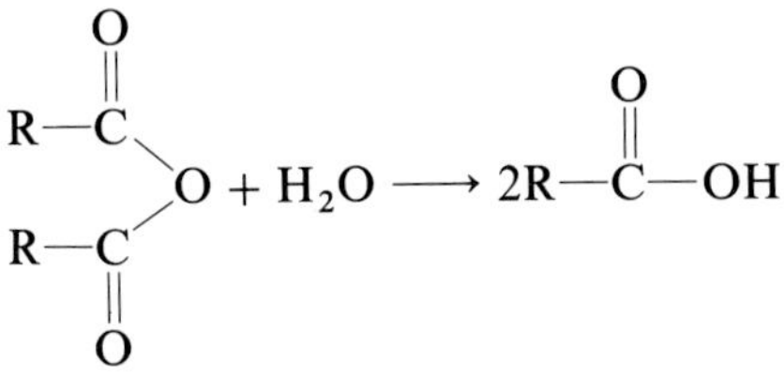

Slow $\quad R-\overset{\overset{\displaystyle O}{\|}}{C}-O-R' + H_2O \xrightarrow[\Delta]{H^+ \text{ (or OH}^-)} R-\overset{\overset{\displaystyle O}{\|}}{C}-OH + R'-OH$

Very slow $\quad R-\overset{\overset{\displaystyle O}{\|}}{C}-\underset{|}{N}-R' + H_2O \xrightarrow[\Delta]{H^+ \text{ (or OH}^-)} R-\overset{\overset{\displaystyle O}{\|}}{C}-OH + R-N\overset{\displaystyle H}{\diagdown}$

Examples are

$$CH_3CH_2CH_2\overset{\overset{\displaystyle O}{\|}}{C}-O-CH_3 \xrightarrow[\Delta, H_2O]{H^+} CH_3CH_2CH_2\overset{\overset{\displaystyle O}{\|}}{C}-OH + CH_3OH$$

REACTION SUMMARY FLOW DIAGRAM—CARBOXYLIC ACIDS AND THEIR DERIVATIVES

SYNTHETIC FIBERS

In Chapter 6 we discussed polymers made from alkene monomer units, and you may recall that when many small molecular units are linked together the resulting long polymeric molecules (macromolecules) sometimes exhibit unusual physical properties that allow the formation of useful products. Synthetic fibers are polymeric in nature, and several of the functional groups used to produce fibers belong to the class of carboxylic acids or their derivatives. Two of the fibers with biggest sales volumes are polyester and polyamide. In this section we will present the structures of each along with the monomer units used to prepare them. The unique physical behavior of polyester is discussed in "Applied Organic Chemistry F" (see page 415).

Polyester

The wrinkle resistance of polyester makes it one of the most popular of the modern synthetic fibers. The trade name used by the major producer, Du Pont, is Dacron. It can be used alone or mixed with other fibers such as cotton (in about a 60:40 ratio of cotton:polyester) to produce a more comfortable fabric. Polyester ribbon, formulated with metal oxides, is used in the manufacture of audio and video recording tape. Tough sheets of polyester are also used for various purposes. The trade name used for these sheets or ribbons is Mylar.

If we start with a difunctional acid (one containing two —COOH groups) and a difunctional alcohol (one containing two —OH groups), continuous polymer chains can be produced. The two compounds used are shown below:

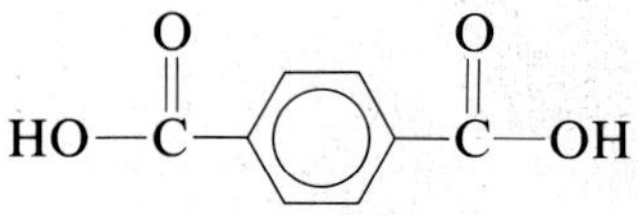

$$\underset{\text{Terephthalic acid}}{\underset{\text{(difunctional)}}{HO-\overset{\overset{O}{\|}}{C}-\langle\bigcirc\rangle-\overset{\overset{O}{\|}}{C}-OH}} \qquad \underset{\text{Ethylene glycol}}{\underset{\text{(difunctional)}}{HO-CH_2-CH_2-OH}}$$

When the two compounds react and give up water molecules, continuous chains are formed. The polymeric **copolymer** (one having two different monomer units) is called **polyethyleneterephthalate** (see formula on page 403 and Figure 12-5).

Polyethyleneterephthalate polymer

Ester functional groups

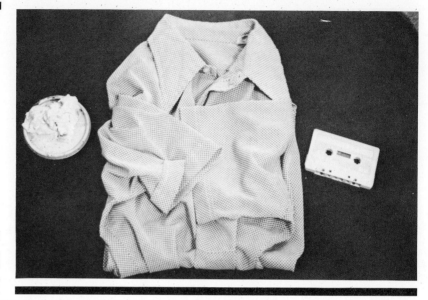

Different forms of
polyethylene terephthalate.
Left, unformed material;
center, polyester shirt; *right*,
sound recording tapes.

FIGURE 12-5

Polyamide

The earliest synthetic fiber was discovered and developed by Du Pont
(see page 2). It is called nylon and was originally used as a substitute for
the natural fiber silk. Now it is used, as well, for ropes and threads (i.e.,
fishing line) and is machined into gears for small appliances, tips for chair
legs, and a host of other objects.

The most common type of nylon is prepared from the diacid and diamine shown below.

$$NH_2—CH_2—CH_2—CH_2—CH_2—CH_2—CH_2—\boxed{NH_2}$$

Hexamethylene diamine

Amine functional group

Acid functional group

$$HO—\overset{\overset{\displaystyle O}{\|}}{C}—CH_2—CH_2—CH_2—CH_2—\overset{\overset{\displaystyle O}{\|}}{C}—OH$$

Adipic acid

These polymerize as follows:

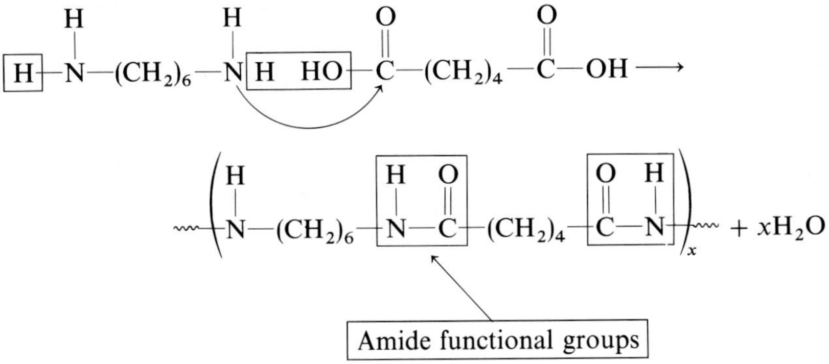

$$\boxed{H}-\underset{\underset{H}{|}}{N}-(CH_2)_6-\underset{\underset{H}{|}}{N}\boxed{H \quad HO}-\underset{\overset{O}{\|}}{C}-(CH_2)_4-\underset{\overset{O}{\|}}{C}-OH \longrightarrow$$

$$\sim\!\!\!\left(\underset{\underset{H}{|}}{N}-(CH_2)_6-\boxed{\underset{\overset{H}{|}}{N}-\underset{\overset{O}{\|}}{C}}-(CH_2)_4-\boxed{\underset{\overset{O}{\|}}{C}-\underset{\overset{H}{|}}{N}}\right)_{\!\!x}\!\!\sim + \; xH_2O$$

Amide functional groups

Nylon

CLEANING PRODUCTS

One of the oldest synthetic chemicals used by human beings is soap. As shown below, it is a salt of a long chain carboxylic acid.

$$CH_3-(CH_2)_{16}-\overset{\displaystyle O}{\overset{\displaystyle \|}{C}}-O^-Na^+$$

Sodium stearate (soap)

Soap is prepared by reacting animal or vegetable fats with a strong, aqueous base such as sodium hydroxide (NaOH). Fat molecules are composed of three ester groups joined to three long-chain fatty acids and a glycerol backbone. The NaOH breaks the ester bonds, producing a trialcohol (glycerol) and the sodium salt of the fatty acid (soap).

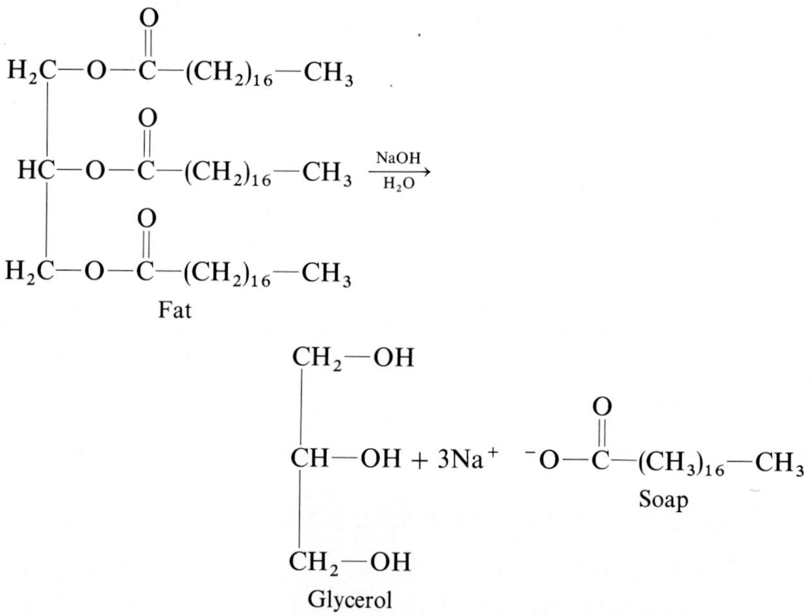

$$
\begin{array}{l}
H_2C-O-\overset{\overset{\displaystyle O}{\displaystyle \|}}{C}-(CH_2)_{16}-CH_3\\[2mm]
HC-O-\overset{\overset{\displaystyle O}{\displaystyle \|}}{C}-(CH_2)_{16}-CH_3 \quad \xrightarrow[H_2O]{NaOH}\\[2mm]
H_2C-O-\overset{\overset{\displaystyle O}{\displaystyle \|}}{C}-(CH_2)_{16}-CH_3
\end{array}
$$

Fat

$$
\begin{array}{l}
CH_2-OH\\[1mm]
|\\
CH-OH \quad + \quad 3Na^+ \quad {}^-O-\overset{\overset{\displaystyle O}{\displaystyle \|}}{C}-(CH_3)_{16}-CH_3\\[1mm]
| \qquad\qquad\qquad\qquad\qquad\qquad\qquad\qquad Soap\\
CH_2-OH
\end{array}
$$

Glycerol

In ancient times, and up until about 1920 in this country, it was a common practice to make soap at home. The practice died out slowly, and by about 1960 only a few people were still making their own soap. Originally the base was obtained by letting rainwater run through wood ashes. The water was evaporated to produce a concentrated solution, which was then boiled with waste animal fat over an open fire. In the early and middle 1900s, the NaOH was purchased as lye and boiled with fat cut from pork and beef. This rather crude soap was harsh on hands because it contained some residual NaOH, which reacted with, and thus removed, the natural oils from the skin.

Once modern commercial soap is prepared, it is formulated in various ways. Some is simply pressed into bars for sale to the public. Some has color and perfume added to make a more pleasant soap, while some has deodorant or a topical bactericide added.

Liquid soaps for hands or dishes are composed of soap suspended in water to make a thick concentrated solution, which can easily be expelled from a plastic squeeze bottle or pump container. For use on very dirty hands, soap is mixed with sand or powdered pumice, which serves as an abrasive; and for use as a scouring powder both abrasives and bleaches are added to powdered soap.

Ordinary soap belongs to a large class of molecules called **surfactants** or **emulsifiers**. These are compounds that break down the incompatibility barriers (surfaces) between polar and nonpolar materials and allow them to form suspensions that will not separate into two layers. Many skin creams contain both oil and water, and thus surfactants are needed to give the skin creams a smooth consistency.

When soap dissolves in water, it does so by forming **micelles**. These are special clusters of molecules positioned in such a way as to have the nonpolar tails together in the center of the cluster and the polar heads outward toward the continuous water phase. Since these micelles are actually much like very small oil drops and are larger than simple dissolved molecules, they interfere with light transmission and the mixture looks cloudy. The micelles are too small to settle out; they stay suspended as a result of the natural thermal motion of the water molecules. Such mixtures are called **colloidal suspensions**, and the visualization of a light beam passed through them is called the **Tyndall effect**. True solutions are homogeneous (the same throughout) and are transparent to light (they are clear, not cloudy), although they are often colored. Figure 12-6 shows

FIGURE 12-6

The Tyndall effect. *Left:* Light beam shining through a true solution. *Right:* Light beam shining through a colloidal suspension (soap in water).

a light beam shining through a true solution and a colloidal suspension. The Tyndall effect can be seen in the colloidal suspension, but in the true solution the light beam is not visible. Figure 12-7, a diagram of soap micelles, shows why soap-water mixtures are cloudy.

Most dirt on skin, clothing, dishes, or floors is combined with grease and is not soluble in water (grease is nonpolar and water is polar). Since soap molecules have two rather well defined regions and thus a dual nature, the charged portion with the carbon-oxygen bonds is polar and tends to dissolve in water. The long hydrocarbon end is nonpolar and tends to be insoluble in water but soluble in the nonpolar grease (see Figure 12-8a). If we attempt to dissolve fat or oil in water, small particles of the nonpolar phase become suspended in the water, but no dissolving occurs (see Figure 12-8b). When soap is added, the soap molecules align themselves so that the hydrocarbon "tails" are in the oil droplets and the polar "heads" are outside the oil and in the water. The oil droplets become surrounded by negatively charged—COO⁻ groups and can be transported

FIGURE 12-7

Soap micelles.

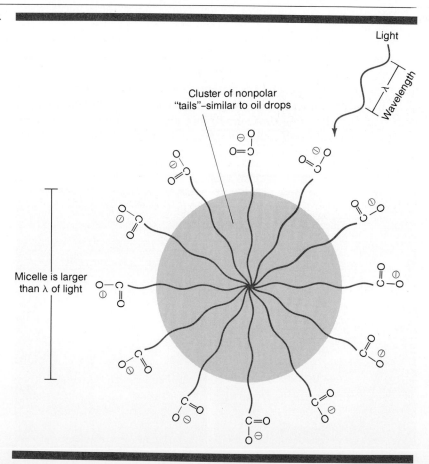

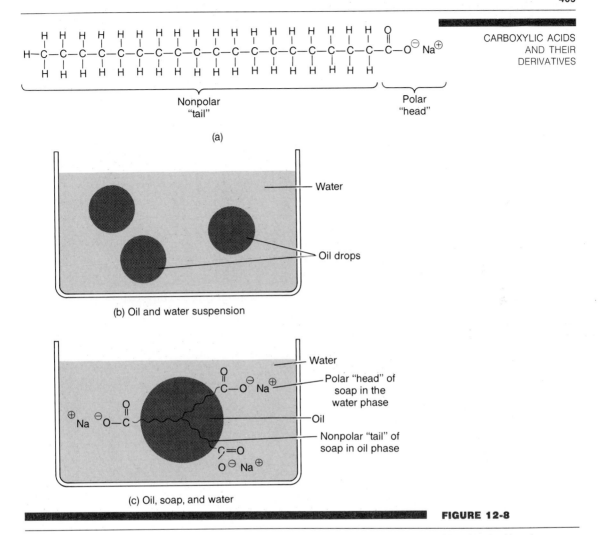

(a)

(b) Oil and water suspension

(c) Oil, soap, and water

FIGURE 12-8

Cleaning action of soap.

by the water. The water molecules contact only the outer negative layer and readily associate with it. The grease (along with any associated dirt) is now soluble (or at least well suspended) in the water and can be washed away. This is shown in Figure 12-8c.

SUMMARY

1 Acids are systematically **named** by designating the number of carbon atoms in the longest sequence, followed by the ending *-oic acid*. Esters are named by first naming the alkyl group attached to the oxygen atom followed as a separate word by the base name of the acid from which it

was prepared, ending in *-ate*. Amides are named by adding the syllable *-amide* to the base name of the corresponding carboxylic acid.

2 Carboxylic **acid strength** (acidity of the compound) is changed by various substituents on the carbon chain near the COOH group. Electronegative atoms tend to increase acidity, while larger alkyl groups tend to decrease acidity.

3 **Carboxylic acids** are **prepared** by **oxidation** of 1° alcohols and aldehydes, by oxidation of alkyl benzenes, by the **malonic ester synthesis**, and by carbonation of Grignard reagents.

4 **Acyl chlorides** and **anhydrides** are **formed** by treating the corresponding carboxylic acid with $SOCl_2$ and by dehydration with heat, respectively.

5 **Esters** and **amides** are **prepared** by reacting the carboxylic acid, its anhydride, or its acyl chloride with an alcohol and with an amide (or ammonia), respectively.

6 All derivatives of carboxylic acids can be converted back to the acid by **hydrolysis**.

7 Many flavoring agents are **esters**, while a number of medicinal products are esters or carboxylic acids. The two biggest sales volume **synthetic fibers** are polyester and polyamide. **Soaps** are salts of long chain carboxylic acids.

KEY TERMS

Acyl halide	Ester	Polymer
Amide	Hydrolysis	Salt
Anhydride	Inductive effect	Side chain oxidation
Carboxylic acid	K_a value	Soap
Claisen condensation	Malonic ester synthesis	Surfactant
Decarboxylation	Micelle	

SKILL PRACTICE PROBLEMS

1 Name these compounds.

(a)

$$CH_3CH_2CH_2CH_2\overset{O}{\overset{\|}{C}}-O-CH_2CH_2CH_3$$

(b)

(c)

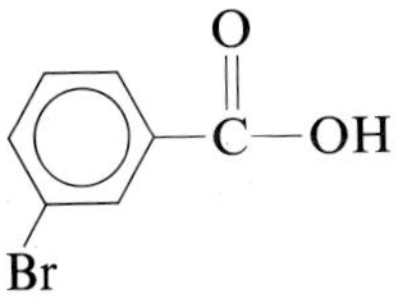

(d)

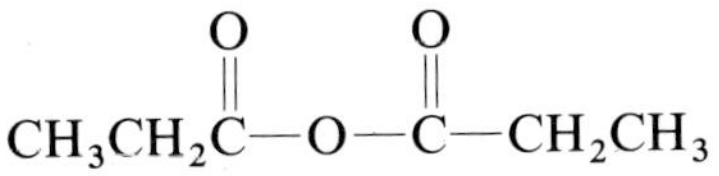

(e) 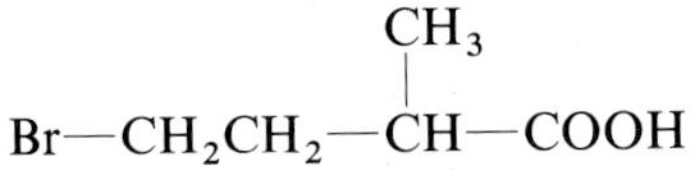 Br—CH$_2$CH$_2$—CH—COOH with CH$_3$

(f) HOOC—COOH

2 Name these compounds.

(a)

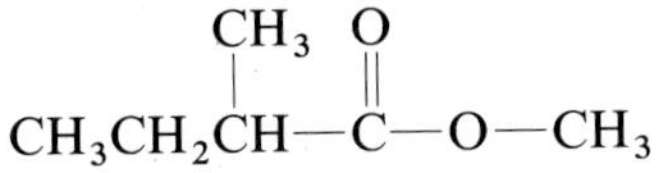

(b)

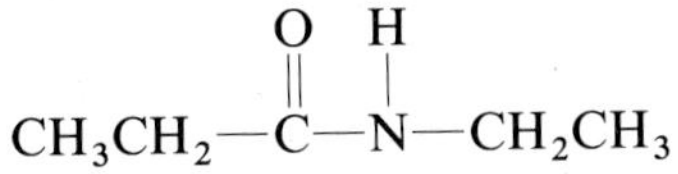

(c)

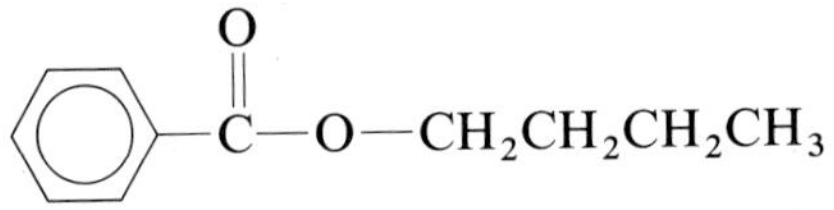

(d)

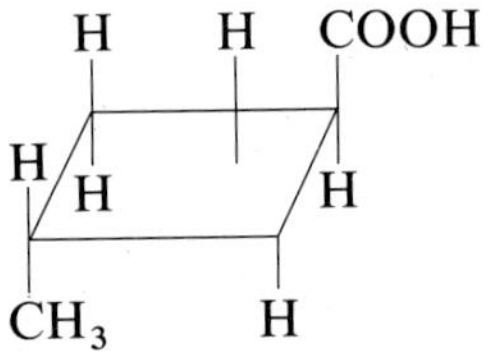

(e) 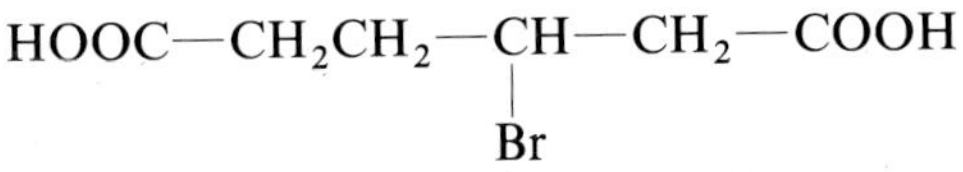 HOOC—CH$_2$CH$_2$—CH—CH$_2$—COOH with Br

(f)

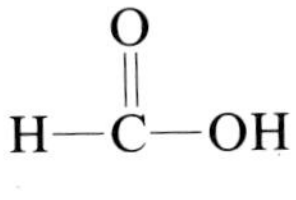

3 Which one of each acid pair would be the strongest acid?

(a) CH$_3$CH$_2$COOH   and   CH$_3$—CH—COOH with CH$_3$

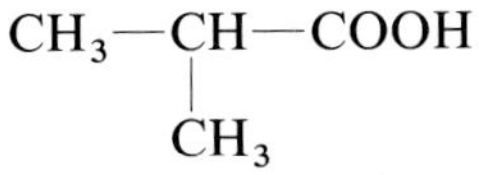

(b) 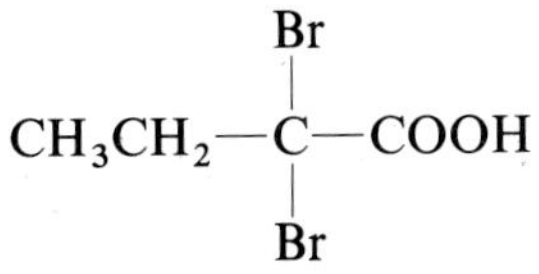 CH$_3$CH$_2$—C(Br)(Br)—COOH   and   CH$_3$CH$_2$CH—COOH with Br

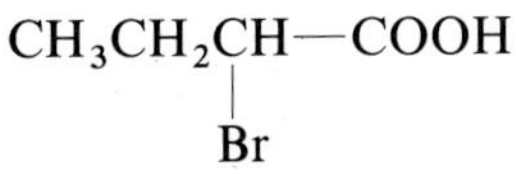

(c) $CH_3CH-COOH$ and CH_3CH_2COOH
              |
              I

(d) $CH_3CH_2CHCOOH$ and CH_3CHCH_2COOH
                    | |
                    Cl   Cl

4 Complete these reactions.

(a)

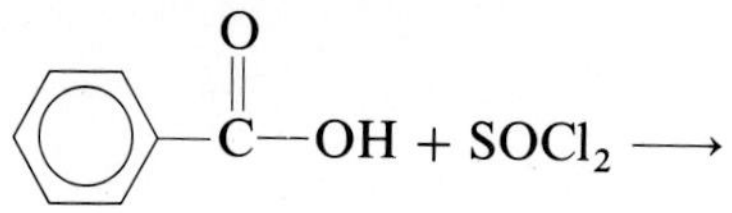

(b)

$$CH_3\overset{O}{\overset{\|}{C}}-O-CH_2CH_2CH_3 \xrightarrow[H_2O, \Delta]{NaOH}$$

(c)

$$CH_3\overset{O}{\overset{\|}{C}}-O-\overset{O}{\overset{\|}{C}}-CH_3 + H_2O \longrightarrow$$

(d)

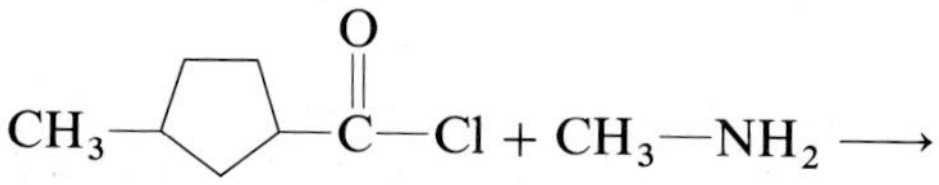

5 Complete these reactions.

(a)

$$CH_3-\underset{\underset{CH_3}{|}}{CH}-\overset{O}{\overset{\|}{C}}-OH + LiOH \longrightarrow$$

(b) $CH_3-\underset{\underset{O}{\|}}{C}-Cl + (CH_3)_3N \longrightarrow$

(c)

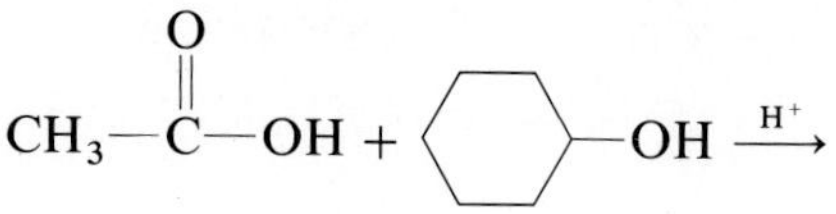

(d)

$$CH_3CH_2CH_2-\overset{O}{\overset{\|}{C}}-O-CH_3 \xrightarrow{CH_3CH_2O^-}$$

(e)

$$HO-\overset{O}{\overset{\|}{C}}-CH_2-CH_2-\overset{O}{\overset{\|}{C}}-OH \xrightarrow{\Delta}$$

6 Design a malonic acid synthesis for 2,3-dimethylbutanoic acid.

7 Name uses for the following materials.
  (a) Tartaric acid   (b) Ethyl 4-aminobenzoate
  (c) Acetic acid   (d) Sodium benzoate
  (e) Valproic acid   (f) Methyl salicylate

8 How would you synthesize propanamide using 1-propanol as your only organic starting material?

9 Give the product of the reaction of 2-methylpropanoic acid with each of the following reagents:

    (a) $SOCl_2$

    (b) heat or dehydrating agent

    (c) $CH_3-CH_2-CH-OH$ (plus acid catalyst)

$$\underset{\displaystyle CH_3}{|}$$

    (d) RbOH

10 Indicate the product you would expect from the use of two moles of 1-bromoethane in the malonic ester synthesis of carboxylic acids.

11 Give the compound that would result from treating benzoic acid with thionyl chloride followed by the addition of aniline. Name the final product.

12 Give the compound that would result from treating ⬡—CH_2OH

with $KMnO_4$ followed by reaction with ethanol/acid catalyst. Name the resulting compound.

13 Give the structure of the polyester that would result from the reaction of oxalic acid and 1,4-butanediol.

14 Give the structure of the polyamide that would be produced if malonic acid reacted with $NH_2-CH_2CH_2-NH_2$.

15 Would you expect oxalic or malonic acid to have the higher K_a value? (Consider only the first ionization constant.) Explain your answer.

16 Give the product of the reaction of caproic acid with thionyl chloride followed by treatment with water.

17 Write structures of the products for the following reactions:

(a)

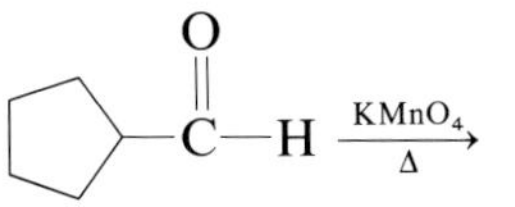

(b)

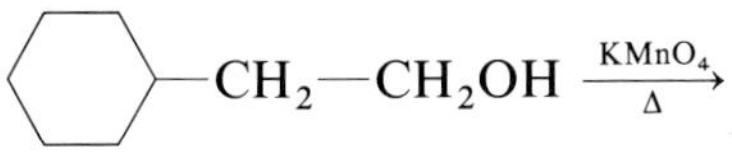

(c) $CH_3-CH_2-C(CH_3)_2-OH \xrightarrow[\Delta]{KMnO_4}$

(d)

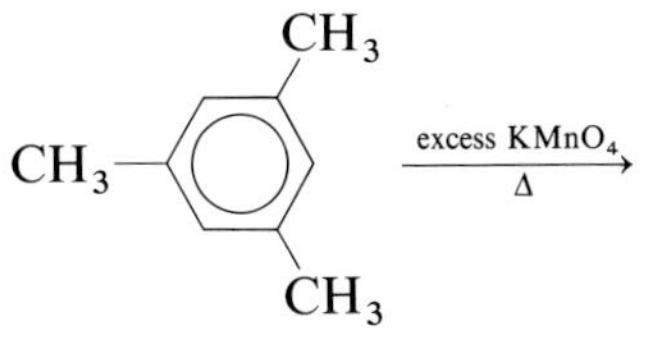

18 Give the product of the Claisen condensation of methyl pentanoate.

19 Give the structure of the product(s) of the hydrolysis of the compound responsible for the flavor of bananas.

REVIEW QUESTIONS

20 Sketch the NMR spectrum you would expect for 3,3-dimethylbutanoic acid.

21 Give three ways to produce a C=C group from other functional groups.

22 What test would you use in the laboratory to distinguish visually between the following pairs?

(a)

$$CH_3-\underset{\underset{O}{\|}}{C}-CH_3 \quad \text{and} \quad CH_3-\underset{\underset{OH}{|}}{CH}-CH_3$$

(b) ⬠—C≡C—CH₃   and   ⬠—CH₂—C≡C—H

(c) ⬠   and   CH₃CH₂CH=CHCH₃

We all know that many synthetic fibers, such as polyester, do not wrinkle when worn, while natural fibers, such as cotton, wrinkle easily. These two fibers also vary in comfort. Cotton feels warm and soft, while polyester is often cold and uncomfortable when worn next to the skin. These **properties**, like all physical and chemical properties, are the **result of the molecular structures** of the materials in question. Let's consider the behavior of cotton and polyester—why they vary in both comfort and resistance to wrinkles.

The structure of polyester is shown in Chapter 12 (see page 403) and the structure of cellulose, of which cotton is composed, is shown in Chapter 14 (see page 457). Cotton has three OH groups on each monomer unit contained in the polymeric chain. Because the OH groups are polar and can form hydrogen bonds, the cotton fiber can absorb water molecules (see Chapter 7, page 216 for a review of hydrogen bonds). Thus, cotton removes the water of perspiration from the skin by allowing it to soak into the fiber rather than evaporate or coat the outside of the fiber. The cotton does not feel wet, because the water is inside the fiber. Polyester, on the other hand, has no OH groups and is nonpolar. Therefore, it cannot absorb water, and perspiration wets the outside of the polyester fiber, causing it to feel cold and clammy. A 60-to-40 mixture of cotton to polyester helps to solve this comfort problem. The cotton in the mixture absorbs the water, adding comfort, while the polyester contributes other desirable properties, such as wrinkle resistance.

To explain why cotton wrinkles easily while polyester does not, we must examine a phase of matter we have thus far ignored. Most matter can exist only as a gas, liquid, or solid. Solids are completely rigid, and liquids have no structural integrity at all. For most pure materials, there is no state between a solid and a liquid. Water, for example, goes directly from rigid ice to fluid liquid water. But polymeric materials, such as the fibers we have been examining, have a flexible solid or rubbery state. Consider the common material polyethylene. At very cold temperatures it is brittle, like most other organic solids. As the temperature is raised, polyethylene reaches a point where it changes to a rubbery state. This is called the **glass transition temperature** and is symbolized by T_g. The T_g of each polymer—including polyester, nylon, cotton, and silk—is characteristic of each material, just as are melting and boiling points. Eventually these materials melt or decompose if the temperature is high enough.

The T_g of cotton is about 50°C, and that of polyester is 100°C. As long as a fiber is below its T_g temperature it does not wrinkle. If it is bent, it springs back to its original shape when released. But when a fiber is above its T_g (but below the melting temperature), it is flexible; when bent, it stays in the new shape. In this state it acts like a copper wire or a piece of clay.

The T_g of fibers is lowered by moisture, and the T_g of moist cotton is about 20°C while that of moist polyester is about 80°C.

When you wear a cotton shirt or blouse and lean against the back of a chair, perspiration lowers the T_g to 20°C. Since this is below body temperature (37°C), the cotton goes into the rubbery state and the natural folds become bends. When you stand up, the cloth cools down and the water evaporates. The fiber is now below its T_g temperature,[1] and the

---

[1] The T_g is back up to 50°C, since the moisture is gone; in addition, the cloth has cooled down to about 30°C.

FIGURE F-1

Wrinkle resistance of polymers: (a) cotton, (b) polyester.

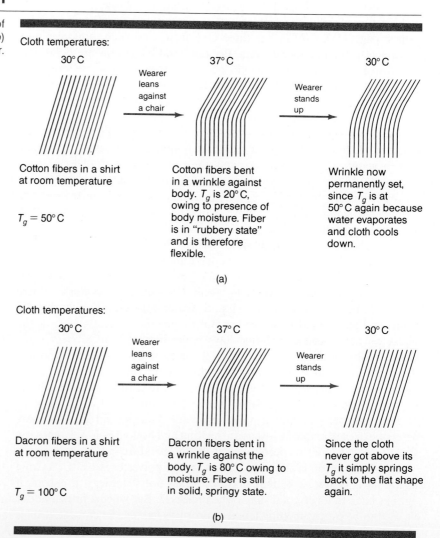

Cloth temperatures:

30°C   37°C   30°C

Wearer leans against a chair → Wearer stands up →

Cotton fibers in a shirt at room temperature

$T_g = 50°C$

Cotton fibers bent in a wrinkle against body. T_g is 20°C, owing to presence of body moisture. Fiber is in "rubbery state" and is therefore flexible.

Wrinkle now permanently set, since T_g is at 50°C again because water evaporates and cloth cools down.

(a)

Cloth temperatures:

30°C   37°C   30°C

Wearer leans against a chair → Wearer stands up →

Dacron fibers in a shirt at room temperature

$T_g = 100°C$

Dacron fibers bent in a wrinkle against the body. T_g is 80°C owing to moisture. Fiber is still in solid, springy state.

Since the cloth never got above its T_g it simply springs back to the flat shape again.

(b)

bends are permanent (i.e., the shirt is wrinkled). When you wear polyester clothing, the perspiration only lowers the T_g to 80°C, which is well above body temperature. When you lean against the chair this time, the fibers remain in the solid state, and they spring back into their straight shape when you stand up. (See Figure F-1.)

Ironing cotton cloth involves this same principle. To flatten cotton you must get it above its T_g so that it can be forced into a flat shape. This can be done with a hot clothes iron but is easier if the cloth is moistened first or steam is used in ironing. This moisture lowers the T_g and therefore lowers the temperature needed to remove wrinkles.

CHAPTER 13

AMINES

LEARNING GOALS

1 To learn the definitions of 1°, 2°, and 3° amines, which differ from the definitions of similar designations for other functional group classes

2 To be able to use the nomenclature systems for amines

3 To understand the base character of amines along with the relationship between basicity and molecular structure

4 To learn the methods of preparing amines and the reactions characteristic of amines

5 To recognize the structure of those amines which are commercially useful, biologically active, and otherwise of interest to consumers and scientists in other fields

Amines are characterized by the presence of a nitrogen atom singly bonded to one, two, or three carbon atoms (other than carbonyl carbon atoms). Compounds in the amine functional group class can be thought of as alkyl- or aryl- (aromatic) substituted ammonia compounds. Amines are classified as primary (1°), secondary (2°), or tertiary (3°) on the basis of the **number of alky or aryl groups attached to the nitrogen atom; not** by the nature of the alkyl groups. The R groups shown below can be either alkyl or aryl.

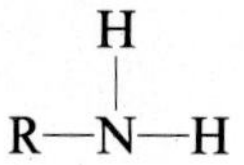

$$
\begin{array}{ccc}
\overset{\displaystyle H}{\underset{|}{R-N-H}} & \overset{\displaystyle R}{\underset{|}{R-N-H}} & \overset{\displaystyle R}{\underset{|}{R-N-R}} \\
\text{Primary, 1}° & \text{Secondary, 2}° & \text{Tertiary, 3}°
\end{array}
$$

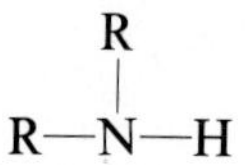

NOMENCLATURE

The classical names for alkyl amines are generated by naming all the alkyl groups attached to the nitrogen atom in alphabetical succession followed by the syllable -*amine* (all one word). The following examples illustrate this system.

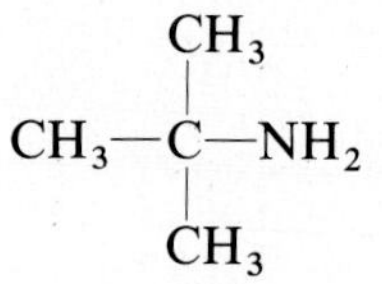

$$
\begin{array}{ccc}
CH_3-\overset{\displaystyle CH_3}{\underset{\displaystyle CH_3}{\overset{|}{\underset{|}{C}}}}-NH_2 & CH_3-\overset{\displaystyle H}{\underset{|}{N}}-\bigcirc & H_3C-CH_2-\overset{\displaystyle CH_2-CH_3}{\underset{|}{N}}-CH\overset{\displaystyle CH_3}{\underset{\displaystyle CH_3}{}} \\
\textit{tert}\text{-Butylamine} & \text{Cyclohexylmethylamine} & \text{Diethylisopropylamine} \\
(1°) & (2°) & (3°)
\end{array}
$$

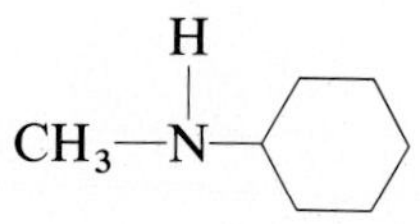

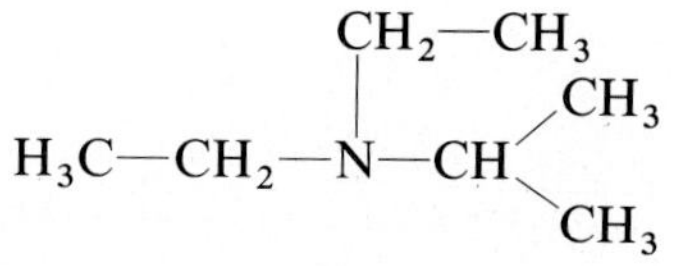

The systematic naming of amines is most conveniently done by a method developed by Chemical Abstracts Service for indexing purposes. The IUPAC method is somewhat bulky and now appears to be less commonly used. We will present and use the Chemical Abstracts Service method in this text. To use this system we identify the largest carbon chain in the molecule along with the nitrogen atom, and name this as an **alkanamine**. The position of the nitrogen is also indicated. (This is similar to the IUPAC system for naming alcohols except that the ending -*amine* is used instead of -*ol*.) The remaining R groups attached to the nitrogen atom are listed alphabetically and their position designated by an "*N*" (*N* is in italics). The following examples illustrate the Chemical Abstracts Service system names.

$$
CH_3CH_2CH_2CH_2CH_2NH_2 \qquad CH_3CH_2\overset{\displaystyle}{\underset{\displaystyle NH_2}{\overset{|}{CHCH_3}}}
$$

1-Pentanamine   2-Butanamine

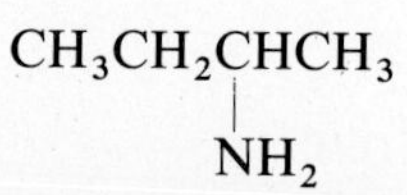

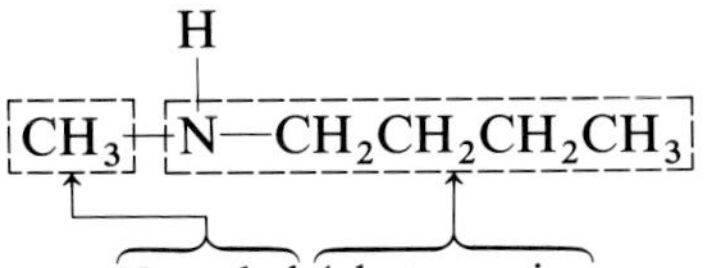

$$\underbrace{CH_3}_{} \underbrace{\overset{\overset{\displaystyle H}{|}}{N}—CH_2CH_2CH_2CH_3}$$

N-methyl-1-butanamine

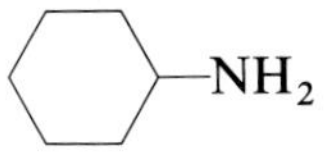

Cyclohexanamine ⟨⟩—NH₂

$$CH_3—N—CH_2—\overset{\overset{\displaystyle CH_3}{|}}{\underset{\underset{\displaystyle CH_3}{|}}{C}}—CH_3$$
$$\overset{\underset{\displaystyle CH_3}{|}}{}$$

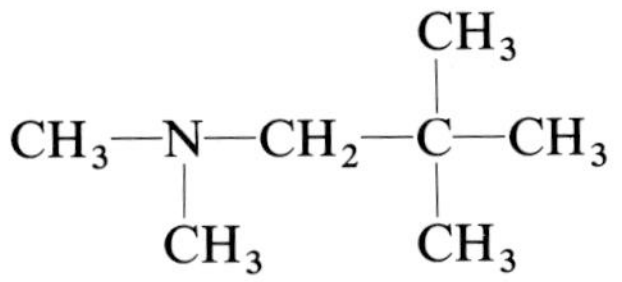

2,2,N,N-tetramethyl-1-propanamine

Amines in which a benzene ring is attached to the nitrogen atom are named as **N-substituted anilines**. For example:

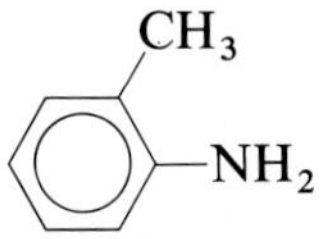

2-Methylaniline

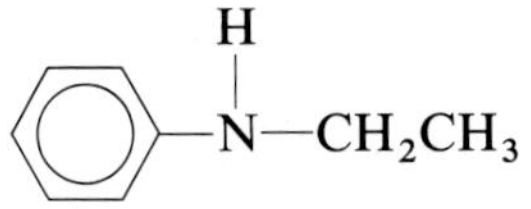

N-Ethylaniline

Frequently, the classical method of naming amines is simpler and therefore preferred for use outside the scientific literature, especially for the lower molecular weight amines. In fact, professional chemists frequently use the classical method for naming compounds in all functional group classes, because of the method's simplicity.

Amines are named as mono-, di-, or trialkyl substituted amines using the classical system. They are named as substituted alkanamines in the Chemical Abstracts Service system. Aryl amines are named as substituted anilines.

BIOLOGICALLY ACTIVE AMINES

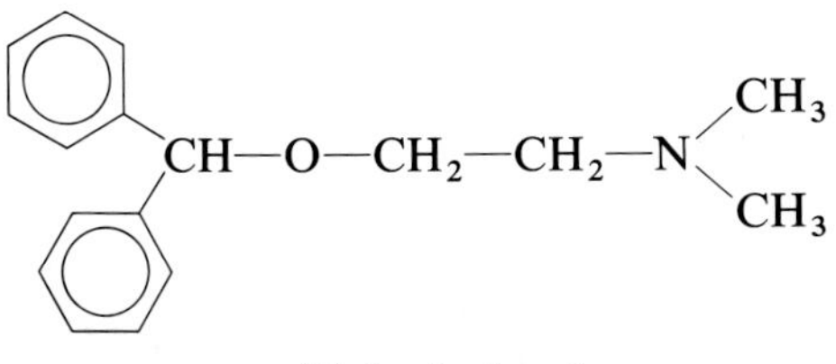

Diphenhydramine
(Benadryl, antihistamine)

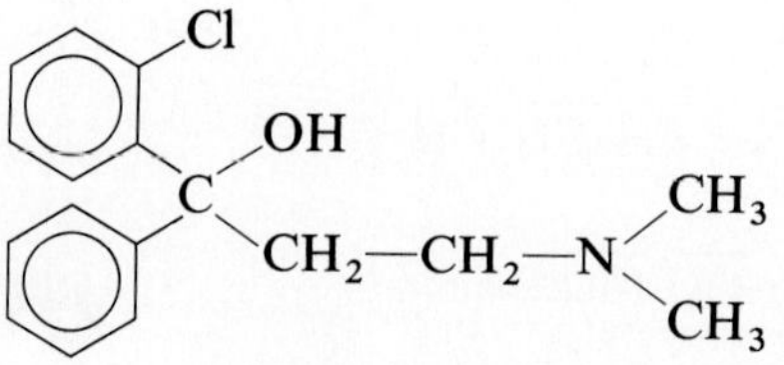

Chlorphedianol
(chlorphedianol, antitussive)

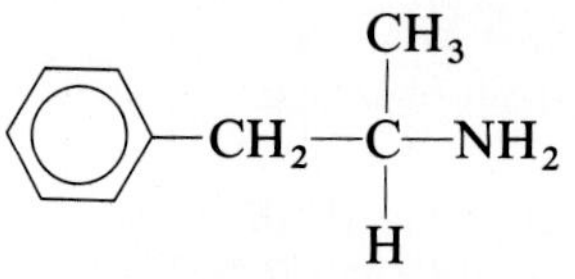

Amphetamine
(mood elevator, "upper")

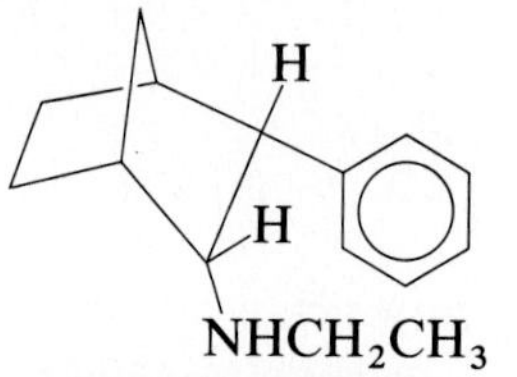

Fencamfamine
(fencamfine, central nervous
system stimulant)

In addition to the medically useful compounds shown above, a number of natural products found in plants are biologically active amines. Those natural, plant-derived materials containing an amine group, some of which are shown below, are called **alkaloid** (see Figure 13-1). Two of these are stimulants of the central nervous system (CNS). See Figure 13-1.

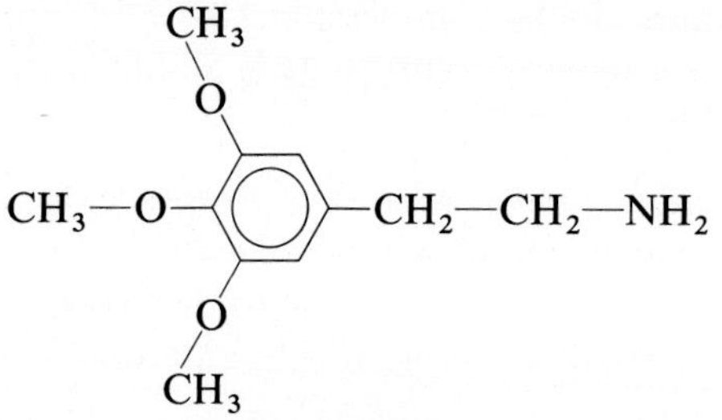

Mescaline
(hallucinogen
found in
cactus buds)

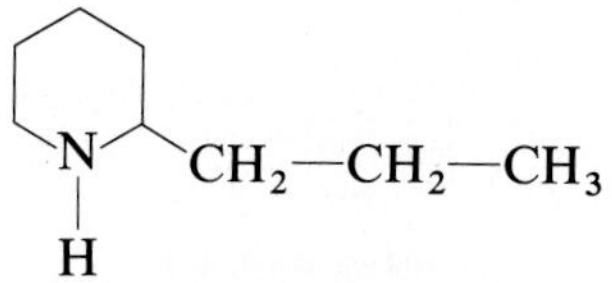

Coniine
(toxic component of
poison hemlock; used
to execute Socrates)

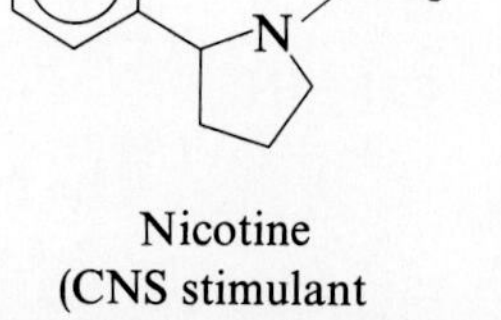

Nicotine
(CNS stimulant
found in tobacco)

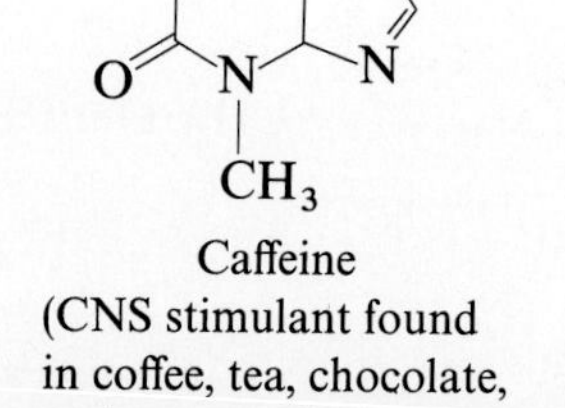

Caffeine
(CNS stimulant found
in coffee, tea, chocolate,
and many soft drinks)

Poison hemlock plant
which contains the toxic
alkaloid coniine.

FIGURE 13-1

Amines are frequently foul-smelling, as are each of the two materials shown below. Many amines have a characteristic odor reminiscent of ammonia.

$$CH_3—NH_2 \qquad H_2N—CH_2—CH_2—CH_2—CH_2—CH_2—NH_2$$

Methylamine
(first odor)

1,5-Pentanediamine
(cadaverine—odor of
decaying flesh)

BASICITY OF AMINES

Amines are the only class of organic materials that show significant base character, although they are classified as **weak bases**. They (1) react with acids (they are proton acceptors), (2) share a pair of electrons (Lewis definition), and (3) produce solutions with a pH greater than 7 when dissolved in water. [While you have likely encountered the concept of acids and bases, you may want to refer back to Table 12-1 (page 380) which summarizes the commonly used definitions of acids and bases.] These three aspects of the base behavior of amines are shown by the three reactions below.

1 Amines react with acids (Brønsted definition).

$$R—NH_2 \xrightarrow{\text{HCl}} R—NH_3{}^+Cl^-$$

Proton acceptor \qquad\qquad A salt

2 Amines donate an unshared pair of electrons (Lewis definition).

$$R—\overset{..}{N}H_2 + \ \ BCl_3 \longrightarrow R—\underset{\underset{\displaystyle H \ Cl}{|\ \ \ |}}{\overset{\overset{\displaystyle H \ Cl}{|\ \ \ |}}{N:B}}—Cl$$

Lewis base   Lewis acid

3 Amines produce solutions with an excess of OH^- ions when added to water (Arrhenius definition).

$$R—NH_2 + H_2O \rightleftharpoons \qquad R—NH_3{}^+OH^-$$

Basic solution; excess OH^-
compared to pure water (pH > 7)

While all amines are weak bases, their basicity varies according to the nature and number of alkyl or aryl groups attached to the nitrogen atom. Alkyl amines are much more basic than are aromatic ones. Within the alkyl amines, 2° amines are somewhat more basic than 1° amines, which in turn are slightly more basic than 3° amines.

These relative basicities of amines are summarized as follows:

2° alkyl > 1° alkyl > 3° alkyl > NH_3 ≫ aromatic

The K_b value is a measure of how basic a material is. From the equation of definition 3, above, the equilibrium constant for the production of OH^- in aqueous media is given by the following expression. Although water is a reactant, it is present in great excess and does not show up in the K_b expression.

$$K_b = \frac{[R—NH_3{}^+][OH^-]}{[R—NH_2]}$$

The stronger the base, the more H^+ is accepted from water and the higher the hydroxide ion (OH^-) concentration that results. Thus a higher K_b value (more OH^- and less $R—NH_2$ present) indicates a stronger base.

The K_b values for a few selected amines are shown in the table below (page 425). These values illustrate the trends in base strength-structure relationships outlined above. Note that the 2° amine (dimethylamine) is the strongest and that the aromatic amine (aniline) is much weaker than the alkyl amines.

The aromatic amines are weaker bases because the unshared electron pair on the nitrogen atom (which is the source of the base character of the amines) is partially delocalized into the pi electron cloud of the aromatic ring. This "ties them up," so to speak, and makes the unshared electrons less available for sharing with an acidic substance. The greater strength of 2° amines than 1° amines is due to the fact that alkyl groups

STRUCTURE	TYPE OF AMINE	K_b
$\begin{array}{c}CH_3\\|\\CH_3\text{—}N\text{—}H\end{array}$	2°	5.2×10^{-4}
$CH_3\text{—}NH_2$	1°	4.4×10^{-4}
$\begin{array}{c}CH_3\\|\\CH_3\text{—}N\text{—}CH_3\end{array}$	3°	5.5×10^{-5}
NH_3	Ammonia	1.8×10^{-5}
⬡—NH_2	Aromatic	3.8×10^{-10}

tend to "feed" electron density through the sigma bond toward the nitrogen atom to which the alkyl groups are attached. This is called a **positive inductive effect**. (See Chapter 12, especially Figure 12-1, for a more detailed description of inductive effects.) A greater positive inductive effect is exhibited by the two alkyl groups. More electron density is fed onto the nitrogen atom than would be the case for the one alkyl group present in 1° amines. This facilitates the sharing of the unshared electrons on the nitrogen atom with an acid. We might expect, from the preceding reasoning, that 3° amines would be still stronger than 2° amines. Such is indeed the case in the gas phase, but in aqueous solutions, which are our focus here, 3° amines are less basic than 2° amines. In water solutions, solvent effects apparently place 3° amines out of the expected order, but this is poorly understood.

Amines are weak organic bases. The relative base strengths are dependent on the nature and number of the organic groups attached to the nitrogen atom. Aromatic groups greatly weaken the base character of the amine (lower K_b values), while secondary amines are stronger than primary and tertiary amines.

PREPARATION OF AMINES

Reactions of alkyl halides

Primary and secondary alkyl halides (RX) react with NH_3 to produce primary amines (usually via an S_N2 mechanism). The 1° amines can react with another alkyl halide to produce 2° amines. Similarly, 2° amines react to produce 3° amines. Finally, a 3° amine can react with another mole of alkyl halide to produce an ionic compound called a **quarternary (4°) ammonium salt**. This reaction sequence is summarized by the scheme below.

$$R-X + NH_3 \longrightarrow R-NH_2 \xrightarrow{R'-X}$$
$$(1°)$$

$$R-\underset{\underset{R'}{|}}{N}-H \xrightarrow{R''-X} R-\underset{\underset{R'}{|}}{N}-R'' \xrightarrow{R'''-X} R-\underset{\underset{R'}{|}}{\overset{\overset{R'''}{|}}{N^+}}-R'' \quad X^-$$
$$(2°) \qquad\qquad (3°) \qquad\qquad (4°)$$

Thus we can produce 1°, 2°, or 3° amines, or the related quarternary ammonium salts, by using the appropriate alkyl halide(s) in the correct ratios. For those reactions that produce amines, we actually get a salt at first. This salt must be neutralized with a strong base in order to isolate the free amine. The general reaction expressing this situation for a primary amine is as follows:

$$R-Br + NH_3 \longrightarrow \boxed{RNH_3{}^+Br^-} \xrightarrow{NaOH} \boxed{R-NH_2} + H_2O + NaBr$$
$$\text{Amine salt} \qquad\qquad \text{Free amine}$$

Hereafter in this chapter when we write reactions of ammonia or amines with alkyl halides, we will not be concerned with the intermediate salt but will simply write the final amine product. Below are a few examples of the preparation of amines using alkyl halides. These reactions illustrate the idea that various numbers of moles of alkyl halides, in various combinations, can be used to produce a great many different amines.

$$\langle\rangle\!-Br + NH_3 \longrightarrow \langle\rangle\!-NH_2$$
Cyclohexylamine

$$2CH_3-CH_2-Cl + NH_3 \longrightarrow (CH_3CH_2)_2-NH$$
Diethylamine

$$CH_3-Br + NH_3 \longrightarrow CH_3NH_2 \xrightarrow{CH_3-CH_2-I} CH_3-\underset{\underset{H}{|}}{N}-CH_2-CH_3$$
Ethylmethylamine

$$3CH_3-CH_2-CH_2-Cl + NH_3 \longrightarrow (CH_3-CH_2-CH_2)_3-N$$
Tripropylamine

Reduction of amides and nitriles

Strong reducing agents, such as lithium aluminum hydride ($LiAlH_4$), can change **amides** into **amines** by reducing the C=O group to CH_2. In this reaction, the remainder of the carbon structure remains the same. We can produce 1°, 2°, or 3° amines of the alkyl or aryl type using this reaction. The general reaction is as follows:

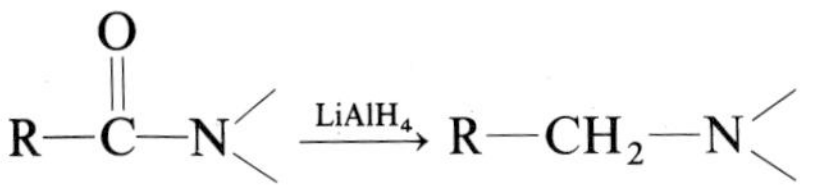

$$R-\overset{\overset{\displaystyle O}{\|}}{C}-N\diagdown \xrightarrow{LiAlH_4} R-CH_2-N\diagdown$$

Examples of the conversion of amides to amines are shown below.

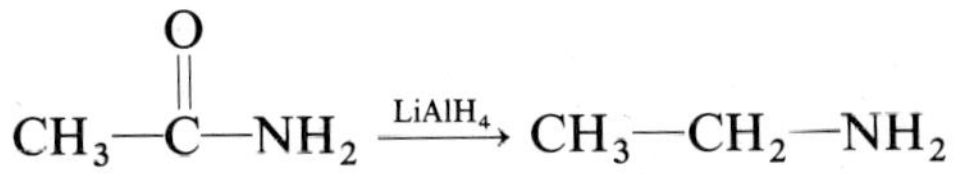

$$CH_3-\overset{\overset{\displaystyle O}{\|}}{C}-NH_2 \xrightarrow{LiAlH_4} CH_3-CH_2-NH_2$$
Ethyl amine

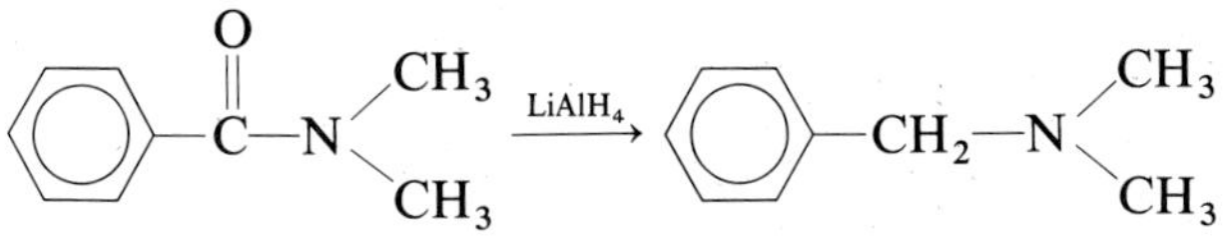

Catalytic hydrogenation of **nitriles** produces **primary amines** only. Nitriles are prepared, as you remember, from alkyl halides (RX) and cyanide ion (CN^-). The general reaction for this reduction is

$$R-C\equiv N \xrightarrow[Pt]{2H_2} R-CH_2-NH_2$$

Examples of nitrile production from alkyl halides, followed by reduction of the nitriles are shown below.

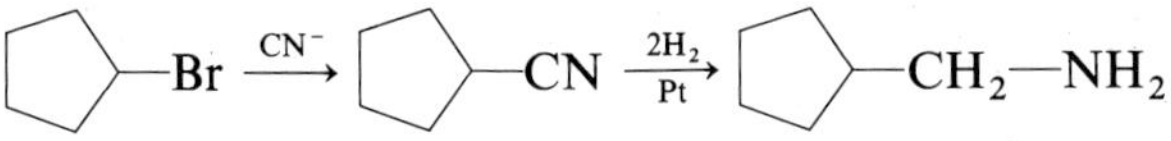

$$Cl-CH_2-CH_2-CH_2-Cl \xrightarrow{2CN^-} NC-CH_2-CH_2-CH_2-CN \xrightarrow[Pt]{4H_2}$$
$$H_2N-(CH_2)_5-NH_2$$
Cadaverine

Aryl amines (substituted anilines) are frequently prepared by reduction of the corresponding nitro compound with iron/HCl or tin/HCl mixtures. These reactions were covered in Chapter 9 along with the method of preparing the nitro compound. For example

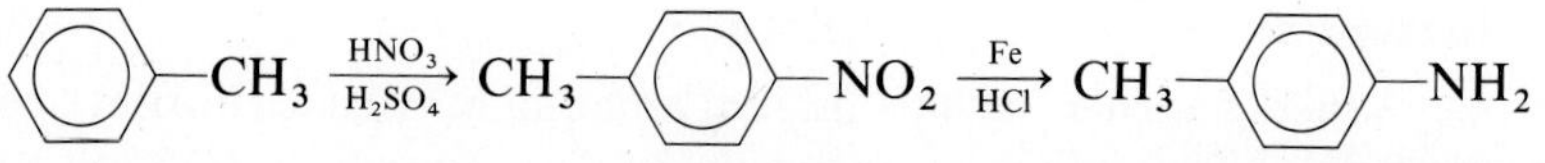

$$\text{Toluene} \xrightarrow[\text{H}_2\text{SO}_4]{\text{HNO}_3} \text{CH}_3 \longrightarrow \text{NO}_2 \xrightarrow[\text{HCl}]{\text{Fe}} \text{CH}_3 \longrightarrow \text{NH}_2$$

Toluene   p-Nitrotoluene   p-Methylaniline

Once formed, the substituted aniline can be further alkylated at the nitrogen atom, like any other amine. This is illustrated by the following reaction:

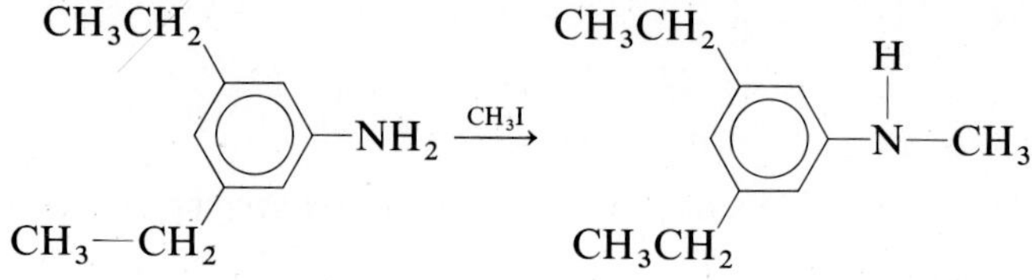

3,5-Diethylaniline   N-Methyl-3,5-diethylaniline

Amines can be prepared by the reaction of ammonia with various alkyl halides in various molar ratios or by the reduction of amides or nitriles. Aryl amines can be prepared by reduction of the corresponding nitro compound.

REACTIONS OF AMINES

Amide formation

Primary and secondary amines react with reactive carboxylic acid derivatives, such as acid chlorides or anhydrides, to produce the corresponding amides according to the following general reaction:

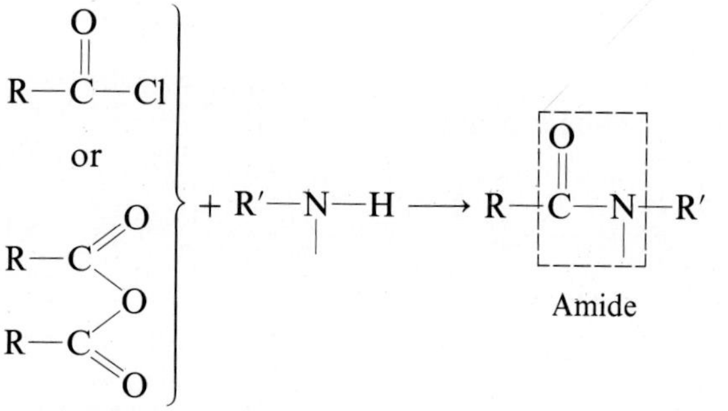

Amide

Examples of these types of reactions are shown by the equations that follow. Note that tertiary amines **do not react** with acid derivatives to form amides, as shown by the last example.

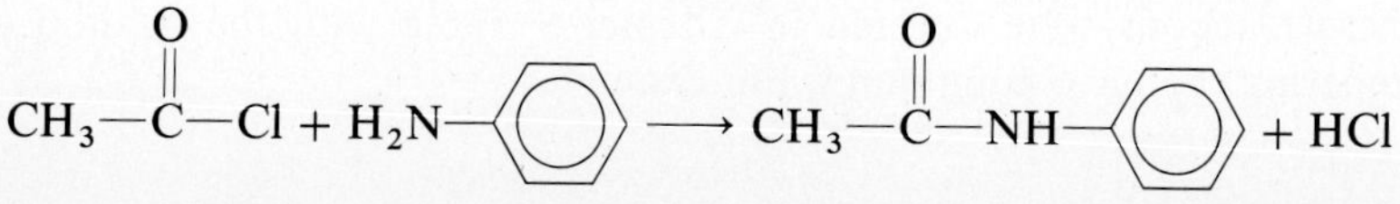

$$\text{CH}_3-\overset{\text{O}}{\overset{\|}{\text{C}}}-\text{Cl} + \text{H}_2\text{N}-\bigcirc \longrightarrow \text{CH}_3-\overset{\text{O}}{\overset{\|}{\text{C}}}-\text{NH}-\bigcirc + \text{HCl}$$

$$\text{C}_6\text{H}_5-\overset{\overset{\displaystyle O}{\|}}{\text{C}}-\text{Cl} + \text{HN}-(\text{CH}_3)_2 \longrightarrow \text{C}_6\text{H}_5-\overset{\overset{\displaystyle O}{\|}}{\text{C}}-\text{N}\overset{\text{CH}_3}{\underset{\text{CH}_3}{}} + \text{HCl}$$

$$\underset{\text{CH}_3-\text{C}}{\overset{\text{CH}_3-\text{C}}{}}\overset{O}{\underset{O}{}} + \text{CH}_3-\text{CH}_2-\text{NH}_2 \longrightarrow$$

$$\text{CH}_3-\overset{\overset{\displaystyle O}{\|}}{\text{C}}-\text{NH}-\text{CH}_2-\text{CH}_3 + \text{CH}_3\text{COOH}$$

$$\text{CH}_3-\text{CH}_2-\overset{\overset{\displaystyle O}{\|}}{\text{C}}-\text{Cl} + (\text{CH}_3)_3\text{N} \longrightarrow \text{no reaction}$$

Acid-base reactions

As already mentioned, amines react with acids to form salts. These acids can be strong mineral acids or organic carboxylic acids. All types of amines form salts. The following general equations show this type of reaction:

$$\text{R}-\overset{\overset{\displaystyle O}{\|}}{\text{C}}-\text{OH} + \text{R}'-\text{NH}_2 \longrightarrow \text{R}-\overset{\overset{\displaystyle O}{\|}}{\text{C}}-\text{O}^- \quad \text{R}'-\text{NH}_3{}^+$$

$$\text{R}-\text{NH}_2 \overset{\text{HX}}{\longrightarrow} \text{R}-\text{NH}_3{}^+\text{X}^-$$

Examples of amine salt formation are

$$\text{CH}_3-\overset{\overset{\displaystyle O}{\|}}{\text{C}}-\text{OH} + \text{CH}_3\text{NH}_2 \longrightarrow \text{CH}_3-\overset{\overset{\displaystyle O}{\|}}{\text{C}}-\text{O}^- \quad \text{CH}_3\text{NH}_3{}^+$$

Acetic acid   Methylammonium acetate
(ethanoic acid)   (methylammonium ethanoate)

$$\text{C}_6\text{H}_5-\text{NH}_2 + \text{HCl} \longrightarrow \text{C}_6\text{H}_5-\text{NH}_3{}^+ \quad \text{Cl}^-$$

Aniline   Anilinium chloride
(aniline hydrochloride)

$$\text{CH}_3\text{CH}_2\text{CH}_2-\underset{\overset{\displaystyle |}{\text{CH}_3}}{\text{N}}-\text{H} + \text{HNO}_3 \longrightarrow \text{CH}_3\text{CH}_2\text{CH}_2\overset{+}{\underset{\overset{\displaystyle |}{\text{CH}_3}}{\text{N}}}\text{H}_2 \quad \text{NO}_3{}^-$$

Methylpropylamine   Methylpropylammonium nitrate

Salts of amines are named as substituted ammonium salts followed by the anion name, as in methylpropylammonium nitrate. Or they can be

The odor of amines in fish can be reduced by an acidic substance such as vinegar or lemon juice.

FIGURE 13-2

referred to simply as the salts of amines (e.g., the hydrochloride salt of aniline, or aniline hydrochloride).

The **salts of amines**, like many salts, are quite **soluble** in water compared to free amines, which are insoluble if the molecule contains more than four carbon atoms. Amine salts are also **nonvolatile**. The first reaction above shows what happens when fish is soaked in vinegar (acetic acid). Soaking in vinegar converts the methylamine (CH_3NH_2) into a salt and, thus, prevents it from evaporating during cooking (see Figure 13-2). This reduces the amount of odor formed from cooking fish. Likewise, washing one's hands in vinegar or lemon juice (citric acid) will remove unwanted fish odor after cleaning or otherwise handling fish. Acid reacts with the amine which causes the odor, converting it to a salt which is soluble in water and is easily washed off. Acid also makes amines nonvolatile, and hence odorless.

$$R\text{—}NH_2 \quad \xrightarrow{\text{acid}} \quad R\text{—}NH_3^+$$

Volatile,   Nonvolatile (odorless),

water insoluble   water soluble (washes away)

Salt formation can also be used to increase the water solubility of amines found in medications. Dextromethorphan hydrobromide, a cough suppressant, can be formulated into a useful product as the HBr salt. It is found as such in most cough drops and syrups. Dextromethorphan hydrobromide is the salt formed from an amine and hydrobromic acid (HBr). See Figure 13-3.

Dextromethorphan
(an insoluble 3° amine)

$$CH_3 \xrightarrow{HBr}$$

Dextromethorphan hydrobromide
(a soluble salt)

Another group of compounds related to amines are quarternary ammonium salts ("quats"). As mentioned earlier in the chapter, they are formed by reacting a 3° amine with another mole of alkyl halide (see page 426). They are charged, like the amine salts discussed above, and are nonvolatile and water soluble. Quarternary ammonium salts are named as substituted ammonium salts, followed by the name of the anion. For example

$$(CH_3)_3\!-\!N + CH_3\!-\!Br \longrightarrow (CH_3)_4\!-\!N^+Br^-$$
Tetramethylammonium bromide

$$4CH_3\!-\!CH_2\!-\!Cl + NH_3 \longrightarrow (CH_3\!-\!CH_2)_4\!-\!N^+Cl^- + 3HCl$$
Tetraethylammonium chloride

Quarternary ammonium salts prepared by using long chain alkyl halides are compounds with strong **detergent** and **antibacterial** properties. Two such compounds used commercially are shown below.

$$\overset{+}{N}\!-\!(CH_2)\!-\!CH_3 \; Cl^-$$

$$CH_3\!-\!\overset{\overset{CH_3}{|}}{\underset{\underset{}{N}}{\overset{+}{N}}}\!-\!(CH_2)_{13}\!-\!CH_3 \quad Cl^-$$

Cetylpyridinium chloride
(hexadecylpyridinium chloride; mouth wash and commercial dish washing detergent; Cepacol mouth wash)

Tetradecyldimethylbenzyl ammonium chloride
(Lysol cleaners)

FIGURE 13-3

Typical ingredient label for an over-the-counter anticough drug. Note that dextromethorphan hydrobromide is the active ingredient.

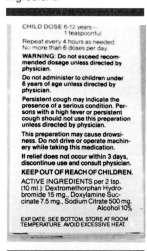

CHILD DOSE 6-12 years—
1 teaspoonful
Repeat every 4 hours as needed.
No more than 6 doses per day.
WARNING: Do not exceed recommended dosage unless directed by physician.
Do not administer to children under 6 years of age unless directed by physician.
Persistent cough may indicate the presence of a serious condition. Persons with a high fever or persistent cough should not use this preparation unless directed by physician.
This preparation may cause drowsiness. Do not drive or operate machinery while taking this medication.
If relief does not occur within 3 days, discontinue use and consult physician.
KEEP OUT OF REACH OF CHILDREN.
ACTIVE INGREDIENTS per 2 tsp. (10 ml.): Dextromethorphan Hydrobromide 15 mg., Doxylamine Succinate 7.5 mg., Sodium Citrate 500 mg. Alcohol 10%
EXP DATE. SEE BOTTOM. STORE AT ROOM TEMPERATURE. AVOID EXCESSIVE HEAT.

Amines react with alkyl halides to form higher-order amines and quarternary ammonium salts. Salts are formed when amines are treated with mineral acids or carboxylic acids. Amines react with reactive carboxylic acid derivatives such as anhydrides and acid chlorides to form amides. Salts of amines are more soluble in water than are the free amines and are nonvolatile.

REACTION SUMMARY FLOW DIAGRAM—AMINES

$$R-CH_2-X \qquad R-\overset{\overset{\displaystyle O}{\|}}{C}-NH_2 \qquad R-C\equiv N$$

$$\xrightarrow{\quad NH_3 \quad} \qquad \Big\downarrow LiAlH_4 \qquad \xrightarrow[2H_2]{Pt}$$

$$R-CH_2-NH_2$$

$$\overset{O}{\underset{\displaystyle R'-C-Cl}{\|}} \qquad \Big\downarrow H^+ \qquad \xrightarrow{\quad R'-X \quad}$$

$$\underset{\displaystyle H}{R-\overset{\overset{\displaystyle O}{\|}}{C}-N-CH_2R} \qquad R-CH_2NH_3{}^+ \qquad \underset{\displaystyle H}{R'-N-CH_2R}$$

$$\Big\downarrow R''-X$$

$$\underset{\displaystyle R''}{R'-N-CH_2R}$$

$$\xleftarrow{\quad R'''-X \quad}$$

$$\underset{\displaystyle R''\quad X^-}{\overset{\displaystyle R'''}{\underset{\displaystyle |}{R'-N^+-CH_2R}}}$$

SUMMARY

1   Unlike other functional group classes, amines are **classified** as **1°**, **2°**, or **3°** on the basis of the **number of organic groups** attached to the nitrogen atom, not according to the nature of those groups.

2   Amines are **named** classically as **alkyl**, **dialkyl** or **trialkyl amines**. Systematically, they are named **alkanamines** or *N*-**substituted alkanamines**. Aryl amines are named as **substituted anilines**.

3 Amines are **weak bases** whose base strengths decrease in the following order: 2° alkyl, 1° alkyl, 3° alkyl, aryl.

4 Amines are **prepared** by reacting ammonia or another amine with an alkyl halide, by reduction of nitriles, or by reduction of amides.

5 Amines **react** with acids to form salts, react with acyl chlorides or anhydrides to form amides, and react with alkyl halides to form higher-order amines and quarternary salts.

KEY TERMS

Acyl chloride (acid chloride)	Amine salt	Quarternary ammonium salt
Alkaloid	Base	Secondary amine
Amide	Inductive effect	Tertiary amine
Amine	K_b value	
	Primary amine	

SKILL PRACTICE PROBLEMS

1 Define the following terms in your own words:
   (*a*) Amine salt   (*b*) Alkaloid
   (*c*) Secondary amine (*d*) Secondary alcohol
   (*e*) "Quat"

2 Name the following compounds:

(*a*)
$$CH_3-\underset{\underset{CH_3}{|}}{CH}-NH_2$$

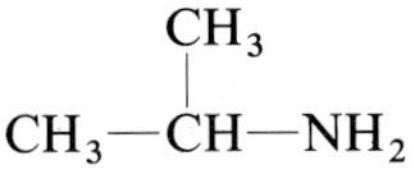

(*b*)

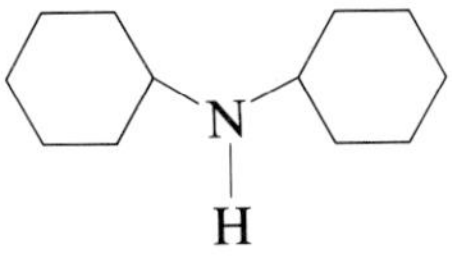

(*c*) $(CH_3)_3-N$

(*d*) $CH_3-CH_2-\underset{\underset{\underset{\underset{CH_3}{|}}{CH_2}}{\underset{|}{CH_2}}}{N}-CH_3CH_2CH_3$

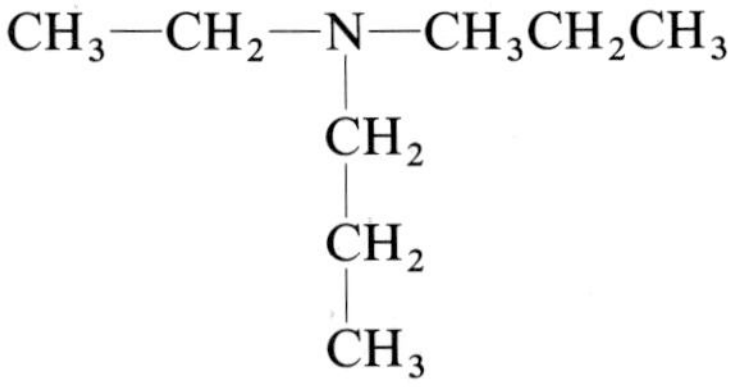

(*e*) $CH_3-CH_2-NH_3{}^+ \quad Br^-$

(f)

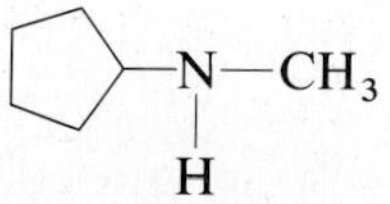

$$\text{cyclopentyl}-\underset{\underset{\text{H}}{|}}{N}-CH_3$$

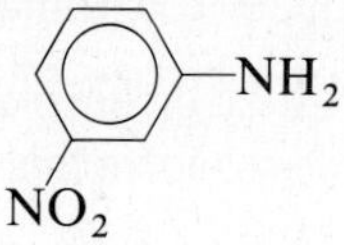

(g)

benzene ring with $-NH_2$ and NO_2 substituents

(h)

benzene ring with $-NH-CH_2CH_2CH_3$ and Br substituents

(i)

$$\text{cyclopentyl}-\overset{+}{N}(CH_3)_3 \quad I^-$$

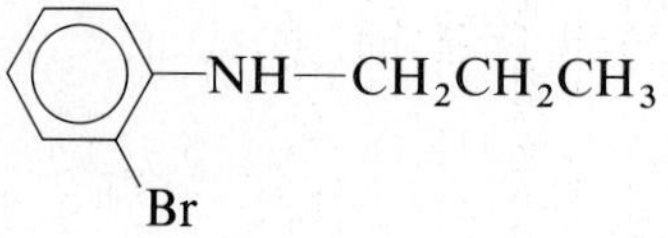

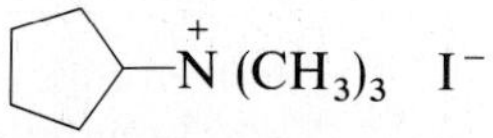

3 Which of the compounds in question 2 are 3° amines? Which are 1°? Which is a quarternary ammonium salt? Which is an amine salt?

4 Complete these reactions, giving the major organic products.

(a)

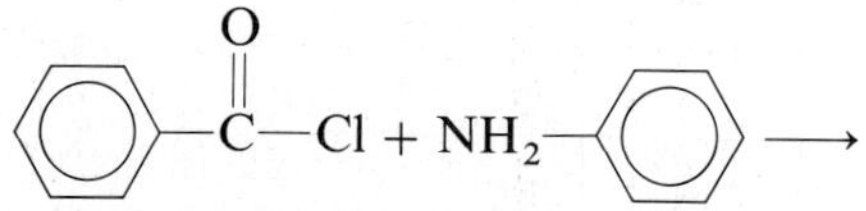

$$\text{phenyl}-\underset{\underset{}{\overset{O}{||}}}{C}-Cl + NH_2-\text{phenyl} \longrightarrow$$

(b) $CH_3-\underset{\underset{Br}{|}}{CH}-CH_3 + NH_3$

(c)

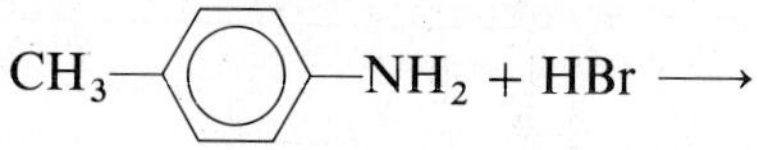

$$CH_3-\text{phenyl}-NH_2 + HBr \longrightarrow$$

(d)

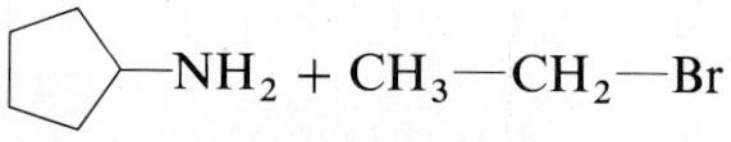

$$\text{cyclopentyl}-NH_2 + CH_3-CH_2-Br$$

(e) $CH_3-CH_2-CH_2-CN \xrightarrow[\text{Pt}]{2H_2}$

(f)

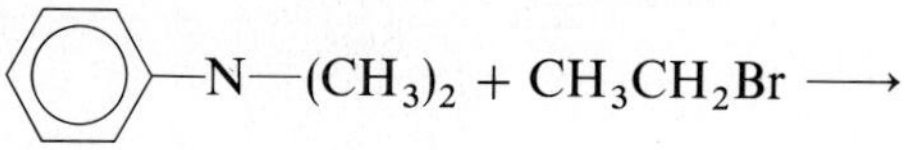

$$\text{phenyl}-N-(CH_3)_2 + CH_3CH_2Br \longrightarrow$$

(g)

$$CH_3-\underset{\underset{H}{|}}{\overset{\overset{O}{||}}{C}}-N-CH_2CH_3 \xrightarrow{\text{LiAlH}_4}$$

5 Show how to synthesize amphetamine from $\text{phenyl}-CH_2-\underset{}{\overset{\overset{O}{||}}{C}}-H$ and CH_3MgBr.

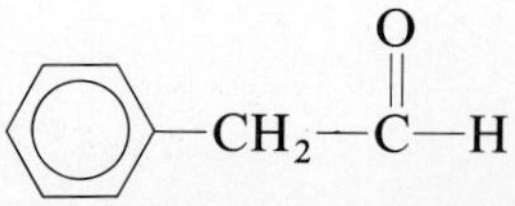

6 Which of the following amines is the most basic? Which is the least?

(a)

—NH$_2$

(b) HN—(CH$_3$)$_2$

(c)

CH$_3$——NH$_2$

How would you prepare the following amines from the indicated starting materials and any inorganic materials? (Three steps are not necessarily involved in each one.)

7 Ethane $\longrightarrow \longrightarrow \longrightarrow$ N—(CH$_2$—CH$_3$)$_3$

8 $\longrightarrow \longrightarrow \longrightarrow$ —NH$_3{}^+$Br$^-$

9

$$CH_3-\overset{\overset{\displaystyle O}{\|}}{C}-Cl + CH_3-CH_2-CN \longrightarrow \longrightarrow \longrightarrow$$

$$CH_3-CH_2-\overset{\overset{\displaystyle H}{|}}{N}-CH_2$$
$$\overset{|}{C}H_2$$
$$\overset{|}{C}H_3$$

10 Give the classical names of the following amines:

(a)

$$CH_3-\overset{\overset{\displaystyle NH_2}{|}}{C}H-CH_3$$

(b) $CH_3-CH_2-\overset{\overset{}{|}}{C}H-CH_3$
      $\overset{|}{N}H_2$

(c)

$$CH_3-\overset{\overset{\displaystyle CH_3H}{|}}{C}-N-\overset{\overset{\displaystyle CH_3}{|}}{C}-CH_3$$
$$\overset{|}{C}H_3 \quad \overset{|}{C}H_3$$

(d) $CH_3-\overset{\overset{}{|}}{C}H-CH_2-NH_2$
      $\overset{|}{C}H_3$

11 Which of the nitrogen atoms in the structure of caffeine (see page 422) are of the amine type?

12 Which of the following compounds are amines?

(a) CH$_3$—CH$_2$—CH=N—OH

(b)

N—H

(c)

$$CH_3-CH_2-\overset{\overset{\displaystyle O}{\|}}{C}-\overset{\overset{\displaystyle H}{|}}{N}-CH_3$$

(d)

N

REVIEW QUESTIONS

13 An amine has an infrared absorbance at 3400 cm^{-1} and a singlet at about 1.0 ppm on the NMR spectrum. The molecular weight is 73 amu. Suggest a structure for the compound.

14 Of those biologically active amines shown on pages 421 through 423 which would be optically active?

15 What is the absolute configuration of the chiral center in the amphetamine structure shown here?

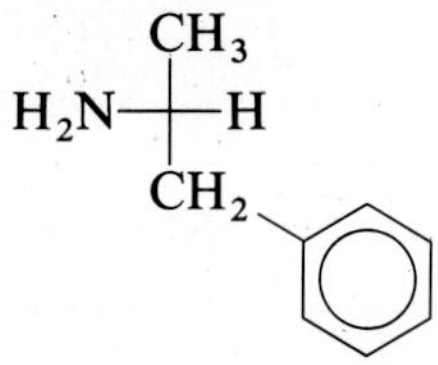

16 Would you expect the enantiomers of the compounds referred to in question 14 to be biologically active? If so, why?

17 What would be the expected optical activity and biological potency of the product **synthesized** in Problem 5 compared to the same compound isolated from a **natural** source?

BIODEGRADABLE POLYMERS

Most synthetic polymers are notably inert to decomposition in the environment. This property is desirable if we want to produce a material that will last a long time. But it is an undesirable property when synthetic polymers are used to make disposable containers, because the biological inertness of the materials causes a pollution problem. When materials such as discarded polyethylene (see page 192) food wrappers are thrown along roadways, they remain for a very long time. Other inert materials are polyester (see page 403) and nylon (see page 405). If chemists could synthesize **biodegradable** polymers—synthetic materials that would be broken down by nature—this pollution problem could be eliminated or greatly reduced. A plastic food wrapper would, if discarded, simply decay in a week or two.

Even more interesting uses of such biodegradable materials are found in agriculture. Biodegradable polymers are used to make containers for tree seedlings. These containers are designed in such a way that the seedlings are planted by dropping them from an airplane. The containers are made with a point, so that the force of falling causes them to penetrate the soil. Because the containers are biodegradable, they decay after planting and allow the tree roots to grow. This planting process is less expensive than planting by hand (see Figure G-1).

The tree-planting technique mentioned above has been successfully used. Other biodegradable polymers are being developed for a number of potential applications, but most of them are not yet in commercial use. In the future, no doubt, a number of such polymers will be marketed.

For example, temporary ground cover can be made of such biodegradable polymers. Polyethylene sheets sometimes are placed on the ground between rows of crops to prevent weed growth and help retain moisture in the soil. But since polyethylene is inert, it must be removed later. If, instead, sheets of a **biodegradable** plastic are used, they simply decay along with other organic matter before the following year.

Slow release of fertilizer and pesticides might also be accomplished using biodegradable polymers. The fertilizer or pesticide could be placed in a matrix of the degradable polymer and this could be formed into small particles. As the particles slowly disintegrated, the fertilizer or pesticide would be slowly released into the environment. Because only one application would be needed annually, the expense of several applications would be avoided. Biodegradable polymers could also possibly be used in human and animal medicine for absorbable sutures and slow-releasing drugs.

An example of such a polymer, developed by William J. Bailey at the University of Maryland, is shown below. The research being carried out

Tree seedling containers
made of biodegradable
polymers.

FIGURE G-1

in his laboratory is aimed specifically at solving a particular problem by designing macromolecules with the desired function, as well with the properties of strength, good appearance, ease of fabrication, and biodegradability.

$$\left(\text{--N--CH}_2\text{C}\right.\overset{\displaystyle H}{\underset{\displaystyle \|}{\overset{\displaystyle|}{\text{N}}}}\text{---}\left.\begin{matrix} \overset{\displaystyle H}{|} \\ \text{NCH}_2\text{CH}_2\text{CH}_2\text{CH}_2\text{CH}_2\text{C} \\ \end{matrix}\overset{\displaystyle O}{\underset{\displaystyle \|}{}}\text{---}\right)_x$$

Glycine unit   6-Aminohexanoic acid unit

This is an amide copolymer (two monomers used in an alternating sequence) of glycine and 6-aminohexanoic acid (or ε-amino caproic acid). While nylon, which has a similar structure (it is also a polyamide—see page 405), will stay in the environment indefinitely, the above polyamide will disintegrate in two weeks.

CHAPTER 14

CARBOHYDRATES

LEARNING GOALS

1 To gain a comprehensive view of the field of biochemistry

2 To learn the structure of several simple sugars

3 To understand the internal bonding that occurs in sugar molecules and learn terms used to describe the behavior and molecular structure of sugars

4 To understand the types of bonding that occur between simple sugar units in disaccharides and polysaccharides, and to understand the effects of this bonding on the structure and behavior of various carbohydrate materials

The study of carbohydrates is an area of **biochemistry**; before we begin our discussion of this class of compounds, let us take a brief overview of biochemistry as a whole. We will then discuss carbohydrates in this chapter and other areas of biochemistry in the subsequent three chapters.

BIOCHEMISTRY–AN OVERVIEW

The human body, for many purposes, can be thought of as an extremely complex chemical system. Many different kinds of chemical changes involving numerous biochemical substances occur simultaneously in the body. Consider the simple act of putting a piece of food into your mouth. You first must see the location of the food, which involves light hitting the back of the eye and causing chemical changes in the eye. These chemical changes in turn initiate chemical changes at each nerve cell, which result in the transmission of signals to the brain. The brain, through chemical changes, recognizes the combination of signals as "food." Then more chemical changes have to occur in order for you to decide to eat the food. Other signals that originate from chemical changes go to the muscles, which cause the molecules in the muscles to contract, each one contracting just the right amount so that you can grasp the utensil and move it to your mouth. The simple act of putting a piece of food into your mouth involves changes in literally thousands of different substances, all taking place in a few seconds. Yet it all happens so smoothly that you are not aware of its complexity. All life processes, even relatively inactive ones, such as your reading (and understanding!) this chapter, are quite complex. Biochemistry is the most incompletely understood of all areas of chemistry, and while the structure and function of many biochemical substances have been unraveled in recent years, there is much more to be done.

We have only just begun to fathom the complexity of the chemical compounds of living systems, and we hardly understand most of the processes, except on a superficial level.

While the general principles of biochemistry apply to all living organisms, there are significant differences in the details of the processes taking place in various life systems. In this book, we will focus on the relevant human biochemistry.

There are four basic categories of biomolecules: carbohydrates, proteins, lipids (fats), and nucleic acids. Figure 14-1 shows how these classes of biomolecules fit into the overall scheme of chemical and biological knowledge. Each of these four types of biochemical substances will be discussed in some detail later in this book. In the scheme shown in Figure 14-1, the complexity increases as we go down the figure. Simple inorganic compounds are composed of elements. The more complex compounds can be thought of as being composed of simpler compounds.

This does not mean, however, that organic materials are necessarily produced from inorganic compounds. It does mean that organic materials are more complex than inorganic materials. As the organic molecules polymerize (form large chains), biomolecules are formed. These combine

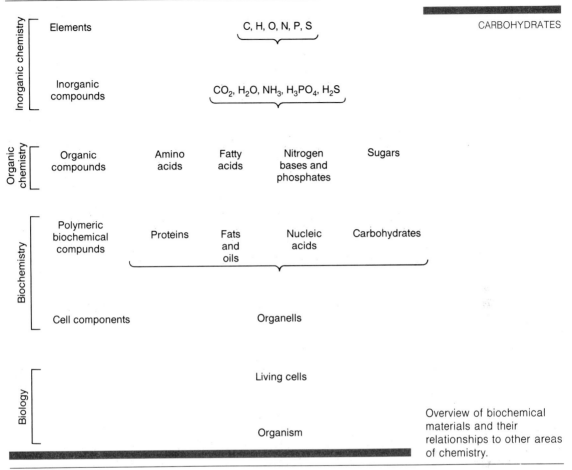

Overview of biochemical materials and their relationships to other areas of chemistry.

FIGURE 14-1

to form the components of cells. The cells form multicellular organisms. The classical areas of science that have traditionally studied each level are shown on the left in Figure 14-1.

Human nutritional needs

Human nutritional needs fall into six categories: **fats, carbohydrates, proteins, vitamins, minerals,** and **water**. Figure 14-2 shows the fate of these nutrients in the human body. Dietary fats are used to produce hormones, body fat, and energy, while almost all digestible carbohydrates are changed to glucose. The glucose is converted to energy or changed to body fat or glycogen if not needed for body functions. Nondigestible materials (fibers—mostly carbohydrate fibers) aid in the digestive process. Proteins in food are broken down into amino acids. Some of these are built back into body proteins for use in body tissues, including muscles and structural parts such as bones and tendons; other amino acids are changed to enzymes (catalysts needed for each biochemical process). Vitamins are or-

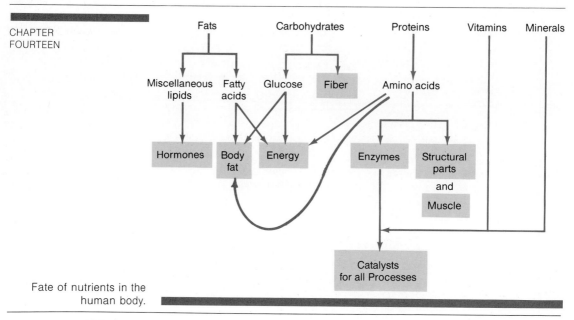

Fate of nutrients in the human body.

FIGURE 14-2

ganic materials needed in trace amounts, and minerals are inorganic ions also needed in small amounts (compared with the amounts of fats, carbohydrates, and proteins). Vitamins and minerals serve many functions, but frequently they are needed in order for enzymes to function. Their role is to activate the enzymes so that the various chemical processes that these enzymes catalyze can be maintained at the proper rate. Water is needed as a solvent or medium for the entire system and as a reactant in many chemical changes.

The living cell

Table 14-1 shows the approximate composition of a living cell. Different organs have cells that vary somewhat from these, but the composition of each cell is usually in the range given. The important point is that there are **several thousand different materials in each cell**. Proteins, for example, are all synthesized in the cell as needed in just the correct amounts for the functioning of that cell at a given moment. As we will see later, each protein is quite complex, and its synthesis requires many steps (50 to 100 in most cases). All proteins are produced synthetically in a minute or less. There are no unwanted by-products, and each reaction has a nearly 100 percent yield. This is nothing short of amazing.

Enzymes are proteins that serve as catalysts for **all** biochemical processes and greatly speed up these processes. Each of the steps in the synthesis of each biomolecule requires its own enzyme. Thus a large number of enzymes are required at a given time in the functioning of a living cell. Each enzyme must itself be synthesized before it can catalyze other syntheses.

This general overview of biochemistry should give us a sense of the extreme complexity involved. When we consider all the processes producing and using biomolecules in all cells of all organs in the human body, we must surely stand in awe. An appreciation for the wonder of life from a chemical point of view is certainly one goal of this section.

The goal of the biochemist is to **isolate all cell components** and determine the **molecular nature of each**, and also to **understand all processes** in which they are involved. There is much yet to be learned before this goal can be realized. We do not yet completely understand even **normal** biochemistry; the various disease states are usually understood even less well. Eventually, of course, we would hope not only to have a thorough understanding of the biochemistry of each system but also to know the chemical basis for malfunctions. This could lead to a rational approach to designing drugs or other remedies for each medical problem encountered. We are not even close to reaching this goal, nor is the prospect of realizing it in the near future very great.

Biochemistry is the chemistry of living systems. Biochemists study the molecular structures of biochemicals and attempt to understand the processes that take place in living cells. The four major classes of biochemicals are proteins, carbohydrates, lipids, and nucleic acids. Various combinations of these materials, along with the ever-present water, account for most of the material in the cells. All biochemical processes are catalyzed by enzymes. Biochemicals are complex materials, but they are made from a relatively few simpler materials. Because of the complexity of biochemical processes and molecular structures, we are just beginning to understand this vast field.

TABLE 14-1

TYPE OF MATERIAL	PERCENT BY WEIGHT	NUMBER OF KNOWN DIFFERENT MATERIALS OF THIS TYPE	BIOCHEMICAL COMPOSITION OF LIVING CELLS
Water	70–80	1	
Proteins	13–17	3000	
Nucleic acids	6–9	1000	
Carbohydrates	3–5	50	
Lipids	1–10	40	
Inorganic ions	1	10	
Miscellaneous	2	500	

SIMPLE SUGARS

All **carbohydrates** contain carbon atoms associated with the elements of water (hydrated carbon or "carbo-hydrates"). The most important member of this class, and the one most others are made from, is glucose, $C_6H_{12}O_6$. This formula could be written $C_6(H_2O)_6$, which illustrates the fact that for each carbon atom there are two hydrogen atoms and one oxygen atom. The structure of glucose is shown below.

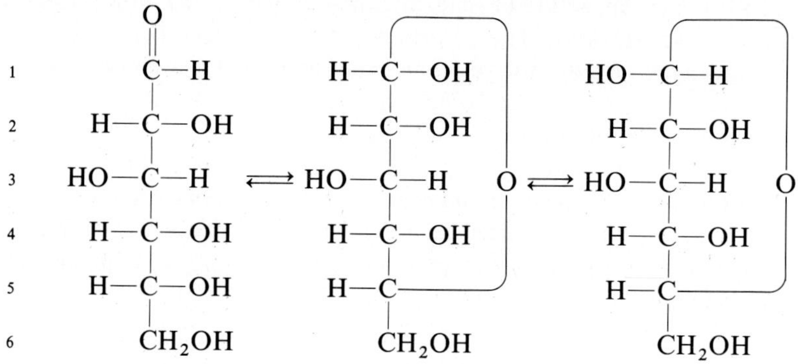

Open chain D-glucose   Cyclic α-D-glucose   Cyclic β-D-glucose

This method of showing a structure of glucose is known as a **Fischer formula**. It is an older and less accurate method than the one we will present shortly, but since it is still used, it is one with which you should become familiar. The first Fischer formula above (the one on the left) shows glucose as an open chain rather than as a cyclic structure. Actually, the open form of glucose exists only to the extent of about 1 percent, in equilibrium with the α- and β-cyclic forms in a water solution.

A newer and better representation of glucose is shown below. It is known as the **Haworth formula**.

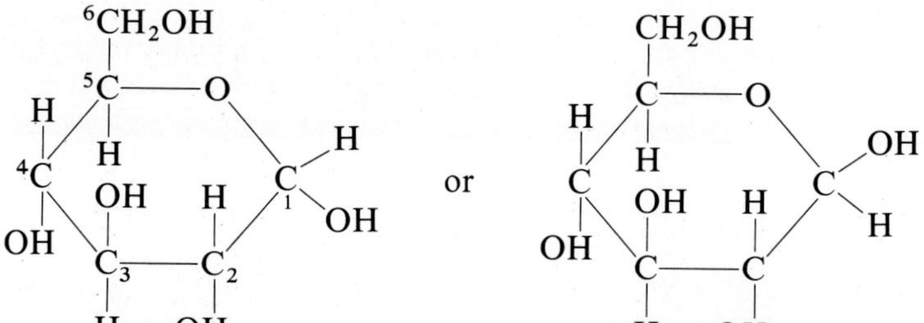

α-D-glucose   or   β-D-glucose

Haworth formulas

A stereo drawing indicates that the cyclic form of glucose has a conformation very similar to the chair form of cyclohexane. In this stereo drawing of the β isomer, notice that all groups larger than hydrogen are

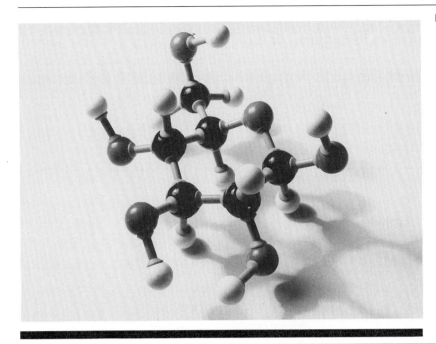

Molecular model of glucose.

FIGURE 14-3

in the equatorial positions. Figure 14-3 shows a molecular model of cyclic glucose in the β form.

Stereo drawing of β-D-glucose

The OH groups written to the right in Fischer formulas are written in a downward direction in the Haworth method. There are five chiral centers in cyclic glucose; this induces optical activity (see Chapter 4). Carbon atom number 1 is called the **anomeric carbon** and is the only one whose stereochemistry can vary in the three forms of glucose. The two cyclic forms (α and β) are referred to as **anomers** (special types of stereoisomers).

Simple sugars are designated D or L according to the stereochemistry at the highest-numbered chiral carbon atom which is called the reference carbon. Thus for glucose, carbon atom number 5 is used to indicate stereochemistry. If the —OH group on carbon atom number 5 is to the right in the Fischer open formula, it is the D-isomer; if the —OH is to the left, it is the L-isomer. Natural sugars are all of the D type, although they may rotate light in either direction depending on the configuration at the other chiral centers. Remember that the direction and magnitude of rotation of light by optically active materials must be determined experimentally—it cannot be predicted by examining molecular structure.

Glucose is called a **simple sugar** or **monosaccharide** because it is one of the building blocks for more complex carbohydrates. Other simple sugars are shown below using the Fischer (open chain and α-cyclic) and the Haworth formulas.

D-Fructose   (See Figure 14-4.)

D-Galactose

D-Ribose

D-Mannose

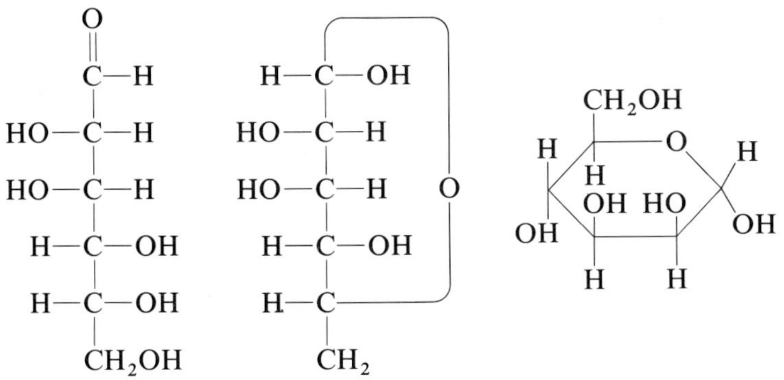

Notice that all these monosaccharides are **aldehydes** or **ketones**. Sugars are referred to in general terms according to whether they are aldehydes (aldoses) or ketones (ketoses), and according to the total number of carbons. A six-carbon sugar is a hexose, a five-carbon sugar is a pentose, etc. Putting these two references together, the term *aldopentose*, for example, means a five-carbon aldehyde sugar, like ribose, while fructose is referred to as a ketohexose.

Biochemists sometimes give simple sugars names that are more systematic or informative than are the common names we have listed so far. For example the α form of glucose is called α-D-($+$) glucopyranose. The various parts of this name have the following meanings:

α The OH at the anomeric carbon is **down** in the Haworth drawing.

D   The configuration at the reference carbon is the same as that in D-glyceraldehyde, i.e., *R*.

($+$)   This material rotates plane polarized light in a dextrorotatary or clockwise manner. (See Chapter 4.)

gluco   This is some form of glucose.

pyran   It is a cyclic ether with five carbons and an oxygen atom in the ring. 1,4-Pyran itself has the structure below.

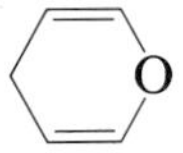

ose   sugars usually have this ending.

The complete names for the other cyclic sugars shown on page 446 are listed in the following table.

COMMON NAME	COMPLETE NAME
D-fructose	α-D(−) fructofuranose
D-galactose	α-(D) (+) galactopyranose
D-ribose	α-(D) (+) ribofuranose
D-mannose	α-(D) (+) mannopyranose

Furan is a ring of four carbons and one oxygen.

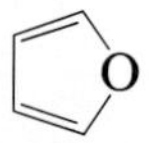

Furan

All these sugars are either aldehydes or ketones, and the cyclic forms are really the **hemiacetal** or **hemiketal** formed from the carbonyl group and the —OH group of the reference carbon atom. This is carbon atom number 5 in glucose, number 4 in ribose, etc. (See Chapter 8 for a review of hemiacetals and hemiketals.)

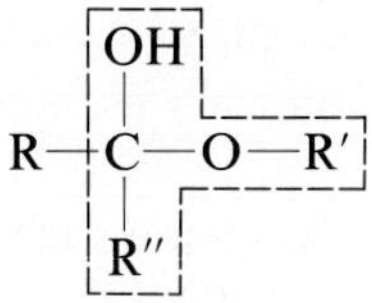

General formula
for a hemiketal

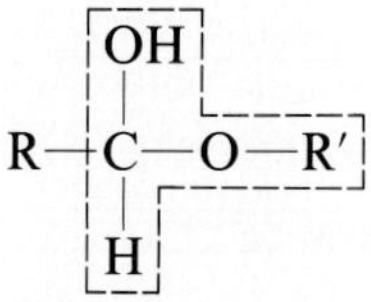

General formula
for a hemiacetal

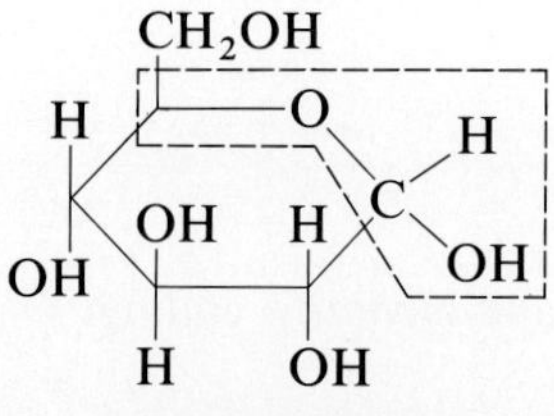

Cyclic glucose,
a hemiacetal

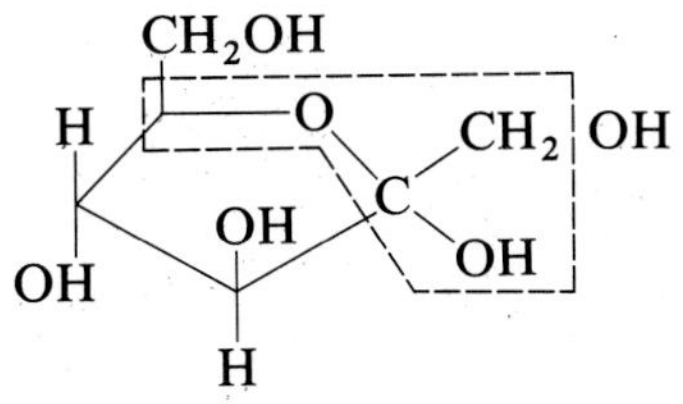

$$CH_2OH$$

Cyclic fructose,
a hemiketal

Simple sugars (monosaccharides) are polyhydroxy aldehydes or ketones which can exist in an open or two cyclic forms. They are optically active, and their stereochemistry is indicated by the name (glucose, mannose, etc.) and a D or L designation for the reference carbon atom. Molecular structure is shown by Fischer or Haworth formulas.

REACTIONS OF SIMPLE SUGARS

Oxidation

Those sugars that are aldehydes are easily oxidizable, as are all aldehydes. Ketoses isomerize in a basic medium to aldoses and thus also are readily oxidizable. Such carbohyrates are referred to as **reducing** sugars—all simple sugars are reducing sugars. The laboratory tests used to detect reducing sugars are **Fehling's test** and **Benedict's test**. Both use Cu^{2+} as the oxidizing reagent, and a positive test is shown by a Cu_2O precipitate, which is a red-yellow color.

In Benedict's test

$$Cu^{2+} + \text{reducing sugar} \xrightarrow[\text{ion}]{\text{citrate}} \text{oxidized sugar} + Cu_2O\downarrow$$
Clear blue   Cloudy red-yellow

In Fehling's test

$$Cu^{2+} + \text{reducing sugar} \xrightarrow[\text{ion}]{\text{tartrate}} \text{oxidized sugar} + Cu_2O\downarrow$$
Clear blue   Cloudy red-yellow

When heated, reducing sugars give a color change from blue to red-yellow with these tests, while nonreducing sugars remain blue. The reducing sugars are themselves oxidized—the aldehyde functional group is converted to the corresponding carboxylic acid salt, as shown below for glucose.

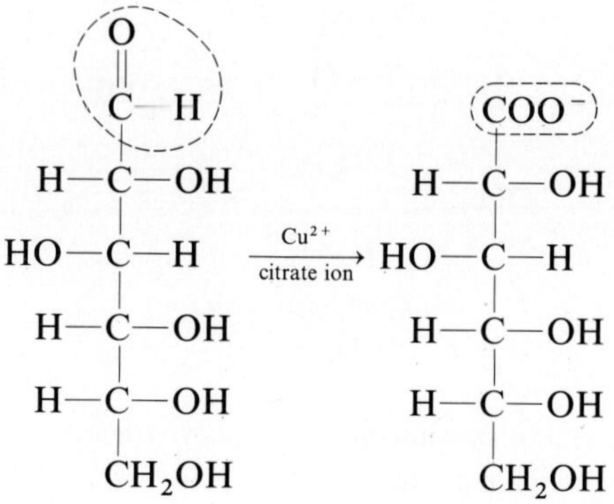

$$
\begin{array}{ccc}
\overset{O}{\underset{\displaystyle \|}{}} & & \\
C-H & & COO^- \\
H-C-OH & & H-C-OH \\
HO-C-H & \xrightarrow[\text{citrate ion}]{Cu^{2+}} & HO-C-H \\
H-C-OH & & H-C-OH \\
H-C-OH & & H-C-OH \\
CH_2OH & & CH_2OH
\end{array}
$$

D-Glucose   D-Gluconate ion

A sugar is classified as a reducing sugar if it is an aldehyde even if it is found primarily in the cyclic hemiacetal form. This is because of the small amount of the open chain aldehyde form in equilibrium with the cyclic form. Disaccharides (see later in this chapter) are also classified as reducing or nonreducing based on the nature of the free anomeric carbon. Sucrose (a disaccharide) is the only common sugar that is a nonreducing sugar.

Reduction—sugar alcohols

The aldehyde or ketone groups of sugars can be reduced to alcohol groups by catalytic hydrogenation or $NaBH_4$ reduction. This reduction gives a product containing an —OH group on each carbon. The commercial treatment of glucose in this manner yields sorbitol, a nonmetabolizable compound used in "diet" (or "sugarless") candies and chewing gums.

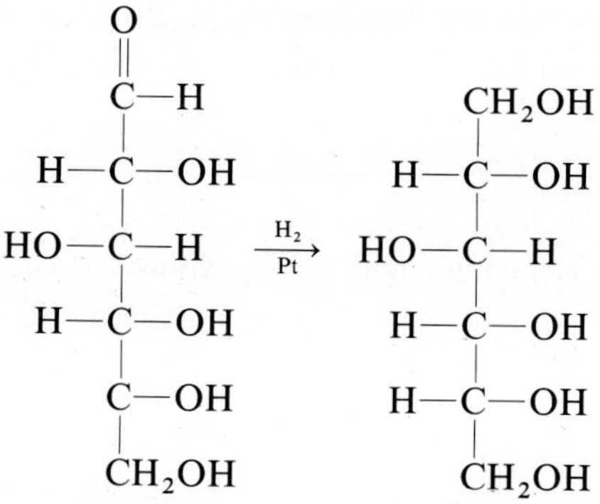

$$
\begin{array}{ccc}
\overset{O}{\underset{\displaystyle \|}{}} & & \\
C-H & & CH_2OH \\
H-C-OH & & H-C-OH \\
HO-C-H & \xrightarrow[\text{Pt}]{H_2} & HO-C-H \\
H-C-OH & & H-C-OH \\
C-OH & & H-C-OH \\
CH_2OH & & CH_2OH
\end{array}
$$

D-Glucose   D-Sorbitol
(open form)   (also called glucitol)

Mutarotation

We have already seen that glucose exists in open, α-cyclic, and β-cyclic forms. All forms are in equilibrium in water solution, but the cyclic forms can be isolated and stored as dry crystals. The equilibrium proportions, along with physical data on each form, are shown below.

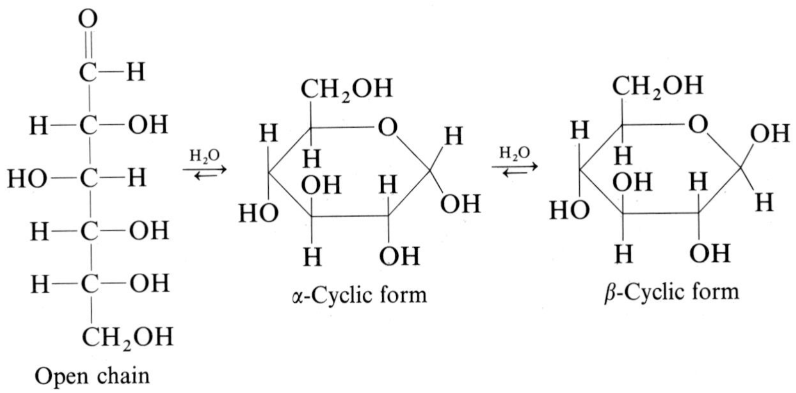

α-Cyclic form   β-Cyclic form

Open chain

When either cyclic form is placed in water, it gradually equilibrates to the 1:36:63 ratio, which has a specific rotation ($[\alpha]_D^{20}$) of $+52.5°$. A solution of either form will gradually attain a rotation value of $+52.5°$, the value for the equilibrium mixture. This process is called **mutarotation** and is observed for other sugars as well.

FORM OF GLUCOSE	EQUILIBRIUM PROPORTION	MELTING POINT	SPECIFIC ROTATION,* $[\alpha]_D^{20}$
Open chain	1%		
α-Cyclic*	36%	146°C	+113°
β-Cyclic	63%	150°C	+19.7°

* There is no connection between the symbol α used to designate stereochemistry at the anomeric carbon and the α which stands for specific rotation

Monosaccharides can be oxidized at the aldehyde functional group; they therefore are called reducing sugars. The open and cyclic forms of sugars interconvert in water solution and reach an equilibrium mixture. This process is called mutarotation. The aldehyde functional groups of sugars can also be reduced to produce sugar alcohols.

SYNTHESIS OF SUGARS

All sugars can be synthesized in the laboratory by using glyceraldehyde as the starting material. One method for accomplishing this is called the **Kiliani-Fischer synthesis**; it was used by Emil Fischer, a pioneer in the field of sugar chemistry. The reaction sequence is shown below. After this sequence is completed, a mixture of two diastereomers is produced. This mixture can be separated to obtain the two new sugars in pure form. Each of these new diastereomers can be used, in turn, to produce two new sugars by the Kiliani-Fischer sequence.

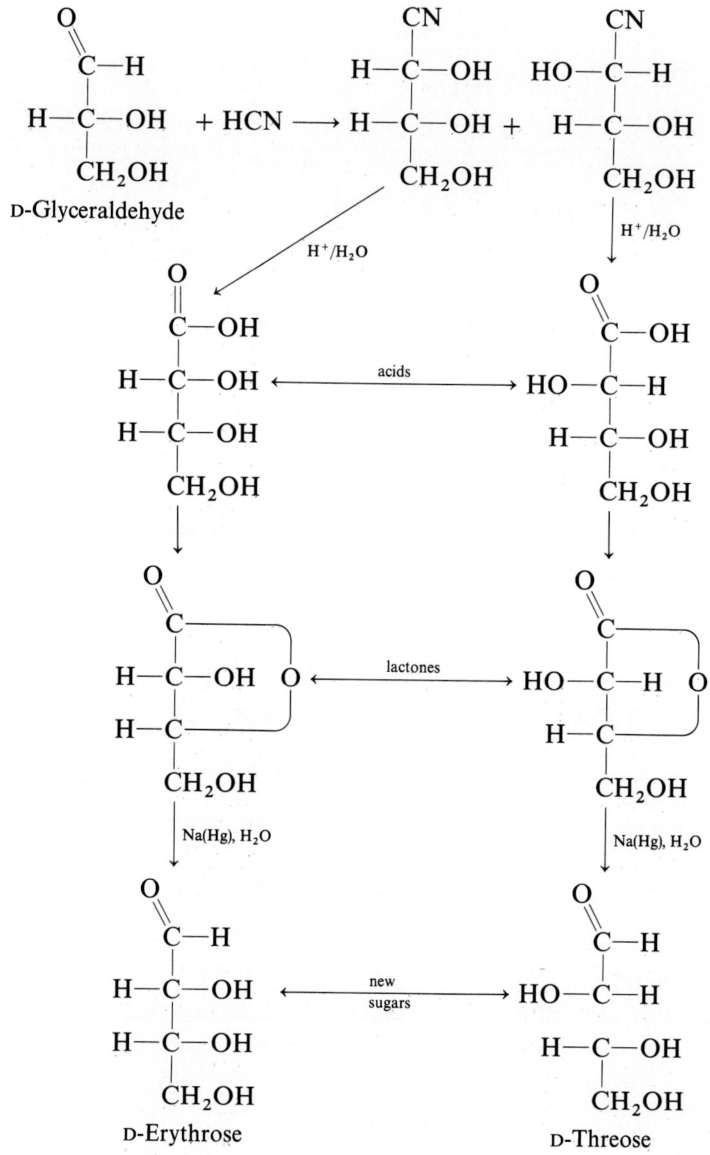

$$
\begin{array}{c}
\underset{\text{D-Glyceraldehyde}}{\overset{\displaystyle \overset{O}{\|}}{\underset{\displaystyle}{}} }
\end{array}
$$

O=C—H
H—C—OH + HCN ⟶
CH₂OH
D-Glyceraldehyde

CN	CN
H—C—OH	HO—C—H
H—C—OH +	H—C—OH
CH₂OH	CH₂OH

H⁺/H₂O   H⁺/H₂O

O=C—OH
H—C—OH ←— acids —→ HO—C—H
H—C—OH   H—C—OH
CH₂OH   CH₂OH

O=C
H—C—OH   O ←— lactones —→ HO—C—H   O
H—C—   H—C—
CH₂OH   CH₂OH

Na(Hg), H₂O   Na(Hg), H₂O

O=C—H
H—C—OH ←— new sugars —→ HO—C—H
H—C—OH   H—C—OH
CH₂OH   CH₂OH
D-Erythrose   D-Threose

This sequence involves the addition of CN⁻ to aldehydes to produce the nitrile, which is also called a cyanohydrin (see Chapter 8). The nitrile is hydrolyzed to the corresponding carboxylic acid. This acid spontaneously reacts with one of its own —OH groups to form a cyclic ester commonly called a **lactone**. The lactone is reduced with sodium amalgam, Na(Hg), in water to the aldehyde. The result is two four-carbon sugars called **threose** and **erythrose** which, since they are diastereomers, can be separated.

This sequence can be repeated on the threose and erythrose to produce two five-carbon sugars from each. It can be repeated again to produce

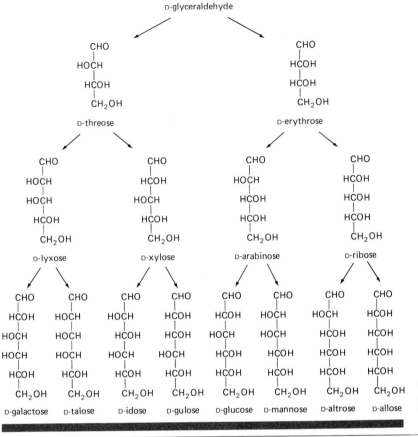

Sugars produced by three successive Kiliani-Fischer treatments of D-glyceraldehyde.

FIGURE 14-5

eight more sugars. Figure 14-5 shows the sugars that can be produced in this way. They include all possible D-aldoses.

All simple sugars can be synthesized in the laboratory by the Kiliani-Fischer sequence. Each sequence produces two diastereomeric sugars, each with one more carbon atom than the starting sugar. These new sugars can be separated physically and each subjected again to the Kiliani-Fischer sequence to produce two more diastereomeric sugars with still one more carbon atom.

DISACCHARIDES

Disaccharides are carbohydrates, the molecules of which are composed of **two** simple sugar units bonded together. Disaccharides can be hydrolyzed back to their simple sugar components. Two glucose units may link together as shown below.

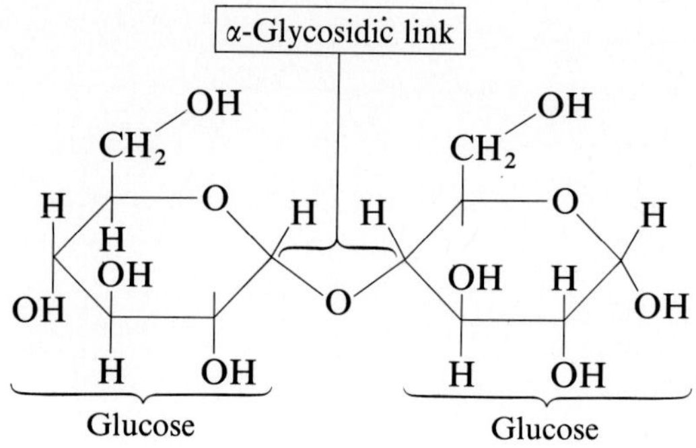

Maltose

The oxygen link (actually an ether or acetal) is called a **glycosidic link** and can have two forms. The form shown above is called an **α-glycosidic link** because the —OH group of carbon atom number 1 in the left glucose was pointing **down** before it formed the glycosidic link in maltose.

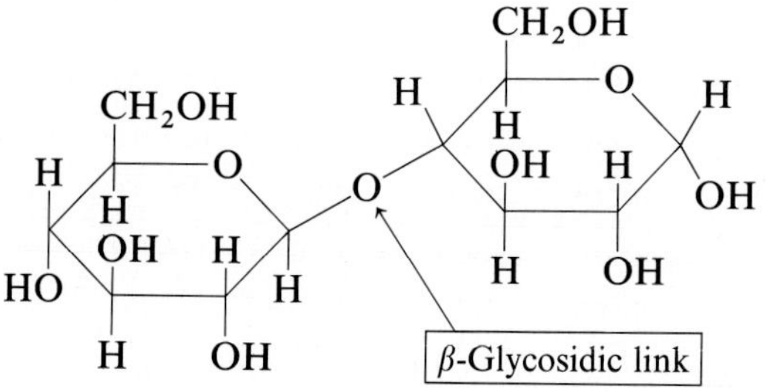

Cellobiose

Another way in which glucose units can link together is called a **β-glycosidic bond** and is shown above. This kind of bond is designated as **beta**, because the —OH group of the anomeric carbon atom in the left glucose unit is in the **beta (up)** position. The compound formed when two glucose molecules are linked together by an **alpha** link is called **maltose**, while the beta-linking of two glucose units produces **cellobiose**. Both of these compounds are disaccharides. Other important members of this class are **lactose** (milk sugar), which constitutes 5 to 8 percent of whole milk, and **sucrose**, which is common table sugar, commercially extracted from sugar cane and sugar beets. The structures of lactose and sucrose are shown below; sucrose is shown in Figure 14-6. You will notice that sucrose can be hydrolyzed into glucose and fructose, while lactose is composed of glucose and galactose units.

Ordinary table sugar is the disaccharide sucrose.

FIGURE 14-6

Glycosidic links are further classified according to the carbon atoms in the two monosaccharides that are linked by the glycosidic bond. In maltose, the α link is between carbon number 1 of the left glucose and carbon number 4 of the right glucose; it is thus called an $\alpha(1 \rightarrow 4)$ glucosidic link. The arrow ($\rightarrow$) points from the anomeric carbon number (whose molecule is written on the left) to the nonanomeric carbon number. Alternatively, this type of bond can be simply designated as an α-1,4-glycosidic bond (with the arrow omitted).

Maltose is a reducing sugar because the anomeric carbon atom of the right-hand glucose part can exist in the open chain (aldehyde) form as well as in the β-cyclic form. The left-hand glucose unit cannot open, however, since its anomeric oxygen atom is bound to another carbon atom by the glycosidic link. This prevents equilibration to the open chain or β-cyclic form.

Disaccharides are carbohydrate molecules composed of two monosaccharides linked by a glycosidic bond. This bond can be of the alpha (α) or beta (β) type, depending on the stereochemistry at the anomeric carbon atom(s) involved in this link.

POLYSACCHARIDES

Polysaccharides are polymeric carbohydrates that contain many monosaccharide units linked by glycosidic bonds. The more common polysaccharides (complex carbohydrates) are polymers of glucose. Starch, which is produced in plants, is composed of two materials, amylose and amylopectin. Amylose is composed of very long molecules made from glucose units connected by $\alpha(1 \rightarrow 4)$ links. Amylopectin, the other component of starch, is branched polyglucose (see Figure 14-7). Glycogen, which is found in animals, is a highly branched polyglucose connected by $\alpha(1 \rightarrow 4)$ links and is used to store a small amount of energy in the liver and muscle for quick release when needed. Notice that the branches in glycogen and amylopectin are connected to the main polymer chain by a glycosidic bond. This bond is between carbon atom number 1 of the first glucose unit in the branch and carbon atom number 6 of the glucose unit in the main chain. These bonds are called $(1 \rightarrow 6)$ glycosidic bonds. Cellulose (see Figures 14-7 and 14-8), which is the main component of the structural parts of plants, is linear polyglucose connected by $\beta(1 \rightarrow 4)$ links.

Digestion of starch takes place as follows. An enzyme in human saliva (salivary amylase) is able to break some of the α-glucosidic links in starch to produce dextrin, a polyglucose with a much smaller molecular weight. In the small intestine, pancreatic amylase (another enzyme) catalyzes the breakdown of dextrin to maltose. Other enzymes change maltose and dietary disaccharides (sucrose, etc.) into monosaccharides prior to their absorption into the blood stream. The β links of cellulose, on the other hand, cannot be broken by human enzymes, and thus cellulose passes

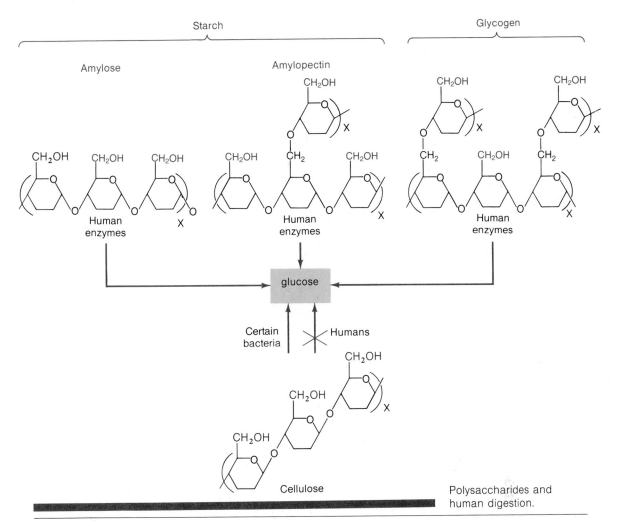

Polysaccharides and human digestion.

FIGURE 14-7

through the body undigested and constitutes what is commonly called **fiber** or **roughage**—an important part of a well-balanced diet.

Enzymes found in the bacteria that live in the digestive systems of termites and ruminants (such as cattle) are able to break the β links in cellulose. This is why termites can digest wood and ruminants can digest hay or straw—the cellulose in wood and hay is converted to glucose just as starch is converted to glucose in human beings. This illustrates the extreme specificity of most enzymes. The very small difference between the molecular structures of cellulose and starch (a β versus an α linkage) completely changes the ability of an enzyme to cleave them. It should be pointed out, however, that human enzymes **can** cleave the β links in lactose (milk sugar). However, not all people have the enzyme necessary for hydrolyzing lactose; some are born without it and some lose the ability to produce this enzyme on reaching adulthood. These processes are summarized

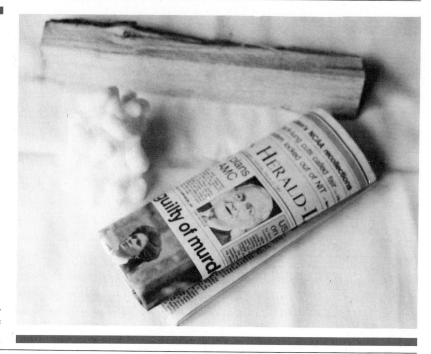

Wood, cotton, and paper
are common forms of
cellulose.

FIGURE 14-8

in Figure 14-7. Some complex carbohydrate materials such as pectin (found in fruits) have units other than glucose present.

Some of the physical and chemical behavior of biochemicals can be attributed to **hydrogen bonding**—one of the most important intramolecular forces between biomolecules. The structural integrity of wood, for example, can be attributed to hydrogen bonding between the adjacent cellulose strands. Wood is normally fairly rigid, but it can be bent if water and heat (steam) are applied.

Under conditions of wet heat, some of the OH groups of wood cellulose form external hydrogen bonds with water molecules rather than with another cellulose molecule. This reduces the intermolecular attraction and, thus, decreases the rigidity of the wood. This allows for shaping of the wood for chair backs, curved table aprons, etc. This is the same phenomenon that occurs when wood is treated with liquid ammonia (NH_3). In the latter case, the wood becomes very flexible (like a piece of rubber) and can be bent into any shape. In either of these cases, after evaporation of NH_3 or the drying of the H_2O and cooling, the wood retains its new shape because new hydrogen bonds are formed between cellulose molecules.

Polysaccharides (complex carbohydrates) are biomolecules composed of many simple sugar units linked via glucosidic bonds. The α or β nature of these bonds determines the chemical behavior of polysaccharides in the digestive systems of various organisms. In addition to the 1 → 4 glycosidic links, some complex carbohydrates have branching via 1 → 6 links as well.

CHAPTER SUMMARY

1 **Biochemistry** is the study of the molecules and processes occurring in living systems.

2 The classes of biomolecules are **carbohydrates**, **proteins**, **lipids**, and **nucleic acids**. All biochemical processes are catalyzed by **enzymes**.

3 Simple sugars (**monosaccharides**) are chiral, polyhydroxy aldehydes or ketones which can exist in an open chain and in two cyclic forms. The two cyclic forms are called **anomers**.

4 **Disaccharides** are carbohydrates composed of two simple sugars linked by an etherlike glycosidic bond of either the α or β type.

5 **Polysaccharides** are composed of many monosaccharide units (usually glucose units). They are used for energy storage in plants in the form of starch and in animals in the form of glycogen. They are also used for the structural components of plants (as cellulose).

KEY TERMS

Anomeric carbon atoms	Fischer formula	Monosaccharide
Anomers	Furan	Mutarotation
Benedict's test	Glycosidic link	Pyran
Disaccharide	Haworth formula	Reducing sugar
Fehling's test	Kiliani-Fischer synthesis	Reference carbon atom
Fiber	Lactone	

SKILL PRACTICE PROBLEMS

1 Which of the sugars shown on page 446 are reducing sugars?

2 Is a reducing sugar one that will cause you to lose weight?

3 What is the product of D-ribose and Fehling's solution?

4 D-deoxyribose is D-ribose without an —OH group on carbon number 2. Draw its structure.

5 Draw the β anomer of D-galactose.

6 What is the structure of the product of $NaBH_4$ reduction of D-mannose?

7 Can sugar molecules be meso and thus not rotate polarized light? If not, why not? If so, give an example.

8 Draw the structure of the disaccharide that would result from a β-1,4-glycosidic link between two D-mannose molecules. Use Haworth formulas.

9 If starch and cellulose are hydrolyzed completely to simple sugars, will there be any difference in the sugar(s) obtained from the two polysaccharides?

10 Figure 14-5 shows eight D-aldohexoses. If they all exist in cyclic form, how many cyclic D-aldohexoses exist?

11 Define the following terms:
    (a) Glycosidic link   (b) Mutarotation
    (c) Anomers   (d) Fiber
    (e) Ketopentose   (f) Pyranose
    (g) Polysaccharide

12 Classify the glycosidic links in lactose and cellobiose according to the $\alpha(1 \rightarrow 4)$ type of designation used for maltose.

13 Classify lactose and sucrose as reducing or nonreducing.

14 From what you know about ring stabilities from Chapter 3, can you suggest a reason for the fact that the β-cyclic form constitutes 63 percent of glucose at equilibrium? (Why is the beta form more stable?)

15 Draw the structure of the disaccharide composed of two galactose units connected by a $\beta(1 \rightarrow 4)$ glycosidic link.

16 Draw the Haworth structure of β-D-$(-)$-ribofuranose.

DIETARY ASPECTS OF CARBOHYDRATES

We are constantly bombarded with claims by people with medical or other scientific training that a given type of diet is particularly harmful, or helpful, as the case may be. Some of these claims are difficult to evaluate, since gathering solid scientific data is very difficult. Each person's diet is complex, and isolating the effect of only one component is virtually impossible. For example, what are the long term effects of drinking coffee? Some people who drink coffee do so with doughnuts, others with scrambled eggs and toast. Some have watermelon for dessert after the coffee while others eat chocolate cake. These other components of the diet probably change the effects of the coffee itself. To isolate the effects of coffee, it would be necessary to feed two large groups of people who have similar heredities identical diets (except for coffee) over a **long period of time**. One group would get coffee, and the other group would not. This is, practically speaking, impossible, and thus a firm conclusion is elusive.

In this unit, we will discuss three aspects of carbohydrates in the human diet.

REFINED CARBOHYDRATES

One such aspect is the claim that refined carbohydrates such as white flour and table sugar are responsible for many health problems. The claim has been made that ordinary table sugar (refined sugar) greatly reduces muscular strength. Such statements are usually to the effect that a few grains placed in the mouth will cause a strong person to lose most of his or her strength. These are **not** the results obtained when this experiment is tried by objective investigators, and these statements should not be taken as fact. Nothing is added to crude (or natural) sugar during the refinery process; all that happens is that substances other than sucrose are removed. It is unlikely that removing such "impurities" causes refined sugar to become harmful. It is true that large excesses of sugar may cause a dietary imbalance, and it is also true that the average American consumes about 100 pounds of sugar annually. We as a group **do** overconsume sweets, and each person should be aware of this trend, but it is **doubtful** that relatively small amounts of sucrose are harmful. It is probably true that an unbalanced diet rich in carbohydrates and very low (or lacking) in fats and proteins causes docility and lethargy in addition to other nutritional problems.

Use of carbohydrates as sweeteners

Sugars are used for sweetening, but not all sugars are equally sweet. Table H-1 gives the relative sweetness of several sugars and some artificial

TABLE H-1

<table>
<tr><td>SWEETNESS OF
CARBOHYDRATES AND
SYNTHETIC SWEETENERS</td><td>SUGAR</td><td>RELATIVE SWEETNESS
NUMBER*</td><td>DESCRIPTION</td></tr>
<tr><td></td><td>Monosaccharides</td><td></td><td></td></tr>
<tr><td></td><td>Glucose</td><td>69</td><td>Sweet</td></tr>
<tr><td></td><td>Galactose</td><td>63</td><td>Sweet</td></tr>
<tr><td></td><td>Fructose</td><td>120</td><td>Very sweet</td></tr>
<tr><td></td><td>Disaccharides</td><td></td><td></td></tr>
<tr><td></td><td>Sucrose</td><td>100</td><td>Very sweet</td></tr>
<tr><td></td><td>Maltose</td><td>46</td><td>Slightly sweet</td></tr>
<tr><td></td><td>Lactose</td><td>39</td><td>Slightly sweet</td></tr>
<tr><td></td><td>Polysaccharide</td><td></td><td></td></tr>
<tr><td></td><td>Starch</td><td>0</td><td>Not sweet</td></tr>
<tr><td></td><td>Artificial sweeteners</td><td></td><td></td></tr>
<tr><td></td><td>Saccharin</td><td>300</td><td>Extremely sweet</td></tr>
<tr><td></td><td>Aspartame</td><td>200</td><td>Extremely sweet</td></tr>
<tr><td></td><td>Acesulfame</td><td>10,000</td><td>Extremely sweet</td></tr>
<tr><td></td><td>Thaumatin</td><td>200,000</td><td>Extremely sweet</td></tr>
</table>

* For equal weights

TABLE H-2

<table>
<tr><td>SUGARS PRESENT IN
SELECTED SWEETENERS</td><td>SOURCE</td><td>TYPE OF SUGAR</td></tr>
<tr><td></td><td>Table sugar</td><td>Sucrose</td></tr>
<tr><td></td><td>Honey</td><td>Fructose</td></tr>
<tr><td></td><td>Fruit</td><td>Fructose</td></tr>
<tr><td></td><td>Maple syrup</td><td>Sucrose</td></tr>
<tr><td></td><td>Corn syrup</td><td>Glucose, maltose,
higher oligosaccharides</td></tr>
<tr><td></td><td>Molasses</td><td>Sucrose</td></tr>
<tr><td></td><td>Sugar beets</td><td>Sucrose</td></tr>
</table>

sweeteners. Table H-2 shows which sugar is the primary component of selected common sources of sweeteners.

ARTIFICIAL SWEETENERS

Several compounds are useful as artificial sweeteners in products for people who must not consume sugar, either because they are trying to reduce their calorie intake or because they have other health problems. **Saccharin** has been used for a long time in this capacity.

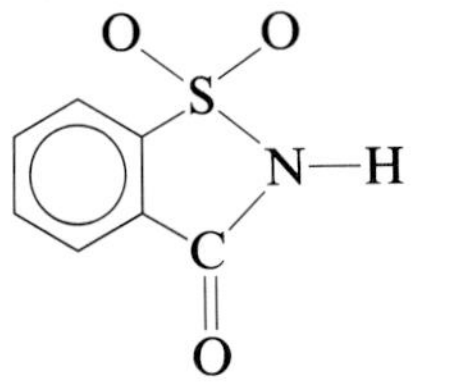

$$
\underset{\text{Saccharin}}{
\begin{array}{c}
\text{O} \quad \text{O} \\
\diagdown \text{S} \diagup \\
\\
\text{N—H} \\
\text{C} \\
\parallel \\
\text{O}
\end{array}}
$$

Saccharin

However, Saccharin has several disadvantages. It leaves a bitter aftertaste; it does not taste exactly like sugar; and it is weakly carcinogenic.

Cyclamates were previously used as sweeteners but now are banned. Calcium cyclamate is shown below.

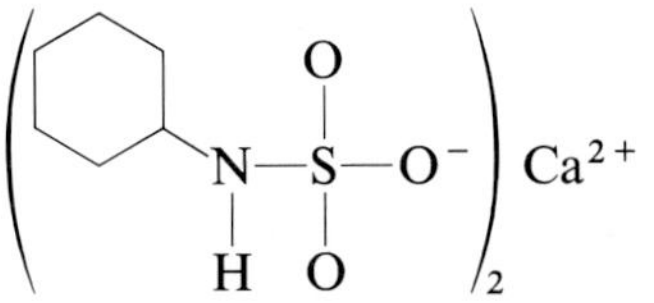

$$
\left(
\begin{array}{c}
\text{O} \\
\parallel \\
\text{N—S—O}^- \\
\mid \quad \mid \\
\text{H} \quad \text{O}
\end{array}
\right)_2 \text{Ca}^{2+}
$$

Calcium cyclamate

The only nonsugar sweetener besides saccharin now approved by the U.S. Food and Drug Administration is **aspartame**. Its structure is shown below.

$$
\begin{array}{c}
\quad\quad \text{O} \quad \text{H} \quad\quad \text{O} \\
\quad\quad \parallel \quad \mid \quad\quad \parallel \\
\text{H}_2\text{N—CH—C—N—C—C—O—CH}_3 \\
\quad\quad \mid \quad\quad\quad\quad \mid \\
\quad\quad \text{CH}_2 \quad\quad\quad \text{CH}_2 \\
\quad\quad \mid \\
\quad\quad \text{COOH}
\end{array}
$$

Aspartic acod

Phenylalanine

Methyl ester

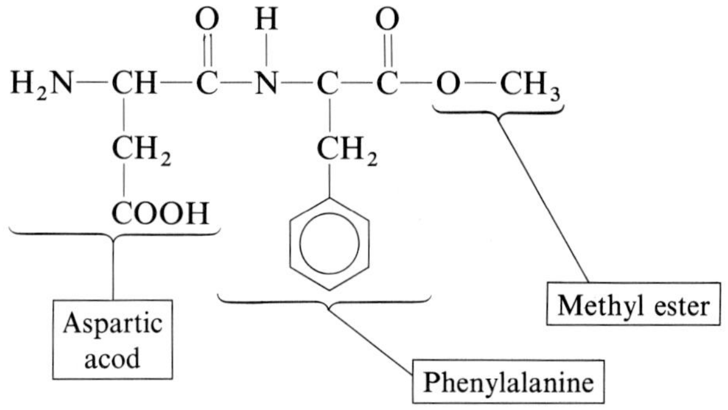

Aspartame
(trade-named Nutrasweet)

As can be seen, aspartame is composed of an aspartic acid moiety along with the methyl ester of phenylalanine. A dilute solution of this material is sweeter than sucrose (table sugar)—up to two times as sweet . Since aspartame is composed of two natural **amino acids**, it is not surprising that tests have shown no medical problems, and it is presumed to be completely safe. Amino acids are discussed in Chapter 17.

Another material, **acesulfame** (as the potassium salt), is expected to be marketed soon. Its structure is shown below.

Acesulfame-K

Acesulfame is over 100 times as sweet as sucrose, and tests have shown this unusual molecule to be safe for human consumption.

A protein called **thaumatin** (Talin), isolated from an African plant, is several thousand times as sweet as sugar; it has a complex molecular structure with 20 amino acids. Its applications and safety are currently being evaluated in several countries, and it is actually in use in some places.

It is not known why substances such as these are sweet. Most of them do not have similar structures, and indeed some materials with structures similar to those that are sweet are not sweet at all.

Another approach to "artificial" sweetening is **sorbitol**.

Sorbitol

Sorbitol is made from glucose, but it cannot be broken down by bacteria to cause tooth decay, nor can it pass through cell walls. Because it cannot get into the cells, it cannot be metabolized; therefore, it does not contribute to the caloric value of foods (such as "diet candy") in which it is used.

DIETARY FIBER

It is generally recognized that a high fiber diet is beneficial to most people. Fiber is composed of the nondigestible carbohydrate **cellulose**, which, when eaten, makes the stomach feel full and aids in the proper movement of food through the intestines. It also helps to prevent colon cancer. Table H-3 shows the approximate fiber content of some foods. Wheat products are

FOOD	FIBER (CELLULOSE), PERCENT	PERCENT FIBER IN SELECTED FOODS
Bran	50	
Whole wheat flour	10	
White flour	3	
Peas	8	
Carrots	4	
Apples	1.5	
Wheat flake cereal (Wheaties)	7	
Oatmeal	1.5	
Bran cereal (40 percent bran flakes)	10–18	

the only source of large amounts of fiber, while vegetables provide an important but less concentrated source. Cooking does not destroy fiber. Cooked carrots and raw carrots both contain about 4 percent fiber. The softer feel of the cooked product is due to a breakdown of the integrity of the cell structure—not the breaking of the β-glucosidic links in the cellulose. Thus, the fact that food is "hard" or "crunchy" is not indicative of a high fiber content.

CHAPTER 15

AMINO ACIDS AND PROTEINS

LEARNING GOALS

1 To understand the molecular structure and chemical behavior of amino acids

2 To understand the acid-base properties of amino acids

3 To understand the various aspects of protein structure and the relationship between structure and function

4 To understand the nature and importance of enzymes

5 To understand some experimental methods used by biochemists for analysis of proteins and amino acids

Proteins constitute one of the most important classes of biomolecules. Muscle, skin, hair, nails, and connective tissue are all composed principally of proteins. Enzymes, which catalyze **all** biochemical processes, are proteins also. In addition, protein portions of cell membranes help control what substances pass in and out of the cell, and some hormones (regulators) are protein in nature.

Proteins are complex polymeric materials composed of monomeric building blocks called **amino acids**. In this chapter we will examine the structure and chemistry of amino acids, and will study the way in which amino acids are combined to produce proteins. We will also see how the structure of a protein molecule allows it to serve a particular function or behave in a certain way in the cell.

AMINO ACID

Amino acid molecules contain both the **carboxylic acid** (COOH) group and the **amino** (NH_2) group. The general formula is

where R stands for any one of 20 different groups. All amino acids except proline have the portion **outside** the box in common and differ only in the nature of the R group. Table 15-1 gives information about the 20 amino acids that occur in proteins. There are several others found in biosystems, but they are not used to produce proteins.[1] Notice that each one has a standard abbreviation.

You will notice that in glycine, which is the simplest amino acid, the R group is an atom of hydrogen, while alanine has a methyl group at that location. Each amino acid has an R group with a different **size**, **shape**, **polarity** (some are polar and some are not), and **chemistry** (some have an alcohol group, some have an acid group, some have an aromatic portion). It is these factors (size, shape, polarity, and chemistry) that allow different amino acids to function in various ways and determine the shape and function of the proteins containing them. The human body can synthesize all but 8 of the 20 amino acids from other amino acids. These 8, listed in

---

[1] Several other amino acids, such as cystine and hydroxyproline, are formed from these 20 once they have been incorporated into the protein molecule. Only 20 amino acids are used by the body to produce proteins, however.

TABLE 15-1

AMINO ACIDS

NAME	STANDARD SYMBOL	FORMULA*
Alanine	Ala	$H_3C-\underset{\underset{NH_2}{|}}{\overset{\overset{H}{|}}{C}}-C\overset{O}{\underset{OH}{}}$
Arginine	Arg	$\underset{HN}{\overset{H_2N}{}}C-NH-CH_2-CH_2-CH_2-\underset{\underset{NH_2}{|}}{\overset{\overset{H}{|}}{C}}-C\overset{O}{\underset{OH}{}}$
Asparagine	Asn	$\underset{H_2N}{\overset{O}{}}C-CH_2-\underset{\underset{NH_2}{|}}{\overset{\overset{H}{|}}{C}}-C\overset{O}{\underset{OH}{}}$
Aspartic acid	Asp	$\underset{HO}{\overset{O}{}}C-CH_2-\underset{\underset{NH_2}{|}}{\overset{\overset{H}{|}}{C}}-C\overset{O}{\underset{OH}{}}$
Cysteine	Cys	$HS-CH_2-\underset{\underset{NH_2}{|}}{\overset{\overset{H}{|}}{C}}-C\overset{O}{\underset{OH}{}}$
Glutamic acid	Glu	$\underset{HO}{\overset{O}{}}C-CH_2-CH_2-\underset{\underset{NH_2}{|}}{\overset{\overset{H}{|}}{C}}-C\overset{O}{\underset{OH}{}}$
Glycine	Gly	$H-\underset{\underset{NH_2}{|}}{\overset{\overset{H}{|}}{C}}-C\overset{O}{\underset{OH}{}}$
Glutamine	Gln	$\underset{H_2N}{\overset{O}{}}C-CH_2-CH_2-\underset{\underset{NH_2}{|}}{\overset{\overset{H}{|}}{C}}-C\overset{O}{\underset{OH}{}}$
Histidine	His	imidazole-$CH_2-\underset{\underset{NH_2}{|}}{\overset{\overset{H}{|}}{C}}-C\overset{O}{\underset{OH}{}}$
Isoleucine	Ile	$H_3C-CH_2-\underset{}{\overset{\overset{CH_3}{|}}{CH}}-\underset{\underset{NH_2}{|}}{\overset{\overset{H}{|}}{C}}-C\overset{O}{\underset{OH}{}}$

(Continued)

TABLE 15-1

Continued

NAME	STANDARD SYMBOL	FORMULA*
Leucine	Leu	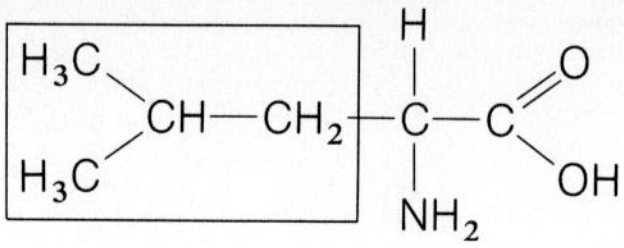
Lysine	Lys	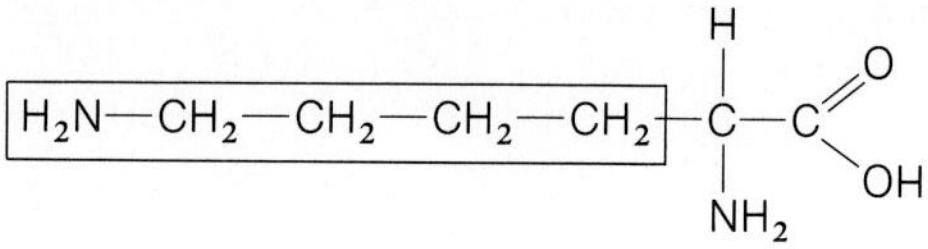
Methionine	Met	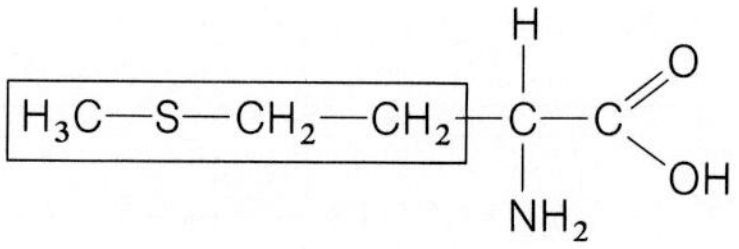
Phenylalanine	Phe	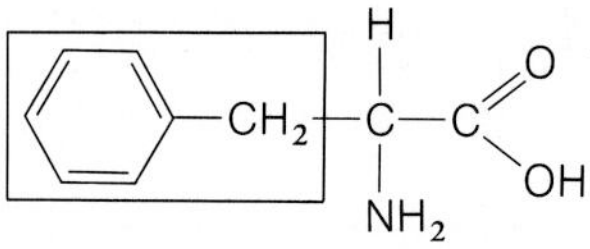
Proline	Pro	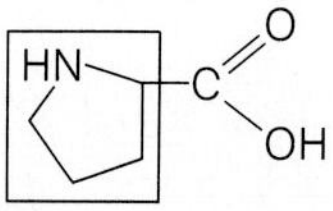
Serine	Ser	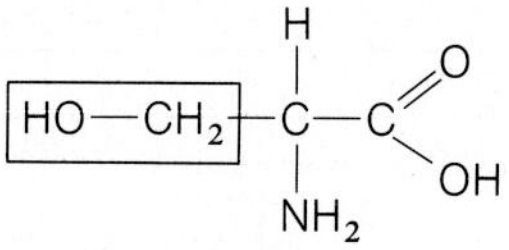
Threonine	Thr	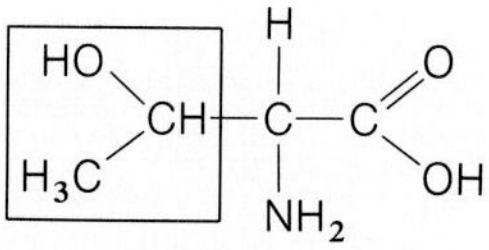
Tryptophan	Trp	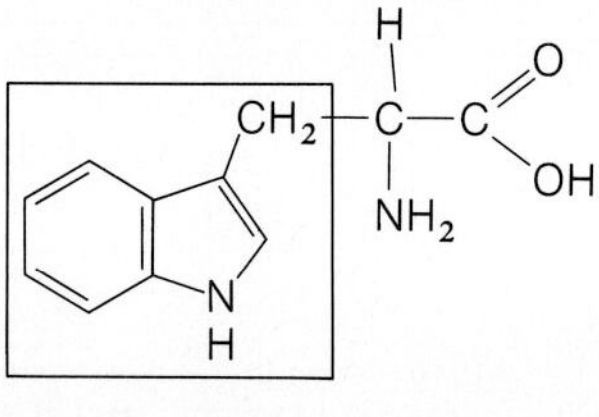
Tyrosine	Tyr	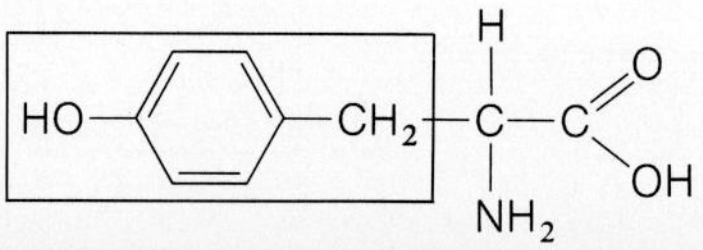

(Continued)

TABLE 15-1

NAME	STANDARD SYMBOL	FORMULA*	
			Continued
Valine	Val	$\begin{array}{c} H_3C \\ \diagup \\ CH-C-C \\ \diagdown \quad | \quad \diagdown \\ H_3C \quad NH_2 \quad OH \end{array}$ (with H above C and O double-bonded)	

* R group is enclosed in box.

Table 15-2, cannot be synthesized by human beings and must be obtained in the diet. They are therefore **essential** to the diet. Not all proteins contain all the essential amino acids. The combination of bread, which is 5 to 15 percent protein, and peanuts, which are a source of vegetable protein, provides a nearly complete complement of the essential amino acids. A good source of this combination is a peanut butter and jelly sandwich. Eggs and milk have the best balance of the essential amino acids, and in general, animal proteins have an essential amino acid balance that is better than that of vegetable proteins. Brown rice is the best of the vegetable protein sources.

All naturally occurring amino acids except glycine have a chiral alpha carbon, and the configuration around that carbon is always L (or *S*).

Proteins are composed of 20 amino acids. All of these amino acids contain a carboxyl (COOH) group and an amino (NH_2) group in the alpha position. The 20 amino acids vary among themselves as to the

TABLE 15-2

THE ESSENTIAL AMINO ACIDS

For adults
  Isoleucine (Ile)
  Leucine (Leu)
  Lysine (Lys)
  Methionine (Met)
  Phenylalanine (Phe)
  Threonine (The)
  Tryptophan (Trp)
  Valine (Val)

For children (less than 6 years old)
  All of the above 8 amino
    acids
  Arginine (Arg)
  Histidine (His)

nature of the remaining portion of the molecule—some have additional acidic or basic groups present while others have OH or SH groups, and still others have nonpolar alkyl groups. All of these amino acids except glycine are chiral, and naturally occurring ones are of the *S* configuration.

ACID-BASE BEHAVIOR OF AMINO ACIDS

An interesting feature of amino acids is that their exact structure is dependent on the pH of the medium in which they are found. This fluctuation in structure with changes in pH occurs because amino acids contain acidic and basic groups. Figure 15-1 shows what happens to alanine if we start with a highly acidic medium (pH = 1) and then slowly add base to raise the pH to 10.

FIGURE 15-1

Titration curve of alanine. Note structures at different pH values.

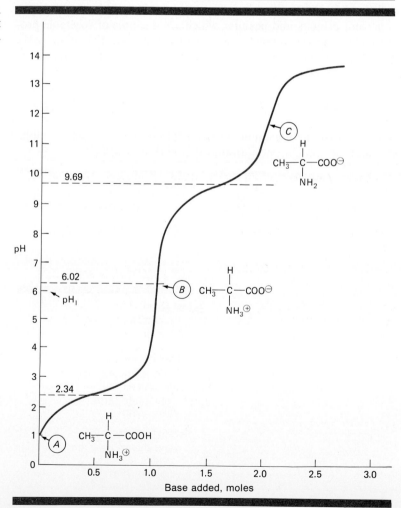

At point A, the acid is not ionized, and the amino group is in the salt form. The molecule has a net charge of $+1$. As the base (NaOH) is added, the COOH group is changed into the ionic COO^- group (see Chapter 12 for a review of the chemistry of carboxylic acids). At point B, all the molecules have both a negative and a positive charge and are, thus, neutral overall. This neutral structure occurs for many amino acids around pH 6 to 8 and represents the actual structure of those amino acids in pure water and in living cells, which have a pH of about 7.4. This neutral form of the amino acid is called a **zwitterion** (German for double ion). As more base is added, the pH of the medium becomes so high that there is not enough H^+ to protonate the amino group, and the NH_3^+ group changes into the neutral amine (NH_2) form at point C. The molecule now has a charge of -1.

The pH at which the amino acid is in the zwitterion form is called the **isoelectric point**, or pH_I. Each acid has its own unique pH_I depending upon the nature of the other functional groups present. While many have an isoelectric point between a pH of 6 and 8, some have isolectric points that are lower and some have ones that are higher. If the pH of the medium is above pH_I, the amino acid will be predominantly in the negative form; if the pH is below the pH_I, the amino acid will be predominantly in the positive form. This situation is shown below for two amino acids.

AMINO ACID	pH_I	PREDOMINANT FORM AT pH 7.4	PREDOMINANT FORM AT pH 5.0
Leucine	5.98	—	+
Aspartic acid	3.47	—	—

The structure, and therefore the behavior, of an amino acid is very much dependent on the pH of the solution in which it exists.

The form of the acidic and basic groups in amino acids varies with the pH of the medium. The electrically neutral form containing a negative and a positive ion is called the zwitterion, and the unique pH at which a given amino acid exists in the zwitterion form is called its isoelectric point.

ANALYSIS OF AMINO ACIDS

One scheme for determining the structure of proteins is to hydrolyze them and then analyze them qualitatively and quantitatively for the amino acids they contain. Several methods that are commonly used are discussed in the following sections.

Thin layer chromatography (TLC)

In this technique, a mixture of unknown amino acids is placed on a spot near the bottom of a glass plate covered with a thin layer of SiO_2 or Al_2O_3. High quality paper without a coating may also be used. See Figure 15-2. The coated plate or paper is then placed in a chamber containing a small amount of solvent. The solvent gradually rises up the plate by capillary action, carrying the various components of the mixture with it. Because of the variation in the exact molecular structure of the different amino acids, each is carried along at a different rate. The rate of movement up the plate is based primarily on the relative polarities of the plate's coating material (or the paper) and the solvent. If, for example, the solvent is of a nonpolar nature, then the nonpolar amino acids will move faster (being carried along by the solvent); a polar amino acid, on the other hand, will not be as soluble in the solvent and will not be carried along as quickly. This variation in rate of migration for the different amino acids

FIGURE 15-2

Diagram of thin layer chromatography (TLC) operation.

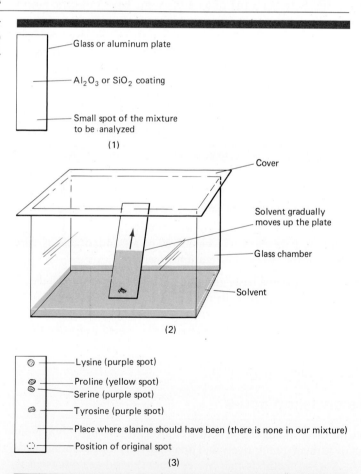

Glass or aluminum plate

Al_2O_3 or SiO_2 coating

Small spot of the mixture to be analyzed

(1)

Cover

Solvent gradually moves up the plate

Glass chamber

Solvent

(2)

Lysine (purple spot)

Proline (yellow spot)
Serine (purple spot)

Tyrosine (purple spot)

Place where alanine should have been (there is none in our mixture)

Position of original spot

(3)

causes a separation of the compounds of the mixture. After the solvent has reached the top of this plate (or paper), the plate is removed from the chamber, dried, and sprayed with a substance called **ninhydrin**. The ninhydrin causes the otherwise colorless (and, therefore, invisible) amino acids to develop a purple-colored complex, which allows us to see where each one is on the plate. By knowing beforehand the location to which each of the 20 amino acids will move (for a given solvent and thin layer), we can determine which amino acids were present in the mixture. For example, if there are colored spots where proline, tyrosine, serine, and lysine should be, then we know that these four acids were present in the mixture. TLC provides a qualitative analysis of a protein. A semiquantitative analysis can be made by determining the relative intensities of the purple-colored spots produced with ninhydrin. A darker spot means that more of that acid is present.

Electrophoresis

Another method of determining what amino acids are present is electrophoresis; it is similar to TLC. In this method, we place the mixture to be analyzed in the center of a piece of paper held horizontally and wet with a buffer solution at the desired pH. The components of the mixture move along the paper at various rates and are visualized with ninhydrin just as they are in TLC. However, the movement of various amino acids is caused by an electric current and is based on the relative charge on the amino acid molecules. Migration can be in either direction. A diagram is shown in Figure 15-3.

If the pH of the buffer solution is above the pH_I of a given acid, then the amino acid will be in the negative form and will move toward the positive pole (anode). If the pH is below the pH_I, then the amino acid will be in the positive form and will move toward the negative pole (cathode). The greater the difference between the pH and the pH_I, the farther (faster) a given amino acid will move. Below are shown some amino acids, their pH_I values, and their relative migration rates at pH 7.4.

AMINO ACID	ABBREVIATION	pH_I	DIRECTION OF MIGRATION AT pH 7.4	RELATIVE DISTANCE TRAVELED OR RATE OF MIGRATION*
Leucine	(Leu)	5.98	toward anode	1.42
Aspartic acid	(Asp)	3.47	toward anode	3.93
Lysine	(Lys)	9.79	toward cathode	2.39
Phenylalanine	(Phe)	5.48	toward anode	1.92

* Calculated by subtracting the pH from the pH_I (relative migration rate = pH_I − pH).

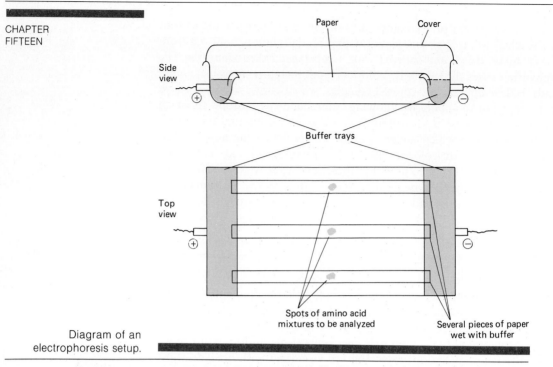

Diagram of an
electrophoresis setup.

FIGURE 15-3

The resulting electrophorogram is shown below.

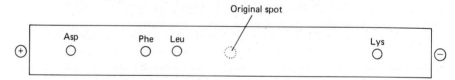

Electrophoresis can be used to analyze amino acids obtained from the hydrolysis of proteins. Sometimes a disease can be diagnosed by detecting abnormal amino acids in body fluids.

Amino acid analyzer

Figure 15-4 shows a diagram of the operation of this sophisticated device. The amino acid analyzer is capable of both qualitative and quantitative analysis of amino acid mixtures obtained from protein hydrolysis.

A protein whose amino acid content is to be determined is mixed with HCl. This causes hydrolysis of the protein into the component amino acids when the sample is heated in the water bath at point A in Figure 15-4. This mixture is then passed through a tube (column) of Al_2O_3 or ion exchange resin, which causes separation of the amino acids (point B). The amino acids each come out of the bottom of the tube at different times.

The individual amino acids are mixed with ninhydrin as they come out of the column, and as they are passed through the heating bath at point C a purple color develops. The stream of effluent from the column then

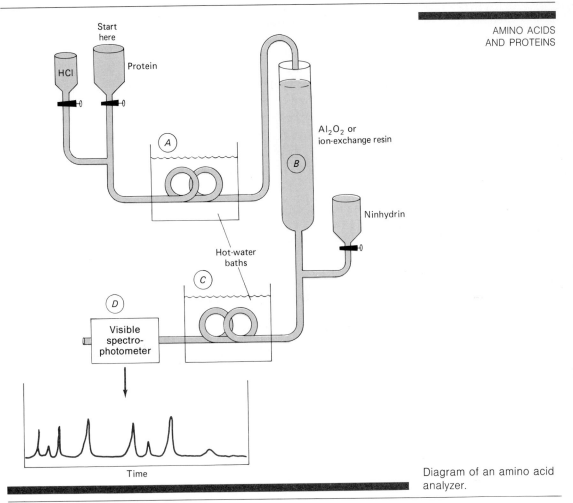

Start
here

HCl

Protein

A

Al_2O_2 or
ion-exchange resin

B

Ninhydrin

Hot-water
baths

C

D

Visible
spectro-
photometer

Time

Diagram of an amino acid
analyzer.

FIGURE 15-4

passes through a spectrophotometer which measures the presence and
intensity of the purple color and plots this on a graph. The time each
amino acid takes to come through the column, and therefore its position
on the graph, is known for each of the 20 acids. By observing where peaks
appear on the graph we can determine which acids are present, and by
measuring the size of each peak we can determine the relative amounts of
the amino acids.

**The amino acids present in a given protein can be determined experi-
mentally by several techniques. After the protein is broken down into
the component amino acids, the mixture can be analyzed by electrophoresis or thin layer chromatography, both of which give a qualitative
indication of the acids present. An amino acid analyzer can be used
to give both a qualitative and quantitative measure of the amino acids
in a protein.**

THE STRUCTURES OF PROTEIN

Proteins are large, polymeric molecules containing 50 to 5000 amino acid units. These units are linked together by an **amide bond** (see Chapter 12); in proteins, this is usually called a **peptide bond** by biochemists.

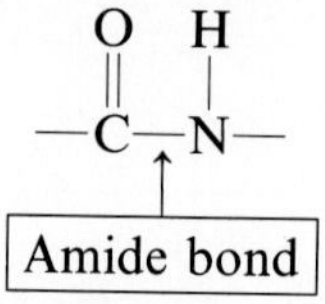

$$
\begin{array}{cc}
\text{O} & \text{H} \\
\parallel & | \\
-\text{C}-\text{N}- \\
\end{array}
$$

$$\boxed{\text{Amide bond}}$$

For example, glycine and alanine can react by using the carboxylic acid group of one and the amino group of the other to form an amide bond, which links the two molecules together.

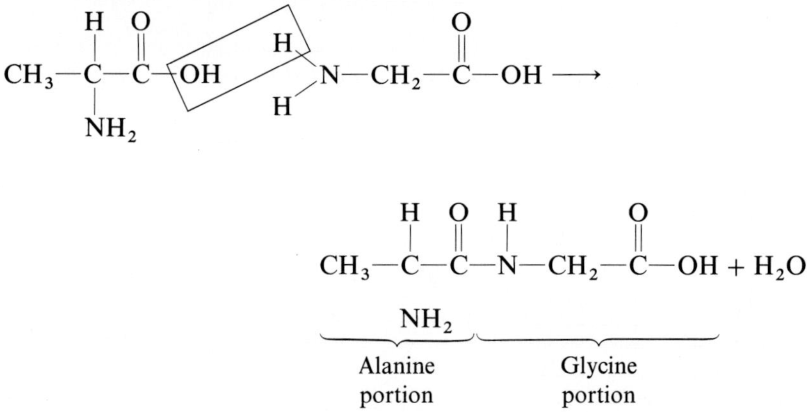

$$
\text{CH}_3-\overset{\overset{\text{H}}{|}}{\underset{\underset{\text{NH}_2}{|}}{\text{C}}}-\overset{\overset{\text{O}}{\parallel}}{\text{C}}\text{OH} \quad \text{H}\,\text{N}-\text{CH}_2-\overset{\overset{\text{O}}{\parallel}}{\text{C}}-\text{OH} \longrightarrow
$$

$$
\text{CH}_3-\overset{\overset{\text{H}}{|}}{\underset{\underset{\text{NH}_2}{|}}{\text{C}}}-\overset{\overset{\text{O}}{\parallel}}{\text{C}}-\overset{\overset{\text{H}}{|}}{\text{N}}-\text{CH}_2-\overset{\overset{\text{O}}{\parallel}}{\text{C}}-\text{OH} + \text{H}_2\text{O}
$$

Alanine portion	Glycine portion

The carboxylic acid end of the glycine can then react with the amino group of a third amino acid to form another amide bond. This process can continue until there are 100 or more amino acids in a sequence. Since there are 20 amino acids, the number of possible combinations and therefore the number of possible protein molecules are extremely large.

To illustrate this point, let's consider just three amino acids: glycine, alanine, and serine. The possible combinations of these three amino acids in a small molecule containing only three amino acid units linked together are shown below.[2] (By convention, the amino acid with the free —COOH group is written to the right; the one with the free NH_2— group is written to the left.) These are called the **C-terminal** and **N-terminal** ends of the proteins, respectively.

---

[2] Note that the sequences shown in numbers 4 and 6 are **not** the same, since in number 4 the Ser has the free (uncombined) COOH and in number 6 the Gly has the free COOH. Likewise, 10 and 12, 13 and 15, and 16 and 18 (as well as other similar combinations) are not identical.

1 Gly-Gly-Gly	10 Gly-Gly-Ser	19 Ala-Ala-Ser
2 Ala-Ala-Ala	11 Gly-Ser-Gly	20 Ala-Ser-Ala
3 Ser-Ser-Ser	12 Ser-Gly-Gly	21 Ser-Ala-Ala
4 Gly-Ala-Ser	13 Gly-Gly-Ala	22 Ser-Ser-Ala
5 Gly-Ser-Ala	14 Gly-Ala-Gly	23 Ser-Ala-Ser
6 Ser-Ala-Gly	15 Ala-Gly-Gly	24 Ala-Ser-Ser
7 Ser-Gly-Ala	16 Ala-Ala-Gly	25 Ser-Ser-Gly
8 Ala-Gly-Ser	17 Ala-Gly-Ala	26 Ser-Gly-Ser
9 Ala-Ser-Gly	18 Gly-Ala-Ala	27 Gly-Ser-Ser

Each of these 27 small molecules has different physical, chemical, and physiological properties. The possibilities increase dramatically as the number of amino acids used is increased and as the number of them in the sequence becomes greater. When we calculate the number of possible proteins that have 50 amino acids in a sequence using all 20 possible amino acids, we arrive at the staggering value of 10^{65}, which is relatively meaningless as a number, since it cannot readily be conceptualized. It does serve to show, however, that the number of possible proteins is virtually beyond comprehension. Yet organisms synthesize only those proteins tailored to their own specific needs.

Proteins can be divided into two broad groups. The **first** is called the **soluble**, or **globular, proteins**. These are materials in which the chain formed by the amino acids is bent and folded much like a clump of string, as shown in Figure 15-5. The exact nature of the bending is dictated by the nature of the R groups on each amino acid in the sequence. The more polar R groups are on the outside folds, so they can dissolve in the polar water medium. Each amino acid sequence produces a different folding pattern. Enzymes are globular proteins, and their ability to catalyze a given reaction is the result of the overall three-dimensional structural pattern and the spatial relationship of R groups to each other.

FIGURE 15-5

General arrangement of globular and structural proteins.

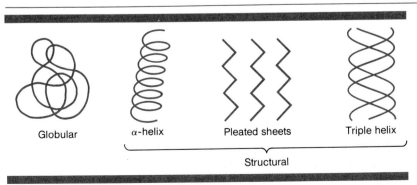

Globular α-helix   Pleated sheets   Triple helix

Structural

The **second** class of proteins is called the **structural proteins** and is found in structural materials of the body, including bone, muscle, hair, ligaments, cartilage, fingernails, and skin. In these materials the protein chains are found in a helix (much like a coiled wire) or flat sheets. These spatial arrangements and the nature of the R groups (mostly nonpolar groups) prevent the molecules from dissolving in water, and the interactions between adjacent coils or between adjacent parts of one chain make these materials strong.

Hair, for example, is composed of three closely linked parallel helices called a **fibril**. A hair strand (a strand visible to the eye) is composed of many of these parallel fibrils. Collagen, a protein found in skin, tendons, and bones, is composed of three mutually interlacing protein strands called a **triple helix**. This triple helix gives great strength to collagen-containing structures. The ability of different parts of the body to function in their own unique ways is a result of the molecular structure of the materials of which they are composed. In the case of proteins, the amino acids present and their sequence determine the structure of the protein chain and consequently the protein's function.

The term **dipeptide** refers to two amino acids bonded together, **tripeptide** refers to three, and so forth. The term **oligopeptide** refers to any peptide having 2 to 10 amino acids, and **polypeptide** refers to those with 11 to 50 amino acids. Those with 50 or more are referred to as **proteins**. An oligopeptide is shown below.

complete structure:

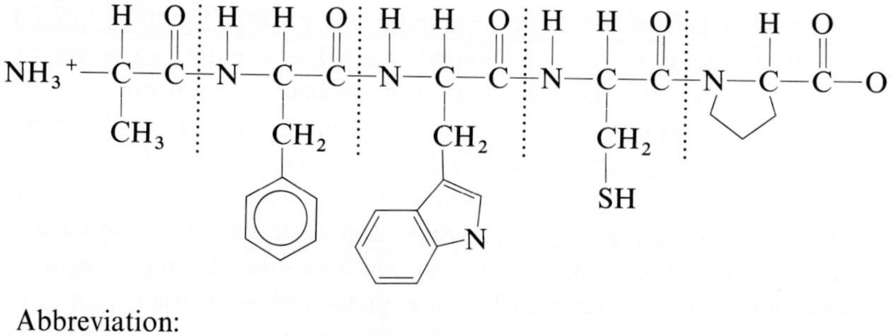

Abbreviation:

Ala-Phe-Trp-Cys-Pro

Protein biochemists use the terms **primary** (1°), **secondary** (2°), and **tertiary** (3°) **structure** to refer to the **amino acid sequence**, the **local stereochemistry**, and the **overall three-dimensional shape** of the molecule, respectively. The primary structure (the amino acids present and their order) determines the 2° and 3° structures. A given sequence of amino acids, because of the nature of the R groups, will, under a given set of conditions, naturally take a particular shape. When the conditions change, the shape may change.

For example, polyglycine exists in the α-helical form at all pH values. Polylysine, on the other hand, exists as random molecules at pH 1 to 10, where the R groups are all positively charged, but takes a helical shape when the pH is raised to 12 or above. At the lower pH values, the positive $-NH_3{}^+$ groups repel each other, preventing a helix from forming, but when they change to the uncharged $-NH_2$ groups, the more stable helix forms spontaneously.

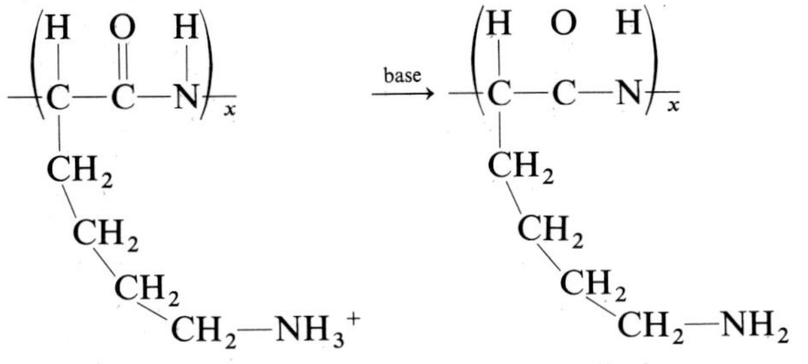

Random coil
pH = 1 to 10

α-helix form
pH > 12

FIGURE 15-6

α-helix structure of proteins.

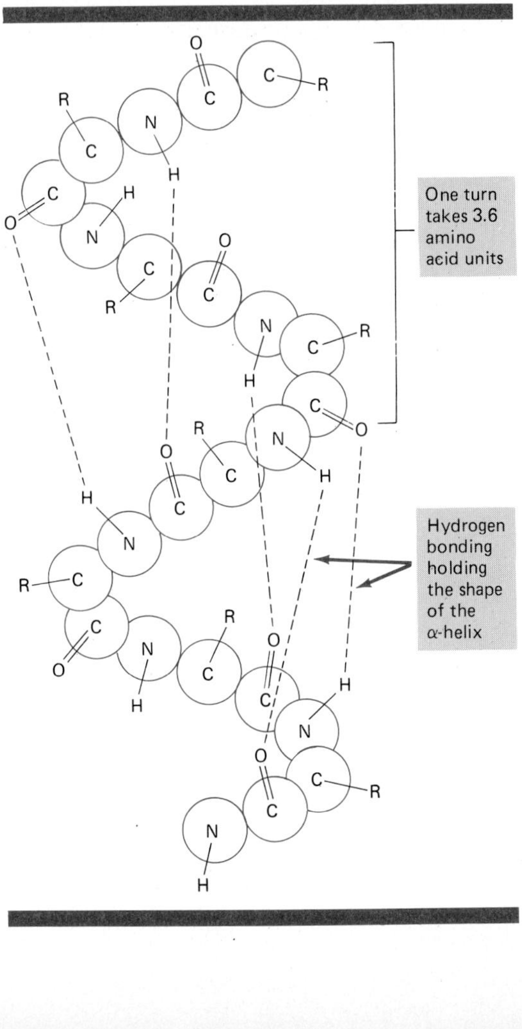

One turn takes 3.6 amino acid units

Hydrogen bonding holding the shape of the α-helix

Figure 15-6 shows the forces that hold the α helix in place. Note that the hydrogen atoms on all of the N—H groups are hydrogen-bonded to the C=O group of another amino acid.

Figure 15-7 shows a pleated sheet arrangement.

The α helix and pleated sheet are examples of secondary (2°) structures. Figure 15-8 shows the overall shape of a hypothetical protein. This is the tertiary structure, and includes local areas (2° structure) of α helix and random coil.

Hydrogen bonding, dipole attractions, hydrophilic-hydrophobic interactions, and disulfide bonds determine the 3° structure. Hydrogen bonding between various parts and attraction between two polar R groups are shown in Figure 15-8. In globular proteins that are in water solution, the polar (hydrophilic or water-loving) R groups tend to be on the outside of the protein. These include the R groups of serine, lysine, and aspartic acid, among others. The nonpolar (hydrophobic or water-repelling) groups such as those of leucine, phenylalanine, and tryptophan tend to clump together toward the center of the molecule. This is much like molecules of oil grouping together to form droplets when shaken with water. The protein assumes the conformation that provides the most stabilizing interactions of all types.

As an illustration of how protein structure is a function of environment,

FIGURE 15-7

Pleated sheet structure of proteins.

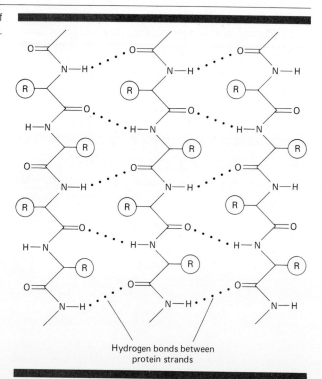

Hydrogen bonds between
protein strands

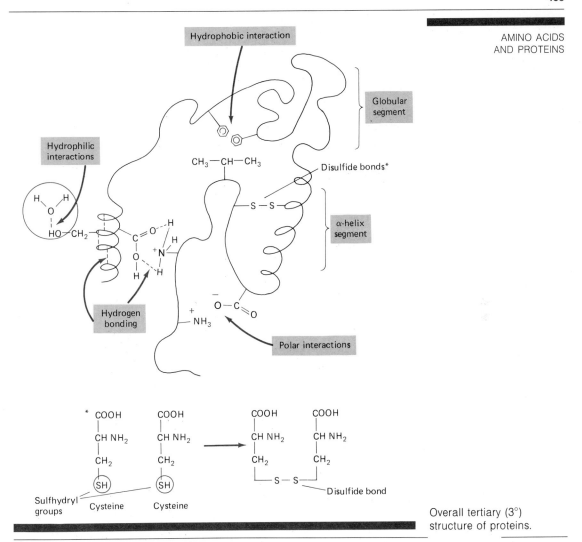

Overall tertiary (3°)
structure of proteins.

FIGURE 15-8

consider the behavior of hair in everyday situations. Figure 15-9 shows
the structure and changes involved.

First we observe the helical nature of hair in the natural, dry state.
When water is added, hydrogen bonds form between the —NH and C=O
groups of the protein and the water molecules. This causes a transition
from helix to pleated sheet, and the hair stretches. If the hair is curled
and then allowed to dry, it tends to stay in the new curled shape because
new hydrogen bonds form as the α helix re-forms. Moisture in the air, or
rewetting, destroys the curl, and the hair reverts to its natural shape.

A permanent change in a hair's shape can be brought about by breaking and then re-forming the disulfide bonds (—S—S—). These are covalent bonds formed between sulfhydryl (—SH) groups of the cysteine
units in different chains. They hold the three protein helices together and

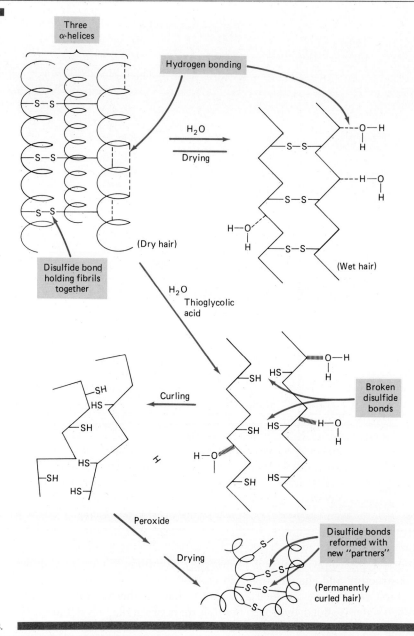

Three
α-helices

Hydrogen bonding

H_2O

Drying

(Dry hair)

Disulfide bond
holding fibrils
together

(Wet hair)

H_2O
Thioglycolic
acid

Curling

Broken
disulfide
bonds

Peroxide

Drying

Disulfide bonds
reformed with
new "partners"

(Permanently
curled hair)

Hair protein transitions.

FIGURE 15-9

determine the natural shape of hair. During a "permanent," thioglycolic acid (or its ammonium salt, ammonium thioglycolate) is used to reduce, and thus break, the disulfide bonds. The hair is then set in the desired shape and treated with a peroxide, which oxidizes the sulfhydryl groups to re-form the disulfide bonds. These latter bonds, because they are covalent and, therefore, much stronger than hydrogen bonds, do not change upon regular wetting or washing of the hair. Only as new hair growth occurs, and the "permed" hair is cut off, does the hair return to its natural appearance, although some "fading" of perms does occur slowly.

The primary (1°) structure of proteins is the sequence of amino acids linked by amide (peptide) bonds. This sequence is normally written with the amino acid with the free α-amino group to the left and the amino acid with the free carboxyl group to the right. The local stereochemistry (secondary or 2° structure) of proteins is determined largely by hydrogen bonding, and the overall stereochemistry (tertiary or 3° structure) is determined by a number of factors, including hydrogen bonding, hydrophobic and hydrophilic interactions, ionic associations, and disulfide bonds.

DETERMINING THE PRIMARY STRUCTURE OF PROTEINS

It is of considerable interest to be able to determine the primary structure of proteins. By determining the primary structures of proteins we can make important scientific and medical advances. For example, some proteins such as insulin are of great medical importance, and some diseases such as sickle-cell anemia are caused by abnormal human protein. Biochemists reasoned that if the complete 1° structure of insulin were known, they could, perhaps, produce it synthetically rather than isolate it from animal tissue. And if they were to ascertain which amino acids are different in the hemoglobin of a victim of sickle-cell anemia, they would be on the path to designing a cure or treatment.

Both of the above mentioned structural determinations have been made. The complete 1° structures of insulin and of normal and abnormal hemoglobin are known, along with those of hundreds of other proteins of the globular and structural types. No cure for sickle-cell anemia has yet resulted, but Eli Lilly and Company succeeded in producing genetically engineered synthetic insulin and began marketing it for the treatment of diabetes in 1984 under the trade name Humulin. This synthetic insulin has an advantage over beef insulin because some diabetics are allergic to the latter. Figure 15-10 shows the primary structure of human insulin.

The question, no doubt, arises in your mind: "How can such a complex molecular structure be determined?" The amino acid analyzer only tells us which acids are present in a given protein and in what proportions they are present; it tells us nothing about the order in which they appear. And the order of amino acids makes a tremendous difference in the 2° and 3° structure and, thus, in the function of the protein.

It is possible to determine the order of amino acids by using a method called **Edman degradation** to remove one amino acid at a time, beginning at the left (—NH_2 end). Each amino acid, upon removal, is placed in a separately numbered container and is later identified by TLC or other forms of chromatography. This process is automated in a machine which

FIGURE 15-10

Primary structure of human insulin.

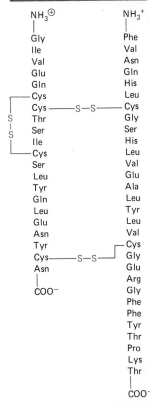

alternately carries out the chemical steps shown below. For this example, alanine is shown as the NH$_2$-terminal amino acid.

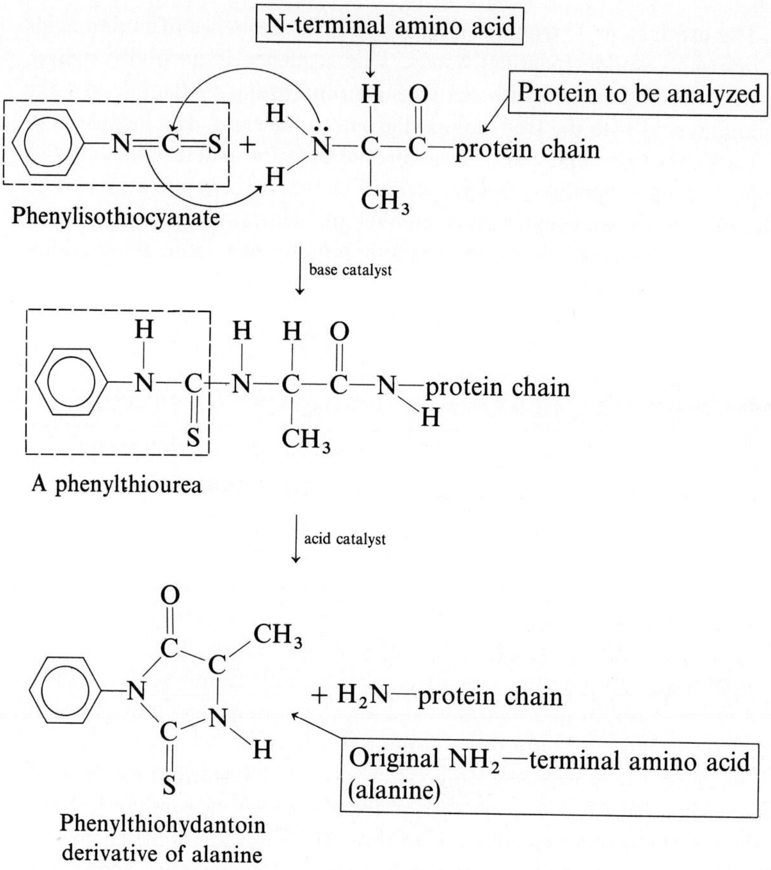

The protein is first treated with phenylisothiocyanate in the presence of a base to produce the phenylthiourea derivative shown. When this phenylthiourea is acidified, the last amino acid is removed from the chain to form the cyclic structure known as a phenylthiohydantoin derivative. This leaves the original second amino acid as the new N-terminal amino acid. The phenylthiohydantoin derivative is removed by filtration and stored. The process is repeated over and over until each amino acid is in turn removed.

Once the primary structure of a protein is determined, it is possible to synthesize a protein with the same amino acid sequence. Such a synthetic protein will be the same in every respect as the natural one. Remember, it is the primary structure that determines the 2° and 3° structures and ultimately the function of that protein in the organism in which it is found.

A small change in a large molecule can make a large difference in function. Figure 15-11 shows the primary structure of normal hemoglobin and

α-chain

Val·Leu·Ser·Pro·Ala·Asp·Lys·Thr·Asn·Val·Lys·Ala·Ala·Trp·Gly·Lys·Val·Gly·Ala·His·Ala·Gly·Glu·Tyr·
Gly·Ala·Glu·Ala·Leu·Glu·Arg·Met·Phe·Leu·Ser·Phe·Pro·Thr·Thr·Lys·Thr·Tyr·Phe·Pro·His·Phe·Asp·Leu·
Ser·His·Gly·Ser·Ala·Gln·Val·Lys·Gly·Hus·Gly·Lys·Lys·Val·Ala·Asp·Ala·Leu·Thr·Asn·
Ala·Val·Ala·His·Val·Asp·Asp·Met·Pro·Asn·Ala·Leu·Ser·Ala·Leu·Ser·Asp·Leu·His·Ala·His·Lys·Leu·Arg·Val·
Asp·Pro·Val·Asn·Phe·Lys·Leu·Leu·Ser·His·Cys·Leu·Leu·Val·Thr·Leu·Ala·Ala·His·Leu·Pro·Ala·Glu·Phe·Thr·
Pro·Ala·Val·His·Ala·Ser·Leu·Asp·Lys·Phe·Leu·Ala·Ser·Val·Ser·Thr·Val·Leu·Thr·Ser·Lys·Tyr·Arg

β-chain

Val·His·Leu·Thr·Pro·*Y·Glu·Lys·Ser·Ala·Val·Thr·Ala·Leu·Trp·Gly·Lys·Val·Asn·Val·Asp·Glu·Val·
Gly·Gly·Glu·Ala·Leu·Gly·Arg·Leu·Leu·Val·Val·Tyr·Pro·Trp·Thr·Gln·Arg·Phe·Phe·Glu·Ser·Phe·Gly·Asp·Leu·
Ser·Thr·Pro·Asp·Ala·Val·Met·Gly·Asn·Pro·Lys·Val·Lys·Ala·His·Gly·Lys·Lys·Val·Leu·Gly·Ala·Phe·Ser·Asp·
Gly·Leu·Ala·His·Leu·Asp·Asp·Leu·Lys·Gly·Thr·Phe·Ala·Thr·Leu·Ser·Glu·Leu·His·Cys·Asp·Lys·Leu·His·Val·
Asp·Pro·Gln·Asp·Phe·Arg·Leu·Leu·Gly·Asn·Val·Leu·Val·Cys·Val·Leu·Ala·His·His·Phe·Gly·Lys·Glu·Phe·Thr·
Pro·Pro·Val·Gln·Ala·Ala·Tyr·Gln·Lys·Val·Val·Ala·Gly·Val·Ala·Asp·Ala·Leu·Ala·His·Lys·Tyr·His

The only difference in the two modules:
*Y = Glu for normal hemoglobin
  Y = Val for sickle-cell hemoglobin

Primary structures of normal and sickle-cell hemoglobins.

FIGURE 15-11

that of the hemoglobin in a person with sickle-cell anemia. Note the **very small** difference. The replacement of amino acid number 6, normally glutamic acid, with valine, changes the shape and oxygen-carrying ability of this large hemoglobin molecule. This, in turn, has serious health implications for the patient. The red blood cells change to an elongated form when deprived of oxygen and, as a result, do not flow easily through the capillaries. This causes restricted blood flow in vital organs. Sickle-cell patients usually do not live past middle age.

The amino acid sequence in proteins can be determined by Edman degradation. This procedure allows us to remove one amino acid (as the phenylthiohydantoin derivative) at a time from the N-terminal end of the protein. Identification of the derivatives in sequence tells us the original order of the amino acids. The purpose of this time-consuming procedure, in addition to providing basic scientific information, is to provide a basis for understanding disease states and to allow for the synthesis of proteins for medical or experimental uses.

ENZYMES

Enzymes are usually **globular proteins** that catalyze biochemical reactions. That is, they enable biochemical processes to occur at useful rates under mild conditions. Enzymes, and all catalysts, lower the activation energy and thus speed up reactions that are spontaneous (have negative ΔH values) but that are slow in the absence of the enzyme. All biochemical processes are catalyzed by enzymes, and since thousands of biochemical processes occur, thousands of enzymes are synthesized in the cell. They aid in the synthesis of all molecules, including enzyme molecules, as well as in hydrolysis, energy production, and other vital cell processes. A very precise 2° and 3° structure is needed in order for an enzyme to function as a catalyst, and because the structures of the proteins are pH and solvent dependent, a small change in cellular pH from the normal 7.4 can destroy enzyme function and spell disaster for the cell. In fact, a cell cannot function if its pH changes by more than a few tenths of a unit. The presence of alcohol or other organic solvents can also change the enzyme structure and stop catalytic activity.

The efficiency of these amazing catalysts can be illustrated by the reaction of urea to form an ammonium ion (NH_4^+) and a bicarbonate ion (HCO_3^-).

$$NH_2-\overset{\overset{\displaystyle O}{\|}}{C}-NH_2 \xrightarrow[\text{urease}]{2H_2O} NH_4^+ + HCO_3^-$$

Without a catalyst, at room temperature and a pH of 7, this reaction is very slow—only 10^{-6} moles react in a year. In the presence of urease (an enzyme) the reaction occurs at the rate of 10^4 moles per second.

Enzymes work by the interaction of three points on the protein with three points on the substrate (the molecule being changed). These points are various functional groups that are in close proximity in both the enzyme structure and the substrate molecule, and the interactions are of the same types used to hold proteins in their tertiary structures. This is usually a very specific interaction sometimes referred to as the "lock and key theory"—**a given enzyme usually will catalyze only one substrate**. Since proteins are chiral, usually only one enantiomer of a substrate will be biologically active. This is because the three points on the enzyme (called the **active site**) match the three points on only one enantiomer. Figure 15-12 shows a hypothetical active site and illustrates how pH, solvent, or other poisons operate to inhibit enzymatic activity.

Enzymes are highly efficient proteins that catalyze all biochemical processes. Many enzymes are very effective in enhancing the rates of biochemical reactions, and they are usually specific for only one reactant. An active site on the enzyme molecule, composed of three functional groups, serves as the catalyst which brings about the change in the substrate molecule.

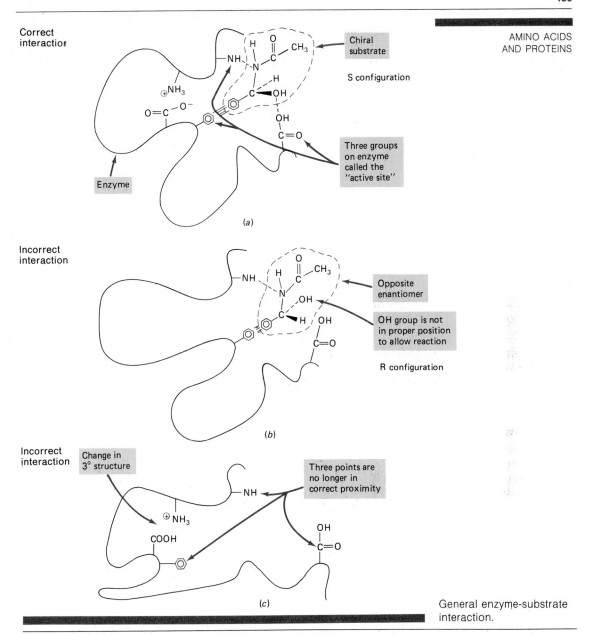

Correct interaction

Chiral substrate

S configuration

⊕NH₃

Enzyme

Three groups on enzyme called the "active site"

(a)

Incorrect interaction

Opposite enantiomer

OH group is not in proper position to allow reaction

R configuration

(b)

Incorrect interaction

Change in 3° structure

Three points are no longer in correct proximity

(c)

General enzyme-substrate interaction.

FIGURE 15-12

SUMMARY

1 **Amino acids** are the monomer units of **protein** molecules.

2 The form in which an amino acid exists depends on the pH of the medium in which it is found.

3 Amino acids can be analyzed by **thin layer chromatography** (TLC), **electrophoresis**, or by an **amino acid analyzer**, which uses **column chromatography** to separate the components of a mixture.

4 Proteins are composed of 50 or more amino acids linked by **peptide bonds**. The sequence of the amino acids (1° structure) determines the molecular shape and the function of the protein.

5 The primary structure of a protein can be determined by **Edman degradation**.

6 Enzymes are usually **globular protein catalysts** that operate on a **three-point, lock-and-key** interaction with the reacting molecule(s). They are highly efficient and specific.

KEY TERMS

Active site	Oligopeptide	Substrate
Amino acid	Peptide bond	Sulfhydryl groups
Amino acid analyzer	Pleated sheet	Tertiary structure of
Disulfide bonds	Polypeptide	proteins
Edman degradation of proteins	Primary structure of proteins	Thin layer chromatography
Electrophoresis	Protein	Zwitterion
Globular proteins	Secondary structure of proteins	
Isoelectric point		
α helix		

SKILL PRACTICE PROBLEMS

1 If the pH_I of an amino acid is 4.9, in what form will the amino acid be at each of the following pH values?
   (a) 2.0   (b) 4.9
   (c) 8.5

2 Which will move faster in an electrophoresis experiment run at pH 6.5: an amino acid with pH_I of 4.8 or one with a pH_I of 5.5? In which direction (i.e., toward which electrode) will it move?

3 Amino acids are the simple molecules from which _____ are made.

4 Which of the following is an essential amino acid?
   (a) Alanine   (b) Leucine
   (c) Glycine   (d) Proline

5 What is the R group in valine?

6 What dipeptide compounds could we prepare by using glycine (Gly) and leucine (Leu)?

7 What do each of the following terms mean?
   (*a*) Zwitterion   (*b*) Primary structure of proteins
   (*c*) Isoelectric point   (*d*) Peptide bond
   (*e*) Hydrophobic   (*f*) Active site of enzymes
   (*g*) Oligopeptide

8 From the following TLC results, what amino acids were present in the unknown?

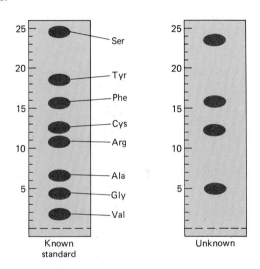

9 Draw the complete structure of the tetrapeptide molecule Tyr-Phe-Gly-Ser.

10 Why does hair get longer when it is wet?

11 Given the rate information on urea being converted to NH_4^+ and HCO_3^- shown on page 488, what is the ratio of the rate of reaction with urease catalyst to the rate of reaction without it?

12 From Figure 15-11 identify the amino acids that differ in the two hemoglobins. What is the main difference in the character of R groups in these two amino acids? Why would this difference cause the hemoglobin structure to be different?

13 Draw methionine in the positively charged, negatively charged, and zwitterion forms.

14 Draw the structure of the Edman degradation product (phenylthiohydantoin) for glutamine (see Table 15-1). Repeat for isoleucine.

15 If the tetrapeptide in question 9 were subjected to Edman degradation, what would be the derivative found in containers 1 through 4? (Draw the molecular structure of each derivative.)

16 What are the factors that determine the 2° and 3° structures of proteins?

17 Which amino acids in Table 15-1 would have nonpolar (alkyl) R groups?

18 Which amino acids have basic (NH_2-containing) R groups? Remember that amide nitrogen atoms are not basic.

19 What is the substrate for urease?

20 Draw the resonance forms of the amide (peptide) functional group in diglycine. See Chapter 1 for a review of resonance forms. Would you expect the C—N bond to have free rotation at ordinary temperatures, or would this bond be rigid (i.e., would it have a high barrier to rotation)?

21 Draw a structure that shows the hydrogen bonding between the R groups of tyrosine and threonine (see Table 15-1).

REVIEW QUESTIONS

22 Complete the following reaction equations:

(*a*)

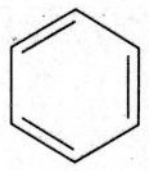

$$\xrightarrow[\text{Pt Heat/pressure}]{H_2}$$

(*b*) $CH_3CH_2CH_2$—$OH + CrO_3/Pyr/CH_2Cl_2$

(*c*) 
$+ O_3 \longrightarrow \xrightarrow[\text{H}_2\text{O}]{\text{Zn}}$

(*d*) CH_3—C=$CH_2 + HBr/peroxide$
       |
       CH_3

23 On the basis of what you learned in Chapter 11, which amino acids would you expect to absorb ultraviolet light?

CHAPTER 16

LIPIDS

LEARNING GOALS

1 To learn the definition of the lipid class of biomolecules

2 To understand how the molecular structures of the fatty acid portions of fats and oils determine the physical and dietary properties of those fats and oils

3 To learn terms used to describe triglycerides

4 To learn some of the reactions of triglycerides

5 To learn the general structures of lipids other than triglycerides

6 To understand the isoprene rule

Lipids are the most diverse category of biomolecules. They include compounds with a wide variety of functional groups, which makes it impossible to give a definition of lipids based on the functional groups present. Instead, we define **lipids** as **those compounds that are soluble in nonpolar solvents** such as hexane or chloroform. This means that lipids are themselves nonpolar and, therefore, have molecules with large hydrocarbon portions in addition to whatever functional group(s) may be present.

We will first consider the chemistry of **triglycerides**. These are the subcategory of lipids that includes fats and oils, which are the most abundant lipids in biosystems. We will then present other less abundant types of lipids.

TRIGLYCERIDES

There are two categories of triglycerides—**fats**, which are **solid** at room temperature, and **oils**, which are **liquids** at room temperature. Most fats have a structure similar to that of lard or solid vegetable shortening, which is shown below.

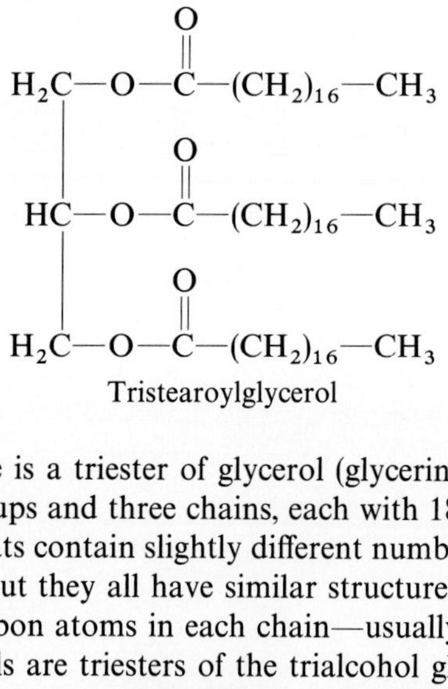

$$H_2C-O-\overset{\displaystyle O}{\overset{\|}{C}}-(CH_2)_{16}-CH_3$$

$$HC-O-\overset{\displaystyle O}{\overset{\|}{C}}-(CH_2)_{16}-CH_3$$

$$H_2C-O-\overset{\displaystyle O}{\overset{\|}{C}}-(CH_2)_{16}-CH_3$$

Tristearoylglycerol

This fat molecule is a triester of glycerol (glycerin)—it contains three ester functional groups and three chains, each with 18 carbon atoms in a sequence. Various fats contain slightly different numbers of carbon atoms in the side chains, but they all have similar structures and most have an even number of carbon atoms in each chain—usually 12, 14, 16, or 18.

Since fats and oils are triesters of the trialcohol glycerol, this class of lipids is often referred to as **triglycerides** or **triacylglycerides**.

Oils (liquids at room temperature) have the same triester structure as do fats, but the carbon chains contain one to three carbon-carbon double bonds (alkene functional groups). Triglycerides that contain no alkene groups are said to be **saturated**, while those which do contain carbon-carbon double bonds are called **unsaturated**. Triglycerides with several double bonds in the side chains are called **polyunsaturated**. Vegetable oils, such as cottonseed oil, have double bonds in each side chain, as shown below:

$$H_2C\!-\!O\!-\!\overset{\overset{\displaystyle O}{\|}}{C}\!-\!(CH_2)_7\overset{\overset{\displaystyle H}{\diagdown}}{C}\!=\!\overset{\overset{\displaystyle H}{\diagup}}{C}(CH_2)_7\!-\!CH_3$$

$$HC\!-\!O\!-\!\overset{\overset{\displaystyle O}{\|}}{C}\!-\!(CH_2)_7\overset{\overset{\displaystyle H}{\diagdown}}{C}\!=\!\overset{\overset{\displaystyle H}{\diagup}}{C}(CH_2)_7\!-\!CH_3$$

$$H_2C\!-\!O\!-\!\overset{\overset{\displaystyle O}{\|}}{C}\!-\!(CH_2)_7\overset{\overset{\displaystyle H}{\diagdown}}{C}\!=\!\overset{\overset{\displaystyle H}{\diagup}}{C}(CH_2)_7\!-\!CH_3$$

Trioleoylglycerol

You may wonder why the presence of a carbon-carbon double bond in the side chain of a triglyceride would lower its melting point and thus cause it to exist as a liquid at room temperature. Most of the double bonds found in oils are cis. The presence of a cis double bond causes a rigid bend in the molecule and prevents close packing of molecules; it therefore **reduces intermolecular forces**. This lowers the melting point below room temperature. This is illustrated by the following diagram.

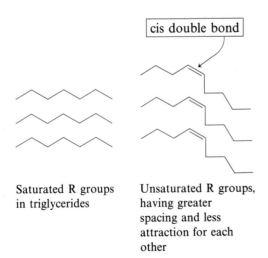

cis double bond

Saturated R groups in triglycerides

Unsaturated R groups, having greater spacing and less attraction for each other

During human digestion of triglycerides, the three ester links are broken by enzymes produced in the pancreas. The breaking of the ester links converts the triglyceride into three molecules of carboxylic acid and one molecule of glycerin. The long chain carboxylic acids are called **fatty acids** because they are derived from fats and oils. The digestion process is shown by the following equation:

$$H_2C-O-\overset{\overset{\displaystyle O}{\|}}{C}-(CH_2)_{16}-CH_3$$

$$HC-O-\overset{\overset{\displaystyle O}{\|}}{C}-(CH_2)_{16}-CH_3 \xrightarrow[3H_2O]{enzyme}$$

$$H_2C-O-\overset{\overset{\displaystyle O}{\|}}{C}-(CH_2)_{16}-CH_3$$

Tristearoylglycerol

$$H_2C-OH$$
$$HC-OH + 3HO-\overset{\overset{\displaystyle O}{\|}}{C}-(CH_2)_{16}-CH_3$$
$$H_2C-OH$$

Glycerin   Stearic acid
(a fatty acid)

Fats and oils are triesters of glycerine and long chain fatty acids and are referred to as triacylglycerides. They are classified as saturated, unsaturated, or polyunsaturated on the basis of the presence and number of carbon-carbon double bonds in the side chains.

FATTY ACIDS

Fatty acids differ from one another in the **number of carbon atoms** they contain, the presence or absence of one or more **double bonds**, and the **location** of any double bonds present. Table 16-1 shows the structures of several fatty acids. The shorthand notation in the last column is used by biochemists to indicate the structure of fatty acids. For saturated acids, the number of carbon atoms alone is given (stearic acid, for example, is designated as 18:0). For unsaturated fatty acids, the number of double bonds is given after a colon, and the position of the double bond or bonds is shown in parentheses. Almost all carbon-carbon double bonds in fatty acids have cis geometry. If one bond does not, then a "t" (for *trans*) is placed after its position designation in the shorthand notation.

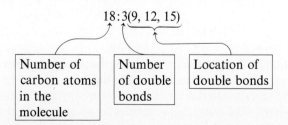

Most of the common fatty acids can be synthesized in the human body from other materials. Since human beings lack the enzyme needed to pro-

TABLE 16-1 SELECTED FATTY ACIDS

NAME	STRUCTURE	SHORTHAND NOTATION
Lauric	$CH_3(CH_2)_{10}COOH$	12:0
Myristic	$CH_3(CH_2)_{12}COOH$	14:0
Palmitic	$CH_3(CH_2)_{14}COOH$	16:0
Stearic	$CH_3(CH_2)_{16}COOH$	18:0
Oleic		18:1(9)
Linoleic		18:2(9, 12)
Linolenic		18:3(9, 12, 15)
Arachidonic		20:4(5, 8)

duce carbon-carbon double bonds beyond carbon atom number 9 in fatty acids, we cannot produce **linoleic** and **linolenic** acids. These materials, therefore, must be contained in the human diet and are called **essential fatty acids**. These acids are needed as precursors for higher molecular weight polyunsaturated fatty acids such as arachidonic acid, which in turn is changed into an important class of lipids called prostaglandins (see page 503).

> Fatty acids are long chain monocarboxylic acids with an even number of carbon atoms. They are the result of enzymatic hydrolysis of fats and oils and are, like triglycerides, classified as saturated (containing no alkene functional groups), unsaturated (containing one alkene group), or polyunsaturated (containing two or three alkene groups). A shorthand designation is sometimes used to communicate fatty acid structures. For human beings, two fatty acids are required in the diet. These are linoleic acid and linolenic acid; they are referred to as essential fatty acids.

NAMING TRIGLYCERIDES

Fats and oils are named as trialkanoyl glycerols. The names of the acyl groups are listed and followed by the ending -*glycerol*. The acyl group names are arrived at by dropping the -*ic* from the name of the corresponding fatty acid and adding the syllable -*oyl*. The structure of the lard shown on page 494 would be named tristearoylglycerol, and the name of the oil on page 495 would be trioleoylglycerol. Two additional examples of triglyceride nomenclature are shown below. When the fatty acids attached to glycerol are not all identical, we indicate the position of each. The carbon atoms of glycerol are numbered sequentially, beginning with number 1 at the top as usually written.

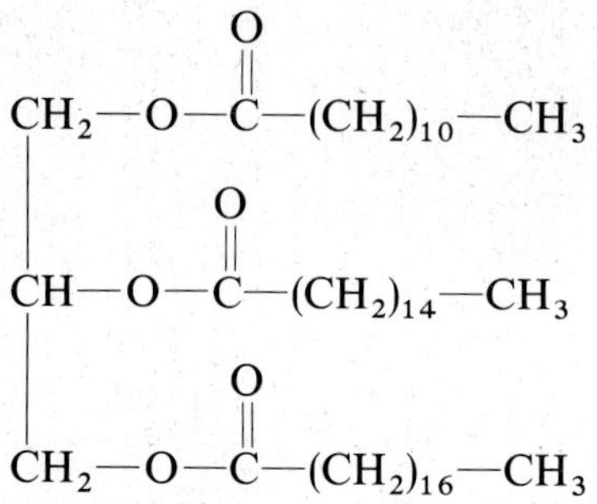

$$CH_2-O-\overset{\overset{\displaystyle O}{\|}}{C}-(CH_2)_{10}-CH_3$$

$$CH-O-\overset{\overset{\displaystyle O}{\|}}{C}-(CH_2)_{14}-CH_3$$

$$CH_2-O-\overset{\overset{\displaystyle O}{\|}}{C}-(CH_2)_{16}-CH_3$$

1-Lauroyl-2-palmitoyl-3-stearoylglycerol

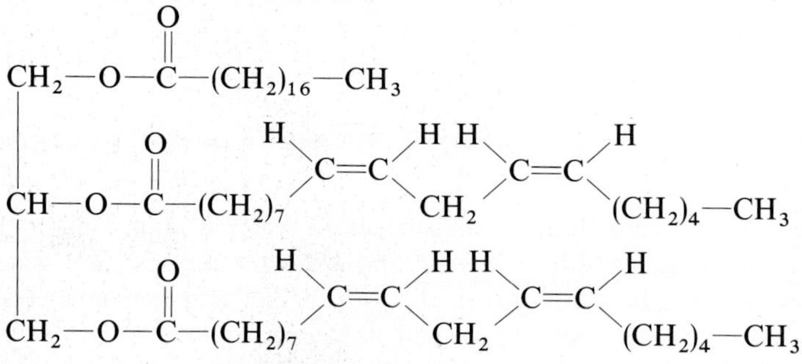

$$CH_2-O-\overset{\overset{\displaystyle O}{\|}}{C}-(CH_2)_{16}-CH_3$$

2,3-Dilinoleoyl-1-stearoylglycerol

Triglycerides are named as trialkanoyl glycerols. If there are different fatty acid groups in the same molecule, the position of each is indicated.

REACTIONS OF TRIGLYCERIDES

Hydrogenation

One of the most important commercial reactions of oils is the catalytic hydrogenation of the side chain carbon-carbon double bonds. Hydrogenation changes oils such as cottonseed, corn, and soybean oils into solid fats such as vegetable shortening (Crisco). This occurs when the unsaturated carbon chains are changed to saturated ones, as follows:

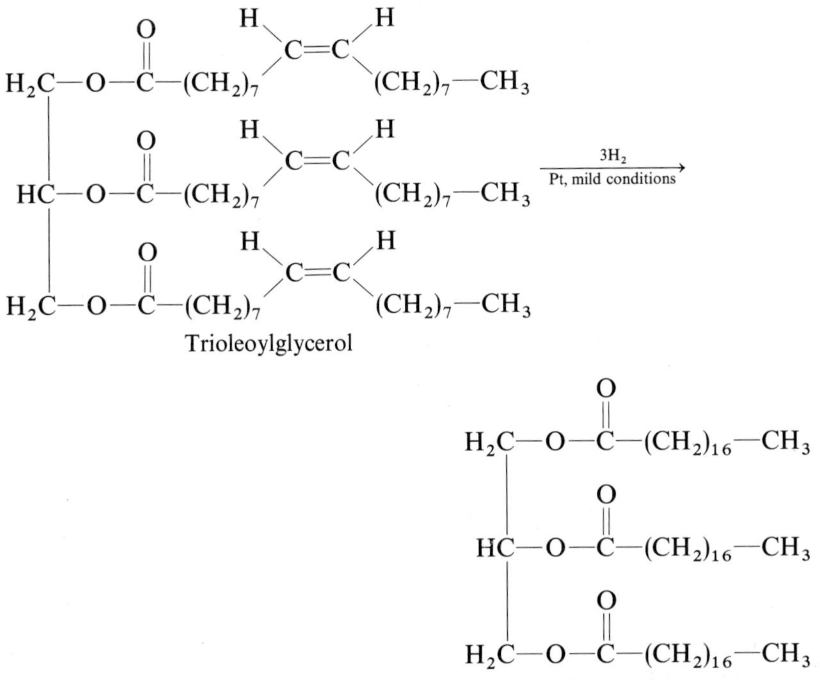

$$H_2C-O-\overset{\overset{\displaystyle O}{\|}}{C}-(CH_2)_7\overset{\overset{\displaystyle H}{\diagup}}{\underset{}{C}}=\overset{\overset{\displaystyle H}{\diagdown}}{\underset{}{C}}-(CH_2)_7-CH_3$$

$$HC-O-\overset{\overset{\displaystyle O}{\|}}{C}-(CH_2)_7\overset{\overset{\displaystyle H}{\diagup}}{\underset{}{C}}=\overset{\overset{\displaystyle H}{\diagdown}}{\underset{}{C}}-(CH_2)_7-CH_3 \quad \xrightarrow[\text{Pt, mild conditions}]{3H_2}$$

$$H_2C-O-\overset{\overset{\displaystyle O}{\|}}{C}-(CH_2)_7\overset{\overset{\displaystyle H}{\diagup}}{\underset{}{C}}=\overset{\overset{\displaystyle H}{\diagdown}}{\underset{}{C}}-(CH_2)_7-CH_3$$

Trioleoylglycerol

$$H_2C-O-\overset{\overset{\displaystyle O}{\|}}{C}-(CH_2)_{16}-CH_3$$

$$HC-O-\overset{\overset{\displaystyle O}{\|}}{C}-(CH_2)_{16}-CH_3$$

$$H_2C-O-\overset{\overset{\displaystyle O}{\|}}{C}-(CH_2)_{16}-CH_3$$

Tristearoylglycerol

Complete hydrogenation changes unsaturated triglycerides into saturated ones. Hydrogenation may be done with less than 1 mole H_2 per mole of $C=C$ to produce a **partially hydrogenated** material that is a soft solid at room temperature. Color and flavor are added to produce margarine. Partially hydrogenated vegetable oil is also used in commercial breads and pastries.

Hydrolysis

Another commercially important reaction of triglycerides is the base-catalyzed hydrolysis of the three ester links to produce soap and glycerine. This reaction, which is called **saponification**, was discussed in Chapter 12, and is shown below for review.

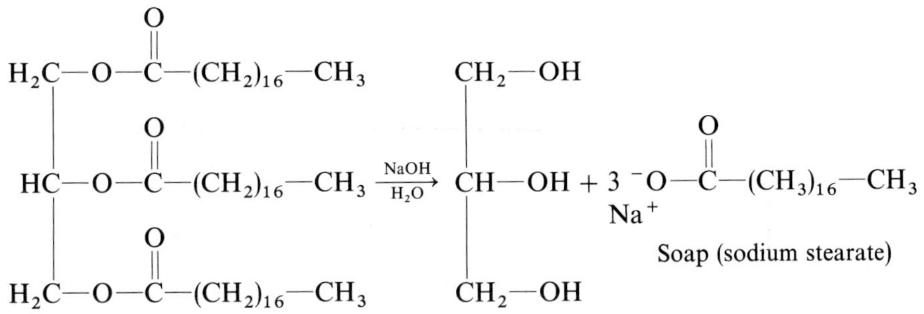

$$H_2C-O-\overset{\overset{\displaystyle O}{\|}}{C}-(CH_2)_{16}-CH_3 \qquad CH_2-OH$$

$$HC-O-\overset{\overset{\displaystyle O}{\|}}{C}-(CH_2)_{16}-CH_3 \xrightarrow[\text{H}_2\text{O}]{\text{NaOH}} CH-OH + 3\ ^-O-\overset{\overset{\displaystyle O}{\|}}{C}-(CH_3)_{16}-CH_3$$
$$\qquad\qquad\qquad\qquad\qquad\qquad\qquad Na^+$$

$$H_2C-O-\overset{\overset{\displaystyle O}{\|}}{C}-(CH_2)_{16}-CH_3 \qquad CH_2-OH \qquad\qquad \text{Soap (sodium stearate)}$$

Polymerization. The double bonds in certain polyunsaturated oils can react with oxygen to produce a polymeric coating. Such oils are found in linseed oil and tung oil, which are used in varnish and oil-based paints. This reaction was discussed in Chapter 6.

Triacyl glycerides can be hydrolyzed with a strong base to produce the salts of the fatty acids (soaps). The double bonds in the side chains of oils can be partially or completely hydrogenated catalytically to produce solid shortening products. Polyunsaturated oils are used in paints and varnishes; they polymerize when exposed to air (oxygen) to produce protective coatings.

MISCELLANEOUS LIPIDS

Phospholipids

Phospholipids are compounds that, like fats and oils, are triglyceride esters; unlike fats and oils, they have one of the —OH groups of glycerine esterified with a phosphoric acid derivative rather than with a carboxylic acid. The most common phospholipid is shown below; it is called dioleoyl phosphatidyl choline, or more simply, **lecithin**. Lecithin is found in cell membranes and is used commercially as an emulsifying agent in baked goods. Eggs are a rich dietary source of lecithin. Lecithin is thought to be a precursor to neurotransmitters necessary for brain function and is therefore believed by some to be a brain enhancer (making the mind clear and sharp). The value of lecithin in the diet is speculative, however.

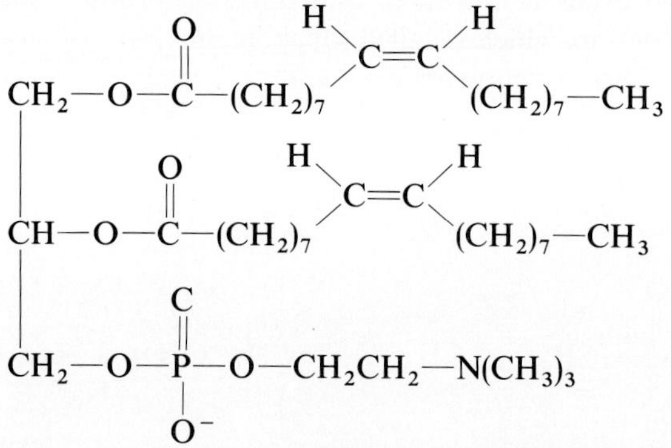

Lecithin

Waxes

Waxes are monoesters of long chain carboxylic acids and long chain alcohols. The structures of the major components of three naturally occurring waxes are shown below. The ranges given in the formulas indicate that these natural materials are actually mixtures of esters. Beeswax, for example, can be hydrolyzed to produce the 26-carbon to 28-carbon fatty acids plus the 30-carbon to 32-carbon alcohols. These waxes consist mostly of compounds within the structural ranges shown, along with small amounts of other esters that vary by a few carbon atoms. The fact that waxes are mixtures rather than pure compounds partly explains why they soften gradually rather than melting sharply. Paraffin (high molecular weight alkanes—see Chapter 3) is also a waxlike material.

$$CH_3-(CH_2)_{24-26}-\overset{\overset{\textstyle O}{\|}}{C}-O-(CH_2)_{29-31}-CH_3$$

Beeswax
(found in honeycombs)

$$CH_3(CH_2)_{23-27}-\overset{\overset{\textstyle O}{\|}}{C}-O-(CH_2)_{31-33}-CH_3$$

Carnuba wax
(found in Brazilian palm leaves; used in
floor and furniture polishes)

$$CH_3-(CH_2)_{14}-\overset{\overset{\textstyle O}{\|}}{C}-O-(CH_2)_{15}-CH_3$$

Spermaceti
(found in sperm whale oil)

Terpenes

Terpenes are compounds that are actually synthesized from, or are composed of, several **isoprene** units. The isoprene units may be rearranged and placed in many different orders, and additional functional groups can be incorporated as well. Isoprene itself is 2-methyl-1,3-butadiene.

$$\overset{\overset{\textstyle CH_3}{|}}{CH_2=C-CH=CH_2}$$

Isoprene

Below are shown the structures of a number of terpenes along with their names, occurrences, and characteristics. The individual isoprene units are shown in outlined blocks. Terpenes are called **steroids** if they contain the following ring structure:

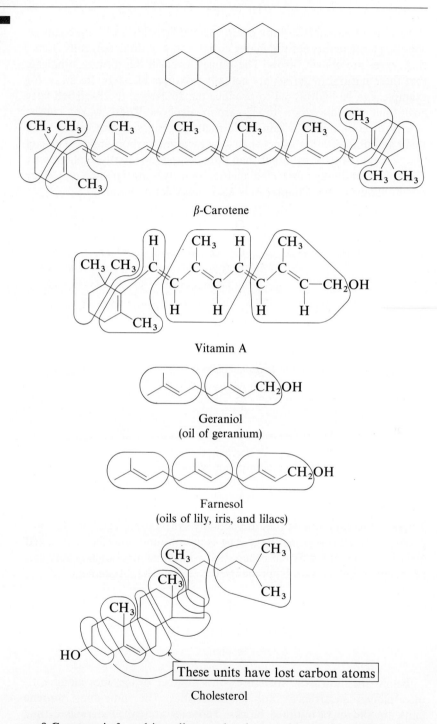

β-Carotene

Vitamin A

Geraniol
(oil of geranium)

Farnesol
(oils of lily, iris, and lilacs)

These units have lost carbon atoms

Cholesterol

β-Carotene is found in yellow and red vegetables and is broken down in our bodies to **vitamin A** (retinol), which is needed for proper visual function. **Geraniol** and **farnesol** are very sweet-smelling oils with the odors of familiar flowers and are used in perfumes. **Cholesterol** is a component of all cell membranes and is necessary for normal cell function. It is synthesized in the body in rather large quantities and contributes, along with a number of other factors, to cardiovascular disease. Dietary aspects of cholesterol and other lipids are covered briefly in "Applied Organic Chemistry I" following this chapter.

Prostaglandins

Prostaglandins were first isolated from the seminal vesicles of sheep by Bergstrom in Sweden in the 1930s. He perceived the powerful biochemical activity of these materials when he observed that they caused the contraction of smooth muscle in vitro. Since that time, biochemists have found prostaglandins to be important hormonal regulators for a number of processes, including the production of certain types of pain, and regulators of contraceptive activity. The common analgesic aspirin stops an aching pain by interfering with the synthesis of the pain-causing prostaglandins. While these compounds are important biochemically, they are found in most mammalian tissue in very small amounts.

All prostaglandins have similar molecular structures. The structural similarities include a cyclopentane ring with two carbon chains in a trans relationship. The various members of the class have different functional groups on these basic structures. Prostaglandins are designated by letter-number codes, and the structures of two of these, along with their designations, are shown below. These compounds are synthesized in the body from arachidonic acid. Notice that prostaglandins have the same number of carbon atoms as does arachidonic acid (see Table 16-1).

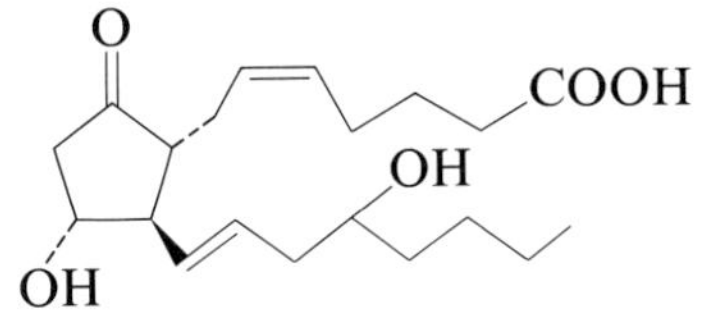

Prostaglandin E$_2$
(PGE$_2$)

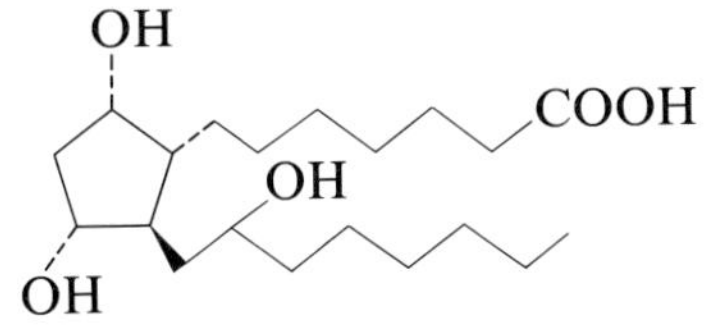

Prostaglandin F$_1$
(PGF$_1$)

A number of structurally diverse materials found in biosystems are classified as lipids because of their solubility in nonpolar solvents. They include waxes, terpenes (including steroids), phospholipids, and prostaglandins.

SUMMARY

1 **Lipids** are biochemical compounds that are **soluble in nonpolar solvents**. Different lipids contain a number of different functional groups.

2 The most abundant lipids are **fats** (solids) and **oils** (liquids), both of which are **triacylglycerides**. Fats contain mostly **saturated** fatty acid moieties while oils are triesters of **unsaturated** fatty acids.

3 Triacylglycerides can be **hydrolyzed** by using a base; they form glycerin and fatty acid salts (soaps). Those triacylglycerides containing unsaturated fatty acid groups (oils) can be **hydrogenated** to form fats (solids). If they contain conjugated double bonds, they can be **polymerized**.

4 The lipid class contains, in addition to triacylglycerides, **waxes**, **phospholipids**, and **terpenes** (such as cholesterol—a steroid—β-carotene, vitamin A, and geraniol) and **prostaglandins**.

5 **Terpenes** are lipids with molecular structures that can be envisioned as consisting of several **isoprene** units.

KEY TERMS

Essential fatty acids	Oil	Terpene
Fat	Phospholipid	Triacylglyceride
Fatty acid	Polyunsaturated	Triester
Hydrogenation	Prostaglandins	Triglyceride
Hydrolysis	Saponification	Unsaturated
Isoprene	Saturated	Wax
Lipid	Steroids	

SKILL PRACTICE PROBLEMS

1 Draw the structure of ethyl palmitate.

2 Draw the structure of potassium oleate.

3 Which fatty acids in Table 16-1 are polyunsaturated?

4 Identify, by circling, the isoprene units in these terpenes:

(a)

(b)

5 Write definitions of the following terms in your own words. Then go to the text and check the correctness of what you have written.
  (*a*) Saturated   (*b*) Unsaturated
  (*c*) Terpene   (*d*) Lipid
  (*e*) Triglyceride   (*f*) Wax
  (*g*) Phospholipid

6 Draw the structure of the triglyceride that has three lauric acid groups esterified to glycerine. Would you expect this to be a solid (fat) or liquid (oil) at room temperature?

7 Repeat question 6 for linoleic acid. Is it a fat or an oil?

8 Write the reaction of the compound whose structure you drew in question 7, with an excess of H_2 in the presence of a catalyst. Repeat using only 4 moles of H_2 per mole of triglyceride. How would you describe each of your products in terms of the extent of saturation?

9 Name the compound in question 6. Repeat for question 7.

10 Arrange the structure of arachidonic acid so as to show how it could be converted into a prostaglandin by bond rearrangement.

11 Draw the structure of hypothetical fatty acids with the following shorthand notations.
  (*a*) 16:2(9, 12)   (*b*) 14:2(9*t*, 11)

12 Write the equation for the base-catalyzed hydrolysis of spermaceti.

13 How many chiral centers are in a molecule of PGE_2?

14 Why are triglycerides insoluble in water but soluble in nonpolar solvents? Would you expect lecithin to be more or less soluble in water than are triacylglycerides?

15 Give the product of the digestion of the lipid referred to in question 7.

REVIEW QUESTIONS

16 Give the product for the reaction of oleic acid with each of the following reagents:
  (*a*) NaOH and H_2O (*b*) $SOCl_2$
  (*c*) Ethyl alcohol and acid catalyst   (*d*) $SOCl_2$ followed by NH_3
  (*e*) $KMnO_4$ (cold, dilute)   (*f*) O_3 followed by Zn/H_2O
  (*g*) H_2/Pt (*h*) H_2O/H^+
  (*i*) Br_2 (*j*) HBr

17 Which of the products in the answers to question 16 would be optically active?

DIETARY ASPECTS OF LIPIDS:

BODY WEIGHT CONTROL

A problem frequently encountered in our culture is dieting to lose weight or eating to maintain a desirable weight. As you will recall, combustion of different materials produces different amounts of heat energy. The complete metabolism of biochemicals to CO_2 and water in the living system produces the same total energy as if the same material were burned in a flame. Carbohydrates produce about 4.5 Calories[1] (Cal),[1] or kilocalories (kcal) of energy per gram; proteins produce 4.5 Calories per gram (Cal/g); fats and oils produce about 9.0 Cal/g.

$$1 \text{ g carbohydrate} + O_2 \xrightarrow{\text{enzyme}} CO_2 + H_2O$$
$$\text{(Glucose)} \qquad \Delta H = -4.5 \text{ Cal} \quad (-4.5 \text{ kcal or } -4500 \text{ cal})$$

$$1 \text{ g} \quad \text{protein} \quad + O_2 \xrightarrow{\text{enzyme}} CO_2 + H_2O + \text{other products}$$
$$\text{(Amino acids)} \qquad \Delta H = -4.5 \text{ Cal}$$

$$1 \text{ g} \quad \text{fat} \quad + O_2 \xrightarrow{\text{enzyme}} CO_2 + H_2O$$
$$\text{(Fatty acids)} \qquad \Delta H = -9 \text{ Cal}$$

The principle of weight control is simple. We take in a certain amount of energy stored in the chemical bonds of food. That energy is released when this food is digested and metabolized. This energy is then used (for driving energy-requiring synthesis reactions, moving muscles, and producing heat) or it is stored, primarily as fat. If more energy is consumed than required by body processes, heat, and exercise, fat builds up (see Figure I-1).

Body processes use a relatively small and fairly constant amount of energy. The heat needed to maintain normal body temperature under normal conditions is also fairly constant. The main controls we have over body fat are the amounts and kinds of food we eat and the exercise we do. Since fats have a higher energy content, lowering the proportion of them in the diet will lower energy intake. However, it is not desirable to eliminate them completely, since they are part of our overall nutritional needs. Since fat takes longer to digest than do carbohydrates and proteins, it stays in the digestive system longer and delays hunger. This can help us to eat less during a given day. Intake of carbohydrates likewise can be

---

[1] In nutrition, energy is measured in "big" calories, written as Calories. 1 Calorie = 1 kilocalorie = 1000 calories.

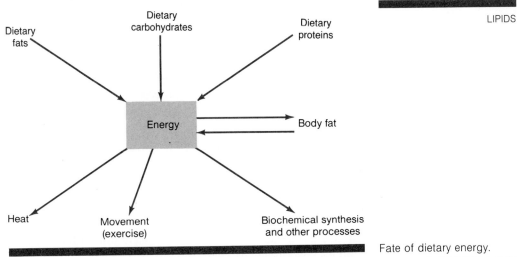

Fate of dietary energy.

FIGURE I-1

lowered **but should not be eliminated**. Since carbohydrate metabolism is required for the body to use up stored fat, a person who is trying to lose weight should consume some carbohydrates. The best and safest way to lose weight is to eat a **little less** than usual and to exercise a **little more**. This is better than "crash diets."

Weight-reducing medications may help to reduce appetite but their value is marginal. There is no such thing as "pills that melt fat away"— fraudulent advertisements notwithstanding. Being aware of the caloric values of foods and applying the principles just discussed (using will power!) is the best approach.

We can do some interesting calculations concerning weight control. Human fat has the same caloric value as do other lipids (9.0 Cal/g). Let us take 2000 Cal/day as the standard dietary energy requirement for maintaining a constant weight (this is average for adults). Some people require more and some less, depending on their size, activity and metabolic rate.

One question we can answer is: **"How much weight would you gain in a year if you ate enough food to exceed your caloric requirements by a very small amount, say 1 percent more food than necessary?"**

1   2000 Cal/day × 0.01 = 20 Cal/day excess

2   20 Cal/day × 365 days/year = 7300 Cal/year excess

3   9 Cal/g × 454 g/lb = 4100 Cal/lb.
This means that for every 4100 Cal excess you consume, you will store 1 pound (lb) of body fat.

4   For 1 percent excess

$$\frac{7300 \text{ Cal/year}}{4100 \text{ Cal/lb}} = 1.8 \text{ lb/year weight gain}$$

5 In 10 years, this would be 18 lb. Thus, even a small excess of 1 percent would cause a slow but steady weight gain and, unless corrected by weight control, would cause obesity in late middle age.

We can also calculate the appropriate loss rate during a diet. If you ate no food and continued normal physical activity, your body would obtain its 2000 Cal/day energy requirement from reserves of body fat.

$$\frac{2000 \text{ Cal/day}}{4100 \text{ Cal/lb}} = 0.5 \text{ lb/day}$$

Thus, for a person using 2000 Cal/day, 0.5 lb is the theoretical maximum loss of fat each day. Now it is not healthy, or indeed even possible, to eat nothing and continue a normal life, so in practice about $\frac{1}{3}$ to $\frac{1}{4}$ lb/day is the most that anyone can safely lose in body **fat**. Many diet product advertisements claim the loss of 1 lb/day, and some even make claims such as "You can lose 5 lbs in one night while you sleep with this amazing pill that melts fat." These claims are either false or misleading. Most such products are diuretics, which cause rapid **water** loss, resulting in a large but fleeting weight loss. In such situations, there is no loss of body fat, however.

Diet aids are also available. They contain an appetite suppressant. The most common appetite suppressant is phenylpropanolamine (usually used as the hydrochloride salt), the structure of which is given below.

$$\langle \bigcirc \rangle - \underset{\underset{OH}{|}}{CH} - \underset{\underset{^+NH_3}{|}}{CH} - CH_3 \quad Cl^-$$

Some foods contain nutrients that reduce the appetite. Niacin (vitamin B_3) is reported to be one of these; therefore meats, which are high in this vitamin, may help one to eat less. When dry fibers such as cellulose or dry algae are ingested, they swell when they come in contact with the water in the stomach and give a "full" sensation, which also helps one to eat less. Note, however, that all these aids simply help us to consume fewer calories. Finally, it is claimed by some that regular vigorous exercise not only consumes energy during the activity but also raises the general level of metabolism and helps a great deal with weight control.

CARDIOVASCULAR DISEASE

As mentioned in Chapter 16, lipids (cholesterol in particular) are believed to play a role in cardiovascular disease. This disease of the circulatory system is caused by the following general process:

1 A small injury or break in the inner wall of a blood vessel occurs. This injury may be caused by tension, high blood pressure (caused by several factors), or physical external injury.

2 This injury heals, leaving scar tissue and a material called **plaque**. Plaque is largely deposits of cholesterol, which cause the diameter of the blood vessel to become smaller. (See Figure I-2.)

3 It is possible for a blood clot or a piece of plaque flowing through the vessels near the heart to become lodged in a vessel so that the blood supply to the heart muscle is partially cut off. That part of the heart with an inadequate blood supply dies. A blood vessel that is already badly clogged by plaque can be completely closed off by nicotine (a vessel constrictor) or other materials. A heart attack results.

4 If a small part of the heart dies as a result of a heart attack, it can be repaired by the body; if a large portion dies, the body cannot repair all the damage, and the person dies.

The vessel injuries and subsequent plaque buildup are a result of at least five major factors:

1 *Heredity.* One's blood pressure and the **tendency** to develop plaque buildup are largely genetic.

2 *Exercise.* A regular, vigorous exercise program helps to prevent cholesterol from coming out of solution in the blood and slows down plaque

FIGURE I-2

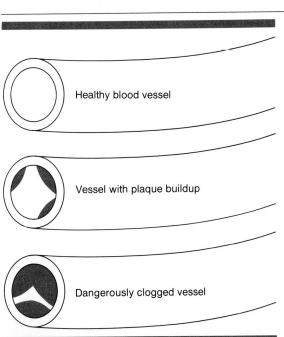

Plaque buildup in blood vessels.

Healthy blood vessel

Vessel with plaque buildup

Dangerously clogged vessel

formation. This also raises the level of high-density lipoproteins (HDLs), which solubilize cholesterol.

3 *Dietary cholesterol.* Regularly eating large amounts of food containing high concentrations of cholesterol probably causes plaque to form faster.

4 *Dietary fats.* The consuming of unsaturated fats (oils) aids in reducing the tendency to develop cardiovascular disease and probably also raises the HDL level.[2]

5 High levels of glucose stimulate the body's system to synthesize cholesterol. This occurs because the insulin needed for glucose metabolism also causes cholesterol to be produced. Fructose, which is available in grocery stores and is the main sugar found in fruit and honey, may not have this effect. Keeping sucrose levels low will, over a period of several months, help to lower serum cholesterol. (Sucrose is a disaccharide with two glucose units.)

---

[2] Some studies suggest that high oil diets may contribute to cancer incidence.

TABLE I-1

FOODS WITH HIGH CHOLESTEROL CONTENT	FOOD	SERVING SIZE	AMOUNT OF CHOLESTEROL, mg
	Brains	$\frac{1}{4}$ lb	1000
	Liver	$\frac{1}{4}$ lb	450
	Oysters	$\frac{1}{4}$ lb	325
	Egg	1 large	252
	Shrimp	$\frac{1}{4}$ lb	125
	Beef	$\frac{1}{4}$ lb	100
	Pork	$\frac{1}{4}$ lb	90
	Chicken	$\frac{1}{4}$ lb	90
	Fish	$\frac{1}{4}$ lb	60
	Whole milk	1 glass	35
	Skim milk	1 glass	5
	Ice cream	$\frac{1}{2}$ cup	50
	Butter	1 teaspoon	12
		$\frac{1}{4}$ lb	300
	Lard	1 teaspoon	4
	Vegetable shortening		0

Table I-1 shows foods that are particularly high in cholesterol. It is wise for those who have a family history of heart disease to keep the level of cholesterol in the diet relatively low, but since it is needed by the body for normal functions and is synthesized by the body, there is no need to attempt to reduce its intake to near zero (except when directed by a physician, of course). A serum cholesterol level below 200 mg per 100 mL of blood is desirable, although the average for Americans is 230 to 250. The daily intake of cholesterol should likely be kept below 200 mg, but recent studies have shown that it is possible to reduce blood cholesterol levels by no more than 5 to 10 percent by dietary means. Those same studies have shown, however, that for every 1 percent reduction in blood cholesterol level, we reduce the risk of a heart attack by 2 percent.

The best approach for reducing the likelihood of cardiovascular disease is to eat a relatively low cholesterol diet, to eat most of your lipids as oils, to get plenty of exercise, not to smoke, and to eat a low sucrose diet.

SATURATED VERSUS UNSATURATED TRIGLYCERIDES

We have already mentioned that the consumption of unsaturated lipids aids in preventing plaque buildup in blood vessels. Remember that the term *unsaturated* means that the fatty acids composing the triglyceride contain carbon-carbon double bonds. The term *polyunsaturated* is also used and refers to those fatty acids having two or more double bonds.

FATTY ACID CONTENT OF SELECTED TRIGLYCERIDE LIPIDS   **TABLE I-2**

LIPID	SATURATED, PERCENT	MONOUNSATURATED, PERCENT	POLYUNSATURATED, PERCENT
Butter	60	35	5
Beef and pork fat	50	45	5
Fish oil	40	25	35
Poultry fat	35	45	20
Cottonseed oil	25	25	50
Corn oil	20	25	55
Margarine	20	25	55
Olive oil	20	70	10
Soybean oil	20	25	55
Peanut oil	10	75	15
Safflower oil	10	15	75

Table I-2 gives the approximate relative amounts of saturated, unsaturated, and polyunsaturated fatty acids in a number of familiar fats and oils. Generally, it is now accepted that the more we include unsaturated lipids in the diet, the smaller is our risk of heart attack.

CHAPTER 17

NUCLEIC ACIDS

LEARNING GOALS

1 To understand the general structure of deoxyribonucleic acids (DNA) and the experimental observations that led scientists to our current knowledge of DNA

2 To understand the general structure of ribonucleic acid (RNA)

3 To understand the structure of important nucleotides, especially adenosine triphosphate (ATP) and adenosine diphosphate (ADP)

4 To understand the roles of the various types of RNA in protein synthesis

The final class of biomolecules we will study includes **nucleic acids** of which there are two general types: **ribonucleic acid (RNA)** and **deoxyribonucleic acid (DNA)**. DNA is important in storing all the **genetic information** of an organism. RNA is involved in the **synthesis** of all the **proteins** in a cell and in the transfer of the necessary information from the DNA molecule to the site where protein synthesis occurs.

DEOXYRIBONUCLEIC ACIDS

In 1944 it was found that two strains of the pneumococcus bacterium existed. One was pathogenic (disease-causing) and the other was not. It also was found that if the pathogenic strain was killed with heat, and the dead organisms were then introduced into a culture of the nonpathogenic organism, then the latter became pathogenic. Moreover, future generations of the originally nonpathogenic organism inherited the disease-causing properties. Later, the DNA of the pathogenic organism was isolated, and when it was introduced into the nonpathogenic culture, it caused the same inherited disease-causing properties. Thus, DNA was shown to be the primary factor in determining the **characteristics** and **heredity** of the organism.

DNA is found as a single large molecule in simple organisms; it is organized into chromosomes in higher organisms. Each cell in a given organism has identical DNA content. However, no two organisms have identical DNA.

The general structure of DNA is as follows:

$$\text{—(phosphate—sugar—phosphate—sugar—phosphate—sugar)}_x\text{—}$$

with Base 1, Base 2, Base 3 attached to the sugars respectively.

There are four possible bases that occur in different sequences in the DNA of each individual, and it is the different arrangement of these bases alone that controls the characteristics of that individual. Your skin color, your hair color, the shape of your nose, and so forth are all controlled by this conceptually simple coding system.

The structure of DNA is shown more completely below. The phosphate-sugar chain, with the attached base units, continues for thousands of units—each with its base side group.

D-ribose (sugar) portions

Adenine

Cytosine

Bases

Guanine

Thymine

Phosphate portions

Deoxyribonucleic acid

The four bases (nitrogen-containing heterocyclic compounds) are shown attached to the sugar-phosphate chain. Each base has a slightly different shape, polarity, and ability to form hydrogen bonds. These differences are used to store (code) information that directs the synthesis of different RNA molecules. The various RNA molecules synthesized, in turn, direct the synthesis of different cellular proteins. This sequence of events determines, directly or indirectly, all the genetic characteristics of species and individuals. Since the DNA is such a large molecule, there are many thousands of base units present, and coding can be stored for **all** characteristics and functions. It is truly an amazing molecule. These four bases (**adenine, cytosine, guanine**, and **thymine**) are the only ones found in DNA, and it is simply various combinations of them (i.e., different sequential orders) that determine ultimately all heredity and all biochemical processes in each organism.

Notice that the sugar portion of the DNA chain is 2-deoxy-D-ribose. The phosphate —OH provides the ionizable hydrogen that makes DNA highly acidic. DNA molecules have 30,000 to 120,000 base-phosphate-sugar units in sequence and a molecular weight of 10 to 40 million.

Deoxyribose nucleic acid (DNA) is a high molecular weight copoly-

mer of 2-deoxy-D-ribose and phosphate units. The sugar units are all bonded to one of four heterocyclic bases. It is by the order of these bases that organisms store genetic information.

RIBONUCLEIC ACIDS

Ribonucleic acid (RNA), like DNA, contains a chain of alternating phosphates and sugars. However, the sugar portion is always D-ribose, rather than 2-deoxy-D-ribose. Like DNA, RNA contains four bases, as shown below. Adenine, cytosine, and guanine are common to both DNA and RNA, but in RNA, **uracil** takes the place of thymine. In addition, RNA sometimes contains other unusual bases. The general structure of RNA is shown below.

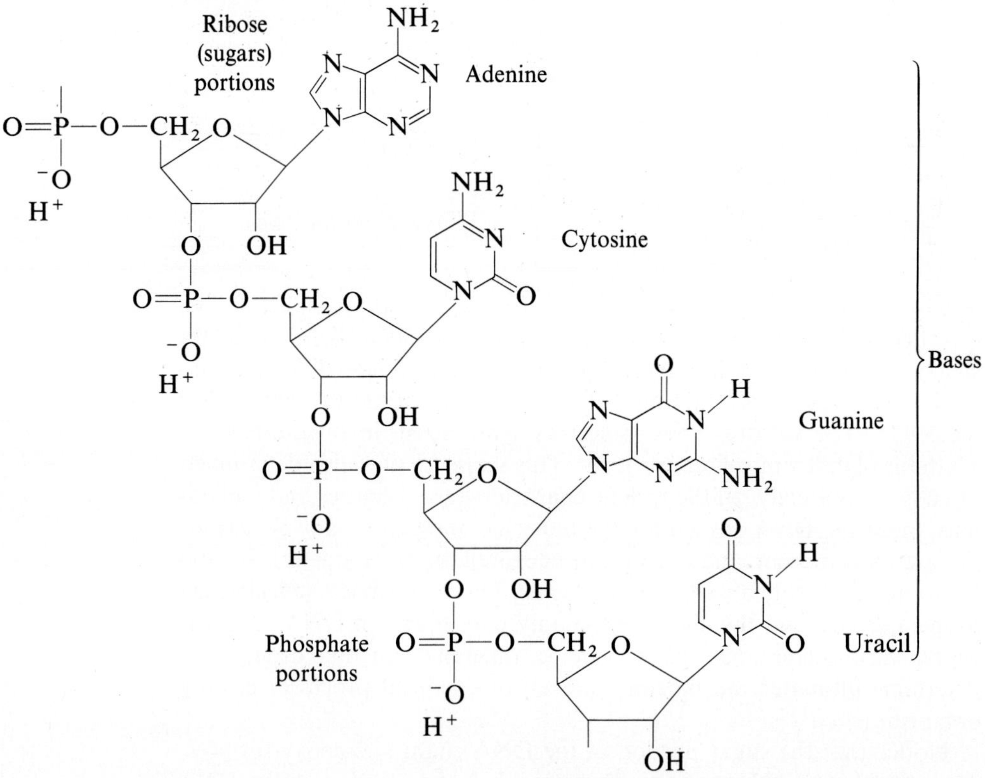

Ribonucleic acid

The nucleic acid bases are classified as **purines** or **pyrimidines** after these simple heterocyclic compounds:

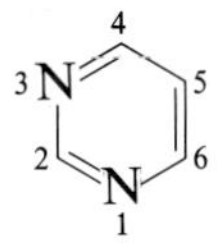

Pyrimidine 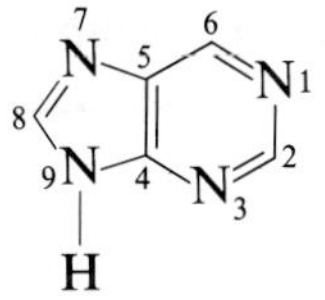   Purine

Adenine and guanine are purine bases, while cytosine, thymine, and uracil are pyrimidine bases.

Ribonucleic acids (RNA) are composed of chains of phosphate and D-ribose copolymer. The ribose units are all bonded to heterocyclic bases. There are several types of RNA, and each serves a different purpose in cell biochemistry.

NUCLEOTIDES

Several monomeric biomolecules, related structurally to nucleic acids, are important to cell function. They are called **nucleotides**, and are composed of a sugar (D-ribose or 2-deoxy-D-ribose), a base attached to carbon number 1 of the sugar, and one to three phosphate groups attached to carbon number 5 of the sugar.

The general structure of a nucleotide is as follows, where Z is H or OH:

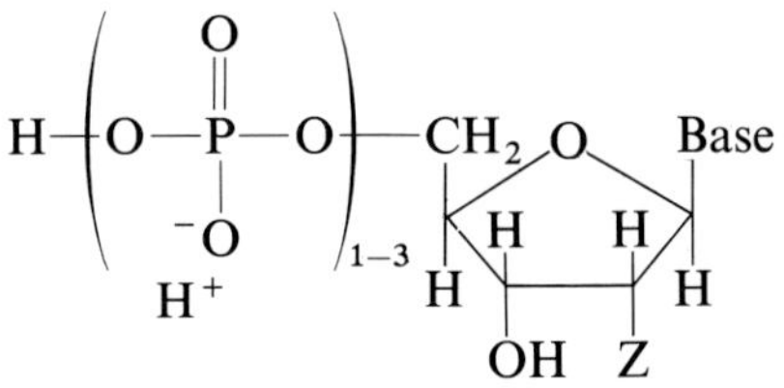

Two of the most commonly encountered nucleotides are **adenosine triphosphate (ATP)** and **adenosine diphosphate (ADP)**. The only difference between the two is in the number of phosphate groups (ADP has two, while ATP has three). ATP is shown below.

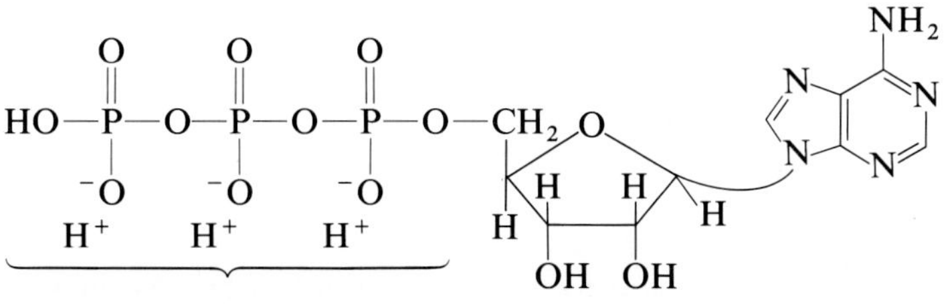

Three phosphate groups   Ribose   Adenine

When a third phosphate group is added to ADP, the potential energy of the molecule increases greatly. Thus, ATP can be used to store and transfer large amounts of energy in the cell.

Nucleotides are compounds containing a sugar bonded to a base and one to three phosphate units. ATP is a nucleotide used by the cell to store and transfer large amounts of energy.

BASE PAIRING—SECONDARY STRUCTURE OF DNA

In the early 1950s, it was discovered that there is a definite relationship between the relative amounts of the various bases in DNA. The adenine:thymine ratio is always 1:1, and the guanine:cytosine ratio is always 1:1. Therefore it was suspected that pairing of these bases occurred in natural DNA molecules. Furthermore, it was found that the **adenine:guanine** and **thymine:cytosine** ratios varied from species to species. In 1953, in a classic publication, Watson and Crick proposed the structure of DNA. Their conclusion, based on x-ray crystallography data and on the ideas of other scientists working on the same puzzle, was that DNA existed as a double-stranded helix. The two polymeric strands are held together by **hydrogen bonding** between pairs of bases (one base from each strand) to form a sort of twisted ladder. This pairing is shown below.

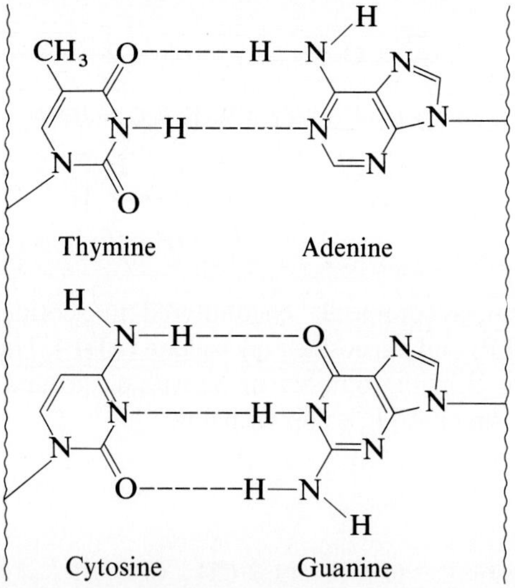

Thymine — Adenine

Cytosine — Guanine

The only pairing relationships that can occur are between adenine and thymine and between cytosine and guanine. Notice that these base-pairing combinations agree with the 1:1 ratios observed earlier. As shown in the diagram above, the specific base pairing occurs because these combinations provide **maximum hydrogen bonding relationships**. This hydrogen bonding

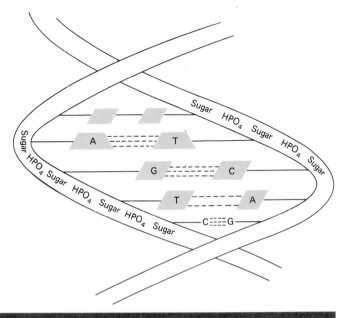

Double helix structure of
deoxyribonucleic acid.

FIGURE 17-1

at each point on the bases stabilizes the system. Other base combinations would allow for less hydrogen bonding and a less stable system. A more general view of the double helix is shown in Figure 17-1.

DNA exists in the living cell as a double helix, the two strands of which are held together by base pairing between thymine and adenine and between cytosine and guanine. This base pairing is the result of hydrogen bonding between a base on one strand and a base on the other strand of the DNA.

SECONDARY STRUCTURE AND FUNCTION OF RNA

Unlike DNA, RNA exists as several different types, each with a different function. The two types of RNA that we will consider are **messenger RNA (mRNA)** and **transfer RNA (tRNA)**. We will examine their structures and roles in protein synthesis.

Messenger RNA

mRNA is a single-stranded polymer which is formed in the cell nucleus according to the base order coding of a portion of the DNA molecule. The order of the bases in a segment of the DNA causes a particular ordering of the bases in the mRNA molecule being formed. Once the mRNA is produced, it moves to the site of protein synthesis, where it serves as a **template** for the ordering of the amino acids in the protein molecule being synthesized. The primary structure of each protein needed by a cell is coded somewhere on the DNA, and a different mRNA is produced for each protein as needed. An overview of this process is shown in Figure 17-2.

The mRNA primary structure (base sequence) contains adjacent groups of three bases which code for a particular amino acid. These groups are called **codons** and are shown below in general terms.

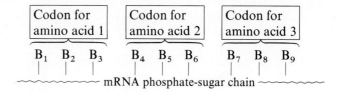

Transfer RNA

tRNA, which also plays an important role in protein synthesis, has an overall "clover leaf" secondary structure as shown below.

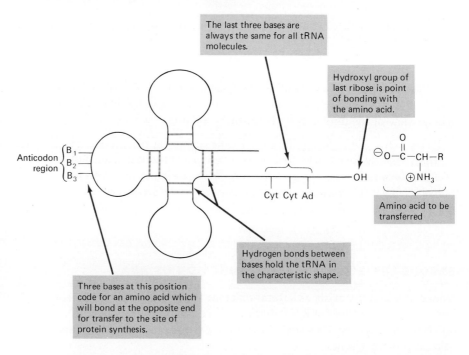

The purpose of tRNA is to transport amino acids from various locations in the cell to the **ribosomes**, where protein synthesis takes place. Three bases at the end of the tRNA form a code for a particular amino acid. A given tRNA molecule will become bonded to the particular amino acid for which its bases code and will move it into place. The region containing the coding bases is called the **anticodon**; in addition to coding for an amino aicd, it also "matches" the codon bases of mRNA via hydrogen bonding. This codon-anticodon matching determines which amino acids are placed in sequence in the protein being synthesized. The amino acid is transferred to the protein being synthesized by the forming of an ester bond between the COOH of the amino acid and the OH attached to the number 3 carbon atom of the last ribose in the tRNA chain. There are 61 known tRNA molecules; several of these code for each of the 20 amino acids used to build proteins.

An overview of the role of RNA in protein synthesis is illustrated in Figure 17-2.

Let's examine Figure 17-2 and follow the processes as they occur. First, mRNA is enzymatically synthesized (**transcribed**) according to the coding in a segment of the DNA molecule in the cell nucleus (point A). Next, this mRNA moves to the ribosomes, where protein synthesis takes place (point B). In the cytoplasm, tRNA molecules become enzymatically bonded to the amino acids indicated by their anticodons (point C). As tRNA molecules move to the ribosomes and diffuse through the medium they "match up" with the codon region (point D) of the mRNA which serves as a

FIGURE 17-2

Overview of protein synthesis and the role of nucleic acids.

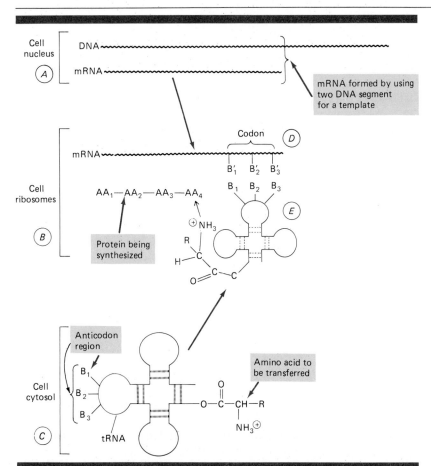

template for the particular protein being synthesized. Once this match is found, the amino acid bonded to the tRNA is transferred to the developing protein and forms an amide bond with the previous amino acid in the developing protein chain (point E).

After all the required amino acids have been added to the protein chain, the protein molecule separates from the mRNA, assumes its natural secondary and tertiary structure, and serves its function in the cell. The efficiency of protein synthesis is dramatic. Several proteins can be produced at the same time in the same region of the ribosomes with no error in the ordering of amino acids. A protein molecule with 50 to 100 amino acids can be perfectly synthesized in a matter of seconds.

Protein synthesis takes place when tRNA moves amino acid units into place according to the ordering dictated by codons on mRNA. The mRNA receives its base sequence code from a segment of the DNA.

SUMMARY

1 **Deoxyribonucleic acid** (DNA) contains a copolymer of alternating sugar (2-deoxy-D-ribose) and phosphate units. The genetic code for a given organism is contained in the exact **sequence of heterocyclic base units** attached to the sugar portions of the polymer chain.

2 There are several types of **ribonucleic acids**, but all are composed of a sugar (D-ribose) and phosphate copolymer chain plus a heterocylic base unit bonded to each sugar unit.

3 **Nucleotides** are monomeric materials that are structurally related to the nucleic acids. Nucleotide molecules are composed of a sugar, a base, and one to three phosphate units.

4 The secondary structure of DNA consists of a **double helix**. The two strands of this helix are held together by **hydrogen bonding** between a base unit on one strand and a base unit on the other strand.

5 Protein synthesis occurs in the cell as a result of coding in a segment of the DNA. **Messenger RNA** is synthesized in the nucleus and serves as a template for the primary structure of a protein. **Transfer RNA** molecules move the needed amino acids to the site of synthesis. There, individual amino acids are placed in sequence by the match between the **codons** on the mRNA and the **anticodons** on the tRNA.

KEY TERMS

ADP	Codon	mRNA
Anticodon	Deoxyribonucleic acid	tRNA
ATP	Nucleotide	Transcription
Base pairing	Ribonucleic acid	

SKILL PRACTICE PROBLEMS

1   After studying Figure 17-2 and the accompanying text, describe in your own words how protein synthesis takes place.

2   What is the single most important factor in determining the interactions of biomolecules with each other?

3   What force holds tRNA in the "clover leaf" general shape?

4   Why are adenine, thymine, cytosine, guanine, and uracil called bases?

5   Draw the free structures of all the bases found in nucleic acids (i.e., what are the structures of the base units when they are unattached to the sugar?).

6   Draw the molecular structure of 5-fluorouracil, an anticancer medication. Refer to the numbering system shown on the general structures of purine and pyrimidine on page 517.

7   Draw the structure of the nucleotide composed of 2-deoxy-D-ribose, guanine, and two phosphate units.

REVIEW QUESTIONS

8   Write the reaction of cytosine with hydrochloric acid (HCl).

9   How many of the base units found in nucleic acids contain ketone functional groups? How many contain amide functional groups?

10   List the infrared spectral absorbances you would expect for uracil.

TYPES OF ORGANIC REACTIONS

Throughout this book special terms are used to describe types of reactions. This appendix defines and illustrates these terms. Eight types of reactions have been chosen. Organic reactions can be categorized in a number of different ways, and this organization is not unique.

The fact that there are eight sections to this appendix does not imply that there are eight and only eight reaction types. This organization is simply a convenient way of presenting the terms used to describe reactions in the text.

1 *Substitution.* One atom, or group of atoms, on the organic molecule is removed and another put in its place. In general

$$-\overset{|}{\underset{|}{C}}-X + Y \longrightarrow -\overset{|}{\underset{|}{C}}-Y + X$$

Examples are

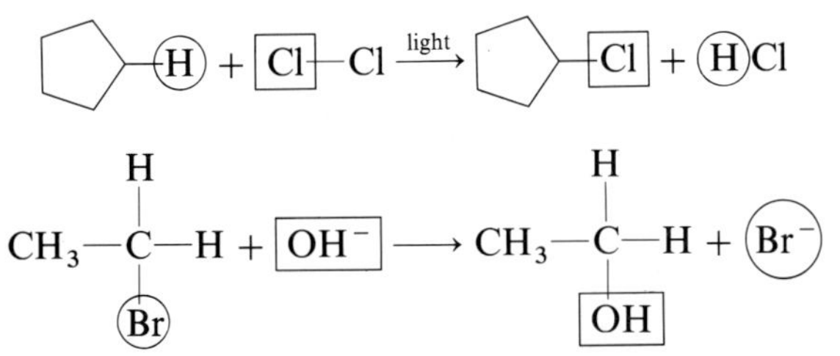

$$\bigcirc\!\!-\!\!\text{(H)} + \boxed{\text{Cl}}\!\!-\!\!\text{Cl} \xrightarrow{\text{light}} \bigcirc\!\!-\!\!\boxed{\text{Cl}} + \text{(H)}\text{Cl}$$

$$CH_3-\overset{\overset{\displaystyle H}{|}}{\underset{\underset{\displaystyle \text{(Br)}}{|}}{C}}-H + \boxed{OH^-} \longrightarrow CH_3-\overset{\overset{\displaystyle H}{|}}{\underset{\underset{\displaystyle \boxed{OH}}{|}}{C}}-H + \text{(Br}^-)$$

In the first example, a Cl atom replaces an H atom; in the second example, an OH group is substituted for a Br atom.

525

2 *Addition.* Two molecules simply add together to make a larger molecule.

$$A + B \longrightarrow A{-}B$$

Examples are

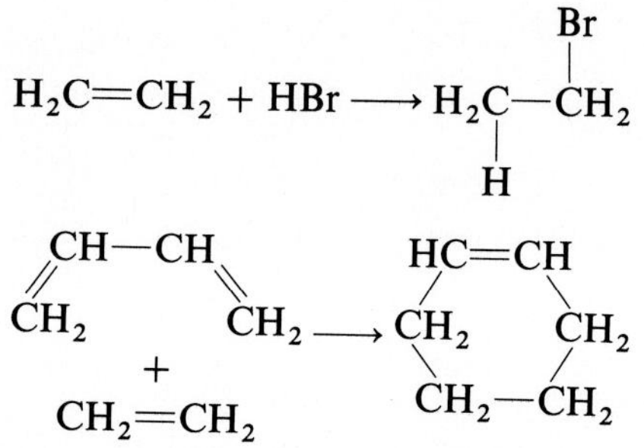

$$H_2C{=}CH_2 + HBr \longrightarrow H_2C{-}\underset{\displaystyle H}{\overset{\displaystyle Br}{C}}H_2$$

Here, in the first example a small HBr molecule adds to an alkene molecule, and in the second example two alkene molecules add together to make a larger cyclic molecule.

3 *Elimination.* This is just the opposite of addition—one molecule splits into two parts. Usually one of the parts is a small molecule such as H_2O or HCl, and the remaining carbon-containing portion has a double or triple bond.

$$A{-}B \longrightarrow A + B$$

Examples are

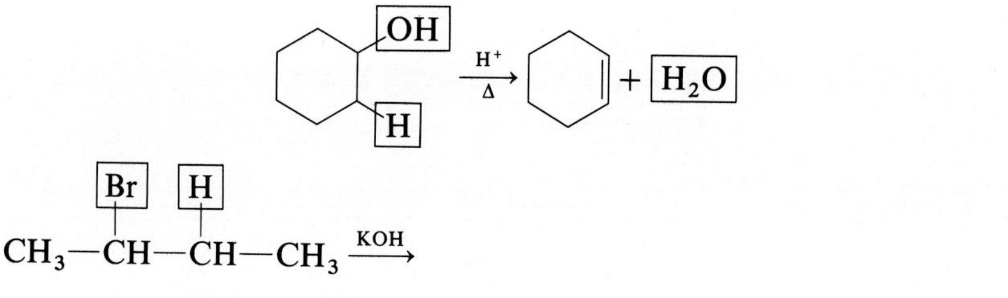

$$CH_3{-}\underset{\displaystyle \boxed{Br}}{CH}{-}\underset{\displaystyle \boxed{H}}{CH}{-}CH_3 \xrightarrow{\text{KOH}}$$

$$CH_3CH{=}CH{-}CH_3 + K^+\boxed{Br^-} + \boxed{H}{-}OH$$

Here an alcohol and an alkyl halide eliminate water and HBr, respectively.

4 *Condensation.* Two organic molecules join together while splitting out a small molecule such as water, HCl, or NH_3 in the process.

$$A{-}X + Y{-}B \longrightarrow A{-}B + XY$$

Examples are

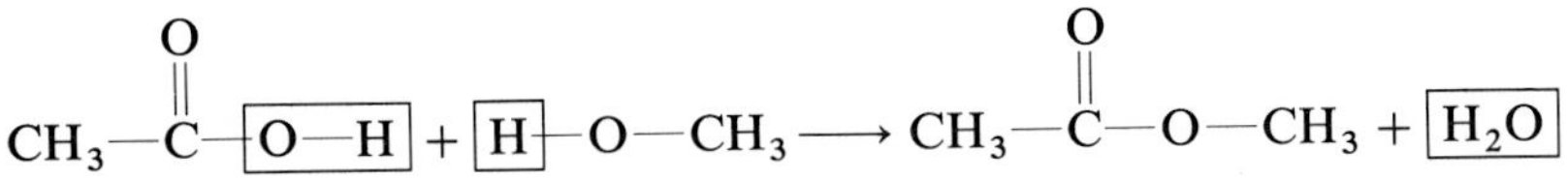

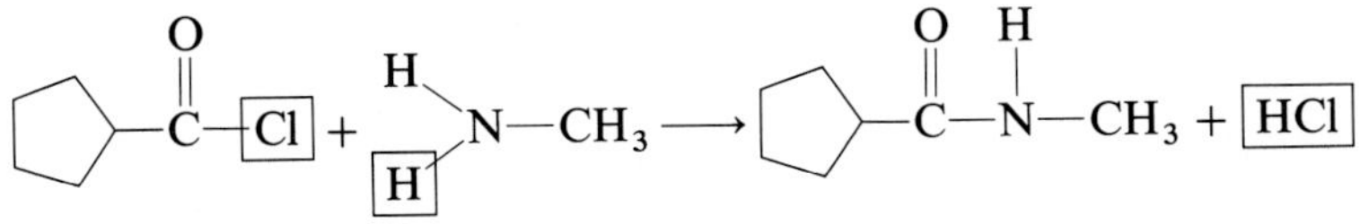

$$CH_3-\overset{\overset{\textstyle O}{\|}}{C}-\boxed{O-H} + \boxed{H}-O-CH_3 \longrightarrow CH_3-\overset{\overset{\textstyle O}{\|}}{C}-O-CH_3 + \boxed{H_2O}$$

Here water and HCl are split out as an ester and an amide respectively, are produced.

5 *Hydrolysis.* A large molecule is split into two parts, and the atoms of water take the place of the broken bonds. The water molecule is split (or lysed) in the process. This is just the opposite of condensation.

$$A-B + X-Y \longrightarrow A-X + C-Y$$

Examples are

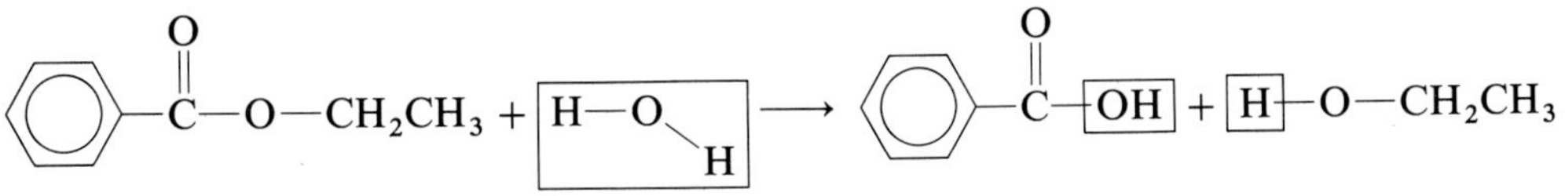

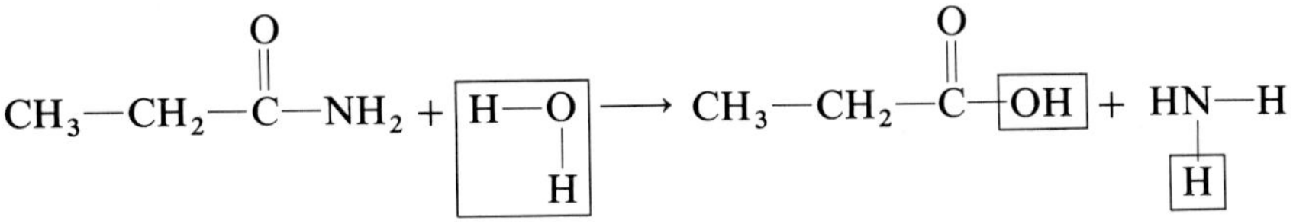

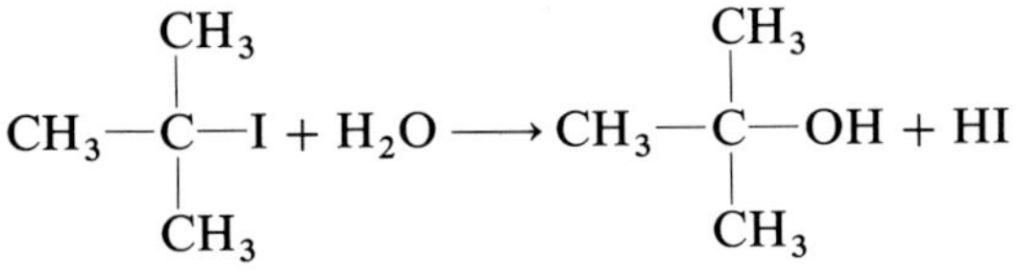

$$CH_3-CH_2-\overset{\overset{\textstyle O}{\|}}{C}-NH_2 + \boxed{H-O}_{\underset{\textstyle H}{|}} \longrightarrow CH_3-CH_2-\overset{\overset{\textstyle O}{\|}}{C}-\boxed{OH} + HN-H \quad \boxed{H}$$

$$\underset{\underset{\textstyle CH_3}{|}}{\overset{\overset{\textstyle CH_3}{|}}{CH_3-C-I}} + H_2O \longrightarrow \underset{\underset{\textstyle CH_3}{|}}{\overset{\overset{\textstyle CH_3}{|}}{CH_3-C-OH}} + HI$$

6 *Rearrangement (isomerization).* No atoms are gained or lost by the molecule. They simply change places.

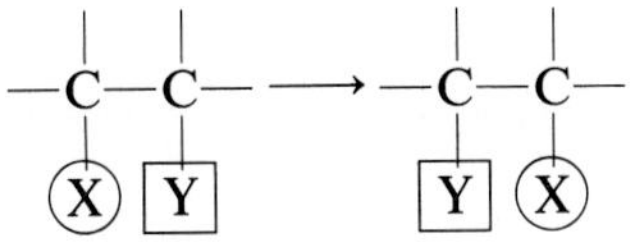

Examples are

The H atom moves to the end of the molecule, and the $C=C$ moves to the center. This is called a 1,3 hydride shift since the H atom moves two carbon atoms to the right (i.e., from one carbon atom to the third atom along the chain).

$$H_2C=CH-O-CH_2-CH=CH_2 \xrightarrow{\Delta}$$

Here an alkene ether changes to an alkene aldehyde.

7 *Oxidation-reduction.* The oxidation state (number) of one or more carbon atoms changes. Some addition, substitution, and elimination reactions also change the oxidation state of carbon atoms. Thus, some reactions can be classified in more than one way. Consider the oxidation states of the carbon atom in each of the functional groups shown in the table below. The oxidation state of a carbon atom is calculated by adding the following numbers: -1 for each hydrogen atom attached; $+1$ for each bond to an atom more electronegative than carbon (such as O, N); zero for any other carbon atoms attached.

COMPOUND	FUNCTIONAL GROUP CLASS	OXIDATION NUMBER OF C ATOM	OXIDATION STATE
CH_4	Alkane	-4	Most reduced
CH_3-OH or CH_3-Cl	Alcohol or alkyl halide	-2	
	Aldehyde	0	
$H-\overset{\overset{\displaystyle O}{\|}}{C}-OH$	Carboxylic acid	$+2$	
CO_2	Carbon dioxide	$+4$	Most oxidized

As one goes downward in the table, the oxidation number increases; thus, oxidation has occurred. Oxidation is the loss of electrons (to produce a more positive oxidation state), the loss of hydrogen atoms, or the bonding to more electronegative atoms such as oxygen. Reduction occurs as we go upward in the table. Reduction is the gain of electrons, the gain of hydrogen atoms, or the bonding to atoms with a lower electronegativity.

An example of oxidation is

$$CH_4 + 2O_2 \longrightarrow O{=}C{=}O + 2H_2O$$

$$\boxed{-4} \qquad \boxed{+4}$$

Carbon has a higher oxidation state after the reaction. It is also bonded to fewer hydrogen atoms and more oxygen atoms.

Another example of oxidation is

$$CH_3{-}\overset{\overset{O}{\|}}{C}{-}H \xrightarrow{KMnO_4} CH_3{-}\overset{\overset{O}{\|}}{C}{-}OH$$

$$\boxed{+1} \qquad \boxed{+3}$$

The carbon atom indicated has changed its oxidation state from $+1$ to $+3$. It also has one less hydrogen atom and one more oxygen atom in the carboxylic acid state than in the aldehyde state. The $-CH_3$ group is not changed during this reaction.

An example of reduction is

$$CH_3{-}\overset{\overset{O}{\|}}{C}{-}OH \xrightarrow{LiAlH_4} CH_3{-}\overset{\overset{H}{|}}{\underset{\underset{H}{|}}{C}}{-}O{-}H$$

$$\boxed{+3} \qquad \boxed{-1}$$

Here the acid has been reduced to an alcohol. The indicated carbon atom has fewer oxygen atoms, more hydrogen atoms, and has gone from an oxidation number of $+3$ to -1.

Another example of reduction is

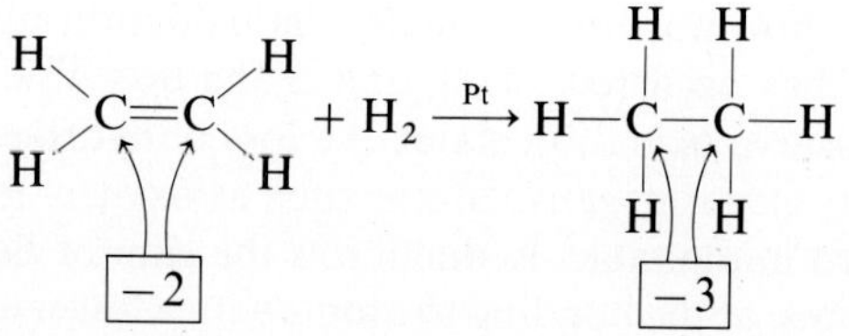

$$\underset{H}{\overset{H}{>}}C=C\underset{H}{\overset{H}{<}} \;+\; H_2 \xrightarrow{Pt} \; H-\underset{\underset{H}{|}}{\overset{\overset{H}{|}}{C}}-\underset{\underset{H}{|}}{\overset{\overset{H}{|}}{C}}-H$$

$$\boxed{-2} \qquad\qquad\qquad \boxed{-3}$$

After this reaction, the carbon atoms are bonded to more hydrogen atoms, thus reduction has occurred. No oxygen atoms are present, and we need not calculate the oxidation numbers, since the added hydrogen atoms provide a means of classifying the reaction. The oxidation number for the carbon atom does go down from -2 to -3, however. Note that this reaction is also an addition reaction. This points out that a given reaction sometimes can be classified in more than one way.

8 *Acid-base reactions.* The three definitions of acids and bases are given in Table 12-1. The Lowery-Brønsted definition is the most useful for organic chemistry. This concept is discussed for carboxylic acid in Chapter 12 and for amines in Chapter 13. For this book, then, the following definitions will be used:

Acid   a compound that donates an H^+

Base   a compound that accepts an H^+ (Lowery-Brønsted) or donates a pair of electrons (Lewis)

Examples are

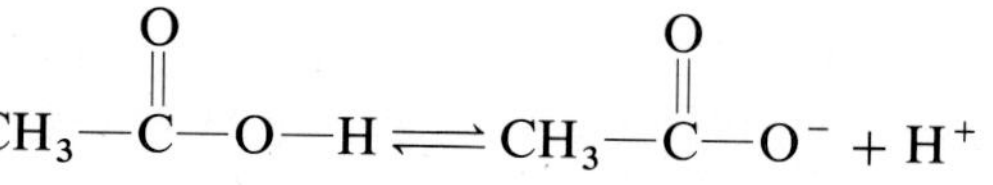

$$\underset{\text{Acid}}{CH_3-\overset{\overset{\displaystyle O}{\|}}{C}-O-H} \;\rightleftharpoons\; CH_3-\overset{\overset{\displaystyle O}{\|}}{C}-O^- + H^+$$

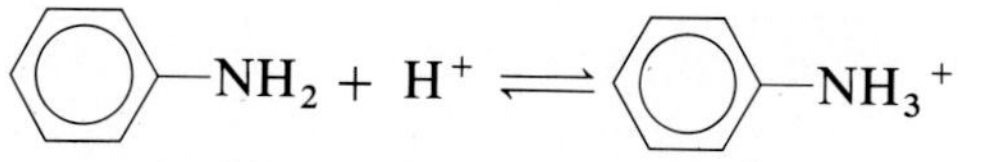

$$\underset{\text{Base}}{\bigcirc\!\!-NH_2} + \underset{\text{Acid}}{H^+} \;\rightleftharpoons\; \bigcirc\!\!-NH_3{}^+$$

$$\underset{\text{Base}}{CH_3-CH_2-O^-\overset{+}{M}gCl} + \underset{\text{Acid}}{H_2O} \longrightarrow CH_3CH_2-OH + OH^-$$

$$\underset{\text{Base}}{CH_3-CH_2-\overset{..}{\underset{..}{O}}-H} + \underset{\text{Acid}}{H^+} \longrightarrow CH_3-CH_2-\overset{\overset{\displaystyle H}{|}}{\underset{..}{\overset{+}{O}}}-H$$

SELECTED
REACTION
MECHANISMS

This appendix contains the accepted reaction mechanisms for selected reactions that were covered in this book, but for which mechanisms were not discussed. Generally, in the main body of the book reaction mechanisms are given only when the mechanism is useful in explaining some aspect of the reaction. This appendix is organized according to chapters. These mechanisms are given without explanation.

CHAPTER 5

Dehydrohalogenation

Concerted

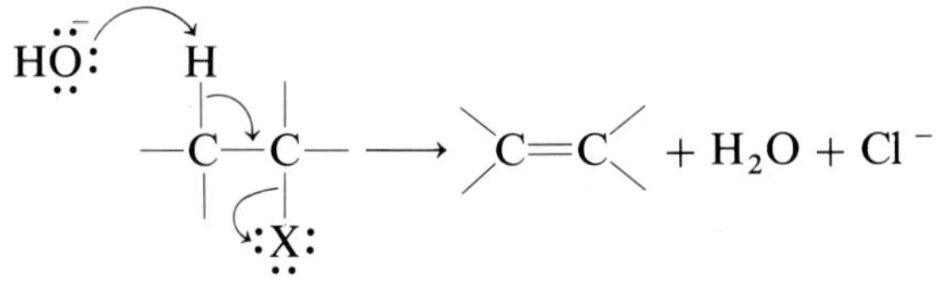

$$HO^{-} \quad H$$
$$-\overset{|}{C}-\overset{|}{C}- \longrightarrow C=C + H_2O + Cl^{-}$$
$$\underset{:X:}{|}$$

CHAPTER 7

Acid cleavage of ethers

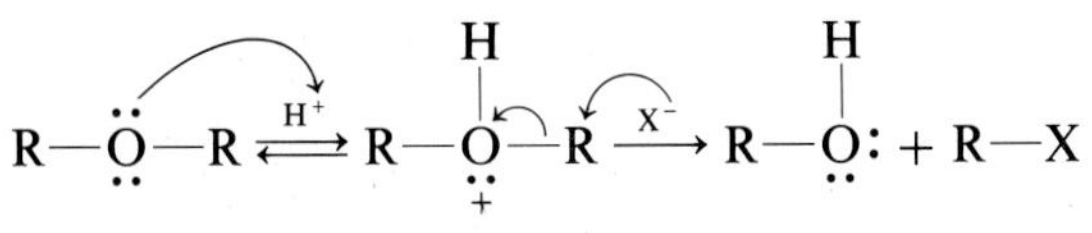

$$R-\ddot{O}-R \xrightarrow{H^+} R-\overset{H}{\underset{\underset{+}{\cdot\cdot}}{O}}-R \xrightarrow{X^-} R-\overset{H}{\underset{\cdot\cdot}{O}}: + R-X$$

CHAPTER 8

Hemiacetal formation

Acid catalyzed

Acetal formation (acid catalyzed)

Formation of ammonia derivatives of aldehydes and ketones

Acid catalyzed

CHAPTER 12

Ester formation

Ester hydrolysis

Base catalyzed

Acid catalyzed

APPENDIX C

COMMON ORGANIC MATERIALS

This appendix contains the names, molecular structures, and uses or occurrences of a number of organic materials of commercial importance, biological or medical use, or consumer interest. The materials listed here are usually those that are not shown in the main body of this book. For the structure of those materials that are given in the book, refer to the index for page references.

NAME	MOLECULAR STRUCTURE	USE OR OCCURRENCE
p-Amino benzoic acid (PABA)	H_2N—⬡—COOH	Sunscreen, protection against ultraviolet rays of the sun
Atrazine	CH_3—CH_2—NH—(triazine ring with Cl)—NH—$CHCH_3$ (CH_3)	Herbicide
Butylate (Sutan)	CH_3—CH_2—S—C(=O)—N—(CH_2—CH—CH_3)$_2$ (CH_3)	Herbicide
Camphor	(bicyclic structure with CH_3, CH_3, CH_3, and O)	Anesthetic

537

NAME	MOLECULAR STRUCTURE	USE OR OCCURRENCE
Carbaryl (Sevin)		Insecticide
Carvone		Oil of spearmint
Chlordiazepoxide (Librium)		Tranquilizer
Citric acid		Found in citrus fruits
Cocaine		Stimulant
Cream of tartar (potassium acid tartrate)		Ingredient in baking powder
Diazepam (Valium)		Tranquilizer and anticonvulsant

NAME	MOLECULAR STRUCTURE	USE OR OCCURRENCE
2,4-Dichlorophenoxyacetic acid (2,4-D)		Herbicide
Diethylstilbesterol		Compound used in estrogen therapy (no longer widely used)
Divinyl ether	$CH_2{=}CH{-}O{-}CH{=}CH_2$	Anesthetic
Ephedrine		Nasal decongestant
Furazolidone		Antibacterial agent
Heroin		Narcotic
Hexylresorcinol		Anesthetic
Lactic acid		Component of sour milk
Lidocaine (Xylocaine)		Local anesthetic
Malathion		Insecticide

NAME	MOLECULAR STRUCTURE	USE OR OCCURRENCE
Maleic hydrazide		Plant growth inhibitor
Melamine polymer (Formica)		Tough polymer used in lamination for desk and counter tops
Meperidine (Demerol)		Pain reliever
Mephenesin		Muscle relaxant
Meprobamate (Miltown)		Tranquilizer
Methadone		Drug used to treat heroin addiction
Morphine		Narcotic and pain killer
Mustard gas	$Cl—CH_2CH_2—S—CH_2CH_2—Cl$	War gas
Nicotine		Compound found in poisons used for pests and in tobacco smoke

NAME	MOLECULAR STRUCTURE	USE OR OCCURRENCE
Paraquat		Herbicide
Penicillin G		Antibacterial agent
Phenobarbital		Anticonvulsant and sedative
Bakelite		Inexpensive plastic
Phenylcyclidine (Angel dust, PCP)		Mind-altering drug
Piperazine		Worm killer in animals
Progesterone		Female sex hormone
Safrole		Flavor in sassafras and root beer

NAME	MOLECULAR STRUCTURE	USE OR OCCURRENCE
Secobarbital		Short-acting hypnotic
TCDD (dioxin)		Toxic contaminant of some herbicide preparations
Testosterone		Male sex hormone
Tetrahydrocannabinol (THC)		Active ingredient in marijuana

ANSWERS TO

EVEN-NUMBERED PROBLEMS

CHAPTER 1

2 (a)

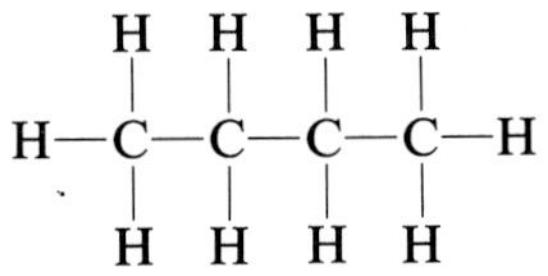

H—C—C—C—C—H with H's above and below each C

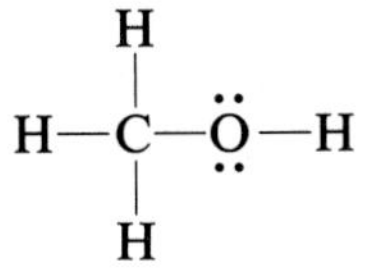

(b)

H—C—Ö—H with H above and below C

(c)

:O:
||
H—C—Ö:

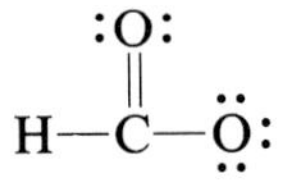

4

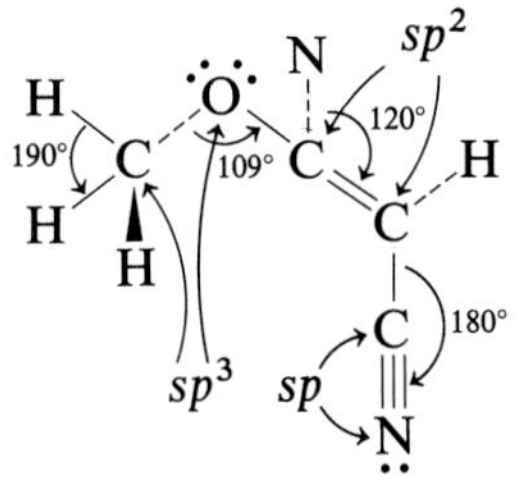

6 See text.

8

CH₂—CH₂
CH₂   CH—CH₂—CH₂
   CH₂

C—C
C   C—C—C
   C

(cyclopentane with ethyl group structure)

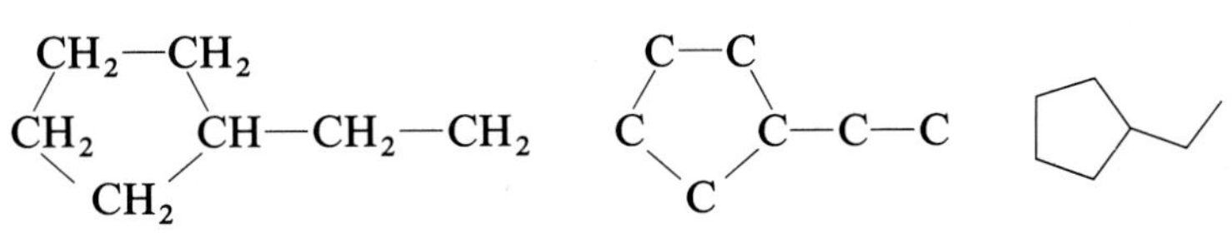

10 Structure (b) is not correct: Cl has two bonds (it normally forms only one) and O has only six electrons instead of the octet required.

12 (a) polar $\delta+$ C—O $\delta-$ (b) not polar
(c) polar $\delta-$ N—H $\delta+$ (d) polar $\delta+$ C—Cl $\delta-$

14 (a)

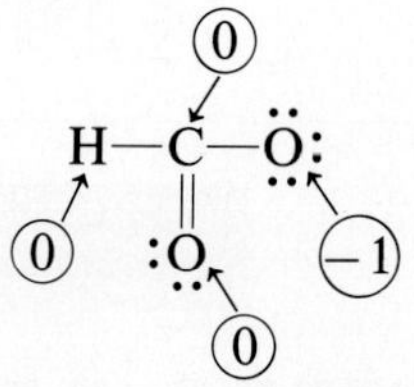

$$H-\overset{\underset{|}{\overset{|}{\circ}}}{\underset{\underset{\circ}{\overset{}{}}}{C}}-\ddot{\overset{..}{O}}:$$

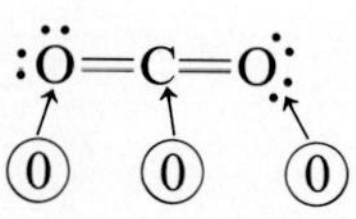

(formal charges shown: 0 on H, 0 on C, O with -1, O below with 0)

(b) $:\ddot{O}=C=\ddot{O}:$ (0, 0, 0)

(c)

$$H-\overset{}{C}=\overset{}{N}-H\leftarrow O$$

with $:\overset{..}{O}:$ (-1) below C, N carrying $(+1)$, and formal charges 0, 0 H, 0 indicated

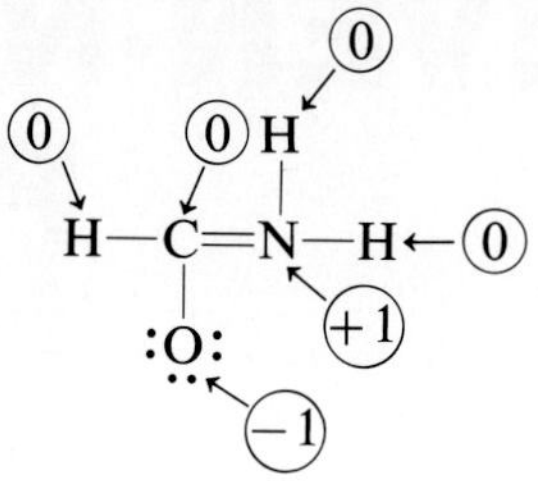

CHAPTER 2

2 $CH_3-CH_2-CH_2-OH$ $CH_3-\underset{\underset{OH}{|}}{CH}-CH_3$

$CH_3-CH_2-O-CH_3$

4 (a) broad leaf weed killer   (b) anesthesia
(c) sun burn protection   (d) beverage
(e) insecticide

6 (a) carboxylic acid, aromatic, amine
(b) ketone, aromatic, phenol
(c) alkene, amide. aromatic
(d) substituted alkane (alkyl halide), alcohol
(e) cyclic alkane

8 (a) $C_6H_{12}O$ (b) C_3H_4
(c) $C_{18}H_{36}O_2$ (d) C_4H_8O
(e) $C_6H_{12}O$ (f) $C_3H_6O_2$

10 See text page 38 for a comparison with your answer.

12 Nitrogen: amine and amide. Oxygen: alcohol, phenol, ester, ketone, aldehyde, ether, carboxylic acid, and amide

14

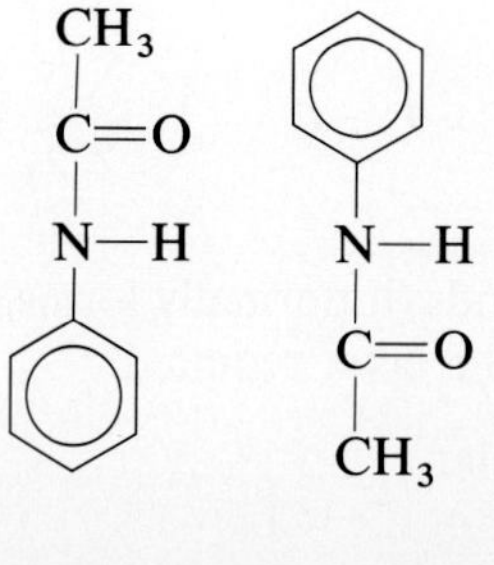

$$\underset{\underset{\underset{\underset{C_6H_5}{|}}{N-H}}{|}}{\overset{\overset{\overset{CH_3}{|}}{C=O}}{}}$$

(one structure: $CH_3-C(=O)-N-H$ attached to phenyl; second structure: phenyl$-N-H-C(=O)-CH_3$)

This indicates that as long as the atoms are connected in the same way, the orientation or direction of drawing a structure is not important.

16 The pairs (b), (e), and (f) are isomers.

18 Carbon must have four bonds; oxygen must have two bonds.

20 All would contain highly polar bonds except the hydrocarbons.

CHAPTER 3

2 The structures are as follows:

(a) $CH_3-CH_2-CH_2-CH_2-CH_2-CH_2-CH_3$

(b)
$$CH_3-CH_2-CH_2-CH_2-\underset{\underset{CH_3}{|}}{CH}-CH_3$$

(c)
$$CH_3-CH_2-CH_2-\underset{\underset{CH_3}{|}}{CH}-CH_2-CH_3$$

(d)
$$CH_3-CH_2-\underset{\underset{\underset{CH_3}{|}}{\overset{|}{CH_2}}}{CH}-CH_2-CH_3$$

(e)
$$CH_3-CH_2-CH_2-\underset{\underset{CH_3}{|}}{\overset{\overset{CH_3}{|}}{C}}-CH_3$$

(f)
$$CH_3-CH_2-\underset{\underset{CH_3}{|}}{\overset{\overset{CH_3}{|}}{C}}-CH_2-CH_3$$

(g)
$$CH_3-CH_2-\underset{\underset{CH_3}{|}}{CH}-\underset{\underset{CH_3}{|}}{CH}-CH_3$$

(h)
$$CH_3-\underset{\underset{CH_3}{|}}{CH}-CH_2-\underset{\underset{CH_3}{|}}{CH}-CH_3$$

(i)

$$\underset{\underset{CH_3}{|}}{CH_3}-\underset{\underset{CH_3}{|}}{CH}-\overset{\overset{CH_3}{|}}{\underset{\underset{CH_3}{|}}{C}}-CH_3$$

Names of these structures are (a) Heptane; (b) 2-Methylhexane; (c) 3-Methylhexane; (d) 3-Ethylpentane; (e) 2,2-Dimethylpentane; (f) 3,3-Dimethylpentane; (g) 2,3-Dimethylpentane; (h) 2,4-Dimethylpentane; (i) 2,2,3-Trimethylbutane

4 Errors are as follows: (a) Position of *both* methyl groups should be given; 2,2-dimethylnonane. (b) Longest chain was not chosen; nonane. (c) Longest chain was not chosen; 3-methylhexane. (d) Prefix di- was omitted; 3,3-dichloro-1-methylcyclohexane.

6 Names are as follows: (a) 3-Bromo-2-methylhexane; (b) 2-Cyclobutylbutane; (c) 3,3-Diethylpentane; (d) 1,1-Dipropylcyclopentane; (e) 3,3-Dichloro-4,5-dimethylnonane.

8 Products of the reactions are

(a) $CH_3CH_2CH_2CH_2CH_3$ (b) $CH_3CH_2CH_3$ (c)

(d)

$$\underset{}{CH_3CH_2CHCH_3} \overset{\overset{CH_3}{\diagup}}{}$$

(e)

$$CH_3-\overset{\overset{CH_3}{|}}{\underset{\underset{CH_3}{|}}{C}}-H$$

(f)

(g)

10

CH_3-CH_2

12 (a) Gasoline; (b) Natural gas; (c) Kerosine

14 $3050 \text{ g/gal}(10.5 \text{ kcal/g}) = 32{,}000 \text{ kcal/gal}$

16 See text.

18

20 (a) Isopropyl; (b) Isobutyl; (c) *sec*-Butyl.

22 (a)

$$\underset{\underset{CH_3}{|}}{CH_3}-\underset{}{CH}-CH_2-CH_3$$

(b)

$$CH_3-\overset{\overset{CH_3}{|}}{\underset{\underset{CH_3}{|}}{C}}-CH_3$$

CHAPTER 4

2 (*a*)

$$
\begin{array}{c}\text{Cl}\\ \text{CH}_3\!-\!\!\!\!\!-\!\text{H}\\ \text{CH}_3\end{array}
\quad\text{or}\quad
\begin{array}{c}\text{CH}_3\\ \text{H}\!-\!\!\!\!\!-\!\text{CH}_3\\ \text{Cl}\end{array}
\quad\text{or}\quad
\begin{array}{c}\text{CH}_3\\ \text{Cl}\!-\!\!\!\!\!-\!\text{H}\\ \text{CH}_3\end{array}
\quad\text{plus others}
$$

(*b*)

$$
\begin{array}{c}\text{Cl}\\ \text{I}\!-\!\!\!\!\!-\!\text{CH}_2\!-\!\text{CH}_3\\ \text{Br}\end{array}
\quad\text{or}\quad
\begin{array}{c}\text{CH}_2\!-\!\text{CH}_3\\ \text{Br}\!-\!\!\!\!\!-\!\text{Cl}\\ \text{I}\end{array}
\quad\text{plus others}
$$

(*c*)

$$
\begin{array}{c}\text{H}\\ \text{Cl}\!-\!\!\!\!\!-\!\text{CH}_3\\ \text{H}\end{array}
\quad\text{or}\quad
\begin{array}{c}\text{H}\\ \text{H}_3\text{C}\!-\!\!\!\!\!-\!\text{Cl}\\ \text{H}\end{array}
\quad\text{plus others}
$$

(*d*)

$$
\begin{array}{c}\text{O}\!\!\diagdown\;\;\diagup\text{H}\\ \text{C}\\ \text{I}\!-\!\!\!\!\!-\!\text{H}\\ \text{CH}_2\!-\!\text{I}\end{array}
\quad\text{or}\quad
\begin{array}{c}\text{I}\\ \text{H}\!-\!\!\!\!\!-\!\text{C}\diagup\!\!\diagdown\!\!{}^{\text{O}}_{\text{H}}\\ \text{CH}_2\text{I}\end{array}
\quad\text{plus others}
$$

4 (*a*)

$$
\begin{array}{c}\text{CH}_3\\ \text{CH}_2\\ \text{H}\!-\!\!\!\!\!-\!\text{Br}\\ \text{CH}_2\\ \text{CH}_2\\ \text{CH}_3\end{array}
\quad\Big|\quad
\begin{array}{c}\text{CH}_3\\ \text{CH}_2\\ \text{Br}\!-\!\!\!\!\!-\!\text{H}\\ \text{CH}_2\\ \text{CH}_2\\ \text{CH}_3\end{array}
\qquad\text{(}b\text{)}\quad
\begin{array}{c}\text{CH}_2\text{Cl}\\ \text{Cl}\!-\!\!\!\!\!-\!\text{H}\\ \text{CH}_3\end{array}
\quad\Big|\quad
\begin{array}{c}\text{CH}_2\text{Cl}\\ \text{H}\!-\!\!\!\!\!-\!\text{Cl}\\ \text{CH}_3\end{array}
$$

6

$$
\begin{array}{c}\text{COOH}\\ \text{H}\!-\!\text{C}\!-\!\text{OH}\\ \text{H}\!-\!\text{C}\!-\!\text{OH}\\ \text{COOH}\end{array}
\qquad
\begin{array}{c}\text{COOH}\\ \text{HO}\!-\!\text{C}\!-\!\text{H}\\ \text{HO}\!-\!\text{C}\!-\!\text{H}\\ \text{COOH}\end{array}
$$

8 (*a*) (S); (*b*) (R); (*c*) (S)

10 (*a*) Same; (*b*) Same; (*c*) $-50°$; (*d*) L; (*e*) Same; (*f*) Same

12 (*a*) (S)-2-bromopentane; (*b*) (R)-3-chloro-3-methylhexane;
(*c*) (S)-2-bromo-2,4-dichlorobutane

CHAPTER 5

2 (*a*) $\text{CH}_3\!-\!\text{CH}_2\!-\!\text{CH}_2\!-\!\text{CH}_2\!-\!\text{I} + \text{NaCl}\!\downarrow$

(*b*)

$\!-\!\text{CH}_2\!-\!\text{SH}$

(c)

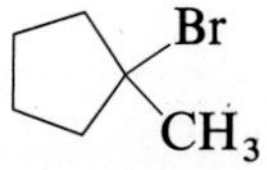

(d)

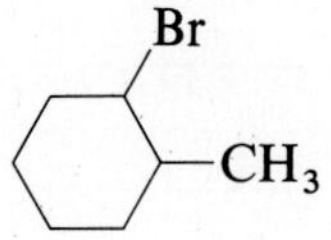

(e) $CH_3-CH_2-CH-CH_3$
$\qquad\qquad\qquad |$
$\qquad\qquad\qquad Cl$

4 (a) 1,1-dichloroethane
(b) 4-bromo-3-iodo-1-methylcyclohexane
(c) 1,2-dichloroethane
(d) 1,2,3-trichloro-4-fluorocyclobutane
(e) chloroform or trichloromethane

6 $CH_3-CH_2-CH_2-CH_2-CH=CH_2 \xrightarrow[\text{peroxide}]{\text{HBr}}$

$CH_3-CH_2-CH_2-CH_2-CH_2-CH_2-Br$

8 (a) S_N1; (b) S_N2; (c) 50 percent S_N1; 50 percent S_N2

10 $Br_2 \xrightarrow{hv} 2Br\cdot$

$CH_3-CH_3 + Br\cdot \longrightarrow CH_3-CH-CH_3 + HBr$

$CH_3-CH_3 + Br_2 \longrightarrow CH_3-CH-CH_3 + Br\cdot$
$\qquad\qquad\qquad\qquad\qquad\qquad\quad |$
$\qquad\qquad\qquad\qquad\qquad\qquad\quad Br$

12 $CH_3-CH_3 \xrightarrow[hv]{Br_2} CH_3-CH_2Br$

14 Markovnikov

16 Because inversion occurs with S_N2 reactions, we obtain the opposite (S) enantiomer:

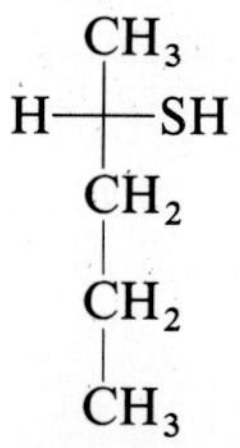

18 No. It is meso.

20 CH_3F is more polar, because F is more electronegative.

22 Both compounds would prefer to have the halogen atom in the equatorial position. Since bromine atoms are larger than fluorine atoms, however, the preference would be larger for the bromocyclohexane. Remember that it is the crowding that makes the axial position relatively less preferred.

CHAPTER 6

2 (a)

sp^3 sp^2

$\triangle \} sp^3$ $CH_3 - CH = CH_2$

(b) For three possible isomers:

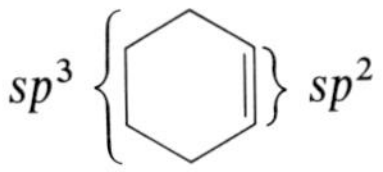

sp^3

$sp^3 \{ \bigcirc \} sp^2$ $CH_3 - CH_2 - CH_2 - CH_2 - C \equiv C - H$ sp

sp^2 sp^2
$CH_2 = CH - CH_2 - CH_2 - CH = CH_2$
sp^3

(c) For two possible isomers:

$\square \} sp^3$ $CH_3 - CH_2 - CH = CH_2$
               sp^3 sp^2

(d) For two possible isomers:

$\hexagon \} sp^2$ $CH_2 = CH - C \equiv C - CH = CH_2$
                    sp^2 sp sp^2

4 (a) $CH_3 - CH_2$ $CH_2 - CH_3$
             $C = C$
             H H

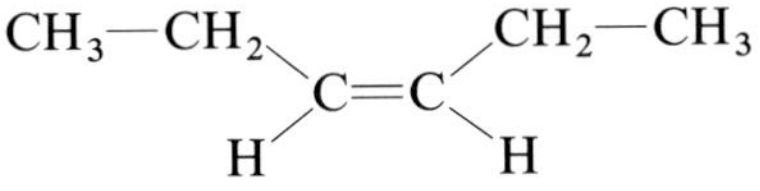

(b) $CH_3 - (CH_2)_3 - C \equiv C - H$

(c) CH_3
     $CH - C \equiv C - CH_3$
  CH_3

(d) CH_3 $CH_2 - CH_3$
       $C = C$
  Cl I

(e) H $CH_2 - CH_2 - CH_3$
                             $C = C$
  $CH_3 - CH_2 - CH_2 - CH_2 - CH_2$ H

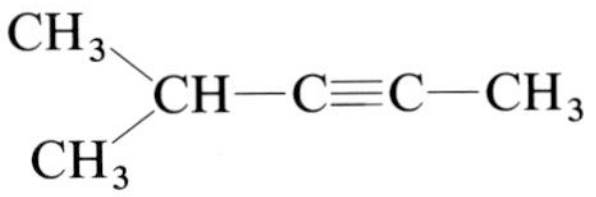

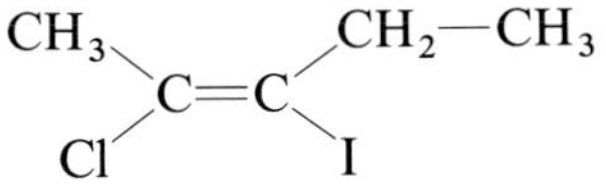

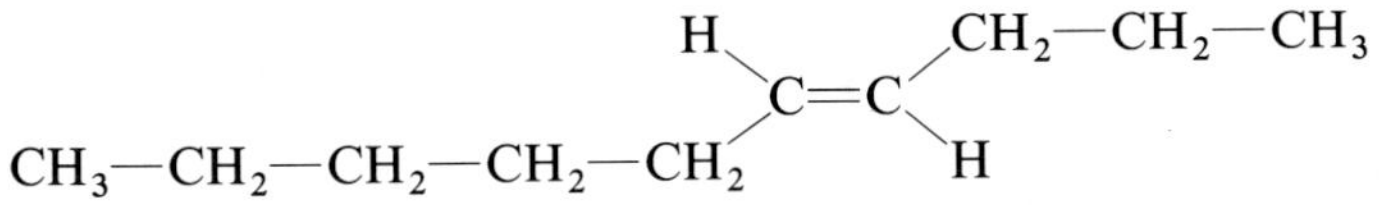

(*f*)

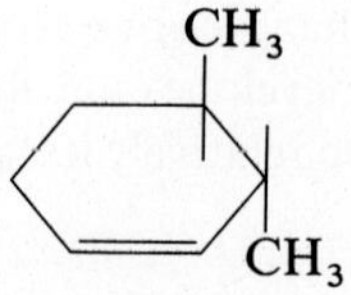

6 (*a*)

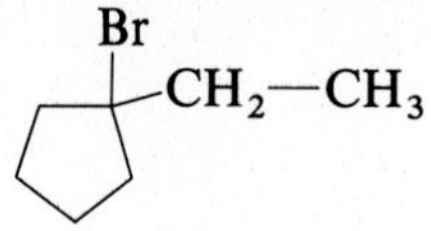

(*b*)

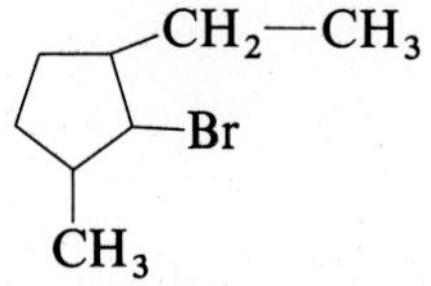

(*c*)

$$2CH_3-\overset{\displaystyle O}{\overset{\|}{C}}-H$$

(*d*) Pentane

(*e*)

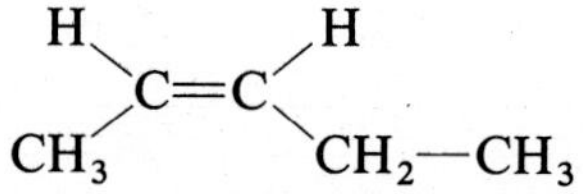

(*f*)

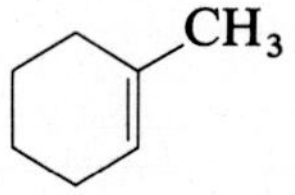

(major) +

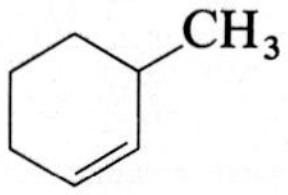

(minor)

(*g*)

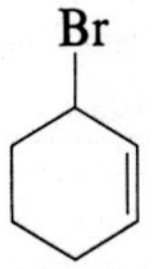

8 (*a*)

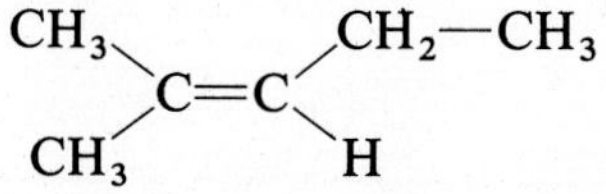

(*b*)

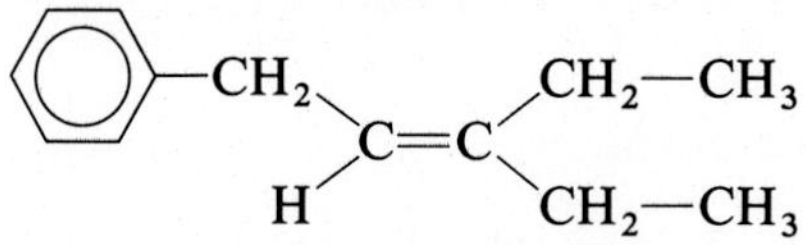

(*c*)

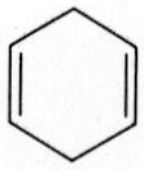

10

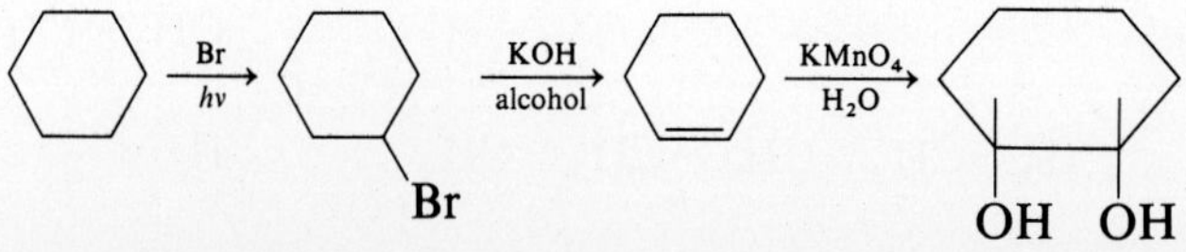

12 (*a*) Baeyer test: purple changes to brown for the alkene; purple remains for the alkane.

(*b*) Ag^+ gives a precipitate for the second (terminal) alkyne but none for the first (nonterminal) alkyne.

(*c*) Ag^+ gives a precipitate for the alkyne but not for the alkene.

14 (*a*) $CH_3-CH_2-C\equiv C-H$ 1-butyne

(*b*) $CH_3-C\equiv C-CH_3$ 2-butyne

(*c*) ▷$-CH_3$ 3-methylcyclopropene

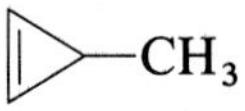

(*d*) ▷$-CH_3$ 1-methylcyclopropene

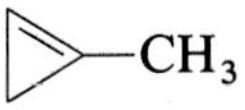

(*e*) ▷$=CH_2$ methylenecyclopropane (we have not covered this nomenclature)

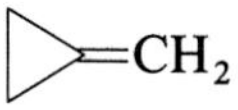

(*f*)  ☐   cyclobutene

(*g*) $CH_2=CH-CH=CH_2$ 1,3-butadiene
(*h*) $CH_2=C=CH-CH_3$ 1,2-butadiene (we have not covered this type of compound)

16 (*a*) $CH_3-CH=CH-CH_3 + HBr \longrightarrow CH_3-CH_2-\underset{\underset{Br}{|}}{CH}-CH_3$

(*b*) $CH_3-CH=CH-CH_3 + $ NBS/peroxides $\longrightarrow$

$CH_3-CH=CH-CH_2-Br$

(*c*) $CH_3-CH=CH-CH_3 + Br_2 \longrightarrow$

$CH_3-\underset{\underset{Br}{|}}{\overset{\overset{Br}{|}}{CH}}-CH-CH_3 \xrightarrow{2NaNH_2} CH_3-C\equiv C-CH_3$

(*d*) $CH_3-CH=CH-CH_3 + H_2 \xrightarrow{Pt} CH_3-CH_2-CH_2-CH_3$

18 See text

20 (*a*) Amide   (*b*) Aldehyde
(*c*) Carboxylic acid   (*d*) Amine, aromatic

22 (*a*)

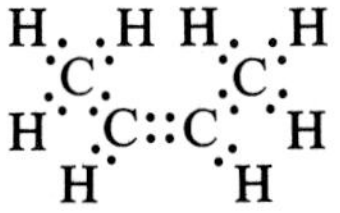

H..C..H H..C..H
H .C::C. H
H   H

(*b*)

H   H
H:C:C:::C:C:H
H   H

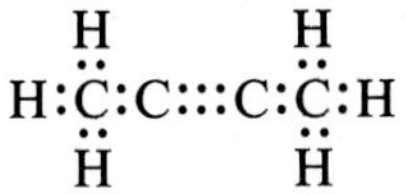

CHAPTER 7

2 (a)

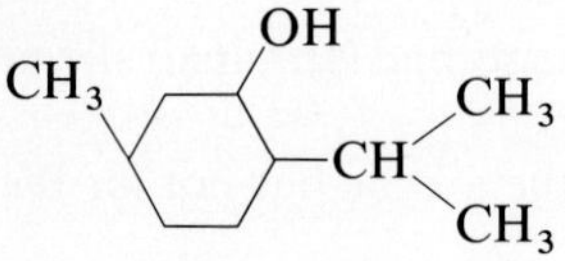

(b) $CH_3-CH-CH_2-OH$
           |
          CH_3

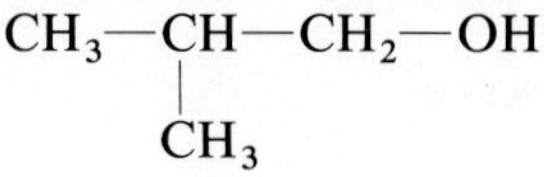

(c)

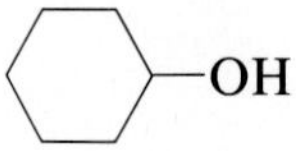

        —OH

(d) $CH_3-CH-CH-CH-CH_2-CH_2-CH_2CH_3$
            | | |
           CH_3 CH_3 OH

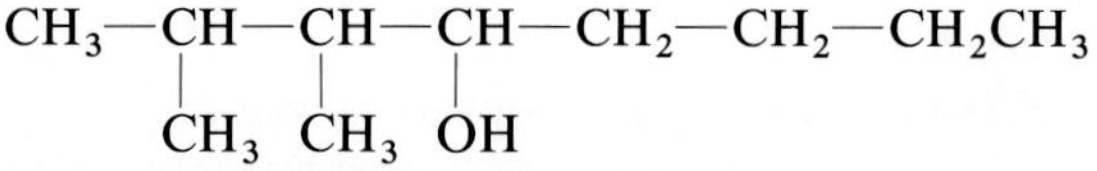

(e)

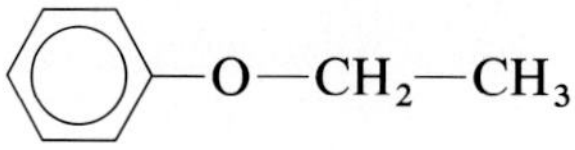

        —O—CH_2—CH_3

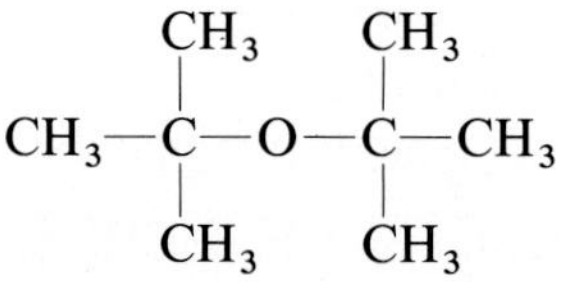

(f) CH_3 CH_3
            | |
   $CH_3-C-O-C-CH_3$
            | |
           CH_3 CH_3

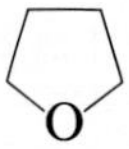

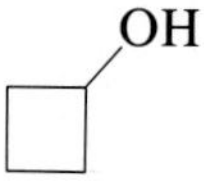

(g)

(h)   OH

(i)   Cl
                  |
   $CH_3-OH-C-CH_2-CH_3$
              | |
             OH CH_3

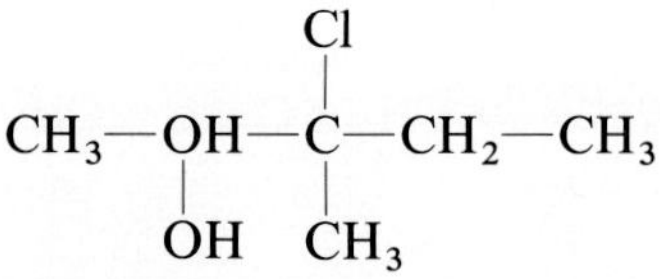

(j) CH_3OH

4 (a)   OH
                    |
   CH_3-CH_2-C—
                    |
                   CH_3

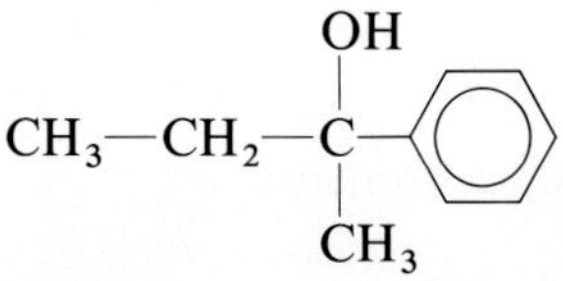

(b) CH_3OH

(c) CH_3Br

(d)   OH
                  |
   $CH_3-CH-CH-CH_3$
          |
         CH_3

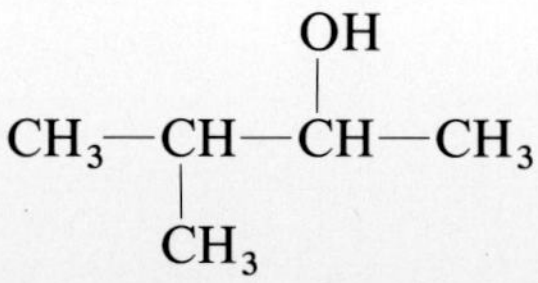

(e)   OH

[structure: cyclobutanol]

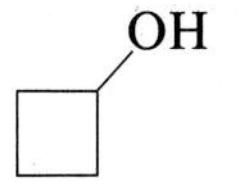

6

[structure: cyclohexene] $\xrightarrow[\text{H}^+]{\text{H}_2\text{O}}$ [structure: cyclohexanol with OH]

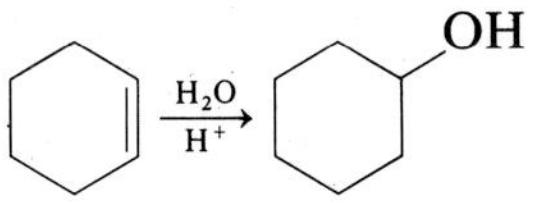

8

$$CH_3{-}CH_2{-}Br \xrightarrow[\text{ether}]{\text{Mg}} CH_3{-}CH_2{-}MgBr \xrightarrow{\substack{O \\ \| \\ H-C-H}} \xrightarrow{H^+}$$

$$CH_3{-}CH_2{-}CH_2{-}OH$$

10 $18 \times 2 = 36$ proof

12 (a) $R{-}O^-$
(b) Ether from alkoxide and R—X
(c) Ethyl alcohol rendered undrinkable by adding a toxic material
(d) Removing water
(e) See text

(f) [structure: epoxide]
     $\overset{O}{\underset{C-C}{\triangle}}$

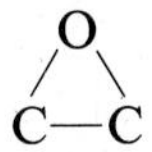

(g) Heating to the point of decomposition in the absence of air

14 1-methyl-1-cyclohexanol

16 1-methyl-1-cyclohexanol

18

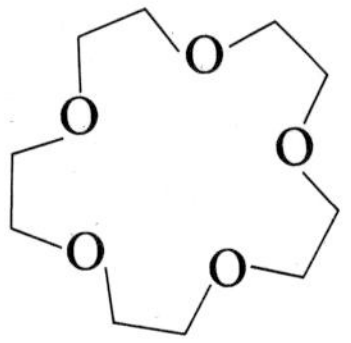

[structure: crown ether ring with six O atoms]

20 SH$^-$

22 (a) $Br_2 \xrightarrow{h\nu} 2Br\cdot$

(b) [cyclopentane]—H + Br· $\longrightarrow$ [cyclopentane]· + HBr

(c) [cyclopentane]· + $Br_2 \longrightarrow$ [cyclopentane]—Br + Br·

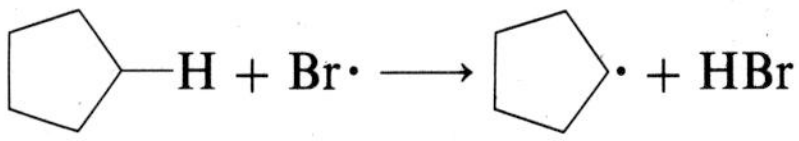

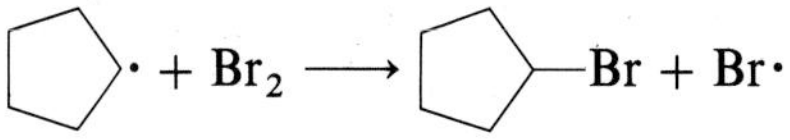

CHAPTER 8

2 4-Chloro-2-methyl-3-pentanone

4 Cyclopropanone

6 2-Bromo-3-methylcyclobutylcarbaldehyde or 2-bromo-1-formyl-3-methylcyclobutane

8

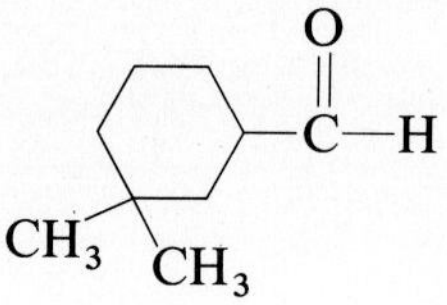

10

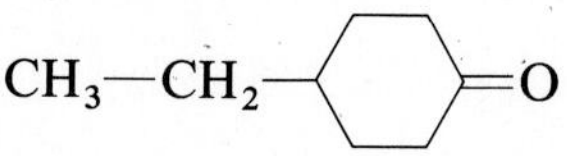

CH_3-CH_2- $=O$

12

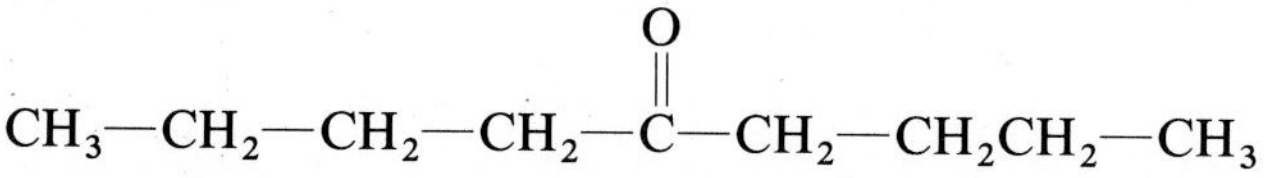

$$CH_3-CH_2-CH_2-CH_2-\overset{\overset{\displaystyle O}{\|}}{C}-CH_2-CH_2CH_2-CH_3$$

14

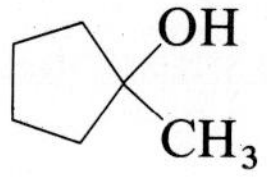

16 No reaction

18

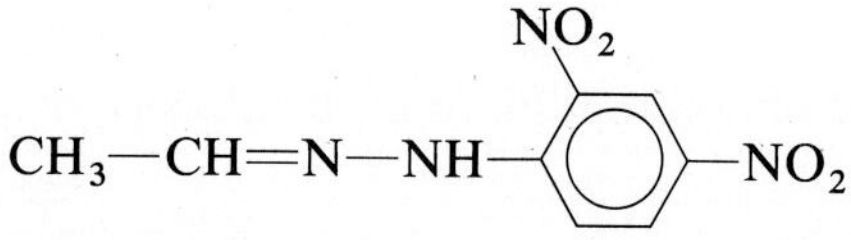

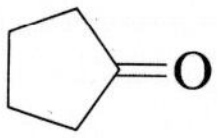

$CH_3-CH=N-NH-$ with NO_2 groups

22

$$CH_3-CH_2-\overset{\overset{\displaystyle O}{\|}}{C}-H$$

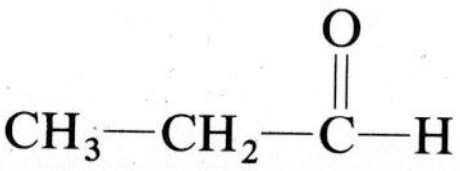

24 Pentanal, acetone, 2-pentanone

26

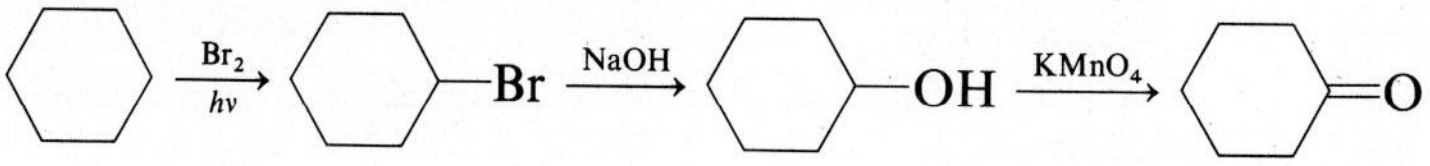

28

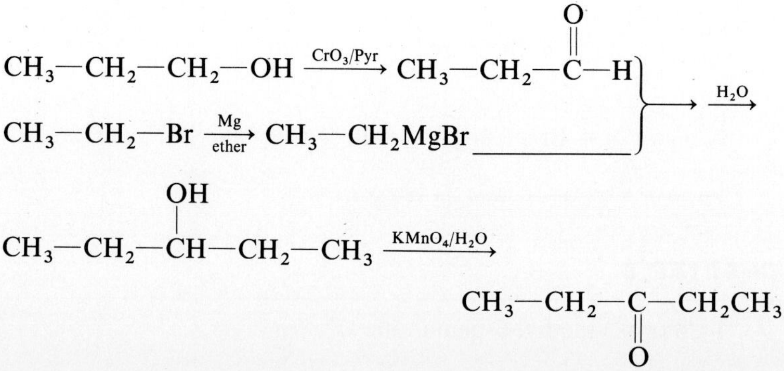

$CH_3-CH_2-CH_2-OH \xrightarrow{CrO_3/Pyr} CH_3-CH_2-\overset{\overset{\displaystyle O}{\|}}{C}-H$

$CH_3-CH_2-Br \xrightarrow[\text{ether}]{Mg} CH_3-CH_2MgBr$

$\xrightarrow{H_2O}$

$$CH_3-CH_2-\overset{\overset{\displaystyle OH}{|}}{CH}-CH_2-CH_3 \xrightarrow{KMnO_4/H_2O}$$

$$CH_3-CH_2-\overset{\overset{\displaystyle O}{\|}}{C}-CH_2CH_3$$

30 (a) Identifying an unknown carbonyl compound
   (b) Preventing an unwanted reaction
   (c) Forming a new, larger carbon skeleton
   (d) Preventing the $KMnO_4$ from oxidizing the primary alcohol all
   the way to the corresponding carboxylic acid

32 $C_xH_{2x}O$; aldehydes have the same general formula as ketones.

34

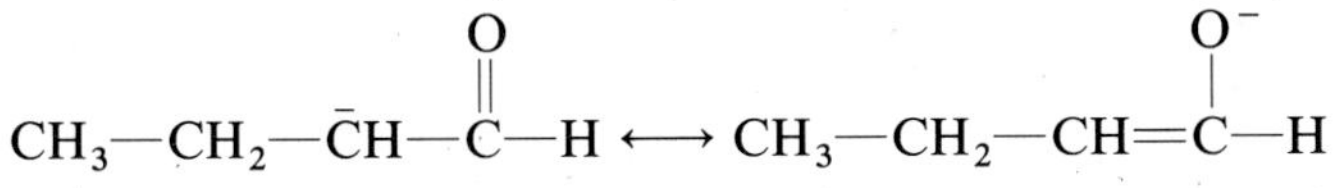

$$CH_3-CH_2-\overset{..}{\underset{}{C}}H-\overset{\overset{O}{\|}}{C}-H \longleftrightarrow CH_3-CH_2-CH=\overset{\overset{O^-}{|}}{C}-H$$

36 Only compound (b) is an aldehyde.

38

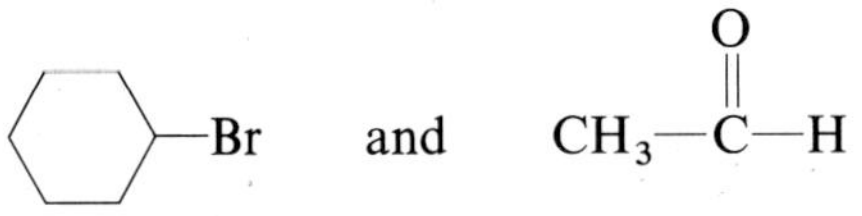

—Br   and $CH_3-\overset{\overset{O}{\|}}{C}-H$

or

CH_3CH_2-Cl and   =O

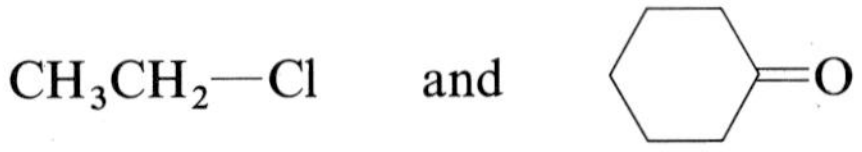

40

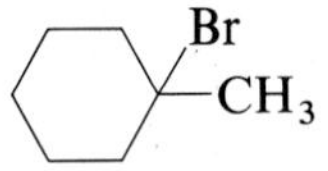

42 Dilute $KMnO_4$ (aqueous)

44 (a) —CH_2CH_3

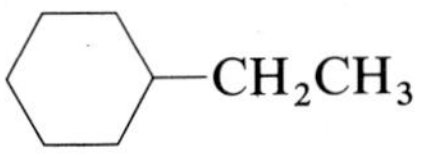

(b)

=O + $CH_3-\overset{\overset{O}{\|}}{C}-H$

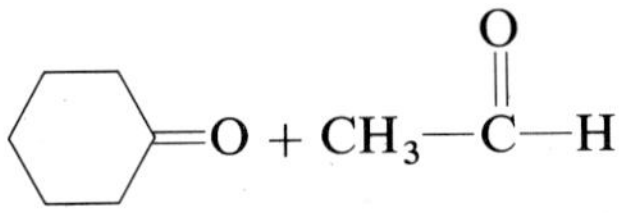

CHAPTER 9

2 (a) o-Nitroanisole   (b) p-Dinitrobenzene
   (c) 1-Ethylnaphthalene   (d) 5-Bromo-1,3-dimethylbenzene
   (e) p-Bromoethylbenzene (f) 4-Bromo-3-methylphenol

4 (a)   (b) See text page 288.

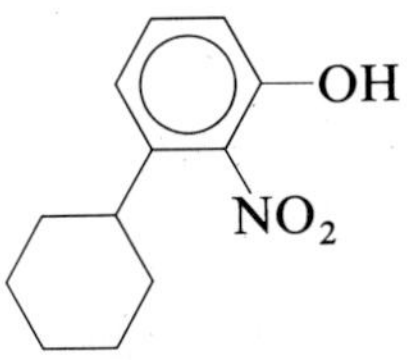

(c)

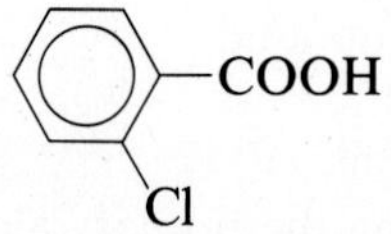

(d)

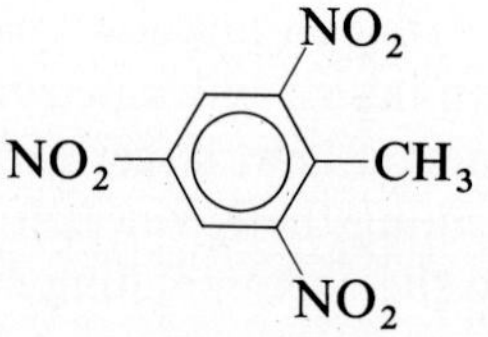

(e)

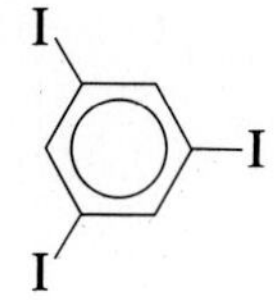

(f)

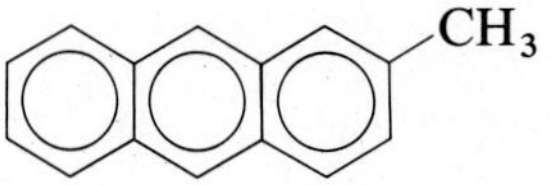

6 (a)

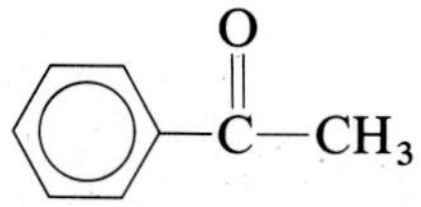

(b)

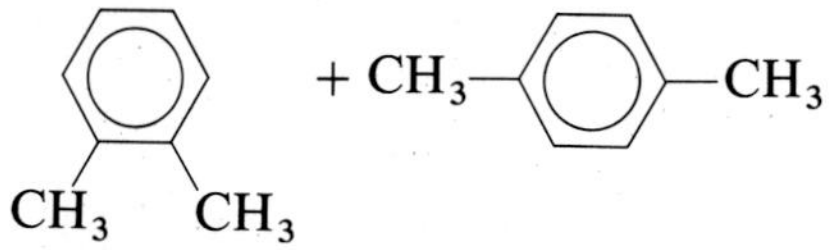

(c)

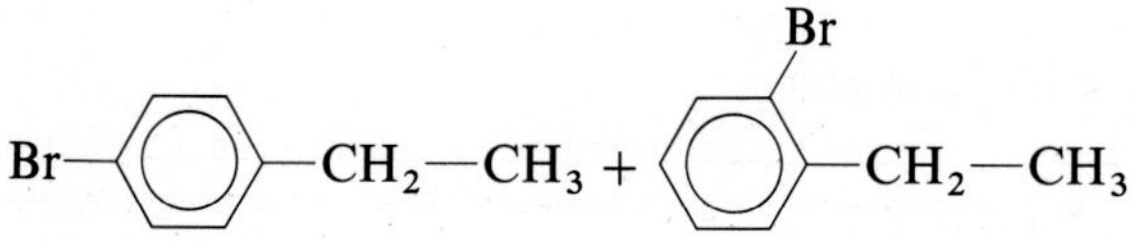

(d)

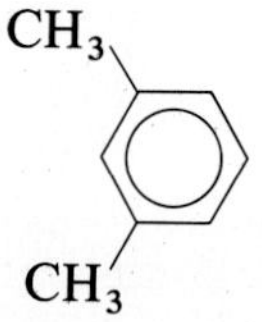

(e)

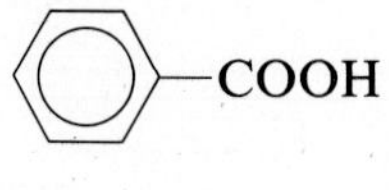

8

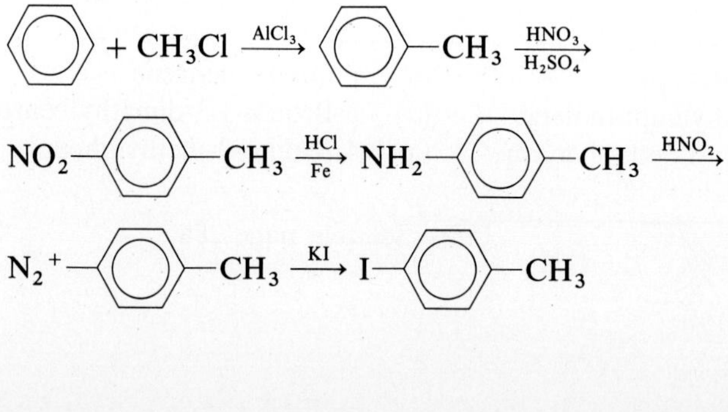

10

12 *trans*-2-Pentene would be more stable, since it has a lower heat of hydrogenation. In Chapter 6 it was stated that the more highly substituted alkenes are more stable. *trans*-2-Pentene is disubstituted (compared to the monosubstituted 1-pentene) and would, therefore, be expected to be more stable.

14 We would expect twice as much ortho as para product since there are two ortho positions and only one para position in each monosubstituted benzene molecule. Large groups already on the ring or large incoming groups might make the ortho position less favorable due to steric crowding and give more of the para isomer. Indeed this is frequently the case.

16 See text for lists of both types.

18 (*a*) One mole; We expect 1 mole of H_2 per double bond.
(*b*) One mole; the benzene portion will not hydrogenate under these conditions.
(*c*) Two moles; two alkene double bonds
(*d*) None

20 Methanol, methyl alcohol, wood alcohol, carbinol

22 Acetone
$$CH_3-\overset{\overset{\textstyle O}{\|}}{C}-CH_3$$

Diethyl ketone
$$CH_3-CH_2-\overset{\overset{\textstyle O}{\|}}{C}-CH_2-CH_3$$

CHAPTER 10

2 $CH_3-CH_3 \xrightarrow[hv]{Br_2} CH_3-CH_2-Br \xrightarrow[alcohol]{KOH}$

$$CH_2{=}CH_2 \xrightarrow{KMnO_4} \underset{\underset{\textstyle OH \quad OH}{|\qquad|}}{CH_2-CH_2}$$

4 $CH_3-CH_2-CH_2-CH_2-CH_2-Cl \xrightarrow[H_2O]{NaOH}$

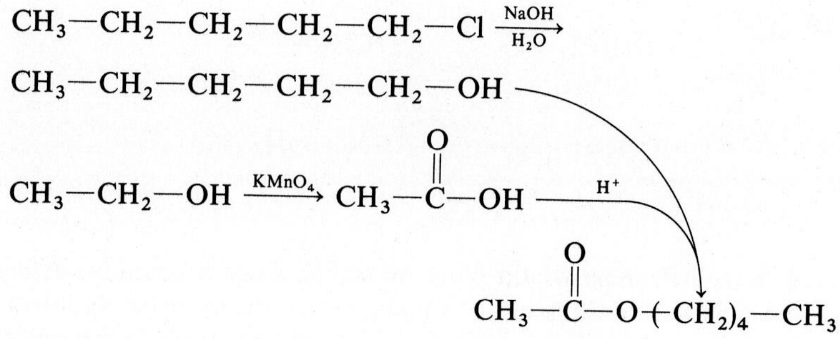

$CH_3-CH_2-CH_2-CH_2-CH_2-OH$

$CH_3-CH_2-OH \xrightarrow{KMnO_4} CH_3-\overset{\overset{\displaystyle O}{\|}}{C}-OH \xrightarrow{H^+}$

$CH_3-\overset{\overset{\displaystyle O}{\|}}{C}-O-(CH_2)_4-CH_3$

6 $CH_3-CH_2-CH_3 \xrightarrow{\underset{h\nu}{Br_2}} CH_3-\underset{\underset{\displaystyle Br}{|}}{CH}-CH_3 \xrightarrow[alcohol]{KOH}$

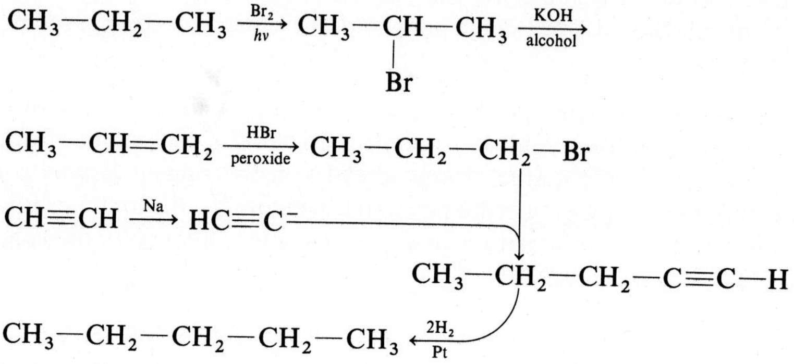

$CH_3-CH=CH_2 \xrightarrow[peroxide]{HBr} CH_3-CH_2-CH_2-Br$

$CH\equiv CH \xrightarrow{Na} HC\equiv C^-$

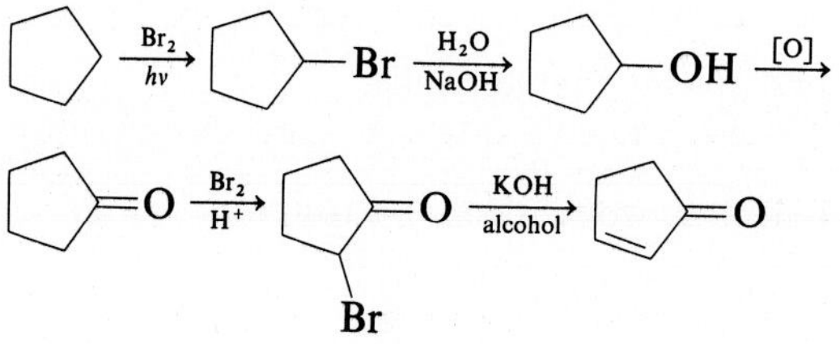

$CH_3-CH_2-CH_2-C\equiv C-H$

$CH_3-CH_2-CH_2-CH_2-CH_3 \xleftarrow[Pt]{2H_2}$

8 $\xrightarrow{\underset{h\nu}{Br_2}}$ $-Br$ $\xrightarrow[NaOH]{H_2O}$ $-OH$ $\xrightarrow{[O]}$

$=O \xrightarrow[H^+]{Br_2}$ $\underset{\underset{\displaystyle Br}{|}}{}=O \xrightarrow[alcohol]{KOH}$ $=O$

10 $CH_3-\overset{\overset{\displaystyle O}{\|}}{C}-CH_3 \xrightarrow[2.)\ H^+]{1.)\ LiAlH_4} CH_3-\underset{\underset{\displaystyle OH}{|}}{CH}-CH_3 \xrightarrow[\Delta]{H^+}$

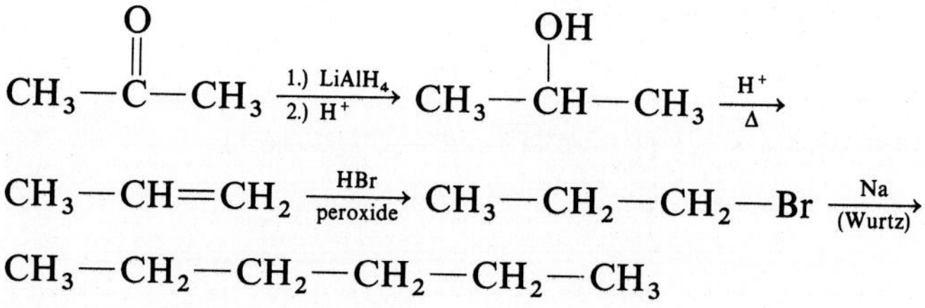

$CH_3-CH=CH_2 \xrightarrow[peroxide]{HBr} CH_3-CH_2-CH_2-Br \xrightarrow[(Wurtz)]{Na}$

$CH_3-CH_2-CH_2-CH_2-CH_2-CH_3$

12 $CH_4 \xrightarrow{\underset{h\nu}{Br_2}} CH_3-Br \xrightarrow[H_2O]{NaOH} CH_3-OH$

$\Big\downarrow Na$

$CH_3-O-CH_3 \longleftarrow CH_3O^-$

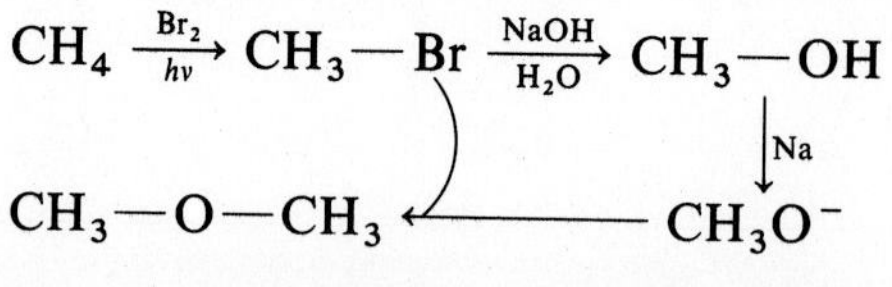

14 $CH_3-CH_2-CH_2-CH_2-CH_2-OH \xrightarrow[\Delta]{H^+}$

$CH_3-CH_2-CH_2-CH=CH_2 \xrightarrow{O_3} \xrightarrow{Zn/H_2O}$

$CH_3-CH_2-CH_2-\overset{\overset{\displaystyle O}{\|}}{C}-H + \underset{H\quad H}{\overset{\overset{\displaystyle O}{\|}}{C}} \xrightarrow[\text{2.) } H^+]{\text{1.) LiAlH}_4}$

$CH_3-CH_2-CH_2-CH_2-OH$

16

$\underset{CH_3}{\bigcirc} \xrightarrow[H_2SO_4]{HNO_3} \underset{CH_3}{\overset{NO_2}{\bigcirc}} \xrightarrow[H_2O]{KMnO_4} \underset{COOH}{\overset{NO_2}{\bigcirc}} \xrightarrow[HCl]{Fe} \underset{COOH}{\overset{NH_2}{\bigcirc}}$

$+$

$\underset{CH_3}{\bigcirc} NO_2$

CHAPTER 11

2 (a) C—O, (lower mass) (b) C≡C, (lower mass)
  (c) C=C, (stronger bond)

4 (a) 3400   (b) 3400
  (c) 2900, 1470, 1370 (d) 1000 to 1200
  (e) 1690 to 1750

6 (a)

$CH_3-CH_2-N-CH_2-CH_3$
$\qquad\quad |$
$\qquad\quad CH_3$

(b)

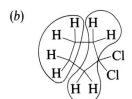

(c)

$\underset{CH_3}{\overset{CH_3}{CH_3-C-CH_2-CH_3}}$

8 (1) Four aromatic H's (7.2 ppm)
(2) A methyl group (1.9 ppm)
(3) An ethyl group (0.9 and 3.2 ppm)
(4) Two oxygens

One would expect CH_3-CH_2-O-⟨○⟩$-O-CH_3$

10 (*a*) IR   acid—broad peak at 3400 cm^{-1}
                 aldehyde—peak at 2700 cm^{-1}
         NMR   acid—peak at 12 ppm
                 aldehyde—peak at 9.5 ppm
(*b*) IR   aromatic—peaks at 3050 and 1900 cm^{-1}
                 cyclohexane—no peaks at 3050 or 1900 cm^{-1}
         NMR   aromatic—peaks at 7.0 and 2.0 ppm
                 cyclohexane—all peaks at 0.9 to 1.5 ppm
(*c*) IR   similar
         NMR   2,2-dichloropropane—one singlet at 2.0 ppm
                 1,2-dichloropropane—three absorbances
(*d*) IR   1° alcohol—C—O at 1050 cm^{-1}
                 3° alcohol—C—O at 1150 cm^{-1}
         NMR   1° alcohol—several complex peaks
                 3° alcohol—only two singlets observed in a ratio of 9:1
(*e*) IR   the ether would have an absorbance around 1200 cm^{-1}
         NMR   the two spectra would be quite similar

12

CH_3-O-⟨⬡⟩$-O-CH_3$

14 Using 253 nm as our reference for three conjugated double bonds and adding 2×30 nm for each additional double bond we get an approximate value for the compound in question of 313 nm.

16 The molecular formula would be C_6H_{12} and a possible structure would be

⟨⬠⟩$-CH_3$

18 (*a*) sp^2 (*b*) sp^3
(*c*) sp^3 (*d*) sp^2
(*e*) sp^2

20 (*a*)

⟨⬠⟩ $\overset{\text{Br}}{-CH_3}$ (major product)

(*b*) $CH_3CH_2CH_2-O^-Na^+ + H_2$

(*c*) No reaction

(d)

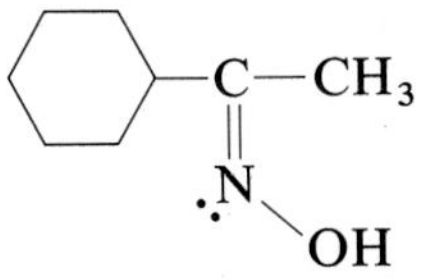

CHAPTER 12

2 (a) Methyl 2-methylbutanoate
  (b) N-Ethylpropanamide
  (c) Butyl benzoate
  (d) trans-3-Methylcyclobutane carboxylic acid
  (e) β-Bromoadipic acid or 3-bromohexanedoic acid
  (f) Formic acid

4 (a)

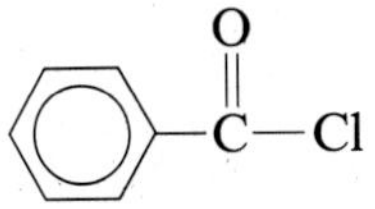

(b)

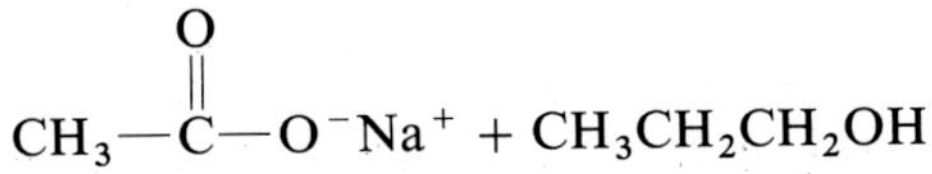

$$CH_3-\overset{\overset{\displaystyle O}{\|}}{C}-O^-Na^+ + CH_3CH_2CH_2OH$$

(c)

$$2CH_3-\overset{\overset{\displaystyle O}{\|}}{C}-OH$$

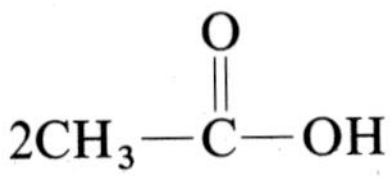

(d)

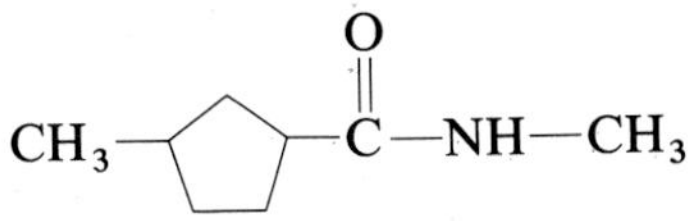

6

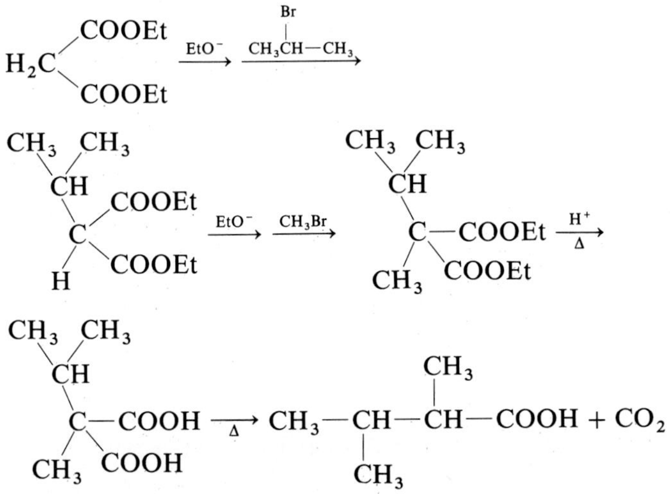

8 $CH_3CH_2CH_2-OH \xrightarrow{[O]} CH_3CH_2COOH \xrightarrow{SOCl_2}$

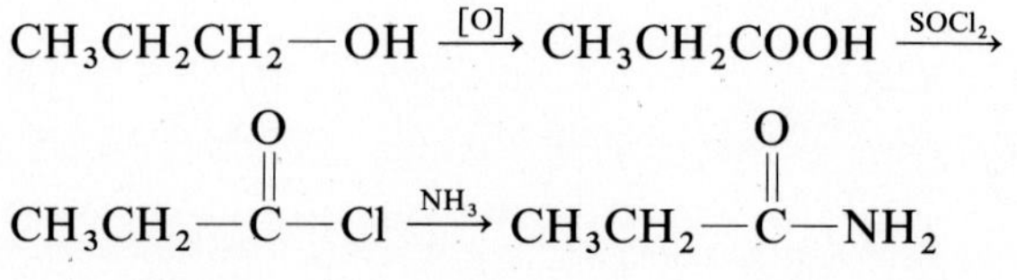

$$CH_3CH_2-\overset{\overset{\displaystyle O}{\|}}{C}-Cl \xrightarrow{NH_3} CH_3CH_2-\overset{\overset{\displaystyle O}{\|}}{C}-NH_2$$

10 $H_2C\overset{\overset{\displaystyle \overset{O}{\|}}{C}-O-CH_2CH_3}{\underset{\overset{\displaystyle \underset{O}{\|}}{C}-O-CH_2CH_3}{}} \xrightarrow{base} \xrightarrow[base]{CH_3CH_2Cl} \xrightarrow{CH_3CH_2Cl} \xrightarrow[\Delta]{H^+} \xrightarrow{\Delta}$

$$\begin{array}{c} CH_3 \\ | \\ CH_2 \\ | \\ CH_3-CH_2-CH-COOH \end{array}$$

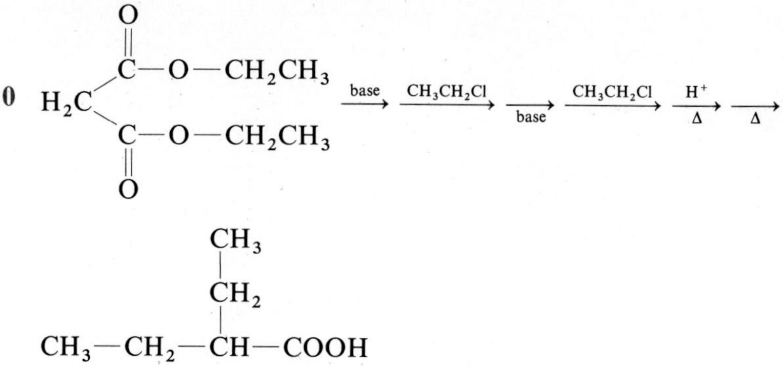

12

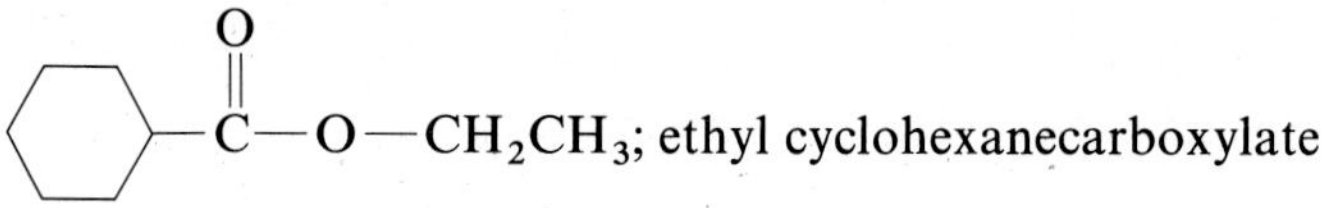

⬡$-\overset{\overset{\displaystyle O}{\|}}{C}-O-CH_2CH_3$; ethyl cyclohexanecarboxylate

14 $\begin{bmatrix} \overset{\overset{\displaystyle H}{\|}}{\sim\!\!N}-CH_2-CH_2-\overset{\overset{\displaystyle H}{\|}}{N}-\overset{\overset{\displaystyle O}{\|}}{C}-CH_2-\overset{\overset{\displaystyle O}{\|}}{C} \end{bmatrix}_x\!\!\sim$

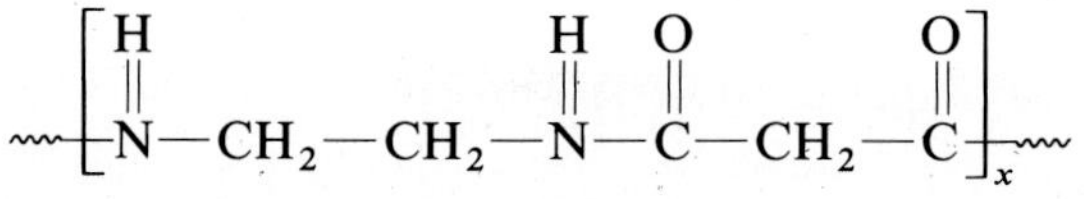

16 Caproic acid would be regenerated (produced again).

18

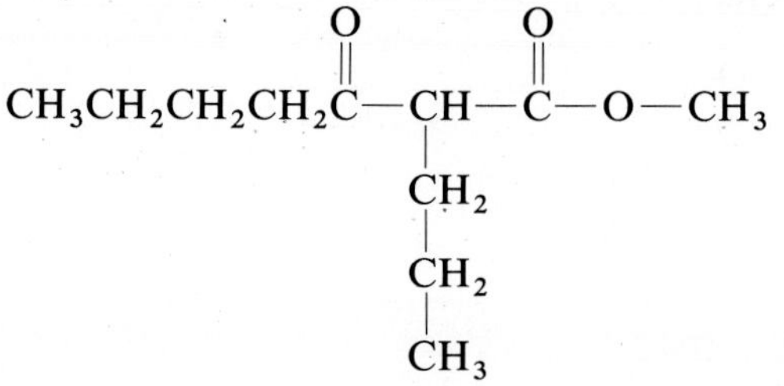

$$CH_3CH_2CH_2CH_2\overset{\overset{\displaystyle O}{\|}}{C}-CH-\overset{\overset{\displaystyle O}{\|}}{C}-O-CH_3$$
$$\begin{array}{c} | \\ CH_2 \\ | \\ CH_2 \\ | \\ CH_3 \end{array}$$

20

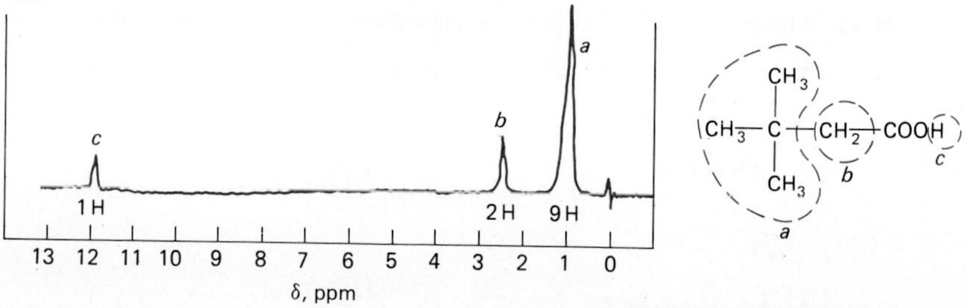

22 (*a*) The ketone would give a colored precipitate with 2,4-dinitro-phenylhydrazine (see Chapter 8).

(*b*) The terminal alkyne would give a precipitate with $AgNO_3$ (see Chapter 6).

(*c*) The alkene would give a positive Baeyer test (the purple color would change to colorless) (see Chapter 6).

CHAPTER 13

2 (*a*) Isopropylamine or 2-propanamine
   (*b*) Dicyclohexylamine or *N*-cyclohexylcyclohexanamine
   (*c*) Trimethylamine or *N,N*-dimethylmethanamine
   (*d*) Ethyldipropylamine or *N*-ethyl-*N*-propylpropanamine
   (*e*) Ethyl ammonium bromide
   (*f*) Cyclopentylmethylamine or *N*-methylcyclopentanamine
   (*g*) *m*-Nitroaniline or 3-nitroaniline
   (*h*) *N*-Propyl-2-bromoaniline or *N*-propyl-*o*-bromoaniline
   (*i*) Cyclopentyltrimethylammonium iodide

4 (*a*)

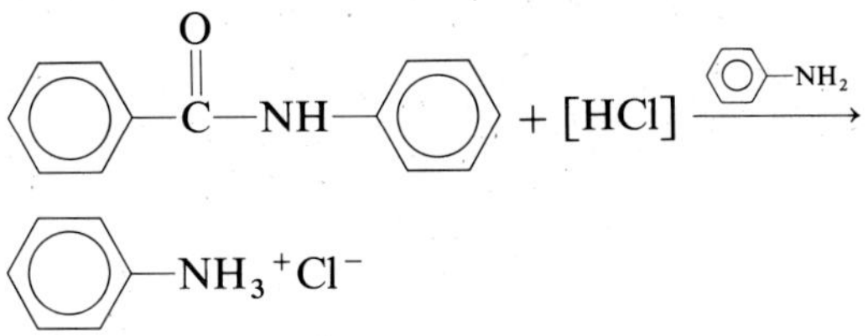

   (*b*) CH_3—CH—CH_3
              |
              NH_2

   (*c*)

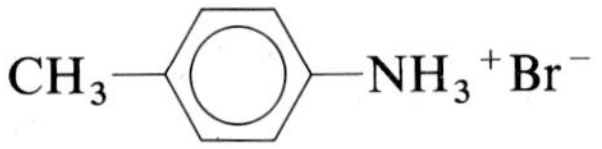

   (*d*)

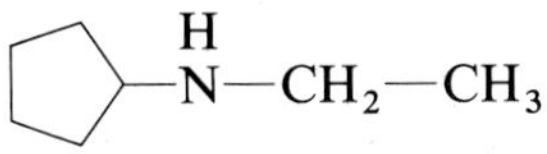

   (*e*) CH_3—CH_2—CH_2—CH_2—NH_2

   (*f*)

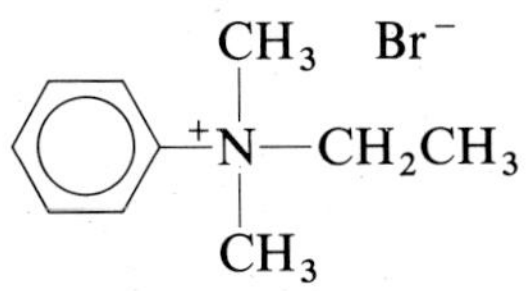

   (*g*) CH_3CH_2—N—CH_2CH_3
                    |
                    H

6 (*a*) Most basic, (*b*) (secondary); least basic, (*c*) (aromatic)

8

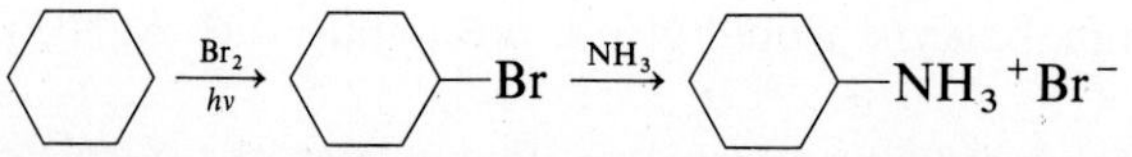

(Remember, the salt is formed naturally before neutralization with base; see page 426.)

10 (*a*) Isopropylamine (*b*) *sec*-Butylamine
(*c*) Di-*tert*-butylamine (*d*) Isobutylamine

12 Compound (*b*) is a secondary amine, and compound (*d*) is a tertiary amine. Compound (*a*) is an oxime (see Chapter 8), and compound (*c*) is an amide.

14 Chlophedianol, Amphetamine, Fencamphine, coniine, caffeine and nicotine

16 No. If one enantiomer is biologically active, the other is usually not active or at least is greatly reduced in activity.

CHAPTER 14

2 No.

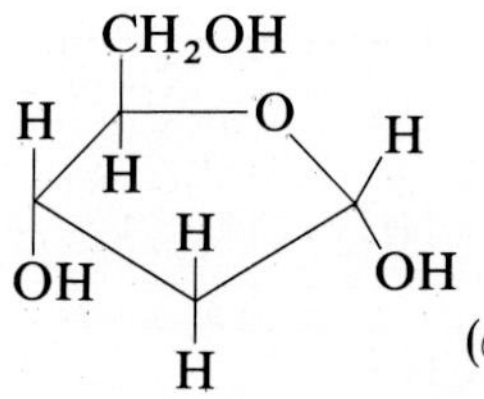

4

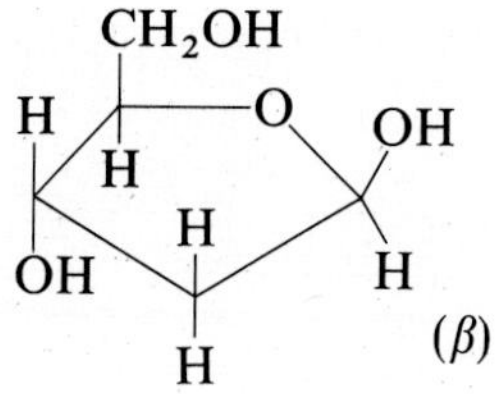

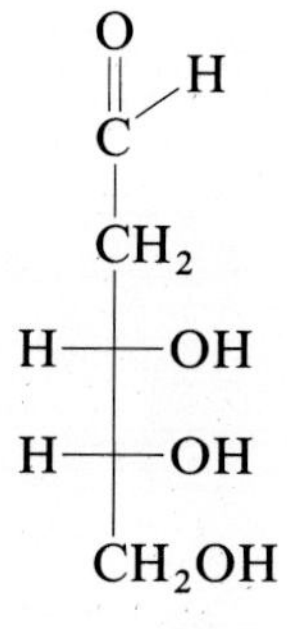

6

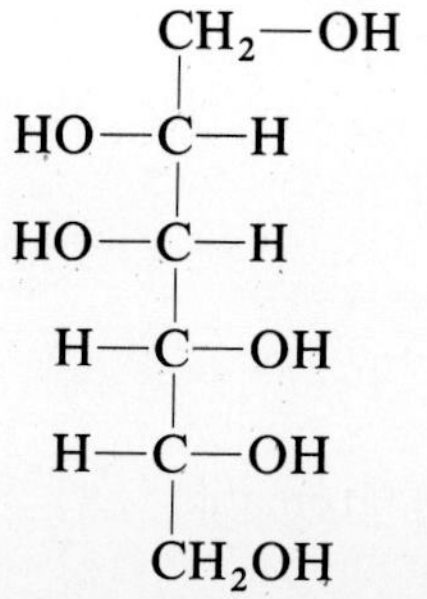

8

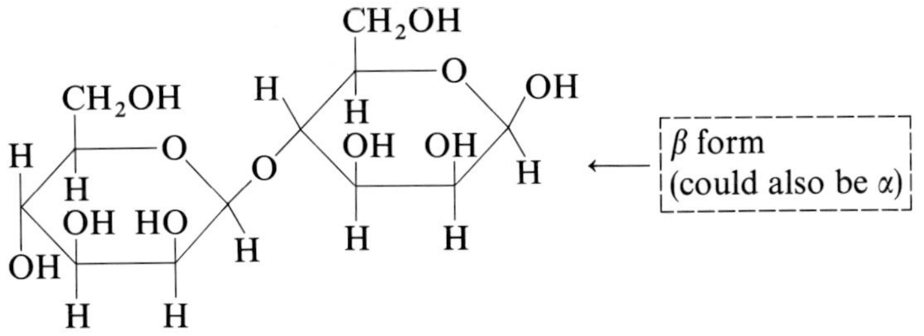

β form
(could also be α)

10 16 (two cyclic forms for each)

12 Lactose: β(1 → 4); cellobiose: β(1 → 4)

14 In the β form, the OH groups at carbon atoms numbers 1 and 2 are trans and in the equatorial position. This makes it more stable than the α form, which has the above mentioned OH groups cis with the anomeric OH group in the axial position. This axial interaction reduces the stability of the α form relative to the β form. See the stereo drawing of cyclic glucose on page 445.

16 The beta designation indicates that the anomeric OH group is drawn upward in the Haworth formula. The term *furan* indicates that the five-membered cyclic form of the monosaccharide is to be drawn. The term *ribo* shows that the structure is a form of the sugar ribose.

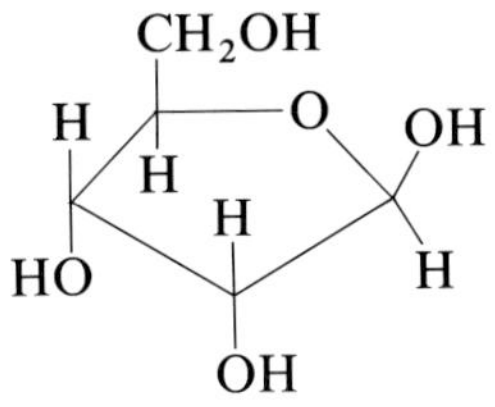

CHAPTER 15

2 Both will be in the negative form, since pH > pH_I.
6.5 − 4.8 = 1.7. This one will move faster.
6.5 − 5.5 = 1.0
Both will move toward the positive pole.

4 Leucine (see Table 15-2)

6 Gly-Leu; Leu-Gly; Leu-Leu; Gly-Gly

8 Gly, Cys, Phe, Ser

10 The pleated sheet form of the protein molecules is longer than the coiled α-helix form.

12 The number 6 amino acid in normal hemoglobin is glutamic acid. In the sickle-cell patient it is valine. These amino acids differ in that valine has a nonpolar R group, while the R group of glutamic acid is polar. This polarity difference and resulting increased hydrophilic character of glutamic acid would result in a secondary structure for normal hemoglobin that is different from that of sickle-cell hemoglobin.

14 (a)

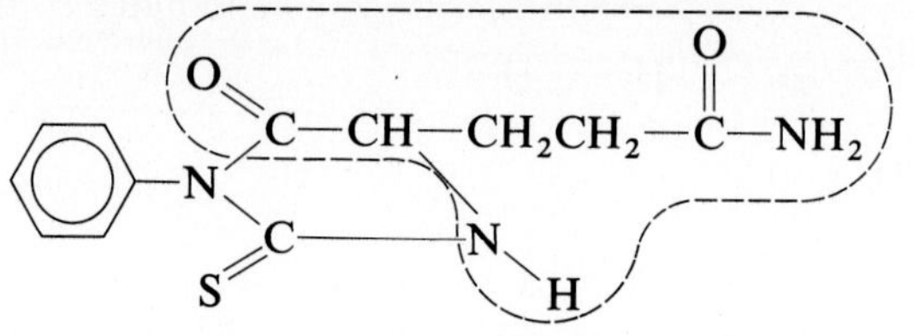

(b)

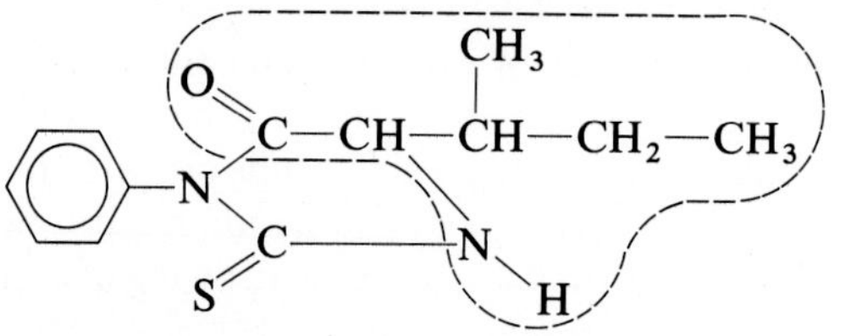

16 Hydrogen bonding, attraction between polar groups, hydrophilic and hydrophobic interactions, disulfide bonds

18 Lysine, histidine, arginine (not asparagine or glutamine—amides are not bases)

20

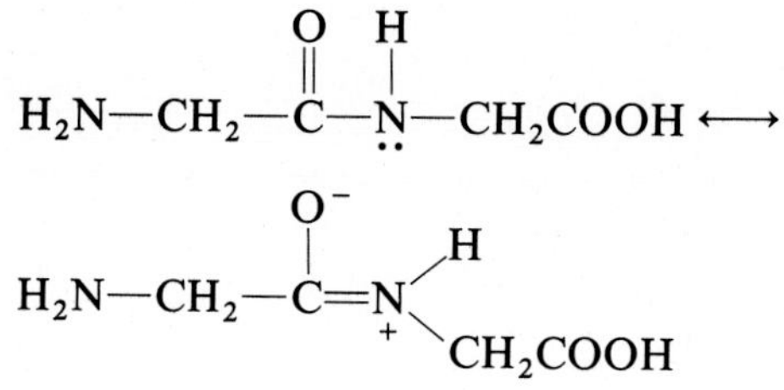

22

(a)

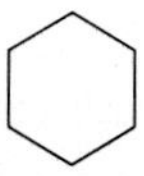

(b)

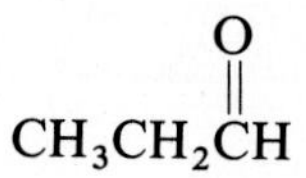

CH_3CH_2CH

(c)

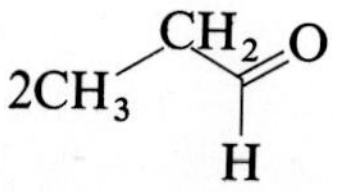

$2CH_3$

(d) $CH_3-CH-CH_2-Br$
$\quad\quad\quad\ \ |$
$\quad\quad\quad CH_3$

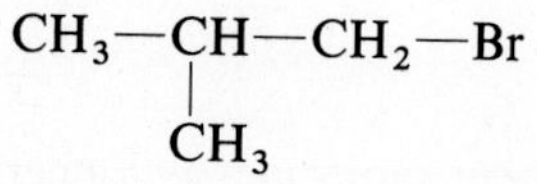

CHAPTER 16

2

$$CH_3(CH_2)_7 \overset{H}{\underset{}{C}}=\overset{H}{\underset{}{C}}(CH_2)_7-\overset{O}{\overset{\|}{C}}-O^-K^+$$

4 (*a*)

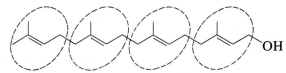

OH

(*b*)

6

$$CH_2-O-\overset{O}{\overset{\|}{C}}-(CH_2)_{10}-CH_3$$

$$CH-O-\overset{O}{\overset{\|}{C}}-(CH_2)_{10}-CH_3$$

$$CH_2-O-\overset{O}{\overset{\|}{C}}-(CH_2)_{10}-CH_3$$

This is a solid (fat) at room temperature.

8

$$\xrightarrow[\text{Pt}]{\text{excess } H_2}$$

$$H_2C-O-\overset{O}{\overset{\|}{C}}-(CH_2)_{16}-CH_3$$

$$HC-O-\overset{O}{\overset{\|}{C}}-(CH_2)_{16}-CH_3$$

$$H_2C-O-\overset{O}{\overset{\|}{C}}-(CH_2)_{16}-CH_3$$

If we used only 4 moles of H_2, four of the double bonds would become single bonds and two double bonds would remain. Their exact positions would be random.

10

COOH

cyclization occurs at these points

12

$$\xrightarrow[H_2O]{\text{NaOH}} CH_3-(CH_2)_{14}-\overset{O}{\overset{\|}{C}}-O^-Na^+ + CH_3-(CH_2)_{15}-OH$$

14 Triglycerides are insoluble in water and soluble in nonpolar solvents because of the large hydrocarbon portions and the relatively small polar portions. Lecithin would be more soluble in water than are most lipids because of the ionic nature of the ionized phosphoric acid portion and the amine salt portion.

16 (a)

$$CH_3-(CH_2)_7 \overset{H}{\underset{}{C}}=\overset{H}{\underset{}{C}} (CH_2)_7 - \overset{O}{\overset{\|}{C}} - O^- Na^+$$

(b)

$$CH_3-(CH_2)_7 \overset{H}{\underset{}{C}}=\overset{H}{\underset{}{C}} (CH_2)_7 - \overset{O}{\overset{\|}{C}} - Cl$$

(c)

$$CH_3-(CH_2)_7 \overset{H}{\underset{}{C}}=\overset{H}{\underset{}{C}} (CH_2)_7 - \overset{O}{\overset{\|}{C}} - O - CH_2CH_3$$

(d)

$$CH_3-(CH_2)_7 \overset{H}{\underset{}{C}}=\overset{H}{\underset{}{C}} (CH_2)_7 - \overset{O}{\overset{\|}{C}} - NH_2$$

(e)

$$CH_3-(CH_2)_7-\underset{OH}{CH}-\underset{OH}{CH}-(CH_2)_7-\overset{O}{\overset{\|}{C}}-OH$$

(f)

$$CH_3-(CH_2)_7-\overset{O}{\overset{\|}{C}}-H + H-\overset{O}{\overset{\|}{C}}-(CH_2)_7-\overset{O}{\overset{\|}{C}}-OH$$

(g)

$$CH_3-(CH_2)_{16}-\overset{O}{\overset{\|}{C}}-OH$$

(h)

$$CH_3-(CH_2)_8-\underset{OH}{CH}-(CH_2)_7-\overset{O}{\overset{\|}{C}}-OH$$

and

$$CH_3-(CH_2)_7-\underset{OH}{CH}-(CH_2)_8-\overset{O}{\overset{\|}{C}}-OH$$

(i)

$$CH_3-(CH_2)_7-\underset{Br}{CH}-\overset{Br}{CH}-(CH_2)_7-\overset{O}{\overset{\|}{C}}-OH$$

(j)

$$CH_3-(CH_2)_8-\underset{\underset{Br}{|}}{CH}-(CH_2)_7-\overset{\overset{O}{\|}}{C}-OH$$

$$\text{and } CH_3-(CH_2)_7-\underset{\underset{Br}{|}}{CH}-(CH_2)_8-\overset{\overset{O}{\|}}{C}-OH^-$$

CHAPTER 17

2 Hydrogen bonding

4 They contain nitrogen atoms of the amine type which can donate their unshared electron pair to a proton (H^+).

6

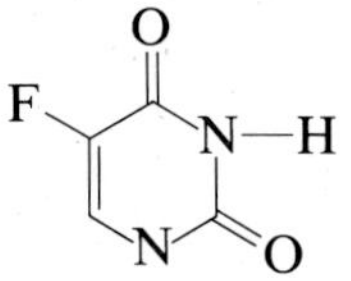

8

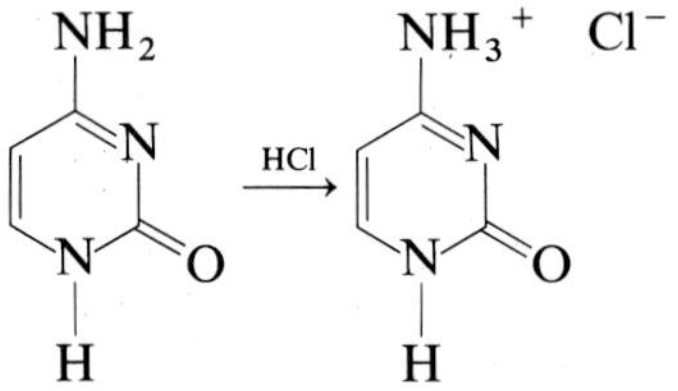

10 3050 cm^{-1} (vinyl C—H); 1690 cm^{-1} (amide C=O); 3400 cm^{-1} (N—H)

INDEX